THE ALGEBRAIC
FOUNDATIONS
OF MATHEMATICS

This book is in the

ADDISON-WESLEY SERIES IN

INTRODUCTORY COLLEGE MATHEMATICS

———————————

Consulting Editors

RICHARD S. PIETERS   GAIL S. YOUNG

THE ALGEBRAIC
FOUNDATIONS
OF MATHEMATICS

by

ROSS A. BEAUMONT

and

RICHARD S. PIERCE

Department of Mathematics
University of Washington

ADDISON-WESLEY PUBLISHING COMPANY, INC.

READING, MASSACHUSETTS · PALO ALTO · LONDON

PREFACE

This book is an offspring of two beliefs which the authors have held for many years: it is worthwhile for the average person to understand what mathematics is all about; it is impossible to learn much about mathematics without *doing* mathematics. The first of these convictions seems to be accepted by most educated people. The second opinion is less widely held. Mathematicians teaching in liberal arts colleges and universities are often under pressure from their colleagues in the humanities and social sciences to offer short courses which will painlessly explain mathematics to students with varying backgrounds who are seeking a broad, liberal education. The extent to which such courses do not exist is a credit to the good sense of professional mathematicians. Mathematics is a big and difficult subject. It embraces a rigid method of reasoning, a concise form of expression, and a variety of new concepts and viewpoints which are quite different from those encountered in everyday life. There is no such thing as "descriptive" mathematics. In order to find answers to the questions "What is mathematics?" and "What do mathematicians do?", it is necessary to learn something of the logic, the language, and the philosophy of mathematics. This cannot be done by listening to a few entertaining lectures, but only by active contact with the content of real mathematics. It is the authors' hope that this book will provide the means for this necessary contact.

For most people, the road from marketplace arithmetic to the border of real mathematics is long and steep. It usually takes several years to make this journey. Fortunately, because of the improving curriculum in high schools, many students are completing the elementary mathematics included in algebra, geometry, and trigonometry before entering college, so that as college freshmen, they can begin to appreciate the attractions of sophisticated mathematical ideas. Many of these students have even been exposed to the new programs for school mathematics which introduce modern mathematical ideas and methods. Too often, such students are shunted into a college algebra or elementary calculus course, where the main emphasis is on mathematical formalism and manipulation. Any enthusiasm for creative thinking which a student may carry into college will quickly be blunted by such a course. It is often claimed that the manipulative skills acquired in elementary algebra and calculus are what a student needs for the application of mathematics to science and engineering, and indeed to the practical problems of life. Although not altogether wrong, this argument overlooks the obvious fact that in almost any situation, the ability to use mathematical technique and reasoning is more valuable than the ability to manipulate and calculate accurately.

Elementary college algebra and calculus courses usually cultivate manipulation at the expense of logical reasoning, and they give the student almost no idea of what mathematics is really like. It is often painfully evident to an instructor in, say, a senior level course in abstract algebra that the average mathematics major in his class has a very distorted idea of the nature of mathematics.

The object of this book is to present in a form suitable for student consumption a small but important part of real mathematics. It is concerned with topics related to the principal number systems of mathematics. The book treats those topics of algebra which are basic for advanced studies in mathematics and of fundamental importance for all working mathematicians. This is the reason that we have entitled our book *"The Algebraic Foundations of Mathematics."* In accord with the philosophy that students should be taught mathematics by exposing them to the mathematics of professional mathematicians, the book should be useful not only to students majoring in mathematics, but also to adequately prepared students of any speciality.

Since mathematics is a logical science, it is appropriate that any book on real mathematics should emphasize mathematical proofs. The student who masters the technique and acquires the habit of mathematical proof is well on his way toward understanding the nature of mathematics. Such a mastery is hard to achieve, but it is within the reach of a large percentage of the college population.

This book is not intended to be an easy one. It is not meant for the college freshman with minimum preparation from high school. An apt student with three years of high school mathematics should be able to study most parts of the book with profit, but his progress may not be rapid. Appropriate places for the use of this book include: a freshman course to replace the standard precalculus college algebra for students who will progress to a rigorous treatment of calculus, a terminal course for liberal arts students with a good background in mathematics, an elementary honors course for mathematics majors, a course to follow a traditional calculus course to develop maturity, and a refresher course for high school mathematics teachers. The book is written in such a way that the law of diminishing returns will not set in too quickly. That is, enough difficult material is included in most sections and chapters so that even the best students will be challenged. The student of more modest ability should keep this in mind in order to combat discouragement.

Some sections digress from the main theme of the book. These are designated by a "star." For the most part, starred sections can be omitted without loss of continuity, although it may be necessary to refer to them for definitions. It should be emphasized that the starred sections are *not* the most difficult parts of the book. On the contrary, much of the material

in these sections is very elementary. A star has been attached to just those
sections which are not sufficiently important to be considered indispensable,
but which are still too interesting to omit.

The complete book can be covered in a two semester or three quarter
course meeting three hours per week. The following table suggests how
the book can be used for shorter courses.

Course	Time required	Chapter
College algebra	1 Semester, 3 hours 1 Quarter, 5 hours	1 (Omit 1–3, 1–5, and starred sections) 2 (Omit starred sections) 4 (Omit 4–1) 5 (Omit starred sections) 6 (Omit 6–1, 6–4, 6–5) 7 (Omit 7–1, 7–2, 7–3, 7–6, and starred sections) 8 9 (Omit starred section) 10 (Omit 10–4)
Development of the classical number systems	1 Semester, 3 hours 1 Quarter, 5 hours	1 through 8 (Omit starred sections)
Theory of equations	1 Semester, 2 hours 1 Quarter, 3 hours	4 (Omit 4–1, 4–3, 4–5, 4–6) 5 (Omit starred sections) 6 (Omit 6–1, 6–4, 6–5) 8 9 (Omit starred section) 10 (Omit 10–3, 10–4)
Elementary theory of numbers	1 Semester, 2 hours 1 Quarter, 3 hours	1 (Omit starred sections) 2 (Omit starred sections) 4 5

Above all, this book represents an effort to show college students some
of the real beauty of mathematics. The appreciation of mathematical
beauty is not like the enjoyment of literature, music, and other art forms.
It requires serious effort and hard study. It is much more difficult for a
mathematician to explain his triumphs and masterpieces than for any other
kind of artist or scientist. Consequently, most mathematicains do not try
to interpret their work to the general public, but only communicate with

colleagues having similar interests. For this reason, a mathematician is often considered to be a rather aloof person who lives partly in this world and partly in some other mysterious realm. This is in fact a fairly accurate conception. However, the door to the world of mathematics is never locked, and anyone who will make the effort can enjoy the beauties of an intellectual domain which comes closer to aesthetic perfection than any other science.

Acknowledgements. Writing a textbook is not a routine chore. Without the help of many people, we might never have finished this one. We are particularly indebted to Professors C. W. Curtis, R. A. Dean, and H. S. Zuckerman, who read most of the manuscript of this book, and gave us many valuable suggestions. Our publisher, Addison-Wesley, has watched over our work from beginning to end with remarkable patience and benevolence. The swift and expert typing of Mary Pierce is sincerely appreciated. Finally, we are grateful to many friends for sincere encouragement during the last two years, and especially to our wives, who have lived with us through these trying times.

Seattle, Washington   R. A. B.
January 1963   R. S. P.

CONTENTS

INTRODUCTION

As we explained in the preface, the purpose of this book is to exhibit a small, but significant and representative, part of the world of mathematics. The selection of a principal subject for this project poses difficulties similar to those which a blind man faces when he tries to discover the shape of an elephant by means of his "sense of feel." Only a few aspects of the subject are within reach, and it is necessary to exercise care to be sure the part examined is truly representative. We might select some important unifying concept of modern mathematics, such as the notion of a *group*, and explore the ramifications of this idea. Alternatively, an older and perhaps familiar topic can be examined in depth. It is this last more conservative program which will be followed.

We will study the principal number systems of mathematics and some of the theories related to them. An attempt will be made to answer the question "what are numbers?" in a way which meets the standards of logical precision demanded in modern mathematics. This program has certain dangers. Familiarity with ordinary numbers hides subtle difficulties which must be overcome before it is even possible to give an exact definition of them. Checking the details in the construction of the various number systems is often tedious, especially for a student who does not see the point of this effort. On the other hand, the end products of this work, the real and complex number systems, are objects of great usefulness and importance in mathematics. Moreover, the development of these systems offers an opportunity to exhibit a wide variety of mathematical techniques and ideas, so that the student is exposed to a representative cross section of mathematics.

It is customary in technical books to tell the reader what he will need to know in order to understand the text. A typical description of such requirements in mathematical textbooks runs as follows: "This book has no particular prerequisites. However, the reader will need a certain amount of mathematical maturity." Usually such a statement means that the book is written for graduate students and seasoned mathematicians. Our prerequisites for understanding this book are more modest. The reader should have successfully completed two years of high-school algebra and a year of geometry. The geometry, although not an absolute prerequisite, will be very helpful. For certain topics in the chapters on the complex numbers and the theory of equations, a knowledge of the rudiments of trigonometry is assumed. We do not expect that the reader will have much "mathe-

1

matical maturity." Indeed, one of the main purposes of this book is to put the reader in touch with mature mathematics.

Some of the obstacles which a beginning student of mathematics faces seem more formidable than they really are. With a little encouragement almost any intelligent person can become a better mathematician than he would imagine possible. The purpose of the remainder of this introduction is to provide some encouraging words on a variety of subjects. It is hoped that our discussion will smooth the reader's way throughout the book. We suggest that this material be read quickly, then referred to later as it is needed.

The number systems. There are five principal number systems in mathematics: the *natural numbers*: 1, 2, 3, 4, etc.; the *integers*: 0, 1, -1, 2, -2, 3, -3, etc.; the *rational numbers*: 0, 1, -1, $\frac{1}{2}$, $-\frac{1}{2}$, $\frac{1}{3}$, $-\frac{1}{3}$, $\frac{2}{3}$, $-\frac{2}{3}$, etc.; the *real numbers*: 0, 1, $\frac{1}{2}$, $-\frac{1}{2}$, $\sqrt{2}$, $-\sqrt{2}$, π, $3 - \sqrt[3]{\pi}$, etc.; and the *complex numbers*: 0, 1, $\frac{1}{2}$, $\sqrt{-1}$, $1 + \sqrt{-1}$, $\pi + \frac{1}{4}\sqrt{-1}$, etc.

With the possible exception of the complex numbers, each of these systems should be familiar. Indeed, the study of these number systems is the principal subject of arithmetic courses in elementary school and of algebra courses in high school. Of course, the names of these systems may not be familiar. For example, the integers are sometimes called *whole numbers*, and the rational numbers are often referred to as *fractions*.

In this book the number systems will be considered at two levels. On the one hand, we will assume at least a superficial knowledge of numbers, and use them in examples from the first chapter on. On the other hand, Chapters 3, 4, 6, 7, and 8 each present a critical study of one of these systems. The reader has two alternatives. He can either skim the material in these chapters, relying on the knowledge of numbers which he already possesses, or he can study these chapters in detail. The latter road is longer and more tedious, but it leads to a very solid foundation for advanced courses in mathematical analysis.

Variables. If a single event can be called the beginning of modern mathematics, then it may possibly be the introduction of variables as a systematic notational device. This innovation, due largely to the French mathematician Francois Vièta (1540–1603), occurred about 1590. Without variables, mathematics would not have progressed very far beyond what we now think of as its "beginnings."

By using variables it is possible to express complicated properties of numbers in a very simple way. Basic laws of operation, such as

$$x + y = y + x \qquad \text{and} \qquad x + (y + z) = (x + y) + z,$$

can be stated *without* using the variables x, y, and z, but the resulting statements lack the clarity of these algebraic identities. For example, the statement that "the product of a number by the sum of two other numbers is equal to the sum of the product of the first number by the second with the product of the first number by the third" is more simply and clearly expressed by the identity

$$x \cdot (y + z) = (x \cdot y) + (x \cdot z).$$

More complicated laws would be almost impossible to state without using variables. The reader who doubts this should try to express in words the relatively simple identity

$$(x^2 + y^2)(z^2 + w^2) = (x \cdot z + y \cdot w)^2 + (x \cdot w - y \cdot z)^2.$$

The variables which are encountered in high-school algebra courses usually range over systems of numbers; that is, it is intended that these variables stand for real numbers, rational numbers, or perhaps only for integers. However, variable symbols are often useful in other contexts. For example, the symbols l and m in the statement "if l and m are two different nonparallel lines, then l and m have exactly one point in common" are variables, representing arbitrary lines in a plane. In this book variables will be used to denote many kinds of objects. However, in all cases, a variable is a symbol which represents an unspecified member of some definite collection of objects, such as numbers, points, or lines. The given collection is called the *range* of the variable, and a particular object in the range is called a *value* of the variable.

The notations used for variables in mathematical literature often puzzle students. In the simplest cases, the letters of the alphabet are used as variable symbols. However, some mathematical statements involve a very large number of variables, and in some cases, even infinitely many. To accommodate the need for many variables, letter symbols with subscripts are usually employed, for example, x_1, x_2, x_7, y_3, z_{15}, a_2, b_7, etc. Sometimes double subscripts are more convenient than single ones. Thus, we find expressions such as $x_{1,2}$, $x_{7,7}$, $x_{21,52}$, etc. Variable symbols are often used to denote a subscript on a variable letter. For instance x_i, y_m, a_k, $z_{i,j}$, etc. In these cases, the variable subscript is usually assumed to stand for a natural number, or possibly an integer.

Mathematical language. One of the difficulties in learning mathematics is the language barrier. Not only must the student master many new concepts and the names of these concepts, but he must also learn numerous abbreviations and symbols for common words. Except for the use of abbreviations, the grammar of mathematics is the same as that of the language in which it is written.

A *sentence* in mathematical writing is any expression which is a meaningful assertion, either true or false. According to this definition, such formulas as

$$1 + 1 = 2, \qquad 2 \cdot \tfrac{1}{2} = 2,$$
$$1 < 3 - 2, \qquad \text{and} \qquad 0 = 0$$

must be counted as sentences. Sentences may contain variables. For example, the statement "There is a real number x such that $x^{100} - 57x^{53} - 25x^7 + 500 = 0$" is an assertion which is either true or false, although it is not obvious which is the case.*

There are other expressions of importance in mathematics which cannot be called sentences. These are formulas, such as

$$.x + y = 1, \qquad x^2 + 2x + 1 = 0, \qquad \text{and} \qquad x > 2,$$

and expressions which have the form of sentences, except that variables occur in place of the subject or object; for example, "x is an integer" and "2 divides n." Expressions such as these are called *sentential functions*. They have the property that substituting numerical values (or whatever objects the variables represent) for the variables converts them into sentences. For instance, by suitable substitutions for x and y, the sentential function $x + y = 1$ is transformed into the sentences

$$1 + 1 = 1, \qquad 2 + (-1) = 1,$$
$$0 + 1 = 1, \qquad 100 + (-100) = 1.$$

It makes no sense to ask whether or not a formula such as $x + y = 1$ is true. For some values of x and y it is true; for others it is not. On the other hand, the formula $x + y = y + x$ has the property that every substitution of numbers for x and y leads to a true sentence. Such a sentential function is usually called an *identity*. Sentential functions which are not formulas may also have the property of being true for all values of the variables occurring in them. For example, the statement "either $x < y$, or $y \leq x$" has this property of universal validity, provided that it is understood that x and y are variables which range over real numbers. A sentential function which is true for all values of the variables in it is said to be *identically true* or *identically valid* (the adjective "identically" is sometimes omitted).

Implications. Many beginning students of mathematics have trouble understanding the idea of logical implication. As many as one-half of all statements in a mathematical proof may be implications, that is, of the form "p implies q," where p and q are sentences or sentential functions.

-----
* It is true.

TABLE 1

Form	Example
p implies q	x positive implies that x is nonnegative
q is implied by p	x nonnegative is implied by x being positive
If p, then q	if x is positive, then x is nonnegative
q if p	x is nonnegative if x is positive
p only if q	x is positive only if x is nonnegative
only if q is p	only if x is nonnegative is x positive
p is a sufficient condition for q	x positive is a sufficient condition for x to be nonnegative
for q it is sufficient that p	for x to be nonnegative, it is sufficient that x be positive
q is a necessary condition for p	x nonnegative is a necessary condition for x to be positive
for p it is necessary that q	for x to be positive, it is necessary that x be nonnegative

For this reason, it is important to be able to recognize an implication, and to understand what it means.

The variety of ways in which mathematicians say "p implies q" is often bewildering to students. The expressions "$x = 1$ implies x is an integer"; "if $x = 1$, then x is an integer"; "$x = 1$ only if x is an integer"; "$x = 1$ is a sufficient condition for x to be an integer"; and "for x to equal 1, it is necessary that x be an integer" all have the same meaning. Such statements as these occur repeatedly in any book or paper on mathematics. For the reader's convenience, we list in Table 1 some of the forms in which "p implies q" may be written, together with examples of these locutions.

If p and q are both sentences, then the implication "p implies q" is a sentence; if either p, or q, or both p and q are sentential functions, then "p implies q" is a sentential function. In case "p implies q" is a sentence, then its truth is completely determined by the truth or falsity of p and q. Specifically, this implication is true either if p is false or q is true. It is false only if p is true and q is false. For example, "$3 = 3$ implies $1 < 3$" is true, "$3 = 2$ implies $1 < 2$" is true, "$3 = 1$ implies $1 < 1$" is true, but "$3 = 3$ implies $1 < 1$" is false.

It may seem strange to consider a sentence "p implies q" to be true even though there is no apparent connection between p and q. The idea which the statement "p implies q" usually conveys is that the validity of the

TABLE 2

Form	Example
p is equivalent to q	$x = y$ is equivalent to $x + 1 = y + 1$
p if and only if q	$x = y$ if and only if $x + 1 = y + 1$
p is a necessary and sufficient condition for q	$x = y$ is a necessary and sufficient condition for $x + 1 = y + 1$
p implies q, and conversely	$x = y$ implies $x + 1 = y + 1$, and conversely

sentence q is somehow a consequence of the truth of p. It is hard to see how the truth of such an implication as "$3 = 1$ implies $1 < 1$" fits this conception. Our convention concerning the truth of an implication becomes more understandable when we consider how a sentence of the form "p implies q" may be obtained from a sentential function by substitution of numerical values for the variables. For example, the implication "$y + 2 = x$ implies $y < x$" is a sentential function which everyone would agree is identically valid. That is, it is true for all values of x and y. However, by substituting 1 for x and 1 for y, we obtain the sentence "$3 = 1$ implies $1 < 1$," whose truth was previously admitted only with reluctance.

Converse and equivalence. From any statements p and q it is possible to form two different implications, "p implies q" and "q implies p." Each of these implications is called the *converse* of the other.

An implication does not ordinarily have the same meaning as its converse. For example, the converse of the statement "if $n > 0$, then $n^2 > 0$" is the implication "if $n^2 > 0$, then $n > 0$." These assertions obviously have different meanings. In fact, the first statement is identically true, whereas the second statement is not true for all n; for example, $(-1)^2 = 1 > 0$ and $-1 < 0$. If the implication "p implies q" and its converse "q implies p" are both true, then the statements p and q are said to be *equivalent*. In practice, the notion of equivalence of p and q is most frequently applied when p and q are sentential functions. For example, if x and y are variables which range over numbers, then the formulas $x = y$ and $x + 1 = y + 1$ are equivalent, since "$x = y$ implies $x + 1 = y + 1$" and "$x + 1 = y + 1$ implies $x = y$" are identically valid.

There are various ways of saying that two statements p and q are equivalent. Most of these forms are derived from the terminology for implications. Several examples are given in Table 2.

TABLE 3

p	q	not p	not q	p implies q	not q implies not p
true	true	false	false	true	true
true	false	false	true	false	false
false	true	true	false	true	true
false	false	true	true	true	true

Contrapositive and inverse. In addition to the implication "p implies q" and its converse "q implies p," two other implications can be formed using p and q. These are "not q implies not p" and "not p implies not q." The implication "not q implies not p" is called the *contrapositive* of "p implies q," while "not p implies not q" is called the *inverse* of "p implies q." For example, the contrapositive of the statement "if $x = 1$, then x is an integer" is the implication "if x is not an integer, then x is not equal to 1."

It is easy to see that the contrapositive of "p implies q" is true under exactly the same circumstances that this implication is itself true. The most convincing way to demonstrate this fact is to make a table listing all of the possible combinations of truth values of any two sentences p and q, together with the corresponding truth or falsity of "p implies q" and its contrapositive (Table 3). The entries in the fifth column of Table 3 are determined by the combinations of true and false in the first two columns, while the entries of the last column are determined from the combinations which occur in the third and fourth columns. Of course, the entries of the third column are just the opposite of those in the first column, and a similar relation exists between the fourth and second columns.

The fact that an implication is logically the same as its contrapositive is often very useful in mathematical proofs. Sometimes, rather than proving a statement of the form "p implies q," it is easier to prove the contrapositive "not q implies not p." This is logically acceptable. Also, if we wish to prove that p and q are equivalent, that is, "p implies q" and "q implies p" are valid, it is permissible to establish that "p implies q" and "not p implies not q." This is because "not p implies not q" is the contrapositive of "q implies p." However, beware; it is *not* correct to claim that if p implies q and not q implies not p, then p is equivalent to q.

Definitions. Simple mathematical proofs often consist of nothing more than showing that the conditions of some definition are satisfied. Nevertheless, beginning students frequently find such arguments difficult to understand. Consider, for example, the problem of showing that 222 is an even integer. We must use the definition that an integer n is *even* if it is equal to twice another integer, that is, $n = 2 \cdot m$ for some integer m. To prove that 222 is even, it is only necessary to observe that $222 = 2 \cdot 111$. Hence 222 satisfies the requirement for being an even integer, so that *by definition, it is an even integer*. This is all that needs to be said; the proof is complete.

Definitions sometimes enter into mathematical proofs in the opposite way. For example, to prove the statement that the square of every even integer is divisible by four, we must use the condition which defines even numbers: if n is even, then $n = 2 \cdot m$ for some integer m. From the equality $n = 2 \cdot m$ and well-known properties of multiplication, it follows that $n^2 = 4 \cdot m^2$. Therefore, 4 divided into n^2 gives the quotient m^2, with no remainder. Since n is an arbitrary even integer, this argument proves the assertion that the square of every even integer is divisible by four.

In this proof we have used the condition which defines "evenness" to show that every even number has a certain property. On the other hand, the proof in the preceding paragraph consists of showing that a certain number satisfies the condition for being even. Sometimes both aspects of a definition are involved in a proof. An example in which this happens is the proof of the statement that the square of every even integer is even.

Proofs. The logic which mathematicians use is no different from that used by any person in the course of his thinking. A typical husband might reason as follows: "I know that my wife is going shopping today, and I know that if she goes shopping, she will want some money; therefore she will no doubt ask me for some money." This deduction is a typical application of what logicians call the *rule of detachment*, or the *modus ponens*.

The modus ponens is the most commonly used rule of deduction in mathematics. Stated in general terms, this rule can be formulated as follows. Let p and q be any two statements. Suppose that p is true, and that the implication "p implies q" is also valid. Then q is true. If p and q are sentential functions, rather than sentences, then the rule of detachment is still applicable, provided that p and "p implies q" are identically valid. The conclusion in this case is that q is identically true. For example, we know that "$x < x + 1$," and "$x < x + 1$ implies $x + y < (x + 1) + y$" are identically valid statements. Therefore, by the rule of detachment, $x + y < (x + 1) + y$ is identically true.

Next to the modus ponens, the most important rule of deduction in mathematical arguments is the *law of substitution*. This is the rule which allows us to infer from the universal validity of a statement p involving variables, that any particular instance of p, obtained by making substitutions for the variables, is true. For example, we know that in the arithmetic of numbers, the identity $x + y = y + x$ is true for all x and y.

From this we can infer such formulas as

$$1 + 2 = 2 + 1, \qquad x + 3 = 3 + x,$$
$$x + x = x + x, \qquad x + (z + 1) = (z + 1) + x.$$

The logical structure of a mathematical proof may have one of two forms. The *direct proof* starts from certain axioms or definitions, and proceeds by application of logical rules to the required conclusion. The second method, the so-called *indirect proof*, is perhaps less familiar, even though it is often used unconsciously in everyday thinking. The indirect proof begins by assuming that the statement to be proved is false. Then, using this assumption, together with the appropriate axioms and definitions, a contradiction of some kind is obtained by means of a logical argument. From this contradiction it is inferred that the statement originally assumed to be false must actually be true.

For example, let us show by an indirect proof that there is no largest natural number. This proof uses three general properties of numbers, which, for our purposes can be considered as axioms:

(a) if n is a natural number, then $n + 1$ is a natural number;

(b) $n < n + 1$;

(c) if $n < m$, then $n \geq m$ is impossible.

Our indirect proof begins with the assumption that the statement to be proved is false, that is, we assume that there is a largest natural number. Let this number be denoted by n. To say that n is the largest natural number means two things:

(i) n is a natural number;

(ii) if m is a natural number, then $n \geq m$.

Applying the rule of detachment to (a) and (i) gives

(iii) $n + 1$ is a natural number.

Substituting $n + 1$ for m in (ii), we obtain

(iv) if $n + 1$ is a natural number, then $n \geq n + 1$.

The rule of detachment can now be applied to (iii) and (iv) to conclude that

(v) $n \geq n + 1$.

However, substituting $n + 1$ for m in (c) gives

(vi) if $n < n + 1$, then $n \geq n + 1$ is impossible.

This, together with (b) and the rule of detachment yields

(vii) $n \geq n + 1$ is impossible.

The statements (v) and (vii) provide the contradiction which completes this typical indirect proof.

In spite of the elementary character of the logic used by mathematicians, it is a matter of experience that understanding proofs is the most difficult aspect of mathematics. Most people, mathematicians included, must work hard to follow a difficult proof. The statements follow each other relentlessly. Each step requires logical justification, which may not be easy to find. The result of this labor is only the beginning. After the step-by-step correctness of the argument has been checked, it is necessary to go on and find the mathematical ideas behind the proof. Truly, real mathematics is not easy.

CHAPTER 1

SET THEORY

1-1 Sets. The notion of a set enters into all branches of modern mathematics. Algebra, analysis, and geometry borrow freely from elementary set theory and its terminology. Indeed, all of mathematics can be founded on the theory of sets. As is to be expected, an idea with such a wide range of application is quite simple, and any intelligent person can learn enough about set theory for most useful applications of the subject.

The central idea of set theory is that of dealing with a collection of objects as an individual thing. Mathematics is not alone in using this idea, and many occurrences of it are found in everyday experience. Thus, for example, one speaks of the Smith family, meaning the collection of people consisting of John Smith, his wife Mary, and their son William. Also, if we referred to Mrs. Smith's wardrobe, we would be treating as a single thing the collection of individual pieces of clothing belonging to Mrs. Smith. The mathematical use of this device of lumping things together into a single entity differs from common usage only in the frequency and systematic manner of its application.

> DEFINITION 1-1.1. A *set* is an entity consisting of a collection of objects.*
> Two sets are considered to be the same if they contain exactly the same objects. When this is the case, we say that the sets are *equal*. The objects belonging to a set are called the *elements* of the set.

A set is usually determined by some property which the elements of the set have in common. In the example given above, the property of being a piece of clothing belonging to Mrs. Smith defines the set which we call Mrs. Smith's wardrobe. It should be emphasized that in thinking of a collection of objects as a set, no account is taken of the arrangement of the objects or any relations between them. Thus, for example, a deck of

---

* This statement cannot be considered as a mathematical definition of the term "set." In mathematics, a definition is supposed to completely identify the object being defined. Here we have only supplied the synonym "collection" for the less familiar term "set." The problem of finding a satisfactory mathematical definition is far more difficult than it might seem. The uncritical use of sets can lead to contradictions which are avoided only by imposing restrictions on the naive concept of a set. Finding a definition of "set" which is free from contradictions and which satisfies all mathematical needs has for 75 years been a central problem of the logical foundations of mathematics. Fortunately, these difficult aspects of set theory can be ignored in almost all mathematical applications of the theory.

52 cards, considered as a set, remains the same whether it is in its original package or is shuffled and distributed into four bridge hands.

EXAMPLE 1. The set consisting of the numbers 0 and 1.

EXAMPLE 2. The set of numbers which are roots of the equation $x^2 - x = 0$.

EXAMPLE 3. The set of numbers which are roots of the equation $x^3 - x^2 = 0$.

EXAMPLE 4. The set of numbers a on the real line (Fig. 1–1) which satisfy $-1 \leq a \leq 1$.

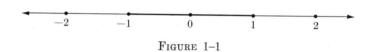

FIGURE 1–1

EXAMPLE 5. The set of all numbers $x/2$, where x is a real number which satisfies $-2 \leq x \leq 2$.

EXAMPLE 6. The set of all points at a distance less than one from a point p in some plane.

EXAMPLE 7. The set of all points inside a circle of radius one with center at the point p in the plane of the preceding example.

EXAMPLE 8. The set of all circles with center at the point p in the plane of Example 6.

EXAMPLE 9. The set consisting of the single number 0.

EXAMPLE 10. The set which contains no objects whatsoever.

According to our definition of equality of sets, we see that the sets of Examples 1, 2, and 3 are the same. Although 0 occurs as a so-called double root of the equation $x^3 - x^2 = 0$ in Example 3, only its presence or absence matters when speaking of the set of roots. The sets of Examples 4 and 5 are the same, as are those of Examples 6 and 7. If we consider a circle to be the same thing as the set of all of its points, then the elements of the set of Example 8 are themselves sets. Sets of sets will be studied more thoroughly in Section 1–5. The set described in Example 9 contains a single element. Such sets are quite common. It is conventional to regard such a set as an entity which is different from the element which is its only member. Even in ordinary conversation this distinction is often made. If Robert Brown is a bachelor with no known relations, then we would say that the Brown family consists of one member, but we would not say that Mr. Brown consists of one member. The reader may feel that the set of Example 10 does not satisfy the description given in

Definition 1–1.1. However, it is customary in mathematics to interpret the term "collection" in such a way that this notion includes the collection of no objects. Actually, the set containing no elements arises quite naturally in many situations. For instance, in considering the sets of real numbers which are roots of algebraic equations, it would be awkward to make a special case for equations like $x^2 + 1 = 0$, which has no real roots. Because of its importance, the set containing no elements has a special name, the *empty set*, and it is represented by a special symbol, Φ. When it is necessary to call attention to the fact that a set A is not the empty set, then we will say that A is *nonempty*.

One reason that set theory is used in so many branches of mathematics is the versatility of its notation. As anyone who has studied elementary algebra might expect, the letters of the alphabet are used to represent sets. In this book, sets will be represented by capital letters, and the elements of sets will usually be represented by small letters.

The statement that an object a is an element of a set A is symbolized by

$$a \in A.$$

We read the expression $a \in A$ as "a is in A," or sometimes, "a in A."

To give a specific example, let A be the set of roots of the equation $x^2 - x = 0$ (Example 2). Then

$$0 \in A \qquad \text{and} \qquad 1 \in A.$$

We often wish to express the fact that an object is not contained in a certain set. If a is not an element of the set A, we write

$$a \notin A,$$

and read this expression "a is not in A." Thus if A again is the set of Example 2, we would have $2 \notin A$, $3 \notin A$, $4 \notin A$, etc.

It was mentioned earlier that a set is often defined by some property possessed by its elements. There is a very useful notational device in set theory which gives a standard method of symbolizing the set of all objects having a certain property. For instance, the sets of Examples 2 and 4 are respectively written

$$\{x | x^2 - x = 0\}, \qquad \text{and} \qquad \{a | -1 \le a \le 1\}.$$

The symbolic form $\{* | *\}$ is sometimes called the *set builder*. In using it, we replace the first asterisk by a variable element symbol (x and a in the examples), and the second asterisk is replaced by a meaningful condition which the object represented by the variable must satisfy to be an element of the set ($x^2 - x = 0$ and $-1 \le a \le 1$ in the examples). Thus, the set builder occurs in the form

$$\{x | \text{condition on } x\}$$

(or with some variable other than x), and this expression represents the set of all elements which satisfy the stated condition. Often, the totality of possible objects for which the variable stands is evident from the condition required of the variable. For example, if the real roots of algebraic equations are under discussion, then in $\{x | x^2 - x = 0\}$, it is clear that x stands for a real number, and that the set consists of the real numbers which satisfy $x^2 - x = 0$. In $\{a | -1 \leq a \leq 1\}$, it may not be clear what kind of numbers are allowed as values of the variable. If it is necessary to be more explicit, we would write

$$\{a \in R | -1 \leq a \leq 1\},$$

where R is the set of all real numbers. Similarly, in Example 6, the set builder notation would be

$$\{q \in P | d(p, q) < 1\},$$

where P is the set of all points in some plane and $d(p, q)$ is the distance between points p and q in the plane. Here, the variable q can take as its value any point in the plane P, and the set in question consists of those points in P which satisfy $d(p, q) < 1$. Other forms of the set builder notation for this example are

$$\{q | q \in P \text{ and } d(p, q) < 1\} \qquad \text{or} \qquad \{q | q \in P, d(p, q) < 1\}.$$

It is often convenient to use general symbols or expressions in place of the variable element in the set builder notation. For example, $\{x^2 | x \in R\}$, where R is the set of all real numbers, is the set of all squares of real numbers; $\{x/y | x \in N, y \in N\}$, where N is the set of all natural numbers, is the set of all positive fractions.

A variation of the set builder notation can be used to denote sets which contain only a few elements. This consists of listing all of the elements of the set between braces. For example, the sets of Examples 1 and 8 would be written

$$\{0, 1\} \qquad \text{and} \qquad \{0\},$$

respectively. It is sometimes convenient to repeat the same element one or more times in the notation for the set. Thus, in Example 3, we might first write the set of roots of $x^3 - x^2 = x \cdot x \cdot (x - 1) = 0$ as $\{0, 0, 1\}$, since 0 is a double root. Of course, by the definition of equality, $\{0, 0, 1\} = \{0, 1\}$. The notation $\{0, 0, 1\}$ conveys no more information about

$x^3 - x^2 = 0$ than $\{0, 1\}$ does. Similarly, $\{a, b, a, a, b\}$ represents the same set as $\{a, b\}$.

There is another good reason for allowing repetition of one or more elements in the notation for a set. Consider the example $\{a, b\}$. We can think of this as the set whose members are the letters a and b. In mathematical applications, however, it is often convenient to regard $\{a, b\}$ as the set containing variable quantities a and b. As such, it would become a specific set if particular values where substituted for a and b. For example, if we allow natural numbers to be substituted for a and b, then each choice of values for a and b determines a set whose members are these selected natural numbers. In this example, a and b may take on the same value. For instance, if $a = 1$, $b = 1$, then $\{a, b\} = \{1, 1\} = \{1\}$. If we did not allow repetition of the elements in designating sets, the collection of sets $\{a, b\}$ determined by substituting values for a and b would be considerably more difficult to describe. This difficulty would be increased in more complicated examples.

Sets containing many elements can often be represented by listing some of the elements between braces and using a sequence of dots to indicate omitted elements. For example, it is clear that

$$\{1, 2, 3, \ldots, 2165\}$$

represents the set of all natural numbers from 1 to 2165. Some infinite sets can also be represented in this way. For example,

$$\{1, 2, 3, \ldots\}$$

denotes the set of all natural numbers.

DEFINITION 1–1.2. A set A is called a *subset* of the set B (or A is *included in* B) if every element of A is an element of B. It is customary to express the fact that A is a subset of B by writing $A \subseteq B$ or $B \supseteq A$.

Any set A is a subset of itself, $A \subseteq A$, according to this definition. If $A \subseteq B$, but $A \neq B$ (that is, A is not the same as the set B), then A is called a *proper subset* of B and in this case we write $A \subset B$ or $B \supset A$. If A is not a subset of B, we write $A \nsubseteq B$ or $B \nsupseteq A$.

EXAMPLE 11. The set of all even integers, $E = \{0, \pm 2, \pm 4, \ldots\}$, is a proper subset of the set Z of all integers.

EXAMPLE 12. The set of all points at distance less than one from a point p in a plane P is a proper subset of the set of points of P at distance less than or equal to one from p.

EXAMPLE 13. $\{0, 1\} \subset \{0, 1, 2, 4\}$.

EXAMPLE 14. $\{a|0 < a \leq 1\} \subset \{a|0 \leq a \leq 1\}$.

EXAMPLE 15. $\Phi \subseteq A$ for every set A.

The reader should carefully check to see that in each of these examples the condition of Definition 1–1.2 is satisfied. The fact that Φ is a subset of every set may seem strange. However, it is certainly true according to our definitions: every element of Φ is an element of A, or in other words, no element of Φ can be found which is not in A. Since Φ has no elements, this condition is certainly satisfied.

The inclusion relation has three properties which, although direct consequences of our definition, are quite important. The first of these has already been noted.

THEOREM 1–1.3. For any sets A, B, and C,
  (a) $A \subseteq A$,
  (b) if $A \subseteq B$ and $B \subseteq A$, then $A = B$,
  (c) if $A \subseteq B$ and $B \subseteq C$, then $A \subseteq C$.

Proof. We will prove property (b) in detail, leaving the proof of (c) to the reader. If $A \subseteq B$ and $B \subseteq A$, then every element of A is an element of B and every element of B is an element of A. That is, A and B contain exactly the same elements. Thus, by Definition 1–1.1, $A = B$.

Certain sets occur so frequently in mathematical work that it is convenient to use particular symbols to designate them throughout any mathematical paper or book. An example is the practice of denoting the empty set by the symbol Φ. In this book, the number systems of mathematics, considered as sets, will occur repeatedly. We therefore adopt the following conventions:

  N designates the set of all natural numbers: $\{1, 2, 3, \ldots\}$;
  Z designates the set of all integers: $\{\ldots, -3, -2, -1, 0, 1, 2, 3, \ldots\}$;
  Q designates the set of all rational numbers: $\{a/b|a \in Z, b \in N\}$;
  R designates the set of all real numbers.

This notation, though not universal, would be recognized by most modern mathematicians. Throughout this book, the letters N, Z, Q, and R will not be used to denote any set other than the corresponding ones listed above.

In mathematical literature, a considerable amount of variation in notation can be found. The terminology and symbolism introduced in this section will be used in the remainder of this book, but it is by no means universal. For the reader's convenience, we list some common alternative terminology.

Set: class, ensemble, aggregate, collection.
Element of a set: member of a set, point of a set.
Empty set: void set, vacuous set, null set, zero set.
Φ: 0, Λ.
$a \in A : A \ni a$.
$a \notin A : a \in' A, a \bar{\in} A, A \not\ni a$.
$\{*|*\} : \{* : *\}, [*|*], [* : *]$.

PROBLEMS

1. Using the set builder form, write expressions for the following sets.
   (a) The set of all even integers.
   (b) The set of all integers which are divisible by five.
   (c) The set of all integers which leave a remainder of one when divided by five.
   (d) The set of all rational numbers greater than five.
   (e) The set of all points in space which are inside a sphere with center at the point p and radius r.
   (f) The set of solutions of the equation $x^3 - 2x^2 - x + 2 = 0$.
2. Tell in words what sets are represented by the following expressions.
   (a) $\{x \in N | x > 10\}$
   (b) $\{x \in Q | x - \frac{1}{2} \in N\}$
   (c) $\{5, 6, 7, \ldots\}$
   (d) $\{a, b, \ldots, y, z\}$
   (e) $\{x | x = y^2 + z^2, y \in R, z \in R, x^2 - y^2 = (x - y)(x + y)\}$
3. Describe the following sets by listing their elements.
   (a) $\{x | x^2 = 1\}$
   (b) $\{x | x^2 - 2x = 0\}$
   (c) $\{x | x^2 - 2x + 1 = 0\}$
4. List the following collections of sets.
   (a) The sets $\{a, b, c\}$, where a, b, and c are natural numbers less than or equal to 3.
   (b) The sets $\{a^2 + a + 1\}$, where a is a natural number less than or equal to 5.
   (c) The three element sets $\{a, b, c\}$, where a, b, and c are integers between -2 and 4.
5. State all inclusion relations which exist between the following sets: N, Z, Q, R, the set of all even integers, $\{n | n = m^2, m \in Z\}$, $\{x | x = y^2, y \in Q\}$, $\{x | x = y^2 - n, y \in R, n \in Z\}$.
6. Prove Theorem 1–1.3(c).
7. Prove that if $A \subseteq B$, $B \subset C$, then $A \subset C$, and if $A \subset B$ and $B \subseteq C$, then $A \subset C$.

1–2 The cardinal number of a set. The simplest and most important classification of sets is given by the distinction between finite and infinite sets. Returning to the examples considered in Section 1–1, the set of Examples 1, 2, and 3, and the sets of Examples 8 and 9 are finite, while the sets of Examples 4 through 7 are infinite. Note that the empty set Φ is considered to be finite. It is not altogether easy to explain the difference between a finite and an infinite set, although almost everyone with some experience learns to distinguish finite from infinite sets. Roughly speaking, a finite set is either the empty set, or a set in which we can designate a first element, a second element, a third element, and so on, until at some stage we reach an nth element and find that there are no more left. Of course, the number n of elements in the set may be one, two, three, four, ... , a million, or any natural number whatsoever.

A set is said to be *infinite* if it is not finite, that is, if its elements cannot be counted. Examples of infinite sets are the set N of all natural numbers, the set Z of all integers, the set Q of all rational numbers, the set R of all real numbers, etc. These examples show that some of the most important sets encountered in mathematics are infinite.

If A is a finite set, it is meaningful to speak of the number of elements of A. This number is called the *cardinal number* (or *cardinality*) of the set A. We will use the notation $|A|$ to designate the cardinal number of A. As examples,

$$|\{0\}| = 1, \qquad |\{a\}| = 1, \qquad |\{0, 1, 4\}| = 3.$$

It was remarked above that the empty set Φ is regarded as being finite. Since Φ has no elements, it is natural to say that the cardinality of Φ is zero. Thus, in symbols, $|\Phi| = 0$.

There are many synonyms for the expression "cardinal number of A." Besides the term "cardinality of A," which we have already mentioned, one finds such expressions as "power of A" and "potency of A." The notation $|A|$ for the cardinal number of the set A is not universal either. The symbolism $\overline{\overline{A}}$ is perhaps even more common (but difficult to print and type), and such expressions as card A or $N(A)$ can also be found.

These descriptions of finite and infinite sets, and of the cardinal number of a finite set are too vague to be called mathematical definitions. Moreover, we have not said anything about the cardinal numbers of sets which are not finite. The first man to systematically study the cardinal number concept for arbitrary sets (both finite and infinite) was Georg Cantor (1845–1918). His researches have had a profound influence on all aspects of modern mathematics. In the remainder of this section, we will examine one of Cantor's most important ideas, and see in particular how it enables us to explain the concept of a finite set in more exact terms.

DEFINITION 1–2.1. A pairing between the elements of two sets A and B such that each element of A is matched with exactly one element of B, and each element of B is matched with exactly one element of A, is called a *one-to-one correspondence* between A and B.

The reader should study the following examples to be sure that he fully understands the meaning of the fundamental concept defined in Definition 1–2.1.

EXAMPLE 1. Let $A = \{1, 2, 3\}$, and $B = \{a, b, c\}$. Then there are six possible one-to-one correspondences between A and B:

$$
\begin{array}{ccc}
1 & 2 & 3\\
\updownarrow & \updownarrow & \updownarrow\\
a & b & c
\end{array}
\quad
\begin{array}{ccc}
1 & 2 & 3\\
\updownarrow & \updownarrow & \updownarrow\\
b & c & a
\end{array}
\quad
\begin{array}{ccc}
1 & 2 & 3\\
\updownarrow & \updownarrow & \updownarrow\\
c & a & b
\end{array}
\quad
\begin{array}{ccc}
1 & 2 & 3\\
\updownarrow & \updownarrow & \updownarrow\\
b & a & c
\end{array}
\quad
\begin{array}{ccc}
1 & 2 & 3\\
\updownarrow & \updownarrow & \updownarrow\\
a & c & b
\end{array}
\quad
\begin{array}{ccc}
1 & 2 & 3\\
\updownarrow & \updownarrow & \updownarrow\\
c & b & a
\end{array}
$$

EXAMPLE 2. It is impossible to obtain a one-to-one correspondence between the set $A = \{1, 2, 3\}$ and the set $B = \{1, 2\}$. No matter how we try to pair off the elements of A and B, we find that more than one element of A must correspond to a single element of B. If $1 \leftrightarrow 1$ and $2 \leftrightarrow 2$, then 3 must correspond to 1 or 2 in B. In the correspondence $1 \leftrightarrow 1$, $2 \leftrightarrow 2$, $3 \leftrightarrow 1$, the element $1 \in B$ is paired with both $1 \in A$ and $3 \in A$, so that the correspondence is not one-to-one. A similar situation occurs in all possible correspondences between A and B. The more general fact that there is no one-to-one correspondence between $\{1, 2, 3, \ldots, m\}$ and $\{1, 2, 3, \ldots, n\}$ if $m < n$ is also true. This can be proved using the properties of the natural numbers, which will be discussed in the next two chapters.

EXAMPLE 3. There is a one-to-one correspondence between the set $Z = \{\ldots, -3, -2, -1, 0, 1, 2, 3, \ldots\}$ of all integers and the set $N = \{1, 2, 3, \ldots\}$ of all natural numbers. The elements of Z and N can be paired off as follows:

$$
\begin{array}{ccccccccc}
0 & -1 & 1 & -2 & 2 & \ldots & -n & & n\\
\updownarrow & \updownarrow & \updownarrow & \updownarrow & \updownarrow & & \updownarrow & & \updownarrow\\
1 & 2 & 3 & 4 & 5 & \ldots & 2n & & 2n+1
\end{array}
$$

Note that in order to construct a one-to-one correspondence between Z and N, not all of the numbers of N can be paired with themselves. Otherwise, we would use up all of N and have nothing left to associate with $0, -1, -2, \ldots$.

Using Definition 1–2.1, we can clarify the notion of a finite set.

DEFINITION 1–2.2. Let A be a set and let n be a natural number. Then the cardinal number of A is n if there is a one-to-one correspondence between A and the set $\{1, 2, 3, \ldots, n\}$, consisting of the first n natural numbers. A set A is *finite* if $A = \Phi$, or there is a natural number n such that the cardinal number of A is n. Otherwise A is called *infinite*.

This definition is no more than a careful restatement of the informal descriptions of finite and infinite sets, and their cardinal numbers, which were given at the beginning of this chapter.

The usual practice of writing a finite set in the form

$$\{a_1, a_2, a_3, \ldots, a_n\} \qquad \text{(without repetition)}$$

exhibits the one-to-one correspondence between A and $\{1, 2, 3, \ldots, n\}$, namely,

$$
\begin{array}{ccccc}
a_1 & a_2 & a_3 & \ldots & a_n \\
\updownarrow & \updownarrow & \updownarrow & & \updownarrow \\
1 & 2 & 3 & \ldots & n
\end{array}
$$

Cantor observed that it is possible to say when two sets A and B have the same number of elements, without referring to the exact number of elements in A and B. This idea is illustrated in the following example. Suppose that in a certain mathematics class, every chair in the room is occupied and no students are standing. Then without counting the number of students and the number of chairs, it can be asserted that the number of students in the class is the same as the number of chairs in the room. The reason is obvious; there is a one-to-one correspondence between the set of all students in the class and the set of all chairs in the room.

DEFINITION 1–2.3. Two sets A and B are said to have the *same cardinal number*, or the *same cardinality*, or to be *equivalent* if there exists a one-to-one correspondence between A and B.

By Example 1, the two sets $\{1, 2, 3\}$ and $\{a, b, c\}$ have the same cardinality. By Example 3, so do the sets N and Z. However, according to Example 2, the sets $\{1, 2, 3\}$ and $\{1, 2\}$ do not have the same cardinal number.

In accordance with Definition 1–2.3, the existence of any one-to-one correspondence between A and B is enough to guarantee that A and B have the same cardinal number. As in Example 1, there may be many one-to-one correspondences between A and B.

EXAMPLE 4. Every set A is equivalent to itself, since $a \leftrightarrow a$ for $a \in A$ is obviously a one-to-one correspondence of A with itself. If A contains more than one element, then there are other ways of defining a one-to-one correspondence of A with itself. For example, let $A = \{1, 2\}$. Then there are two one-to-one correspondences of A with itself: $1 \leftrightarrow 1$, $2 \leftrightarrow 2$ and $1 \leftrightarrow 2$, $2 \leftrightarrow 1$. Any one-to-one correspondence of a set with itself is called a *permutation* of the set.

If $A = \{a_1, a_2, \ldots, a_n\}$ and $B = \{b_1, b_2, \ldots, b_n\}$ are finite sets which both have the cardinal number n, then there is a one-to-one correspondence between A and B:

$$
\begin{array}{cccc}
a_1 & a_2 & \ldots & a_n \\
\updownarrow & \updownarrow & & \updownarrow \\
b_1 & b_2 & \ldots & b_n
\end{array}
$$

so that A and B are equivalent in the sense of Definition 1–2.3. That is, if A and B are finite sets, then A and B are equivalent if $|A| = |B|$.

The important fact to observe about Definition 1–2.3 is that it applies to infinite as well as finite sets. One of Cantor's most remarkable discoveries was that infinite sets can have different magnitudes, that is, in some sense, certain infinite sets are "bigger than" others. To appreciate this fact requires some work. Example 3 has already illustrated the fact that infinite sets which seem to have different magnitudes may in fact have the same cardinality. An even more striking example of this phenomenon is the following one.

EXAMPLE 5. The set N of natural numbers has the same cardinality as the set

$$
F = \{m/n \mid m \in N, n \in N\}
$$

of all positive rational numbers. This can be seen with the aid of a diagram as in Fig. 1–2. By following the indicated path, each fraction will eventually be passed. If we number the fractions in the order that they are encountered, skipping fractions like $\frac{2}{2}$, $\frac{2}{4}$, $\frac{3}{3}$, and $\frac{4}{2}$, which are equal to numbers which have

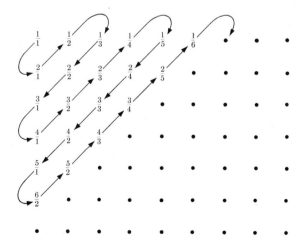

FIGURE 1–2

been previously passed, we get the desired one-to-one correspondence between
N and F:

$$
\begin{array}{ccccccccccccccccc}
1 & 2 & 3 & 4 & 5 & 6 & 7 & 8 & 9 & 10 & 11 & 12 & 13 & 14 & 15 & 16 & 17 \\
\updownarrow & \updownarrow & \updownarrow & \updownarrow & \updownarrow & \updownarrow & \updownarrow & \updownarrow & \updownarrow & \updownarrow & \updownarrow & \updownarrow & \updownarrow & \updownarrow & \updownarrow & \updownarrow & \updownarrow \\
\frac{1}{1} & \frac{2}{1} & \frac{1}{2} & \frac{1}{3} & \frac{3}{1} & \frac{4}{1} & \frac{3}{2} & \frac{2}{3} & \frac{1}{4} & \frac{1}{5} & \frac{5}{1} & \frac{6}{1} & \frac{5}{2} & \frac{4}{3} & \frac{3}{4} & \frac{2}{5} & \frac{1}{6}
\end{array} \quad \ldots
$$

Cantor showed that many important collections of numbers have the same
cardinality as the set N of all natural numbers. For example, this is true for
the set A of all real algebraic numbers, that is, real numbers r which are solutions of an equation of the form

$$ n_0 x^k + n_1 x^{k-1} + \cdots + n_{k-1} x + n_k = 0, $$

where $n_0, n_1, \ldots, n_{k-1}, n_k$ are any integers. The set A includes all rational
numbers, since m/n is a root of the equation $nx - m = 0$; A also includes
numbers like

$$ \sqrt{2}, \sqrt[3]{2}, \sqrt{3}, \sqrt[3]{3}, \ldots. $$

Judging from these examples, one might guess that all infinite sets
have the same cardinality. But this is not the case. Cantor proved that it
is impossible to give a pairing between N and the set R of all real numbers.
Later, we will be able to present Cantor's proof that these sets do not have
the same cardinal numbers. The fact that the set A of real algebraic
numbers has the same cardinality as N and the result that R and N do
not have the same cardinal numbers together imply that $R \neq A$. That
is, there are real numbers which are not solutions of any equation

$$ n_0 x^k + n_1 x^{k-1} + \cdots + n_{k-1} x + n_k = 0 $$

with $n_0, n_1, \ldots, n_{k-1}, n_k$ integers. This interesting fact is by no means
evident. It is fairly hard to exhibit such a real number, but Cantor's
results immediately imply that they do exist.

Although Cantor's work on the theory of sets was highly successful in
many ways, it raised numerous new and difficult problems. One of these
ranks among the three most famous unsolved problems in mathematics
(the other two: the Fermat conjecture, which we will describe in Chapter 5,
and the Riemann hypothesis, which is too technical to explain in this
book.) Cantor posed the problem of whether or not there is some set S
of real numbers whose cardinality is different from both the cardinality
of N and the cardinality of R. The conjecture that no such set S exists

is known as the *continuum hypothesis*. It was first suggested in 1878, and to date, it has been neither proved nor disproved.

An infinite set is called *denumerable* if it has the same cardinality as the set N of all natural numbers. If S is denumerable, then it is possible to pair off the elements of S with the numbers $1, 2, 3, \ldots$. Thus, the elements can be labeled $a_1, a_2, a_3, \ldots$, where a_n is the symbol which stands for the element corresponding to the number n. Hence, if S is denumerable, then S can be written $\{a_1, a_2, a_3, \ldots\}$, with the elements of S listed in the form of a sequence. The converse statement is also true. That is, a set which can be designated $\{a_1, a_2, a_3, \ldots\}$ is denumerable (or possibly finite, since distinct symbols might represent the same element of S). As we have shown in this section, the set of all integers and the set of all positive rational numbers are examples of denumerable sets.

We conclude this section by listing for future reference the following important properties of the equivalence of sets.

(1–2.4). Let A, B, and C be arbitrary sets. Then
   (a) A is equivalent to A;
   (b) if A is equivalent to B, then B is equivalent to A; and
   (c) if A is equivalent to B and B is equivalent to C, then A is equivalent to C.

It has already been noted in Example 4 that (a) is satisfied. Property (b) follows from the fact that the definition of a one-to-one correspondence is symmetric. That is, if A and B are interchanged in Definition 1–2.1, the definition says the same thing as before. Thus, a one-to-one correspondence between A and B is a one-to-one correspondence between B and A. The proof of (c) is left as an exercise for the reader (see Problem 8).

PROBLEMS

1. State which of the following sets are finite.
   (a) $\{\langle x, y, z \rangle | x \in \{0, 1, 2\}, y \in \{3, 4\}, z \in \{0, 2, 4\}\}$
   (b) $\{x | x \in Z, x < 5\}$
   (c) $\{x | x \in N, x^2 - 3 = 0\}$
   (d) $\{x | x \in Q, 0 < x < 1\}$

2. What is the cardinal number of the following finite sets?
   (a) $\{n | n \in N, n < 1000\}$ (b) $\{n | n \in Z, n^2 \leq 36\}$
   (c) $\{n^2 | n \in Z, n^2 \leq 36\}$ (d) $\{n | n \in N, n^3 \leq 27\}$
   (e) $\{n^3 | n \in N, n^3 \leq 27\}$

3. Let $A = \{1, 2, 3, 4\}$ and $B = \{a, b, c, d\}$. List all one-to-one correspondences between A and B.

4. Using the method by which we proved that the positive rational numbers have the same cardinality as the set N of natural numbers, indicate how to prove that N has the same cardinal number as the set of all pairs $\langle m, n \rangle$ of natural numbers. List the pairs which correspond to all numbers up to 21.

5. Prove that the set of all rational numbers Q has the same cardinality as the set of all natural numbers N.

6. Let A be the set of all positive real numbers x, and let B be the set of all real numbers y satisfying $0 < y < 1$. Show that the pairing $x \leftrightarrow y$, where $y = 1/(1 + x)$ is a one-to-one correspondence between A and B.

7. Let A be a denumerable set, and let B be a finite set. Show that the set $S = \{\langle x, y \rangle | x \in A, y \in B\}$ is denumerable.

8. Suppose that sets A and B have the same cardinality, and that sets B and C have the same cardinality. Show that A and C have the same cardinality.

1–3 The construction of sets from given sets. In this section, we will discuss two important methods of constructing sets from given sets. The first process combines two sets X and Y to obtain a set called the product of X and Y. The second construction leads from a single set X to another set called the power set of X. There are several other methods of building sets from given sets, but they will not be considered in this book.

The definition of the product of two sets is based on the concept of an *ordered pair* of elements. Suppose that a and b denote any objects whatsoever. If the elements a and b are grouped together in a definite order $\langle a, b \rangle$, where a is the first element and b is the second element, then the resulting object $\langle a, b \rangle$ is called an ordered pair of elements. Two ordered pairs are the same if and only if they have the same first element and the same second element. Thus we arrive at the following definition.*

DEFINITION 1–3.1. $\langle a, b \rangle = \langle c, d \rangle$ if and only if $a = c$ and $b = d$.

EXAMPLE 1. Let $A = \{1, 2, 3\}$. Then the following distinct ordered pairs of elements of A can be formed: $\langle 1, 1 \rangle$, $\langle 1, 2 \rangle$, $\langle 1, 3 \rangle$, $\langle 2, 1 \rangle$, $\langle 2, 2 \rangle$, $\langle 2, 3 \rangle$, $\langle 3, 1 \rangle$, $\langle 3, 2 \rangle$, $\langle 3, 3 \rangle$. Note that $\langle a, b \rangle = \langle b, a \rangle$ only if $a = b$. By Definition 1–3.1, this is true in general.

EXAMPLE 2. A man has two pairs of shoes, one brown pair and one black pair. If he dresses in the dark, what are the possible combinations of shoes

---

* There is a simple way to define an ordered pair in the framework of set theory, namely, for objects a and b let $\langle a, b \rangle = \{\{a, b\}, a\}$. An ordered pair is then a definite object, and it is possible to prove that $\langle a, b \rangle = \langle c, d \rangle$ if and only if $a = c$ and $b = d$. However, we will use the informal description given in the text and regard this property of ordered pairs as a definition.

which he can put on? Let X = {left brown shoe, left black shoe} and Y = {right brown shoe, right black shoe}. Then the set of all possible combinations which the man might wear is the set of all ordered pairs with the first element taken from the set X and the second element taken from the set Y, that is, the set of all pairs ⟨left brown shoe, right brown shoe⟩, ⟨left brown shoe, right black shoe⟩, ⟨left black shoe, right brown shoe⟩, ⟨left black shoe, right black shoe⟩.

EXAMPLE 3. The set of all ordered pairs of natural numbers is the set

$$S = \{\langle n, m\rangle | n \in N, m \in N\}.$$

Thus,

$$S = \{\langle 1, 1\rangle, \langle 1, 2\rangle, \langle 2, 1\rangle, \langle 1, 3\rangle, \langle 2, 2\rangle, \langle 3, 1\rangle, \langle 1, 4\rangle, \langle 2, 3\rangle, \langle 3, 2\rangle, \langle 4,1\rangle, \ldots\}.$$

DEFINITION 1–3.2. Let X and Y be sets. Then the *product* of the sets X and Y is the set of all ordered pairs $\langle x, y\rangle$, where $x \in X$ and $y \in Y$. The product of X and Y is denoted by $X \times Y$. Thus, in symbols

$$X \times Y = \{\langle x, y\rangle | x \in X, y \in Y\}.$$

EXAMPLE 4. The ordered pairs listed in Examples 1, 2, and 3 are exactly the elements of the products $A \times A$, $X \times Y$, and $N \times N$, respectively.

EXAMPLE 5. Let $U = \{1, 2, 3\}$, $V = \{1, 3\}$, and $W = \{2, 3\}$. Then $U \times V = \{\langle 1, 1\rangle, \langle 1, 3\rangle, \langle 2, 1\rangle, \langle 2, 3\rangle, \langle 3, 1\rangle, \langle 3, 3\rangle\}$, and $V \times U = \{\langle 1, 1\rangle, \langle 1, 2\rangle, \langle 1, 3\rangle, \langle 3, 1\rangle, \langle 3, 2\rangle, \langle 3, 3\rangle\}$. It follows that $U \times V \neq V \times U$. Thus, in forming the product of two sets, the order in which the sets are taken is significant. We also have

$$(U \times V) \times W = \{\langle\langle 1, 1\rangle, 2\rangle, \quad \langle\langle 1, 3\rangle, 2\rangle, \quad \langle\langle 2, 1\rangle, 2\rangle, \quad \langle\langle 2, 3\rangle, 2\rangle, \quad \langle\langle 3, 1\rangle, 2\rangle,$$
$$\langle\langle 3, 3\rangle, 2\rangle, \quad \langle\langle 1, 1\rangle, 3\rangle, \quad \langle\langle 1, 3\rangle, 3\rangle, \quad \langle\langle 2, 1\rangle, 3\rangle, \quad \langle\langle 2, 3\rangle, 3\rangle,$$
$$\langle\langle 3, 1\rangle, 3\rangle, \langle\langle 3, 3\rangle, 3\rangle\},$$

$$U \times (V \times W) = \{\langle 1, \langle 1, 2\rangle\rangle, \quad \langle 1, \langle 1, 3\rangle\rangle, \quad \langle 1, \langle 3, 2\rangle\rangle, \quad \langle 1, \langle 3, 3\rangle\rangle, \quad \langle 2, \langle 1, 2\rangle\rangle,$$
$$\langle 2, \langle 1, 3\rangle\rangle, \quad \langle 2, \langle 3, 2\rangle\rangle, \quad \langle 2, \langle 3, 3\rangle\rangle, \quad \langle 3, \langle 1, 2\rangle\rangle, \quad \langle 3, \langle 1, 3\rangle\rangle,$$
$$\langle 3, \langle 3, 2\rangle\rangle, \langle 3, \langle 3, 3\rangle\rangle\}.$$

Note that the elements of $(U \times V) \times W$ are different from all of the elements of $U \times (V \times W)$. In fact, the elements of $(U \times V) \times W$ are ordered pairs whose first element is an ordered pair of numbers, and the second element is a number. In $U \times (V \times W)$ it is just the other way around: the elements are ordered pairs in which the first element is a number and the second element is an ordered pair of numbers. The reader must be careful to make a distinction between $\langle\langle 2, 1\rangle, 3\rangle$ and $\langle 2, \langle 1, 3\rangle\rangle$, for example.

EXAMPLE 6. If X is any set, then $X \times \Phi = \Phi \times X = \Phi$. Indeed, since the empty set contains no element, there cannot be any ordered pair whose first or second element belongs to the empty set.

Even though $U \times V \neq V \times U$ and $(U \times V) \times W \neq U \times (V \times W)$ in Example 5, it is true that $U \times V$ is equivalent to $V \times U$ and $(U \times V) \times W$ is equivalent to $U \times (V \times W)$, as we see by counting the elements in each of these sets. It is easy to prove that these results hold in general.

THEOREM 1–3.3. Let X, Y, and Z be sets. Then
   (a) $X \times Y$ is equivalent to $Y \times X$, and
   (b) $(X \times Y) \times Z$ is equivalent to $X \times (Y \times Z)$.

Proof. We will prove (a) and leave the proof of (b) as an exercise for the reader. According to Definition 1–2.3, we must show that there is a one-to-one correspondence between $X \times Y$ and $Y \times X$. Every element of $X \times Y$ is an ordered pair $\langle x, y \rangle$, with $x \in X$ $y \in Y$; every element of $Y \times X$ is an ordered pair $\langle z, w \rangle$, with $z \in Y$ and $w \in X$. If $\langle x, y \rangle \in X \times Y$, then $\langle y, x \rangle \in Y \times X$, so that $\langle x, y \rangle$ can be matched with $\langle y, x \rangle$. The pairing $\langle x, y \rangle \leftrightarrow \langle y, x \rangle$ is the desired one-to-one correspondence between $X \times Y$ and $Y \times X$.

The definition of the product of two sets can be generalized to a finite collection of sets $X_1, X_2, \ldots, X_n$. The product of these sets, denoted by $X_1 \times X_2 \times \cdots \times X_n$, is the set of all ordered strings of elements $\langle x_1, x_2, \ldots, x_n \rangle$, where $x_i \in X_i$ for $i = 1, 2, \ldots, n$. For example, if $n = 3$, then

$$X_1 \times X_2 \times X_3 = \{\langle x_1, x_2, x_3 \rangle | x_1 \in X_1, x_2 \in X_2, x_3 \in X_3\}.$$

EXAMPLE 7. Let U, V, and W be the sets defined in Example 5, that is $U = \{1, 2, 3\}$, $V = \{1, 3\}$, and $W = \{2, 3\}$. Then

$$U \times V \times W = \{\langle 1, 1, 2 \rangle, \quad \langle 1, 1, 3 \rangle, \quad \langle 1, 3, 2 \rangle, \quad \langle 1, 3, 3 \rangle, \quad \langle 2, 1, 2 \rangle, \quad \langle 2, 1, 3 \rangle,$$
$$\langle 2, 3, 2 \rangle, \quad \langle 2, 3, 3 \rangle, \quad \langle 3, 1, 2 \rangle, \quad \langle 3, 1, 3 \rangle, \quad \langle 3, 3, 2 \rangle, \quad \langle 3, 3, 3 \rangle\}.$$

It is possible to generalize Theorem 1–3.3 to products of finite collections of sets (see Problems 6, 7, and 8).

We turn now to a second method of obtaining a new set from a given set X.

DEFINITION 1–3.4. Let X be any set. The set of all subsets of X is called the *power set* of X, and is denoted by $P(X)$.

Thus, the elements of $P(X)$ are precisely the subsets of X. In particular, $\Phi \in P(X)$ and $X \in P(X)$.

EXAMPLE 8. If $X = \Phi$, then $P(X) = \{\Phi\}$.

EXAMPLE 9. If $X = \{a\}$, then $P(X) = \{\Phi, \{a\}\}$.

EXAMPLE 10. If $X = \{a, b\}$, then $P(X) = \{\Phi, \{a\}, \{b\}, \{a, b\}\}$.

If X is an infinite set, then it has infinitely many distinct subsets. That is, $P(X)$ is infinite if X is infinite. In fact, if $x \in X$, then $\{x\} \in P(X)$, so that $P(X)$ contains at least as many elements as X.

Suppose that X is a finite set. Let X_1 be a set which is obtained by adjoining to X a new element a which is not in X. That is, the elements of X_1 are all of the elements of X, together with the new element a. Then every subset of X_1 either does not contain a and is therefore a subset A of X, or else it contains a and is therefore obtained from a subset A of X by adjoining the element a to A. Thus, every subset A of X gives rise to two distinct subsets of X_1, the set A itself and the set A_1 obtained by adjoining a to A. Note that all of the sets so constructed are different. That is, $A \neq A_1$, and if $A \neq B$, then $A \neq B_1$, $A_1 \neq B$, and $A_1 \neq B_1$. Therefore, there are just twice as many subsets of X_1 as there are subsets of X. That is, $|P(X_1)| = 2|P(X)|$. Starting with the empty set Φ (for which $|P(X)| = 1$), it is possible to add elements one by one, doubling the cardinality of the resulting power set each time an element is added, until a set X containing n elements is obtained. Our reasoning shows that the power set of X will contain 2^n elements.

THEOREM 1–3.5. If $|X| = n$, then $|P(X)| = 2^n$.

There is another way to prove this theorem which is worth examining, since it gives additional information about the number of subsets of a finite set. Let X consist of the distinct elements $a_1, a_2, \ldots, a_n$. With each a_k in X, associate a symbol x_k, and consider the formal product

$$(1 + x_1)(1 + x_2) \ldots (1 + x_n).$$

If this expression is multiplied out, the result is a sum of distinct products of x's (except the first term, which is 1). There is exactly one such product for every subset $\{a_{m_1}, a_{m_2}, \ldots, a_{m_k}\}$ of $\{a_1, a_2, \ldots, a_n\}$, namely $x_{m_1}x_{m_2} \ldots x_{m_k}$. The empty set corresponds to 1. For instance, if

$$X = \{a_1, a_2, a_3\},$$

then

$$(1 + x_1)(1 + x_2)(1 + x_3)$$
$$= 1 + x_1 + x_2 + x_3 + x_1x_2 + x_1x_3 + x_2x_3 + x_1x_2x_3.$$

Now replace each x_k by the symbol t. Then the product becomes $(1 + t)(1 + t) \ldots (1 + t)$, while in its expansion, all products corresponding to sets containing the same number j of elements become t^j. In the example, $X = \{a_1, a_2, a_3\}$, we obtain $(1 + t)^3 = 1 + t + t + t + t^2 + t^2 + t^2 + t^3 = 1 + 3t + 3t^2 + t^3$. As in this example, all of the terms t^j can be collected into a single expression of the form $N_{j,n}t^j$, where $N_{j,n}$ is precisely the number of subsets of X which have cardinality j. Therefore

$$(1 + t)^n = N_{0,n} + N_{1,n}t + N_{2,n}t^2 + \cdots + N_{n,n}t^n. \qquad (1\text{--}1)$$

We can specialize even more by letting t have the value 1. Then the identity (1–1) becomes

$$2^n = N_{0,n} + N_{1,n} + N_{2,n} + \cdots + N_{n,n}. \qquad (1\text{--}2)$$

The sum on the right-hand side of this identity represents the number of subsets containing no elements of X (the empty set), plus the number of subsets containing one element of X, plus the number of subsets containing two elements of X, and so on, until we reach $N_{n,n}$, the number of subsets containing n elements of X. Clearly, this sum is just the total number of subsets of X, since every subset contains some number of elements of X between zero and n. Thus, we have arrived at the same conclusion as before: there are exactly 2^n subsets of a set X with n elements.

By using the binomial theorem of algebra (see Section 2–2) to expand $(1 + t)^n$, it is possible to squeeze more information from identity (1–1). We get

$$(1 + t)^n = 1 + nt + \frac{n(n - 1)}{2!} t^2 + \cdots + t^n. \qquad (1\text{--}3)$$

The coefficient of t^j is *

$$\frac{n(n - 1) \cdots (n - j + 1)}{j!} = \frac{n!}{j!(n - j)!}.$$

---

* An exclamation mark (!) following a natural number n denotes the number obtained by multiplying together all the numbers from 1 to n. For example, $1! = 1$, $2! = 1 \cdot 2 = 2$, $3! = 1 \cdot 2 \cdot 3 = 6$, $4! = 1 \cdot 2 \cdot 3 \cdot 4 = 24$. It is also customary to define 0! to be 1. With this convention, the formulas for the binomial coefficients are correct in the cases $j = 0$ and $j = n$.

Comparing the identities (1–1) and (1–3) we see that

$$N_{0,n} + N_{1,n}t + N_{2,n}t^2 + \cdots + N_{n,n}t^n = 1 + nt + \frac{n(n-1)}{2}t^2 + \cdots + t^n$$

for all numbers t. This leads us to expect that the coefficients of the same powers of t on each side of the equation must be equal. That is, $N_{0,n} = 1$, $N_{1,n} = n$, $N_{2,n} = n(n-1)/2, \ldots, N_{n,n} = 1$, and in general

$$N_{j,n} = \frac{n!}{j!(n-j)!}. \tag{1–4}$$

Later we will be able to prove that if

$$a_0 + a_1 t + \cdots + a_n t^n = b_0 + b_1 t + \cdots + b_n t^n$$

for all values of t, then $a_0 = b_0$, $a_1 = b_1, \ldots, a_n = b_n$. This will justify (1–4). Thus, our somewhat longer proof of Theorem 1–3.5 yields the interesting fact that in a set X containing n distinct elements, there are $n!/j!(n-j)!$ different subsets containing exactly j elements. For example, in a set containing ten elements, there are $10!/4!6! = 210$ subsets of cardinality 4.

Problems

1. List the elements of the sets $A \times B$, $B \times A$, $(A \times B) \times C$, and $A \times (B \times C)$, where $A = \{x, y, z, w\}$, $B = \{1, 2\}$, and $C = \{a\}$.

2. Prove Theorem 1–3.3(b).

3. Let $U = \{1, 2\}$. Prove that $U \times N$ is equivalent to N, where N is the set of all natural numbers.

4. Prove that if U is a finite nonempty set and V is a denumerable set, then $U \times V$ is equivalent to V.

5. Prove that if U and V are denumerable sets, then the following sets are equivalent: U, V, $U \times V$, $V \times U$.

6. State the generalization of Theorem 1–3.3 for a finite collection of sets $X_1, X_2, \ldots, X_n$.

7. Prove that $U \times V \times W$ is equivalent to $(U \times V) \times W$, where U, V, and W are arbitrary sets.

8. Prove that the following sets are equivalent: $U \times V \times W$, $U \times W \times V$, $V \times U \times W$, $V \times W \times U$, $W \times U \times V$, $W \times V \times U$.

9. For any set X, define

$$X^n = \overbrace{X \times X \times \cdots \times X}^{n \text{ factors}},$$

where n is a natural number. Show that if $X = \{1, 2\}$, and $Y = \{1, 2, \ldots, n\}$, then $|X^n| = |P(Y)|$.

10. List the elements of $P(X)$, where $X = \{1, 2, 3, 4\}$.

11. Let X be a set with 7 objects.
   (a) How many subsets of X of cardinality at most three are there?
   (b) How many subsets of X of cardinality at least three are there?

12. (a) Let $t = -1$ in equation (1–1) and interpret the meaning of the resulting identity.
   (b) What is the number of subsets of even cardinality of a set containing n elements?

13. Show that if the sets A and B have the same cardinality, then so do $P(A)$ and $P(B)$.

14. Cantor proved that if X is an infinite set, then X and $P(X)$ do not have the same cardinal number, that is, it is impossible to give a one-to-one correspondence between the elements of X and the elements of $P(X)$. Prove this fact. [*Hint:* Suppose that $a \leftrightarrow A$ is such a correspondence. Let

$$B = \{a | a \in X, a \leftrightarrow A \text{ and } a \notin A\}.$$

Show that if $b \leftrightarrow B$, then both $b \in B$ and $b \notin B$.]

1–4 The algebra of sets. The ordinary number systems satisfy several important laws of operation, such as $a + b = b + a$, $a \cdot (b \cdot c) = (a \cdot b) \cdot c$ and $a \cdot (b + c) = a \cdot b + a \cdot c$. There are also natural operations of combining sets which satisfy rules analogous to these identities. Modern algebra is largely concerned with systems which satisfy various laws of operation, so it is natural that the algebra of sets should be a part of this subject. Our objective in this section is to study the principal operating rules for sets. The first two basic operations of set theory are analogous to addition and multiplication of numbers. They are *binary operations*, that is, they are performed on a pair of sets to obtain a new set.

DEFINITION 1–4.1. Let A and B be sets. Then

$$A \cup B = \{x | x \in A \text{ or } x \in B\},$$
$$A \cap B = \{x | x \in A \text{ and } x \in B\}.$$

The set $A \cup B$ is called the *union* (or *join* or *set sum*) of A and B. The set $A \cap B$ is called the *intersection* (or *meet* or *set product*) of A and B.

As we pointed out in the Introduction, the word "or" in mathematics is interpreted in the inclusive sense, so that the statement "$x \in A$ or $x \in B$" includes the case where x is in both A and B. Thus, the union of A and B contains those elements which are in A, or in B, or in both A and B. The intersection of A and B contains those elements which are in both A and B.

These sets can be illustrated by means of simple pictures called Venn diagrams. The elements of the sets are represented by the points inside a closed curve in the plane. It should be emphasized that these diagrams are only symbolic, and that the elements of the sets which they represent are not necessarily points in the plane, but can be any objects whatsoever. In Fig. 1–3, the total shaded area is $A \cup B$ and the doubly shaded area is $A \cap B$.

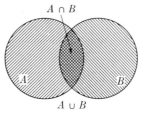

FIGURE 1–3

EXAMPLE 1. $\{1, 3, 4, 5, 7\} \cup \{2, 3, 6\} = \{1, 2, 3, 4, 5, 6, 7\}$.

EXAMPLE 2. $\{1, 3, 4, 5, 7\} \cap \{2, 3, 6\} = \{3\}$.

EXAMPLE 3. $\{1, 3, 4, 5, 7\} \cap \{2, 6\} = \Phi$.

EXAMPLE 4. $\{a|0 < a < 1\} \cup \{0, 1\} = \{a|0 \leq a \leq 1\}$.

EXAMPLE 5. $\{a|0 < a < 1\} \cap \{a|\frac{1}{2} < a < 2\} = \{a|\frac{1}{2} < a < 1\}$.

EXAMPLE 6. If A is the set of all points of a line through the point p and if B is the set of all points of a second (different) line through p, then $A \cap B = \{p\}$.

In most mathematical applications of set theory, all of the sets under consideration will be subsets of some particular set X. This set, called the *universal set*, may be different for different problems, but it will usually be fixed throughout any discussion. For the purposes of developing the algebra of sets, we will fix a universal set X once and for all. All of the sets under consideration are assumed to be subsets of X.

The third basic operation of set theory is analogous to forming the negative of a number. It is a *unary operation*, that is, it is performed on a single set to obtain a new set.

DEFINITION 1–4.2. Let A be a subset of the set X. Then

$$A^c = \{x|x \in X, x \notin A\}.$$

The set A^c is called the *complement* of A in X (or simply the complement of A if it is understood that A is being considered as a subset of the universal set X).

Thus, A^c consists of those elements of X which are not elements of A. There are many different notations in mathematical literature for the complement of a set A. Some which the reader may encounter are A', $\overline{A}$, $C(A)$, and $c(A)$. In Fig. 1–4, the shaded area represents A^c.

FIGURE 1–4

EXAMPLE 7. Let $X = \{1, 2, 3, 4, 5\}$. Then $\{1, 3\}^c = \{2, 4, 5\}$.

EXAMPLE 8. Let $X = \{1, 2, 3\}$. Then $\{1, 3\}^c = \{2\}$.

EXAMPLE 9. Let X be the set of all real numbers. Then $\{a|a < 0\}^c = \{a|a \geq 0\}$.

—————

THEOREM 1–4.3. Let A, B, and C be subsets of X. Then the following identities are satisfied:

(a) $A \cup B = B \cup A$, $A \cap B = B \cap A$;
(b) $A \cup (B \cup C) = (A \cup B) \cup C$, $A \cap (B \cap C) = (A \cap B) \cap C$;
(c) $A \cup A = A$, $A \cap A = A$;
(d) $A \cap (B \cup C) = (A \cap B) \cup (A \cap C)$,
    $A \cup (B \cap C) = (A \cup B) \cap (A \cup C)$;
(e) $A \cup A^c = X$, $A \cap A^c = \Phi$;
(f) $A \cup X = X$, $A \cap \Phi = \Phi$;
(g) $A \cup \Phi = A$, $A \cap X = A$.

Proof. All of these identities are simple consequences of the definition of union, intersection, and complement. We will illustrate this assertion by giving the detailed proofs of (b) and (d). The remaining identities are left for the reader to check.

Suppose that $x \in A \cup (B \cup C)$. Then according to Definition 1–4.1, either $x \in A$ or $x \in B \cup C$. Suppose that $x \in A$. Then by Definition 1–4.1 again, $x \in A \cup B$. Again, by 1–4.1, $x \in (A \cup B) \cup C$. On the other hand, if $x \in B \cup C$, then either $x \in B$ or $x \in C$. If $x \in B$, then $x \in A \cup B$, and consequently $x \in (A \cup B) \cup C$. If $x \in C$, then we conclude immediately that $x \in (A \cup B) \cup C$. Thus, in every case, if $x \in A \cup (B \cup C)$, then $x \in (A \cup B) \cup C$. By Definition 1–1.2, this means that $A \cup (B \cup C)$ $\subseteq (A \cup B) \cup C$. A similar argument shows that $(A \cup B) \cup C \subseteq$ $A \cup (B \cup C)$. Hence, $A \cup (B \cup C) = (A \cup B) \cup C$. This proves the first half of (b).

If $x \in A \cap (B \cap C)$, then by Definition 1–4.1, $x \in A$ and $x \in B \cap C$. Thus, $x \in A$, $x \in B$, and $x \in C$. Consequently, $x \in A \cap B$ and $x \in C$. Therefore $x \in (A \cap B) \cap C$. Hence, $A \cap (B \cap C) \subseteq (A \cap B) \cap C$. Similarly, $(A \cap B) \cap C \subseteq A \cap (B \cap C)$. This shows that $A \cap (B \cap C) = (A \cap B) \cap C$.

To prove the first equality of (d), suppose that $x \in A \cap (B \cup C)$. Then $x \in A$ and $x \in B \cup C$. Hence, either $x \in A$ and $x \in B$ or $x \in A$ and $x \in C$. That is, either $x \in A \cap B$ or $x \in A \cap C$. Consequently, $x \in (A \cap B) \cup (A \cap C)$. We have shown that $A \cap (B \cup C) \subseteq (A \cap B) \cup$ $(A \cap C)$. On the other hand, suppose that $x \in (A \cap B) \cup (A \cap C)$. Then either $x \in A \cap B$ or $x \in A \cap C$. If $x \in A \cap B$, then $x \in A$ and $x \in B$, so that $x \in A$ and $x \in B \cup C$. Therefore $x \in A \cap (B \cup C)$. Similarly, if $x \in A \cap C$, then $x \in A \cap (B \cup C)$. Hence, in any case, $x \in A \cap (B \cup C)$. We have shown that

$$(A \cap B) \cup (A \cap C) \subseteq A \cap (B \cup C).$$

This inclusion relation, combined with the one obtained above, yields

$$A \cap (B \cup C) = (A \cap B) \cup (A \cap C).$$

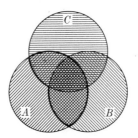

FIGURE 1–5

Let us illustrate by a Venn diagram the identity (d) which we have just proved. The heavily outlined region in Fig. 1–5 represents either side of the identity. The reader should illustrate the other identities of Theorem 1–4.3 by Venn diagrams.

The identities (a) through (g) in Theorem 1–4.3 are the basic rules of operation in the algebra of sets. By algebraic manipulations alone, it is possible to derive from these numerous other laws of operation.

EXAMPLE 10. Let A, B, and C be subsets of a universal set X.

(a) $(A \cup B) \cap C = C \cap (A \cup B) = (C \cap A) \cup (C \cap B) = (A \cap C) \cup (B \cap C)$, and similarly,

$$(A \cap B) \cup C = (A \cup C) \cap (B \cup C).$$

(b) $A \cup (B \cap A) = (A \cup B) \cap (A \cup A) = (A \cup B) \cap A = A \cap (B \cup A) = (A \cap (B \cup A)) \cup \Phi = (A \cap (B \cup A)) \cup (A \cap A^c) = A \cap ((B \cup A) \cup A^c) = A \cap (B \cup (A \cup A^c)) = A \cap (B \cup X) = A \cap X = A$, that is,

$$A \cup (B \cap A) = A \quad \text{and} \quad A \cap (B \cup A) = A.$$

(c) If $A \cap B = A \cap C$ and $A \cup B = A \cup C$, then $B = C$.   Indeed, $B = B \cup (A \cap B) = B \cup (A \cap C) = (B \cup A) \cap (B \cup C) = (A \cup B) \cap (B \cup C) = (A \cup C) \cap (B \cup C) = (A \cap B) \cup C = (A \cap C) \cup C = C \cup (A \cap C) = C$.

Identities such as those of Example 10 can of course always be obtained directly from the definitions of the set operations, as we did for the proof of Theorem 1–4.3. However, identities which involve several sets can usually be derived more easily by algebraic manipulations.

THEOREM 1–4.4. Let A, B, and C be sets.

(a) $A \subseteq A \cup B,\ B \subseteq A \cup B;\ A \supseteq A \cap B,\ B \supseteq A \cap B$.
(b) If $A \subseteq C$ and $B \subseteq C$, then $A \cup B \subseteq C$; if $A \supseteq C$ and $B \supseteq C$, then $A \cap B \supseteq C$.
(c) If $A \subseteq B$, then $A \cup C \subseteq B \cup C$ and $A \cap C \subseteq B \cap C$.
(d) $A \subseteq B$ if and only if $A \cap B = A$; $A \supseteq B$ if and only if $A \cup B = A$.

The proofs of the various statements in Theorem 1–4.4 are again simple applications of the definitions. For example, let us prove the first part of (d). If $A \subseteq B$, then $x \in A$ implies $x \in B$, and hence $x \in A \cap B$. Thus $A \subseteq A \cap B$. If $x \in A \cap B$, then in particular, $x \in A$, so that $A \cap B \subseteq A$. Therefore, $A = A \cap B$. Conversely, if $A = A \cap B$, then every element of A is in $A \cap B$ and, in particular, in B. Therefore $A \subseteq B$.

THEOREM 1–4.5. Let A and B be subsets of the set X.

(a) If $A \subseteq B$, then $A^c \supseteq B^c$.
(b) $(A \cup B)^c = A^c \cap B^c$; $(A \cap B)^c = A^c \cup B^c$.
(c) $(A^c)^c = A$.
(d) $\Phi^c = X$; $X^c = \Phi$.

The statements (a), (c), and (d) of Theorem 1–4.5 should be clear. Let us examine (b). To say that $x \in (A \cup B)^c$ is the same as saying $x \notin A \cup B$, which in turn amounts to $x \notin A$ and $x \notin B$. That is, $x \in A^c$ and $x \in B^c$, which means $x \in A^c \cap B^c$. Thus $(A \cup B)^c$ and $A^c \cap B^c$ contain exactly the same elements, so they are equal. The proof that $(A \cap B)^c = A^c \cup B^c$ is similar.

We illustrate the identity $(A \cap B)^c = A^c \cup B^c$ by a Venn diagram. In Fig. 1–6, the region outside of the doubly shaded region represents each of the sets $(A \cap B)^c$ and $A^c \cup B^c$.

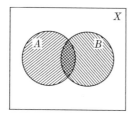

FIGURE 1–6

PROBLEMS

1. If the universal set is the collection N of all natural numbers, determine $A \cup B$, $A \cap B$, and A^c in the following cases.

(a) $A = \{n|n \text{ is even}\}$, $B = \{n|n < 10\}$
(b) $A = \{n|n^2 > 2n - 1\}$, $B = \{n|n^2 = 2n + 3\}$
(c) $A = \{n|(n + 1)/2 \in N\}$, $B = \{n|n/2 \in N\}$

2. Prove Theorem 1–4.3(a), (c), (e), (f), and (g).

3. Justify each step of the computations in Example 10, using the results of Theorem 1–4.3 where they are needed.

4. Prove the following identities by algebraic manipulations, using the results of Theorem 1–4.3 and Example 10.

(a) $A \cup (A^c \cap B) = A \cup B$, $A \cap (A^c \cup B) = A \cap B$
(b) $A \cup (B \cap (A \cup C)) = A \cup (B \cap C)$
(c) $((A \cap B) \cup (B \cap C)) \cup (C \cap A)$
$$= ((A \cup B) \cap (B \cup C)) \cap (C \cup A)$$

5. Illustrate Theorem 1–4.4(c) by a Venn diagram.

6. Show that if $A \subseteq C$, then $A \cup (B \cap C) = (A \cup B) \cap C$.

7. Prove Theorem 1–4.5(a), (c), and (d).

8. Using Theorem 1–4.3(d), (e), (g) and Theorem 1–4.4(d), show that if $A \cup B = X$, then $A^c \subseteq B$. Also, show that if $A \cap B = \Phi$, then $B \subseteq A^c$. Thus, show that $B = A^c$ if and only if $A \cup B = X$ and $A \cap B = \Phi$.

9. Use the result of Exercise 8 to give a new proof of Theorem 1–4.5(b).

10. Make Venn diagrams to illustrate the following identities.

(a) $A \cap (B \cup (C \cup D)) = ((A \cap B) \cup (A \cap C)) \cup (A \cap D)$
(b) $(A \cup (B \cap C))^c = A^c \cap (B^c \cup C^c)$

11. If A and B are any sets, then the *difference* between A and B is defined to be $A - B = \{a \in A | a \notin B\}$. In particular, if A and B are subsets of some universal set X, then $A - B = A \cap B^c$. Show that the following are true.

(a) $(A - B) - C = A - (B \cup C)$
(b) $A - (B - A) = A$
(c) $A - (A - B) = A \cap B$

12. Define $A/B = A^c \cap B^c$. Prove that the following are true.

(a) $A/A = A^c$ (b) $(A/A)/(B/B) = A \cap B$
(c) $(A/B)/(A/B) = A \cup B$

The binary operation $(*/*)$ is called the *Scheffer stroke* operation.

13. Translate the identities of Theorem 1–4.3(d) and Theorem 1–4.4(b) into rules involving only the Scheffer stroke operation.

14. Define $A \oplus B = (A \cap B^c) \cup (A^c \cap B)$. Prove the following.

(a) $A \oplus A = \Phi, A \oplus \Phi = A$
(b) $(A \oplus B) \oplus C = A \oplus (B \oplus C)$
(c) $A \cap (B \oplus C) = (A \cap B) \oplus (A \cap C)$

1–5 Further algebra of sets. General rules of operation. It is possible to extend many of the identities in the previous section to theorems concerning operations on any number of sets.

DEFINITION 1–5.1. Let S be a set whose elements are sets. Then

$$\cup(S) = \{x | x \in A \text{ for some } A \in S\}, \qquad \cap(S) = \{x | x \in A \text{ for all } A \in S\}.$$

As in the case of two sets, $\cup(S)$ is called the *union* of the sets of S and $\cap(S)$ is called the *intersection* of the sets in S.

Thus, $\cup(S)$ contains those elements which are in any one or more of the sets in S, and $\cap(S)$ contains those elements which are in every set in S. For these definitions, S need not be a finite collection of sets (see Example 3 below).

In Fig. 1–7, $S = \{A, B, C, D\}$; $\cup(S)$ is the total shaded area and $\cap(S)$ is the most heavily shaded area, inside the heavy outline.

EXAMPLE 1. Let $S = \{\{1, 2\}, \{1, 3, 5\}, \{2, 5, 6\}\}$. Then $\cup(S) = \{1, 2, 3, 5, 6\}$ and $\cap(S) = \Phi$.

EXAMPLE 2. If $S = \{A, B\}$, then $\cup(S) = A \cup B$ and $\cap(S) = A \cap B$.

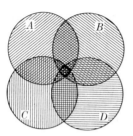

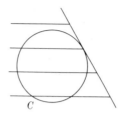

FIGURE 1–7   FIGURE 1–8

EXAMPLE 3. Let C be a circle in some plane P. Let S consist of all sets A which satisfy the following specifications: the elements of A are all points of P lying on the side containing C of some tangent line to C. (See Fig. 1–8.) Then $\cup(S)$ is the set of all points in P, while $\cap(S)$ consists of all points inside C.

EXAMPLE 4. Let S be the empty set of subsets of the universal set X. Then

$$\cup(S) = \Phi, \quad \text{and} \quad \cap(S) = X.$$

The reader should carefully check these examples to be sure that they satisfy the condition of Definition 1–5.1. Example 4 may perhaps be surprising, but it is nevertheless correct according to the definition. Moreover, the intersection or union of the empty set of sets is often encountered. It would be a nuisance if these operations were undefined in this case.

If S is a collection of sets, and if its member sets can be labeled by the elements of another set I, then we write $S = \{C_i | i \in I\}$. For example, let $I = N = \{1, 2, 3, \ldots\}$, and let S be the collection of sets

$$\{\{1\}, \{1, 2\}, \{1, 2, 3\}, \ldots\}.$$

Then the set $\{1, 2, \ldots, i\}$ can be denoted by C_i, and we have $S = \{C_i | i \in N\}$. When this notation is used, the set I is called an *index set*. If $S = \{C_i | i \in I\}$, it is customary to write $\cup_{i \in I} C_i$ for $\cup(S)$ and $\cap_{i \in I} C_i$ for $\cap(S)$.

The identities of Theorem 1–4.3(b) are called the *associative laws* for the operations of set union and set intersection. These are special cases of a general associativity principle.

THEOREM 1–5.2. If the sets of the collection $\{A_1, A_2, \ldots, A_n\}$ are united in any way, two at a time, using each of the sets at least once, the resulting set is equal to

$$\cup(\{A_1, A_2, \ldots, A_n\}).$$

Finally,

$$A \cup B_i = \begin{cases} \{1, 2, \ldots, i, i+2, i+4, \ldots\} & \text{if } i \text{ is even} \\ \{1, 2, \ldots, i, i+1, i+3, \ldots\} & \text{if } i \text{ is odd.} \end{cases}$$

Therefore,

$$\cap_{i \in I}(A \cup B_i) = \{1, 2, 4, 6, \ldots\}.$$

In the ordinary arithmetic of numbers, it is possible to start with a single nonzero number, say 2, and to build from it infinitely many other numbers by addition, subtraction, multiplication, and division. One of the surprising facts about the arithmetic of sets is that only a finite number of different sets can be constructed from a finite number of sets using the operations of union, intersection, and complementation. For example, starting with a set A (contained in the universal set X), we obtain the sets A^c, $A \cap A = A$, $A \cup A = A$. Thus the first step of the construction yields one new set A^c. At the second step, we get $A \cap A^c = \Phi$, $A \cup A^c = X$, as well as A and A^c again. The next step produces no new sets, nor does any step thereafter. A little calculation will show that the only possible sets which can be constructed from two sets A and B in X are Φ, A, B, A^c, B^c, $A \cap B$, $A^c \cap B$, $A \cap B^c$, $A^c \cap B^c$, $A \cup B$, $A^c \cup B$, $A \cup B^c$, $A^c \cup B^c$, $(A \cap B^c) \cup (A^c \cap B)$, $(A \cap B) \cup (A^c \cap B^c)$, X. In this list, the four sets $A \cap B$, $A \cap B^c$, $A^c \cap B$, and $A^c \cap B^c$ are particularly interesting.

An examination of the Venn diagram in Fig. 1–9 indicates why these sets are important. We see that except for Φ, each set in our list is the union of one, two, three, or all of these fundamental sets. For example,

$$A \cup B = (A \cap B) \cup (A \cap B^c) \cup (A^c \cap B).$$

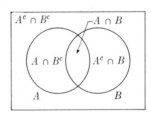

FIGURE 1–9

This is an example of a general theorem which is usually called the *disjunctive normal form* theorem.

THEOREM 1–5.5. Let $A_1, A_2, \ldots, A_n$ be subsets of the set X. Then every set which can be formed from these sets by union, intersection, or complementation is either Φ or has a representation as a union of certain of the sets

$$M_{i_1 i_2 \ldots i_n} = A_1^{i_1} \cap A_2^{i_2} \cap \cdots \cap A_n^{i_n},$$

where $i_1, i_2, \ldots, i_n$ are 0 or 1 and $A_j^{i_j}$ is A_j if $i_j = 0$ and A_j^c if $i_j = 1$.

For example, if $n = 3$,

$$\begin{aligned}
M_{000} &= A_1 \cap A_2 \cap A_3, & M_{001} &= A_1 \cap A_2 \cap A_3^c, \\
M_{010} &= A_1 \cap A_2^c \cap A_3, & M_{011} &= A_1 \cap A_2^c \cap A_3^c, \\
M_{100} &= A_1^c \cap A_2 \cap A_3, & M_{101} &= A_1^c \cap A_2 \cap A_3^c, \\
M_{110} &= A_1^c \cap A_2^c \cap A_3, & M_{111} &= A_1^c \cap A_2^c \cap A_3^c.
\end{aligned}$$

By the theorem, every possible nonempty combination of A_1, A_2, and A_3 can be obtained as a union of one, two, three, four, five, six, seven, or all of these M_{ijk}. For instance,

$$A_2 = M_{000} \cup M_{001} \cup M_{100} \cup M_{101},$$
$$A_1 \cup A_2^c = M_{100} \cup M_{001} \cup M_{010} \cup M_{011} \cup M_{110} \cup M_{111}.$$

The proof of Theorem 1–5.5, like the proof of Theorem 1–5.2, can be carried out only by mathematical induction. Since this result will not be needed in later parts of this book, a formal proof will not be given.

PROBLEMS

1. Suppose that $S = \{A\}$, where A is a set. What is $\cup(S)$? What is $\cap(S)$?

2. Check Theorem 1–5.2 for the following particular combinations of sets: $(A_1 \cup A_2) \cup (A_3 \cup A_4)$, $A_1 \cup (A_2 \cup (A_3 \cup A_4))$, $(A_1 \cup (A_2 \cup A_3)) \cup A_4$.

3. Prove Theorem 1–5.3(b).

4. Let $\{A_i | i \in I\}$ be a set of subsets of X. Show that the following are true.

   (a) $(\cup_{i \in I} A_i)^c = \cap_{i \in I} A_i^c$ (b) $(\cap_{i \in I} A_i)^c = \cup_{i \in I} A_i^c$

5. What is the largest number of different sets which can be constructed from three subsets A, B, C of a universal set X, using the operations of union, intersection, and complementation? If $\Phi \subset A \subset B \subset C \subset X$, how many different sets can be constructed?

*1–6 Measures on sets. One important application of set theory is its use in mathematical statistics. The foundation of statistics is the theory of probability, and in its mathematical form, probability is the study of certain kinds of measures on sets. In this section and the next the concept of measure of a set will be introduced, and some of its simplest properties will be examined.

FIGURE 1–10

Several ways of "measuring" sets are already known to the reader. For example, the measure of a line segment (which may be considered as a set of points) is usually taken to be the length of the segment. A good measure of a finite set A is $|A|$, the number of elements in A. But there are situations where different measures of line segments and finite sets are more useful. For example, a railroad map usually indicates the route between major cities by a sequence of line segments connecting intermediate points as shown in Fig. 1–10. Here the length of each line segment is of little interest. The important measure of these segments is the actual rail line distance between the cities corresponding to the points which the segments connect. Another useful measure for these line segments might be the annual cost of upkeep of that section of the rail line which is represented by them. Note that this measure has a natural extension to those subsets of the map which are unions of two or more segments. For example, if I_1 represents the part of the rail line between Milwaukee and Chicago and if I_2 represents the part between Detroit and Buffalo, then the cost of upkeep of the part of the rail line represented by $I_1 \cup I_2$ would be the cost for I_1 plus the cost for I_2.

We will now consider a measure for finite sets which links our discussion to the application of set theory to probability. Suppose that a pair of dice, labeled A and B, are rolled. Both A and B will come to rest with a number of dots from 1 to 6 on the "up" face. The result of the roll can therefore be represented by an ordered pair $\langle m, n \rangle$ of natural numbers, where m gives the number of dots on the "up" face of A and n gives the number of dots on the "up" face of B. Thus, m and n can be any natural numbers from 1 to 6. If the dice are "honest," then it is reasonable to suppose that for any roll of the dice, the 36 different pairs $\langle m, n \rangle$ are equally likely to occur. Now it is customary to define the "point" which is made on any roll of the dice to be the total number of spots on the two "up" faces. Thus, if the outcome of the roll is represented by $\langle m, n \rangle$, then the point made on the roll is $m + n$. Therefore, the possible points which can be made on a roll of the dice are the numbers from 2 to 12, that is, the set of possible points is $\{2, 3, \ldots, 12\}$. We now assign a measure to the subsets of $\{2, 3, \ldots, 12\}$. If S is such a subset, assign as the measure of S the probability that on a roll of the dice the point made will be a member of S. The probability of making a certain point is the ratio of the number of different ways that the point can be made, to 36, the number of possible results of a roll. For example, the probability of making the point 2 is

$\frac{1}{36}$, since 2 can be made in only one way, by the roll $\langle 1, 1 \rangle$. Thus our measure would assign to the subset $\{2\}$ the number $\frac{1}{36}$. Suppose now that the subset S is the set $\{7\}$. The outcome of the roll will be in $\{7\}$ only if the point made is 7. Since 7 can be made in six possible ways: $\langle 1, 6 \rangle$, $\langle 2, 5 \rangle$, $\langle 3, 4, \rangle$ $\langle 4, 3 \rangle$, $\langle 5, 2 \rangle$, $\langle 6, 1 \rangle$, the probability of making 7 is $\frac{6}{36} = \frac{1}{6}$, and the measure of $\{7\}$ is $\frac{1}{6}$. As another example, take $S = \{7, 11\}$. The point made on a roll will be in this set if it is a 7 or 11. We have seen that there are six ways of making 7. There are two ways of making 11: $\langle 5, 6 \rangle$ and $\langle 6, 5 \rangle$. Thus, the measure of the set $\{7, 11\}$ is $\frac{8}{36} = \frac{2}{9}$. It is clear now that this "probability measure" can be determined for each of the $2^{11} = 2048$ different subsets of possible points.

Let us now look for some common properties of the measures described in the above examples and try to arrive at a suitable mathematical notion of measure. One property is immediately evident. In each case, there is a rule for assigning a certain number to various subsets of a given set. In the example of a railroad map, two different measures were suggested for line segments making up the map. The second of these measures, the cost of upkeep, was actually defined for unions of segments of the map. In both cases, however, the measures are defined only for very special subsets of the whole map. In general, measures need not be defined on all subsets of a given set, but only on some collection of subsets. However, unless these collections satisfy certain "closure" conditions, the measures on them will not be very useful.

DEFINITION 1–6.1. Let X be a set. A nonempty collection S of subsets of X is called a *ring of subsets of X* (or just a ring of sets) if it satisfies the following two conditions.

(a) If $A \in S$ and $B \in S$, then $A \cup B \in S$.
(b) If $A \in S$ and $B \in S$, then $A \cap B^c \in S$.

EXAMPLE 1. If X is any set, then the collection of all subsets of X is a ring of subsets of X.

EXAMPLE 2. Let X be an infinite set. Then the collection of all finite subsets of X is a ring of subsets of X. Moreover, X is not in this ring.

EXAMPLE 3. Let S be the set of all subsets of R which are finite unions of sets of the type

$$I = \{x | a < x \leq b, a \in R, b \in R\}.$$

Such sets are called half-open intervals. That is, each set of S has the form $I_1 \cup I_2 \cup \cdots \cup I_n$, where $I_1 = \{x | a_1 < x \leq b_1\}$, $I_2 = \{x | a_2 < x \leq b_2\}, \ldots,$ $I_n = \{x | a_n < x \leq b_n\}$, for some real numbers $a_1, a_2, \ldots, a_n, b_1, b_2, \ldots, b_n$. Then S is a ring of sets.

The expression "ring of sets" is standard mathematical terminology. It is derived from abstract algebra. The "closure" conditions to which we alluded above are the properties (a) and (b) in Definition 1–6.1. There are other important closure conditions which are satisfied by rings of sets.

THEOREM 1–6.2. Let S be a ring of subsets of X. Then

    (a) $\Phi \in S$;

    (b)   If $A \in S$ and $B \in S$, then $A \cap B \in S$;

    (c)   If $A_1, A_2, \ldots, A_n \in S$, then $A_1 \cup A_2 \cup \cdots \cup A_n \in S$ and $A_1 \cap A_2 \cap \cdots \cap A_n \in S$.

Proof. One of the requirements in Definition 1–6.1 is that S be nonempty. Thus, there is some subset A of X which belongs to S. Consequently, by Definition 1–6.1(b), $A \cap A^c = \Phi$ is in S. Suppose that $A \in S$ and $B \in S$. Then by Definition 1–6.1(b), $A \cap B^c \in S$. Now use Definition 1–6.1(b) again, with $A \cap B^c$ taking the place of B. We obtain $A \cap (A \cap B^c)^c \in S$. However, by Theorems 1–4.5 and 1–4.3, $A \cap (A \cap B^c)^c = A \cap (A^c \cup B) = (A \cap A^c) \cup (A \cap B) = \Phi \cup (A \cap B) = A \cap B$. Thus, $A \cap B \in S$. Finally, if $A_1, A_2, \ldots, A_n$ belong to S, then using Definition 1–6.1(a) repeatedly gives $A_1 \cup A_2 \in S$, $A_1 \cup A_2 \cup A_3 = (A_1 \cup A_2) \cup A_3 \in S, \ldots, A_1 \cup A_2 \cup \cdots \cup A_n \in S$. Similarly, by using repeatedly 1–6.2(b), which we have just proved, we find that $A_1 \cap A_2 \cap \cdots \cap A_n \in S$.

There is one more important property that our examples have in common. In the upkeep cost measure on the segments of the railroad map, we noted that if I_1 and I_2 are distinct segments, then the measure of $I_1 \cup I_2$ is the measure of I_1 plus the measure of I_2. This is still clearly true if I_1 and I_2 are replaced by unions of segments, provided that these unions have no segment in common. This additivity property is shared by the probability measure example. Here, the measure was defined for all subsets of the set of points $\{2, 3, \ldots, 12\}$. If A and B are subsets such that no number of $\{2, 3, \ldots, 12\}$ is in both A and B ($A \cap B = \Phi$), then the measure of $A \cup B$ is the sum of the measures of A and B. For example, the measure of $\{7\}$ is $\frac{1}{6}$, the measure of $\{11\}$ is $\frac{1}{18}$, and the measure of $\{7\} \cup \{11\} = \{7, 11\}$ is $\frac{1}{6} + \frac{1}{18} = \frac{2}{9}$. This simple property is the essence of the mathematical notion of measure.

Two sets A and B are said to be *disjoint* if they have no elements in common, that is, $A \cap B = \Phi$. A collection of sets is called *pairwise disjoint* if each pair of different sets in the collection is disjoint. Note that the term "pairwise disjoint" refers to the collection of sets as a whole and not to the individual sets in the collection.

EXAMPLE 4. The sets $\{7, 11\}$ and $\{2, 12\}$ are disjoint.

EXAMPLE 5. The collection of line segments in the railroad map example are pairwise disjoint, provided we agree that each line segment includes its left-hand endpoint, but not its right-hand endpoint.

EXAMPLE 6. Let A_1, A_2, A_3, ... be the sets of real numbers x defined by $A_1 = \{x \mid 1 < x \leq 2\}$, $A_2 = \{x \mid 2 < x \leq 3\}$, $A_3 = \{x \mid 3 < x \leq 4\}$, etc. Then the collection A_1, A_2, A_3, ... is pairwise disjoint.

DEFINITION 1–6.3. Let X be a set, and let S be a ring of subsets of X. A *measure* on the collection S is a rule which assigns to each set A in the collection S some real number $m(A)$, subject to the condition that if A and B are disjoint sets in S, then

$$m(A \cup B) = m(A) + m(B).$$

We will be concerned principally with measures defined on the set of all subsets of a finite set. For this discussion the following example is important.

EXAMPLE 7. Let X be a set containing n distinct elements x_1, x_2, ..., x_n. Let m_1, m_2 ..., m_n be a sequence of n real numbers. For a nonempty subset A of X, define $m(A)$ to be the sum of all those m_i for which $x_i \in A$. If $A = \Phi$, let $m(A) = 0$. For instance, if $n = 3$,

$$m(\Phi) = 0, \quad m(\{x_1\}) = m_1, \quad m(\{x_2\}) = m_2, \quad m(\{x_3\}) = m_3,$$
$$m(\{x_1, x_2\}) = m_1 + m_2, \quad m(\{x_1, x_3\}) = m_1 + m_3,$$
$$m(\{x_2, x_3\}) = m_2 + m_3, \quad m(\{x_1, x_2, x_3\}) = m_1 + m_2 + m_3.$$

It is left to the reader to show that the condition of Definition 1–6.3 is satisfied, so that a measure is defined on the collection $P(X)$ of all subsets of X.

Particular cases are worth noting.

(1) If $m_1 = m_2 = \cdots = m_n = 1$, then $m(A) = |A|$, the cardinal number of A.

(2) If $m_1 = 1$, $m_2 = \cdots = m_n = 0$, then $m(A) = 1$ if $x_1 \in A$ and $m(A) = 0$ if $x_1 \notin A$. Thus we can say that m measures whether or not x_1 is in A.

(3) Let $x_1 = 1, x_2 = 2, \ldots, x_n = n$. Let $m_1 = -1, m_2 = 1, m_3 = -1, \ldots,$ $m_n = (-1)^n$. Then $m(A)$ is just the number of even numbers in A minus the number of odd numbers in A.

It is not surprising that there are so many interesting special cases of Example 7, since actually every measure on the collection $P(X)$ of all subsets of a finite set S is of this form. This will become clear after we observe that the additive property of measures has a simple generalization.

THEOREM 1–6.4. Let m be a measure defined on a ring S of subsets of a set X. If $\{A_1, A_2, \ldots, A_n\}$ is a collection of sets in S and this collection is pairwise disjoint, then

$$m(A_1 \cup A_2 \cup \cdots \cup A_n) = m(A_1) + m(A_2) + \cdots + m(A_n).$$

If $n = 2$, this theorem is the same as the additivity condition for a measure required in Definition 1–6.3, namely $m(A_1 \cup A_2) = m(A_1) + m(A_2)$ if $A_1 \cap A_2 = \Phi$. Consider the case $n = 3$. The assertion is

$$m(A_1 \cup A_2 \cup A_3) = m(A_1) + m(A_2) + m(A_3).$$

Since the collection $\{A_1, A_2, A_3\}$ is pairwise disjoint, we know in particular, that $A_2 \cap A_3 = \Phi$. Since m is a measure, by Definition 1–6.3,

$$m(A_2 \cup A_3) = m(A_2) + m(A_3).$$

Thus, we have

$$m(A_1) + m(A_2 \cup A_3) = m(A_1) + m(A_2) + m(A_3).$$

Now if A_1 and $A_2 \cup A_3$ are disjoint, we can apply Definition 1–6.3 again to the left side of the last equality to obtain the desired result:

$$\begin{aligned} m(A_1 \cup A_2 \cup A_3) &= m(A_1 \cup (A_2 \cup A_3)) \\ &= m(A_1) + m(A_2 \cup A_3) \\ &= m(A_1) + m(A_2) + m(A_3). \end{aligned}$$

By the distributive law for the set operations (Theorem 1–4.3), we obtain

$$A_1 \cap (A_2 \cup A_3) = (A_1 \cap A_2) \cup (A_1 \cap A_3) = \Phi \cup \Phi = \Phi,$$

so that A_1 and $A_2 \cup A_3$ are indeed disjoint. We used here the fact that $A_1 \cap A_2 = \Phi$ and $A_1 \cap A_3 = \Phi$, which is justified by the assumption that $\{A_1, A_2, A_3\}$ is pairwise disjoint.

By repeated application of the argument used in the case $n = 3$, it is possible to see that Theorem 1–6.4 is true for any n. A formal proof of this theorem will not be given here, because such a proof is based on the principle of mathematical induction. The reader should begin to be aware that mathematics leans heavily on this important method of proof which will be discussed in the next chapter.

Accepting Theorem 1–6.4, we are ready to examine the assertion that every measure defined on $P(X)$ for a finite set X is of the type given in

Example 7.   For simplicity, suppose that $X = \{x_1, x_2, x_3, x_4\}$, where x_1, x_2, x_3, x_4 are distinct. Suppose that m is a measure defined on $P(X)$. Then $m_1 = m(\{x_1\})$, $m_2 = m(\{x_2\})$, $m_3 = (\{x_3\})$, $m_4 = m(\{x_4\})$ are certain real numbers. It is evident that if A is any nonempty subset of X, we can write

$$A = \cup_{x_i \in A} \{x_i\}.$$

For example, $\{x_1, x_2, x_3\} = \{x_1\} \cup \{x_2\} \cup \{x_3\}$.   Moreover, if $i \neq j$, then $\{x_i\} \cap \{x_j\} = \Phi$.   Thus, the collection of all distinct one element sets $\{x_i\}$, with $x_i \in A$, is pairwise disjoint.   Hence, by Theorem 1–6.4, $m(A)$ is the sum of all $m_i = m(\{x_i\})$ for which $x_i \in A$.   For example, if $A = \{x_1, x_2, x_3,\}$, then

$$m(\{x_1, x_2, x_3\}) = m(\{x_1\}) + m(\{x_2\}) + m(\{x_3\}) = m_1 + m_2 + m_3.$$

This argument shows that any measure m on $P(X)$ is a measure of the type described in Example 7, that is, Example 7 is the most general possibility for a measure on the set of all subsets of a finite set.   Indeed, starting with a measure m on $P(X)$ for which nothing is assumed except that it satisfies the conditions of Definition 1–6.3, we have shown that there are numbers m_i corresponding to the distinct elements $x_i \in X$ such that for any nonempty subset A of X, the measure $m(A)$ is precisely the sum of those m_i for which x_i is in A.   But this is just the measure of Example 7, except possibly for $A = \Phi$.   However, in the next section we will show that $m(\Phi) = 0$ for every measure.

PROBLEMS

1. In the dice rolling example, find the measure of the following sets:

$$\{2, 3, 4\}, \ \{10, 11, 12\}, \ \{2, 3, 4, 6, 8, 10, 11, 12\}.$$

2. Find all collections S of subsets of $\{1, 2, 3\}$ which are rings of sets. (There are 15 such collections.)

3. Show that the number of sets in a ring of subsets of a finite set is always a power of 2. [*Hint:* Let S be such a ring. Let $A_1, A_2, \ldots, A_n$ be all those nonempty sets in S which do not contain a smaller nonempty set of S. Show that $I \leftrightarrow \cup_{i \in I} A_i$ defines a one-to-one correspondence between the subsets I of $\{1, 2, \ldots, n\}$ and S.]

4. Show that m, defined in Example 7, is a measure, that is, m satisfies the condition of Definition 1–6.3.

5. Prove Theorem 1–6.4 in the case $n = 4$.

6. Give the details of the proof that if m is a measure defined on a finite set $\{x_1, x_2, \ldots, x_n\}$, then there are real numbers $m_1, m_2, \ldots, m_n$ such that for a nonempty subset A, $m(A)$ is the sum of all m_i for which $x_i \in A$.

7. In a certain game, three pennies are tossed at the same time and points are scored, depending on the outcome of the toss, as follows:

$$3 \text{ heads} = 20 \text{ points}, \quad 3 \text{ tails} = 15 \text{ points},$$
$$2 \text{ heads and a tail} = 10 \text{ points}, \quad 2 \text{ tails and a head} = 5 \text{ points}.$$

Define a probability measure m on the collection of subsets of the possible points $\{20, 15, 10, 5\}$, as was done for the dice rolling example in the text. Find $m(\{20, 15, 10, 5\})$, $m(\{20, 10\})$, and $m(\{5\})$. What is the probability that at least two heads will appear in the outcome of a toss?

8. In a certain card game, two cards are dealt from a standard deck of 52 cards. Aces count 4 points, kings 3 points, queens 2 points, jacks 1 point, and all other cards 0 points. In a given deal, the possible points range from 0 points (neither card is an ace or a face card) to 8 points (a pair of aces). For a subset A of the set $\{0, 1, 2, \ldots, 8\}$ of possible points, define $m(A)$ to be the probability that on a given deal the number of points scored is an element of A. Find $m(\{0\})$, $m(\{8\})$, $m(\{5, 6, 7, 8\})$, and $m(\{1\})$.

*1–7 Properties and examples of measures. In this section we derive some useful properties of measures.

THEOREM 1–7.1. Let m be a measure on a ring S of subsets of a set X.

(a) $m(\Phi) = 0$.
(b) If $A \in S$ and $A^c \in S$, then $m(A^c) = m(X) - m(A)$.

Proof. (a) Since $\Phi \cap \Phi = \Phi$, the empty set is disjoint from itself (and it is the only set having this property). Thus $m(\Phi) = m(\Phi \cup \Phi) = m(\Phi) + m(\Phi)$. Subtracting the number $m(\Phi)$ from both sides of this equality gives $0 = m(\Phi)$.

(b) By Theorem 1–4.3(e), $A \cap A^c = \Phi$ and $A \cup A^c = X$. Thus, A and A^c are disjoint, so that $m(A) + m(A^c) = m(A \cup A^c) = m(X)$. Again, by subtraction, $m(A^c) = m(X) - m(A)$.

THEOREM 1–7.2. Let m be a measure on a ring S of subsets of a set X. Let A, B be in S. Then

$$m(A \cup B) + m(A \cap B) = m(A) + m(B).$$

Proof. An examination of the Venn diagram in Fig. 1–11 shows that

$$A \cup B = (A \cap B^c) \cup (A^c \cap B) \cup (A \cap B),$$
$$A = (A \cap B^c) \cup (A \cap B),$$
$$B = (A^c \cap B) \cap (A \cap B),$$

and that the collection of subsets $\{A \cap B^c, A^c \cap B, A \cap B\}$ is pairwise

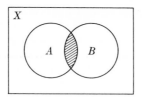

FIGURE 1–11

disjoint. Consequently, by Theorem 1–6.4,

$$m(A \cup B) = m(A \cap B^c) + m(A^c \cap B) + m(A \cap B),$$
$$m(A) = m(A \cap B^c) + m(A \cap B),$$
$$m(B) = m(A^c \cap B) + m(A \cap B).$$

Subtracting the second and third equalities from the first one gives

$$m(A \cup B) - m(A) - m(B) = -m(A \cap B),$$

which when rearranged is the desired identity.

We conclude this chapter by giving some practical examples of measures on finite sets.

EXAMPLE 1. In a certain class, 40% of the students are blonds, the rest are brunettes, 12% are left-handed, and 5% are both blond and left-handed. Find the percentage of students who are right-handed brunettes. Let A be the subset of blonds in the class and B be the subset of left-handed students. Then $A \cap B$ is the subset of left-handed blonds and $A \cup B$ is the subset of students who are either blond or left handed. Moreover $(A \cup B)^c$ is the subset of students who are neither blond nor left handed, that is, the subset of right-handed brunettes. Recalling that cardinality is a measure on the set of all subsets of a finite set, Theorem 1–7.2 gives

$$|A \cup B| = |A| + |B| - |A \cap B|.$$

Now if there are n students in the class, and C is any subset of students, then $|C|/n$ gives the fraction of the class which is in C and $100|C|/n$ gives the percentage of the class which is in C. Thus, we have

$$100|A \cup B|/n = 100|A|/n + 100|B|/n - 100|A \cap B|/n$$
$$= 40\% + 12\% - 5\% = 47\%.$$

Therefore, since 47% of the class is in $A \cup B$, 53% of the class is in $(A \cup B)^c$ that is, are right-handed brunettes.

EXAMPLE 2. A certain type of spring balance is constructed so that it measures only weights between one and two pounds. If we have three steaks each of which is known to weigh between $\frac{1}{2}$ and 1 pound, how can we use the spring balance to determine their weights exactly? Let the steaks be denoted by x_1, x_2, x_3. For a subset A of $X = \{x_1, x_2, x_3\}$, let $m(A)$ be the total weight of the steaks in the set A. Clearly m is a measure on the subsets of X, Let $A_1 = \{x_2, x_3\}$, $A_2 = \{x_1, x_3\}$, $A_3 = \{x_1, x_2\}$. Because of our rough knowledge of the weights of x_1, x_2, and x_3, we are certain that $m(A_1)$, $m(A_2)$, and $m(A_3)$ can be accurately determined by the spring balance, since their weights are between 1 and 2 pounds. Now

$$A_1 \cup A_2 = A_2 \cup A_3 = A_3 \cup A_1 = X,$$
$$A_1 \cap A_2 = \{x_3\}, \qquad A_2 \cap A_3 = \{x_1\}, \qquad \text{and} \qquad A_3 \cap A_1 = \{x_2\}.$$

Thus, by Theorem 1–7.2,

$$m(X) + m(\{x_3\}) = m(A_1) + m(A_2),$$
$$m(X) + m(\{x_1\}) = m(A_2) + m(A_3),$$
$$m(X) + m(\{x_2\}) = m(A_3) + m(A_1).$$

Adding these equalities gives

$$2\big(m(A_1) + m(A_2) + m(A_3)\big)$$
$$= 3m(X) + \big(m(\{x_1\}) + m(\{x_2\}) + m(\{x_3\})\big) = 4m(X)$$

Hence, $m(X) = \frac{1}{2}\big(m(A_1) + m(A_2) + m(A_3)\big)$. Therefore,

$$m(\{x_1\}) = \tfrac{1}{2}\big(m(A_2) + m(A_3) - m(A_1)\big),$$
$$m(\{x_2\}) = \tfrac{1}{2}\big(m(A_1) + m(A_3) - m(A_2)\big),$$
$$m(\{x_3\}) = \tfrac{1}{2}\big(m(A_1) + m(A_2) - m(A_3)\big).$$

It is possible to extend the result of Theorem 1–7.2 to an identity which involves more than two sets. For example, suppose that A, B, and C are subsets of X and that m is a measure defined on a ring of subsets of X. Then using Theorem 1–7.2 repeatedly,

$$m(A \cup B \cup C) = m(A) + m(B \cup C) - m\big(A \cap (B \cup C)\big)$$
$$= m(A) + m(B) + m(C) - m(B \cap C)$$
$$\qquad\qquad - m\big((A \cap B) \cup (A \cap C)\big)$$
$$= m(A) + m(B) + m(C) - m(B \cap C)$$
$$\qquad - [m(A \cap B) + m(A \cap C) - m\big((A \cap B) \cap (A \cap C)\big)]$$
$$= m(A) + m(B) + m(C)$$
$$\qquad - [m(A \cap B) + m(B \cap C) + m(C \cap A)] + m(A \cap B \cap C).$$

EXAMPLE 3. The classification of blood type is made on the presence or absence of three distinct antigens in the blood. These antigens are denoted by A, B, and Rh. The possible blood types are eight in number:

Type	Blood contains
O, Rh negative	no antigens
O, Rh positive	Rh
A, Rh negative	A
A, Rh positive	A and Rh
B, Rh negative	B
B, Rh positive	B and Rh
AB, Rh negative	A and B
AB, Rh positive	all antigens

Suppose that in a group of ten people: 4 have antigen A, 5 have antigen B, 6 have antigen Rh, 2 have antigens A and B, 3 have antigens A and Rh, 3 have antigens B and Rh, and 2 have all antigens. Determine the number of people in the group having type O, Rh positive blood.

Let T_A, T_B, T_{Rh} denote the sets of people having the respective antigens A, B, and Rh. The number of people with type O (Rh positive or negative) is

$$10 - |T_A \cup T_B| = 10 - (|T_A| + |T_B| - |T_A \cap T_B|)$$
$$= 10 - 4 - 5 + 2 = 3.$$

The number of people with type O, Rh negative is

$$10 - |T_A \cup T_B \cup T_{Rh}| = 10 - (|T_A| + |T_B| + |T_{Rh}| - |T_A \cap T_B|$$
$$- |T_B \cap T_{Rh}| - |T_{Rh} \cap T_A| + |T_A \cap T_B \cap T_{Rh}|)$$
$$= 10 - (4 + 5 + 6 - 2 - 3 - 3 + 2)$$
$$= 10 - 9 = 1.$$

The number of people with type O, Rh positive is therefore $3 - 1 = 2$.

By similar considerations, it is possible to determine the number of people with each of the eight possible blood types.

PROBLEMS

1. Use the identities of Section 1–3 to show that

$$A \cup B = (A \cap B^c) \cup (A^c \cap B) \cup (A \cap B),$$
$$A = (A \cap B^c) \cup (A \cap B),$$
$$B = (A^c \cap B) \cup (A \cap B).$$

2. Determine $m(A \cup B \cup C \cup D)$ in terms of $m(A)$, $m(B)$, $m(C)$, $m(D)$, $m(A \cap B)$, $m(A \cap C)$, $m(A \cap D)$, $m(B \cap C)$, $m(B \cap D)$, $m(C \cap D)$, $m(A \cap B \cap C)$, $m(A \cap B \cap D)$, $m(A \cap C \cap D)$, $m(B \cap C \cap D)$, and $m(A \cap B \cap C \cap D)$.

3. Show that the empty set Φ is the only set disjoint from itself.

4. Suppose that a certain spring balance measures only weights between $1\frac{1}{2}$ and 3 pounds. If four steaks are known to weigh between $\frac{1}{2}$ and 1 pound, show how the spring balance can be used to determine their weights exactly.

5. In Example 3, find the number of people with blood types A, Rh negative, A, Rh positive, AB, Rh negative, and AB, Rh positive.

6. Three numbers 1, 2, 3 are written in random order. Assume that each possible ordering is equally likely. What is the probability that at least one of the numbers will occupy its proper place, that is, 1 occurs first, or 2 occurs second, or 3 occurs third?

7. In a certain sample of the population, it is found that lung cancer occurs in 15 cases per 100,000 people. It is estimated that 80% of those with lung cancer smoke and that 65% of those without lung cancer smoke. (These are fictitious estimates.) Determine the approximate ratio of smokers with lung cancer to smokers without lung cancer.

CHAPTER 2

MATHEMATICAL INDUCTION

2–1 Proof by induction. The essence of mathematics is the construction of logically correct proofs for general theorems. A beginning student is apt to look upon a mathematical proof as a sort of magical incantation which somehow gives truth to a theorem. Nothing could be further from the intention of the person who devises the proof. A proof is worthless if it is not convincing, at least to an intelligent person who makes the effort to understand it.

Generally speaking, there are two steps leading to the understanding of a mathematical proof. The first step is the mechanical checking of the proof to see that each statement follows as a logical consequence of statements which precede it. If the argument survives this test, and if the final statement is the assertion which was to be proved, then it must be admitted that the proof is valid. But to really understand the proof it is necessary to take the second, more difficult, step. One must look at the overall pattern of the argument and discover the basic idea behind it. The ideal is to see the proof through the mind of the person who originated it. Of course, this may require a high degree of mathematical talent, to say nothing of hard work, but the reward in self-satisfaction is substantial, every bit as great, perhaps, as the reward which a musician obtains from mastering a difficult piano or violin sonata.

Fortunately there are a few general methods of constructing mathematical proofs which are both elementary and powerful. Our objective in this chapter is to explore in detail one of the most important of these methods, the so-called proof by mathematical induction.

Mathematical induction must be distinguished from logical induction. Roughly speaking, logical induction is the process of discovering general laws by noting some common feature in a number of special cases. As an example, if the sequence of numbers 1, 4, 9, 16, 25, . . . is written down, most people who have had some experience with arithmetic will infer by logical induction that the next term in this sequence will be 36. They recognize that 1, 4, 9, 16, and 25 are, respectively, the squares of 1, 2, 3, 4, and 5, so that the natural choice for the next term is $6^2 = 36$. Logical induction, although it is important for the process of mathematical discovery, is of no use in mathematical proofs. On the other hand, mathematical induction is primarily a technique of proof.

If we examine, say, Theorems 1–5.2, 1–5.5, and 1–6.4, we see that they are statements which involve an arbitrary natural number n. These statements become specific assertions only when particular numbers are substituted for n. For small values of n, the statements are quite easy to prove. The difficulty lies in finding a proof which takes care of all values of n. This is a situation in which mathematical induction can often be used.

We present some examples of mathematical statements which involve an arbitrary natural number n.

EXAMPLE 1. $1 + 2 + 3 + \cdots + n = \frac{1}{2}n(n + 1)$.

EXAMPLE 2. If $a \geq -1$, then $(1 + a)^n \geq 1 + na$.

EXAMPLE 3. (Theorem 1–6.4). Let m be a measure defined on a ring S of subsets of X. Let $\{A_1, A_2, \ldots, A_n\}$ be a pairwise disjoint collection of sets in S. Then $m(A_1 \cup A_2 \cup \cdots \cup A_n) = m(A_1) + m(A_2) + \cdots + m(A_n)$.

In order to illustrate the mechanism of mathematical induction, consider Example 1. As is often the case, our notation is not well adapted for small values of n. For $n = 1, 2, 3$, and 4, the assertions should read

$$1 = \tfrac{1}{2} \cdot 1(1 + 1), \qquad 1 + 2 = \tfrac{1}{2} \cdot 2(2 + 1) = 3,$$

$$1 + 2 + 3 = \tfrac{1}{2} \cdot 3(3 + 1) = 6, \qquad 1 + 2 + 3 + 4 = \tfrac{1}{2} \cdot 4(4 + 1) = 10.$$

For n larger than 4, the notation expresses the asserted identity clearly enough. Thus if allowance is made for the inadequate notation in the cases $n = 1, 2, 3$, and 4, the statement of Example 1, $1 + 2 + 3 + \cdots + n = \frac{1}{2}n(n + 1)$, can be considered as a compact method of writing an infinite sequence of formulas:

$$1 = \tfrac{1}{2} \cdot 1(1 + 1), \qquad 1 + 2 = \tfrac{1}{2} \cdot 2(2 + 1),$$

$$1 + 2 + 3 = \tfrac{1}{2} \cdot 3(3 + 1), \qquad 1 + 2 + 3 + 4 = \tfrac{1}{2} \cdot 4(4 + 1),$$

$$1 + 2 + 3 + 4 + 5 = \tfrac{1}{2} \cdot 5(5 + 1), \qquad \ldots.$$

A person who is not familiar with the identity which we are considering may be somewhat surprised that the formula works for the values $n = 1, 2, 3$, and 4. But he may be justifiably skeptical that this fact makes the assertion true in general. Let us try $n = 5$. Then $1 + 2 + 3 + 4 + 5 = (1 + 2 + 3 + 4) + 5 = \frac{1}{2} \cdot 4(4 + 1) + 5 = 10 + 5 = 15$. Here we have been able to simplify our calculation somewhat by using the formula which we have already checked for the case $n = 4$. It turns out that this simplification is the real key to the general proof of the formula.

For $\frac{1}{2} \cdot 4(4 + 1) + 5$ can be expressed as $15 = \frac{1}{2} \cdot 4(4 + 1) + 5 = 5 \cdot (\frac{1}{2} \cdot 4 + 1) = \frac{1}{2} \cdot 5(4 + 2) = \frac{1}{2} \cdot 5(5 + 1)$, the required result. A similar calculation can now be made for $n = 6$, and, using the same simplification, we find that the formula is also correct in this case. In fact, the process of passing from one formula to the next can be formalized if we are willing to use a variable symbol n instead of a specific number. Thus, suppose that we have already shown that

$$1 + 2 + 3 + \cdots + n = \tfrac{1}{2}n(n + 1).$$

Then

$$
\begin{aligned}
1 + 2 + 3 + \cdots + n + (n + 1) &= (1 + 2 + 3 + \cdots + n) + (n + 1) \\
&= \tfrac{1}{2}n(n + 1) + (n + 1) \\
&= (n + 1)(\tfrac{1}{2}n + 1) \\
&= \tfrac{1}{2}(n + 1)(n + 2) \\
&= \tfrac{1}{2}(n + 1)[(n + 1) + 1].
\end{aligned}
$$

The first, third, fourth, and fifth equality signs in the above identity are justified on the basis of the rules of algebraic operation. The remaining equality, the second, is justified by the assumption that formula n of the sequence, $1 + 2 + 3 + \cdots + n = \frac{1}{2}n(n + 1)$, is valid. Note that $1 + 2 + 3 + \cdots + n + (n + 1)$ and $1 + 2 + 3 + \cdots + (n + 1)$ are both abbreviations for the sum of the first $n + 1$ natural numbers, so that they are equal. Thus, the equality of the first and last terms of the above expression is the n plus first identity in the sequence of formulas which we are trying to prove. In other words, the calculation shows that if some identity of the sequence is valid, then so is the following one. In particular, since the fifth identity is correct (as well as the first, second, third, and fourth), so is the sixth. Consequently, so is the seventh, the eighth, and so on. Since any formula of the sequence will eventually be reached in this way, we conclude that the identity of Example 1 is valid for all n.

The proof we have given for the identity of Example 1 is a proof by mathematical induction. Although this method of attack is usually suggested for mathematical statements which involve an arbitrary natural number n, there are often other types of proof available. For example, we could also prove the formula of Example 1 as follows. Let s be the sum of the first n natural numbers. Then

1	+	2	+	3	$+ \cdots +$	$(n - 2)$	$+ (n - 1) +$	n	$= s$
n	$+ (n - 1) +$	$(n - 2)$	$+ \cdots +$	3	$+$ 2 $+$	1	$= s$

$$(n + 1) + (n + 1) + (n + 1) + \cdots + (n + 1) + (n + 1) + (n + 1) = 2s$$

Therefore, $n(n + 1) = 2s$ and $s = \frac{1}{2}n(n + 1)$.

Let us next consider Example 2: If $a \geq -1$, then $(1 + a)^n \geq 1 + na$. This example is somewhat different from the first one, since it has the form of a mathematical theorem, rather than a mathematical identity.

As in the case of Example 1, the statement of Example 2 can be considered to be an abbreviation for an infinite sequence of statements:

$$\text{If } a \geq -1, \text{ then } (1 + a) \geq 1 + a.$$
$$\text{If } a \geq -1, \text{ then } (1 + a)^2 \geq 1 + 2a.$$
$$\text{If } a \geq -1, \text{ then } (1 + a)^3 \geq 1 + 3a.$$

$$\cdots$$

In these statements, a represents an arbitrary real number, and we require $a \geq -1$ in each statement. Clearly, the first of these statements is true. Let us try to proceed as in Example 1, using the nth statement of the sequence to prove the following statement. Assume then that $(1 + a)^n \geq 1 + na$. Since $a \geq -1$, we have $1 + a \geq 0$. Therefore, multiplying each side of the assumed inequality by $1 + a$ preserves the direction of the inequality and gives

$$(1 + a)^{n+1} = (1 + a)^n(1 + a) \geq (1 + na)(1 + a)$$
$$= 1 + (n + 1)a + na^2$$

Since $a^2 \geq 0$ for every real number a, it follows that

$$1 + (n + 1)a + na^2 \geq 1 + (n + 1)a.$$

Combining these two inequalities gives the desired result,

$$(1 + a)^{n+1} \geq 1 + (n + 1)a.$$

In this example, the argument needed to pass from statement n to statement $n + 1$ is somewhat more complicated than the corresponding proof in Example 1. Nevertheless, it achieves the same end: from the truth of the first statement ($n = 1$), the truth of the second statement ($n = 2$) follows; from the truth of the second statement, the truth of the third statement ($n = 3$) follows; and so on. Eventually every statement of the sequence is proved.

Let us review the methods which we have used to prove the statements given in Examples 1 and 2. It should be evident that both proofs follow the same outline. That outline, stated in general terms, is the *principle of induction*.

The statements in Examples 1 and 2 involve an arbitrary natural number n. Thus, in both cases, we are presented with the problem of proving all of the statements in an infinite sequence P_1, P_2, P_3, . . . of mathematical assertions. The procedure which we followed to prove these statements in the examples consisted of two steps. First, we observed that the first statement P_1 of the sequence is true. Then we showed that for any n, it is possible to construct a proof of the statement P_{n+1}, based on the assumption that P_n is true. This deduction of P_{n+1} from P_n took the form of an ordinary mathematical argument (using logic and known mathematical facts). The number n occurred throughout the proof as a variable. For example, we could have substituted a number like 23 for each occurrence of n in the proof to obtain a deduction of P_{24} from P_{23}. From these two steps in both Examples 1 and 2, it was concluded that all the statements were true. These conclusions were special cases of what is called the *principle of mathematical induction*.

(2–1.1). *Principle of mathematical induction.* Let P_1, P_2, P_3, . . . be a sequence of statements. Suppose that
  (a) P_1 is true, and
  (b) for any n, if P_n is true, then P_{n+1} is true.
Then all of the statements P_1, P_2, P_3, . . . are true.

By assumption (a), P_1 is true. By assumption (b) in the case $n = 1$, if P_1 is true, then P_2 is true. Thus P_2 is true. By (b) in the case $n = 2$, if P_2 is true, then P_3 is true. Thus P_3 is true. We can continue indefinitely in this way. Since any statement of the sequence will ultimately be reached, it follows that every one of the statements is true.

To apply the principle of induction in making a mathematical proof, it is necessary to establish that conditions (a) and (b) are satisfied. The proof of (a) is usually called the *basis* of the induction while the proof of (b) is called the *induction step*. In carrying out the proof of the induction step, it may be assumed throughout the argument that the statement P_n is true. This is called the *induction hypothesis*.

It should be noted however that the validity of the induction step does not necessarily depend on the truth of P_n. For example, if P_n is the assertion "$n^2 + n$ is odd," then P_{n+1} is the statement "$(n + 1)^2 + (n + 1)$ is odd." Since $(n + 1)^2 + (n + 1) = n^2 + n + 2(n + 1)$, it follows that if P_n is true, then so is P_{n+1} (because the sum of an odd number and an even number is odd). That is, condition (b) is satisfied. However, P_n is actually false for every $n \in N$, since $n^2 + n = n(n + 1)$, and at least one of the natural numbers n or $n + 1$ is even. Another aspect of the proof of the induction step which should be emphasized is that n must represent an arbitrary natural number (that is, a variable) throughout the argument. This is essential because the fact that P_n implies P_{n+1} is applied successively with $n = 1, 2, 3, ...$

EXAMPLE 4. We prove Theorem 1–6.4 (Example 3). The proof is a typical application of mathematical induction to establish a mathematical theorem.

The statement to be proved for the basis step is the following: If $\{A_1\}$ is a pairwise disjoint collection of sets, then $m(A_1) = m(A_1)$. This is obviously true. To prove the induction step, we make the induction hypothesis P_n: If

$$\{A_1, A_2, \ldots, A_n\}$$

is a pairwise disjoint collection of sets in S, then $m(A_1 \cup A_2 \cup \cdots \cup A_n) = m(A_1) + m(A_2) + \cdots + m(A_n)$. The statement which has to be proved is P_{n+1}: If $\{A_1, A_2, \ldots, A_n, A_{n+1}\}$ is a pairwise disjoint collection of sets in S, then $m(A_1 \cup A_2 \cup \cdots \cup A_n \cup A_{n+1}) = m(A_1) + m(A_2) + \cdots + m(A_n) + m(A_{n+1})$. Note that by the definition of pairwise disjointness, if

$$\{A_1, A_2, \ldots, A_n, A_{n+1}\}$$

is a pairwise disjoint collection, then so is $\{A_1, A_2, \ldots, A_n\}$. Thus the induction hypothesis can be applied to obtain

$$m(A_1) + m(A_2) + \cdots + m(A_n) = m(A_1 \cup \cdots \cup A_n).$$

Consequently,

$$m(A_1) + m(A_2) + \cdots + m(A_n) + m(A_{n+1})$$
$$= m(A_1 \cup A_2 \cup \cdots \cup A_n) + m(A_{n+1}).$$

We would like to conclude that $m(A_1 \cup A_2 \cup \cdots \cup A_n) + m(A_{n+1}) = m(A_1 \cup A_2 \cup \cdots \cup A_n \cup A_{n+1})$. This conclusion is justified by Definition 1–6.3, provided that $A_1 \cup A_2 \cup \cdots \cup A_n$ and A_{n+1} are disjoint. However by Theorem 1–5.4,

$$A_{n+1} \cap (A_1 \cup A_2 \cup \cdots \cup A_n)$$
$$= (A_{n+1} \cap A_1) \cup (A_{n+1} \cap A_2) \cup \cdots \cup (A_{n+1} \cap A_n)$$
$$= \Phi \cup \Phi \cup \cdots \cup \Phi = \Phi,$$

since $\{A_1, A_2, \ldots, A_n, A_{n+1}\}$ is a pairwise disjoint collection. Thus, we have shown that the truth of P_{n+1} follows from the truth of P_n. By the principle of induction, this proves Theorem 1–6.4.

PROBLEMS

1. Use mathematical induction to prove the following identities.
   (a) $1 + 3 + 5 + \cdots + (2n - 1) = n^2$
   (b) $1^2 + 2^2 + 3^2 + \cdots + n^2 = \frac{1}{6}n(n + 1)(2n + 1)$
   (c) $1^2 + 3^2 + 5^2 + \cdots + (2n + 1)^2 = \frac{1}{3}(n + 1)(2n + 1)(2n + 3)$
   (d) $1^6 - 2^6 + 3^6 - \cdots + (-1)^{n-1} n^6$
   $$= \frac{(-1)^{n-1}}{2} (n^6 + 3n^5 - 5n^3 + 3n)$$

2. Use mathematical induction to prove the following identities.

(a) $\dfrac{1}{1\cdot 2}+\dfrac{1}{2\cdot 3}+\dfrac{1}{3\cdot 4}+\cdots+\dfrac{1}{n(n+1)}=\dfrac{n}{n+1}$

(b) $\dfrac{3}{1^2\cdot 2^2}+\dfrac{5}{2^2\cdot 3^2}+\dfrac{7}{3^2\cdot 4^2}+\cdots+\dfrac{2n+1}{n^2(n+1)^2}=\dfrac{n(n+2)}{(n+1)^2}$

(c) $\dfrac{1}{1\cdot 2\cdot 3}+\dfrac{1}{2\cdot 3\cdot 4}+\dfrac{1}{3\cdot 4\cdot 5}+\cdots$

$$+\dfrac{1}{n(n+1)(n+2)}=\dfrac{n(n+3)}{4(n+1)(n+2)}$$

3. Use mathematical induction to prove the following identities.

(a) $(1\cdot 2\cdot 3)^2-(2\cdot 3\cdot 4)^2+(3\cdot 4\cdot 5)^2-\cdots$

$$+(-1)^{n-1}[n(n+1)(n+2)]^2$$

$$=\dfrac{(-1)^{n-1}}{2}(n^6+9n^5+28n^4+33n^3+7n^2-6n)$$

(b) $(1\cdot 2\cdot 3\cdots r)+[2\cdot 3\cdot 4\cdots(r+1)]+[3\cdot 4\cdot 5\cdots(r+2)]+\cdots$

$$+[n(n+1)(n+2)\cdots(n+r-1)]$$

$$=\dfrac{n(n+1)(n+2)\cdots(n+r)}{r+1}$$

4. Use mathematical induction to prove the following identities.

(a) $1+2+2^2+\cdots+2^{n-1}=2^n-1$

(b) $1+2(\tfrac{1}{2})+3(\tfrac{1}{2})^2+\cdots+n(\tfrac{1}{2})^{n-1}=4-(n+2)(\tfrac{1}{2})^{n-1}$

(c) $3+3^3+3^5+\cdots+3^{2n-1}=\tfrac{3}{8}(9^n-1)$

5. Use mathematical induction to prove the following identities.

(a) $(1-\tfrac{1}{2})(1-\tfrac{1}{3})(1-\tfrac{1}{4})\cdots\left(1-\dfrac{1}{n+1}\right)=\dfrac{1}{n+1}$

(b) $(1+\tfrac{1}{1})(1+\tfrac{1}{2})(1+\tfrac{1}{3})\cdots\left(1+\dfrac{1}{n}\right)=n+1$

(c) $\left(1-\dfrac{1}{2^2}\right)\left(1-\dfrac{1}{3^2}\right)\left(1-\dfrac{1}{4^2}\right)\cdots\left(1-\dfrac{1}{(n+1)^2}\right)=\dfrac{n+2}{2(n+1)}$

6. Let t be any real number different from 1. Use mathematical induction to prove the following identities.

(a) $1+t+t^2+\cdots+t^{n-1}=\dfrac{t^n-1}{t-1}$

(b) $(1+t)(1+t^2)(1+t^4)\cdots(1+t^{2^{n-1}})=\dfrac{t^{2^n}-1}{t-1}$

(c) $\dfrac{1}{1+t}+\dfrac{2t}{1+t^2}+\dfrac{4t^3}{1+t^4}+\cdots$

$$+\dfrac{2^{n-1}t^{2^{n-1}-1}}{1+t^{2^{n-1}}}=\dfrac{2^n t^{2^n-1}}{t^{2^n}-1}-\dfrac{1}{t-1}$$

7. Use mathematical induction to prove the following inequalities.

(a) $n < 2^n$ (b) $2^{n+3} < (n+3)!$

(c) $n!r! < (n+r)!$, where $r \in N$.

8. Prove that for all natural numbers m and n, $m(m+1) \cdots (m+n-1)$ is a multiple of n.

9. Prove by mathematical induction that if $0 \le a_1 \le 1, 0 \le a_2 \le 1, \ldots,$ $0 \le a_n \le 1$, then $(1-a_1)(1-a_2) \cdots (1-a_n) \ge 1 - a_1 - a_2 - \cdots - a_n$.

10. Prove by mathematical induction that if $a_1, a_2, \cdots, a_{2^n}$ are positive real numbers, then

$$a_1 a_2 \cdots a_{2^n} \le \left(\frac{a_1 + a_2 + \cdots + a_{2^n}}{2^n} \right)^{2^n},$$

and the inequality is strict unless $a_1 = a_2 = \cdots = a_n$. [*Hint:* First show that

$$a_1 a_2 = \left(\frac{a_1 + a_2}{2} \right)^2 - \left(\frac{a_1 - a_2}{2} \right)^2.]$$

11. Give a proof by mathematical induction of the case of Theorem 1–5.4 in which $I = \{1, 2, \ldots, n\}$.

2–2 The binomial theorem. In this section, we will use mathematical induction to prove the binomial theorem. The binomial theorem and its generalization, the multinomial theorem, are important results not only in elementary algebra, but also in number theory, probability theory, and combinatorial analysis. An application of the binomial theorem has already been given in Section 1–3. Moreover, the proof of this theorem is a good exercise in the use of mathematical induction.

The formulas

$$(x+y)^2 = x^2 + 2xy + y^2,$$
$$(x+y)^3 = x^3 + 3x^2 y + 3xy^2 + y^3,$$
$$(x+y)^4 = x^4 + 4x^3 y + 6x^2 y^2 + 4xy^3 + y^4$$

are familiar from elementary algebra. They suggest the problem of finding the general expanded version of the power $(x+y)^n$. An examination of the cases $n = 2, 3, 4$ suggests that the general formula should be of the following form:

$$(x+y)^n = x^n + N_{1,n} x^{n-1} y + N_{2,n} x^{n-2} y^2 + \cdots + N_{n-1,n} xy^{n-1} + y^n, \tag{2-1}$$

where the coefficient $N_{i,n}$ of $x^{n-i} y^i$ is some natural number which depends on i and n. For example, if $n = 4$, then $N_{1,4} = 4$, $N_{2,4} = 6$, and $N_{3,4} = 4$. Mathematical induction now provides a means of verifying this guess. Let P_n be the statement that equation (2–1) is valid with $N_{i,n}$ certain positive integers (which will be determined presently). In particular, P_1 is just the statement $x + y = x + y$, which is certainly true. Then, making the induction hypothesis that P_n is true, an algebraic calculation gives

$$
\begin{aligned}
(x + y)^{n+1} &= (x + y)(x + y)^n \\
&= (x + y)(x^n + N_{1,n}x^{n-1}y + N_{2,n}x^{n-2}y^2 + \cdots \\
&\qquad\qquad\qquad\qquad + N_{n-1,n}xy^{n-1} + y^n) \\
&= x^{n+1} + N_{1,n}x^ny + N_{2,n}x^{n-1}y^2 + \cdots \\
&\qquad + N_{n-1,n}x^2y^{n-1} + xy^n + x^ny + N_{1,n}x^{n-1}y^2 + \cdots \\
&\qquad + N_{n-2,n}x^2y^{n-1} + N_{n-1,n}xy^n + y^{n+1} \\
&= x^{n+1} + (N_{1,n} + 1)x^ny + (N_{2,n} + N_{1,n})x^{n-1}y^2 + \cdots \\
&\qquad + (N_{n-1,n} + N_{n-2,n})x^2y^{n-1} \\
&\qquad + (1 + N_{n-1,n})xy^n + y^{n+1}.
\end{aligned}
$$

This identity establishes the validity of P_{n+1}. It is only necessary to note that the coefficients for the identity P_{n+1} will be

$$
N_{1,n+1} = N_{1,n} + 1, \qquad N_{2,n+1} = N_{2,n} + N_{1,n}, \cdots,
$$
$$
N_{n-1,n+1} = N_{n-1,n} + N_{n-2,n}, \qquad N_{n,n+1} = 1 + N_{n-1,n}.
$$

Since the $N_{i,n}$ are natural numbers by the induction hypothesis, so are the coefficients $N_{i,n+1}$. Moreover, these constants, which are usually called *binomial coefficients*, satisfy a simple relationship which makes it possible to obtain their value. For convenience, define

$$
N_{0,n} = N_{n,n} = 1, \qquad \text{for all } n. \tag{2–2}
$$

Then

$$
N_{i,n+1} = N_{i-1,n} + N_{i,n}, \qquad \text{for } 1 \le i \le n. \tag{2–3}
$$

Consider the diagram (known as the Pascal triangle):

$$
\begin{array}{ccccccccccccccc}
 & & & & & & & 1 \\
 & & & & & & 1 & & 1 \\
 & & & & & 1 & & 2 & & 1 \\
 & & & & 1 & & 3 & & 3 & & 1 \\
 & & & 1 & & 4 & & 6 & & 4 & & 1 \\
 & & 1 & & 5 & & 10 & & 10 & & 5 & & 1 \\
 & 1 & & 6 & & 15 & & 20 & & 15 & & 6 & & 1 \\
1 & & 7 & & 21 & & 35 & & 35 & & 21 & & 7 & & 1
\end{array}
$$

The rule of formation should be clear. The edges of the triangle are composed of ones. The position of the numbers in successive rows is staggered, so that every number not on an edge of the triangle has two numbers above it, one of them to the right and the other to the left. Moreover, each such number is the sum of the two numbers above it.

If we write down a similar triangle with the binomial coefficients:

$$
\begin{array}{ccccccc}
N_{0,1} & N_{1,1} \\
N_{0,2} & N_{1,2} & N_{2,2} \\
N_{0,3} & N_{1,3} & N_{2,3} & N_{3,3} \\
N_{0,4} & N_{1,4} & N_{2,4} & N_{3,4} & N_{4,4} \\
N_{0,5} & N_{1,5} & N_{2,5} & N_{3,5} & N_{4,5} & N_{5,5} \\
N_{0,6} & N_{1,6} & N_{2,6} & N_{3,6} & N_{4,6} & N_{5,6} & N_{6,6}
\end{array}
$$

We see that equations (2–2) and (2–3) express exactly the same rules of formation that were used to construct the Pascal triangle, and these rules clearly determine uniquely the numbers which appear in the triangle. Hence, the numbers in the nth row of the Pascal triangle are precisely the binomial coefficients for the expansion of $(x + y)^n$.

EXAMPLE 1. $(x + y)^6 = x^6 + 6x^5y + 15x^4y^2 + 20x^3y^3$
$$+ 15x^2y^4 + 6xy^5 + y^6.$$

EXAMPLE 2. $(x + y)^7 = x^7 + 7x^6y + 21x^5y^2 + 35x^4y^3$
$$+ 35x^3y^4 + 21x^2y^5 + 7xy^6 + y^7.$$

A striking characteristic of the Pascal triangle is its symmetry about the vertical line through its center. This symmetry is expressed in terms of the binomial coefficients by the formula

$$N_{i,n} = N_{n-i,n}. \tag{2–4}$$

The proof that equation (2–4) is actually valid is another simple exercise in mathematical induction. The details are left to the reader.

Another less obvious relationship between binomial coefficients can be discovered from the Pascal triangle by tracing down a diagonal from left to right. For example, on the third diagonal we get the sequence 1, 3, 6, 10, 15, 21, ... The rule of formation here is not immediately evident. However, consider the successive quotients: $\frac{3}{1}$, $\frac{6}{3} = 2 = \frac{4}{2}$, $\frac{10}{6} = \frac{5}{3}$, $\frac{15}{10} = \frac{3}{2} = \frac{6}{4}$, $\frac{21}{15} = \frac{7}{5}$, ... Similarly, down the next diagonal, 1, 4, 10,

20, 35, . . . , the quotients are $\frac{4}{1}$, $\frac{10}{4} = \frac{5}{2}$, $\frac{20}{10} = 2 = \frac{6}{3}$, $\frac{35}{20} = \frac{7}{4}$, ...
These observations suggest another identity:

$$\frac{N_{i+1,n+1}}{N_{i,n}} = \frac{n+1}{i+1}, \qquad 1 \le i \le n. \tag{2–5}$$

This can in fact be proved by induction, using equations (2–2) and (2–3).
We will not carry out this proof. Instead, let us see how equation (2–5)
can be used to determine a numerical expression for the binomial coefficients $N_{i,n}$, $0 < i < n$. By successive cancellation, we obtain

$$\begin{aligned}
N_{i,n} &= \frac{N_{i,n}}{N_{i-1,n-1}} \cdot \frac{N_{i-1,n-1}}{N_{i-2,n-2}} \cdots \frac{N_{1,n-i+1}}{N_{0,n-i}} \cdot N_{0,n-i} \\
&= \frac{n}{i} \cdot \frac{n-1}{i-1} \cdots \frac{n-i+1}{1} \cdot 1 \\
&= \frac{n(n-1)\cdots(n-i+1)}{i(i-1)\cdots 1} \\
&= \frac{n(n-1)\cdots(n-i+1)(n-i)(n-i-1)\cdots 2\cdot 1}{[(n-i)(n-i-1)\cdots 2\cdot 1][i(i-1)\cdots 2\cdot 1]} \\
&= \frac{n!}{(n-i)!\,i!}.
\end{aligned}$$

Recalling the convention that $0! = 1$, we see that the expression
$n!/(n-i)!\,i!$ represents $N_{i,n}$ even for $i = 0$ and $i = n$. For by (2–2),

$$N_{0,n} = 1 = \frac{n!}{(n-0)!\,0!}, \qquad N_{n,n} = 1 = \frac{n!}{(n-n)!\,n!}.$$

The discussion of this section can now be summarized as a theorem.

THEOREM 2–2.1   If n is a natural number, then

$$\begin{aligned}
(x+y)^n = x^n &+ N_{1,n}x^{n-1}y + N_{2,n}x^{n-2}y^2 + \cdots \\
&+ N_{n-1,n}xy^{n-1} + y^n,
\end{aligned}$$

where the binomial coefficients $N_{i,n}$ are natural numbers which are given
by the formula

$$N_{i,n} = \frac{n!}{(n-i)!\,i!} \qquad \text{if } 0 \le i \le n.$$

Except for the inductive proof of (2–5), all of the facts in Theorem 2–2.1,
have been established. Instead of proving (2–5), we will show directly
(by induction on n) that $N_{i,n} = n!/(n-i)!\,i!$ if $0 \le i \le n$.

We have already observed that for all n, $N_{0,n} = n!/(n-0)!\,0!$, and
$N_{n,n} = n!/(n-n)!\,n!$. This provides the basis of the induction. For if

$n = 1$, then $0 \leq i \leq n$ implies that either $i = 0$ or $i = 1$. For the induction step, assume that $N_{i,n} = n!/(n - i)!i!$ for each i between 0 and n (including $i = 0$ and $i = n$). Then by (2–3),

$$N_{i,n+1} = N_{i-1,n} + N_{i,n} = \frac{n!}{(n - i + 1)!(i - 1)!} + \frac{n!}{(n - i)!i!}$$

$$= \frac{n!}{(n - i + 1)!i!} [i + (n - i + 1)] = \frac{(n + 1)!}{(n + 1 - i)!i!},$$

provided that $1 \leq i \leq n$. Since the cases $i = 0$ and $i = n + 1$ are taken care of by the first remark of this paragraph, the proof of the induction step is complete. By the principle of mathematical induction, Theorem 2–2.1 is established.

The notation $N_{i,n}$ for the binomial coefficients seems appropriate for the interpretation of these numbers given in Section 1–3. However, a more common designation of $N_{i,n}$ is $\binom{n}{i}$. That is,

$$\binom{n}{i} = \frac{n!}{(n - i)!i!}, \qquad \text{if } 0 \leq i \leq n.$$

Henceforth, we will use $\binom{n}{i}$ rather than $N_{i,n}$ to denote the binomial coefficients.

There are numerous useful identities involving binomial coefficients. We give one sample of such a relation.

THEOREM 2–2.2. Let m and n be natural numbers, and let k be an integer satisfying $0 \leq k \leq m, 0 \leq k \leq n$. Then

$$\binom{m}{0}\binom{n}{k} + \binom{m}{1}\binom{n}{k - 1} + \binom{m}{2}\binom{n}{k - 2} + \cdots$$

$$+ \binom{m}{k}\binom{n}{0} = \binom{m + n}{k}.$$

It is possible to prove this formula by induction on $m + n$, using (2–2) and (2–3). However, there is a simpler proof, based on Theorem 2–2.1, which makes it clear why such an identity holds. We observe that $\binom{m+n}{k}$ is the coefficient of $x^{m+n-k}y^k$ in the expansion of $(x + y)^{m+n}$. However,

$$(x + y)^{m+n} = (x + y)^m (x + y)^n$$

$$= \left[\binom{m}{0}x^m + \binom{m}{1}x^{m-1}y + \cdots + \binom{m}{m - 1}xy^{m-1} + \binom{m}{m}y^m\right]$$

$$\times \left[\binom{n}{0}x^n + \binom{n}{1}x^{n-1}y + \cdots + \binom{n}{n - 1}xy^{n-1} + \binom{n}{n}y^n\right].$$

If these expressions are multiplied together and the terms with the same powers of x and y are collected, it is clear that the coefficient of $x^{m+n-k}y^k$

will be

$$\binom{m}{0}\binom{n}{k} + \binom{m}{1}\binom{n}{k-1} + \binom{m}{2}\binom{n}{k-2} + \cdots + \binom{m}{k}\binom{n}{0}.$$

For example, with $m = 2$ and $n = 3$,

$$(x + y)^2(x + y)^3 = \left[\binom{2}{0}x^2 + \binom{2}{1}xy + \binom{2}{2}y^2\right]$$

$$\times \left[\binom{3}{0}x^3 + \binom{3}{1}x^2y + \binom{3}{2}xy^2 + \binom{3}{3}y^3\right]$$

$$= \binom{2}{0}\binom{3}{0}x^5 + \binom{2}{0}\binom{3}{1}x^4y + \binom{2}{0}\binom{3}{2}x^3y^2$$

$$+ \binom{2}{0}\binom{3}{3}x^2y^3 + \binom{2}{1}\binom{3}{0}x^4y$$

$$+ \binom{2}{1}\binom{3}{1}x^3y^2 + \binom{2}{1}\binom{3}{2}x^2y^3$$

$$+ \binom{2}{1}\binom{3}{3}xy^4 + \binom{2}{2}\binom{3}{0}x^3y^2$$

$$+ \binom{2}{2}\binom{3}{1}x^2y^3 + \binom{2}{2}\binom{3}{2}xy^4$$

$$+ \binom{2}{2}\binom{3}{3}y^5$$

$$= \binom{2}{0}\binom{3}{0}x^5 + \left[\binom{2}{0}\binom{3}{1} + \binom{2}{1}\binom{3}{0}\right]x^4y$$

$$+ \left[\binom{2}{0}\binom{3}{2} + \binom{2}{1}\binom{3}{1}\right.$$

$$\left. + \binom{2}{2}\binom{3}{0}\right]x^3y^2$$

$$+ \left[\binom{2}{0}\binom{3}{3} + \binom{2}{1}\binom{3}{2}\right.$$

$$\left. + \binom{2}{2}\binom{3}{1}\right]x^2y^3$$

$$+ \left[\binom{2}{1}\binom{3}{3} + \binom{2}{2}\binom{3}{2}\right]xy^4$$

$$+ \binom{2}{2}\binom{3}{3}y^5.$$

The general idea of the proof of Theorem 2–2.2 was used in Section 1–3 to obtain an expression for the number of subsets of cardinality k in a set with n elements. The method consists of obtaining two different expressions for the coefficients of a polynomial in one or more variables, and then equating the corresponding coefficients. The justification for this procedure must wait until the nature of polynomials has been examined more carefully (see Section 9–2). As in the case of Theorem 2–2.2, there are many instances in which an inductive proof can be replaced by this process of "equating coefficients."

Problems

1. Write the binomial formula for the case $n = 15$. (Determine the numerical value of all of the coefficients.)

2. Calculate $n!/i!(n-i)!$ for $n = 7$, $0 < i < 7$, and compare your results with the values of the binomial coefficients obtained from the Pascal triangle.

3. Prove (2–4) by induction on n, using (2–2) and (2–3).

4. Prove (2–5) by induction on n, using (2–2) and (2–3).

5. Show that the binomial formula implies

$$(1 + t)^n = 1 + \binom{n}{1} t + \binom{n}{2} t^2 + \cdots + \binom{n}{n-1} t^{n-1} + t^n.$$

Show conversely that this identity implies the binomial formula. [*Hint:* let $t = y/x$.]

6. (For students familiar with differential calculus.) Prove (2–5) by differentiating both sides of the identity

$$(1 + t)^{n+1} = 1 + N_{1,n+1}t + N_{2,n+1}t^2 + \cdots + N_{n,n+1}t^n + t^{n+1},$$

then expanding the left-hand side and comparing coefficients of equal powers of t.

7. Prove Theorem 2–2.2 by induction on $m + n$.

8. Using Theorem 2–2.2 and (2–4), show that $\binom{n}{0}^2 + \binom{n}{1}^2 + \binom{n}{2}^2 + \cdots + \binom{n}{n}^2 = \binom{2n}{n}$.

9. Prove by induction on n that if m is a natural number satisfying $m \leq n$, then $\binom{n}{m} + \binom{n-1}{m} + \binom{n-2}{m} + \cdots + \binom{m}{m} = \binom{n+1}{m+1}$.

10. Prove by induction on r that

$$(x_1 + x_2 + \cdots + x_r)^2 = x_1^2 + x_2^2 + \cdots + x_r^2$$
$$+ 2(x_1x_2 + x_1x_3 + \cdots + x_1x_r + x_2x_3$$
$$+ x_2x_4 + \cdots + x_2x_r + \cdots + x_{r-1}x_r).$$

2–3 Generalizations of the induction principle. In this section, we will consider some variations of the principle of mathematical induction. It is often difficult to use (2–1.1) directly in a mathematical proof, even though the problem under consideration seems to be accessible to induction. In many such cases, a slight modification of the induction principle (2–1.1) will lead to success.

Our first observation amounts to only a change of the notation in (2–1.1).

(2–3.1). Let r be an integer. Suppose that P_r, P_{r+1}, P_{r+2}, ... is a sequence of statements such that

    (a) P_r is true, and

    (b) for any $n \geq r$, if P_n is true, then P_{n+1} is true.

Then all of the statements P_r, P_{r+1}, P_{r+2}, ... are true.

In many inductive problems, the direct application of (2–1.1) requires an unnatural change in notation. It is better to use (2–3.1) in such cases.

EXAMPLE 1. If $n \geq 4$, $2^n < n!$. In this case $r = 4$. The assertion P_4 is correct: $2^4 = 16 < 24 = 4!$. It is easy to show that if $2^n < n!$, then $2^{n+1} < (n+1)!$. Note that the statements P_1 ($2^1 < 1!$), P_2 ($2^2 < 2!$), and P_3 ($2^3 < 3!$) are false.

Suppose that P_1, P_2, P_3, ... is a sequence of statements, and that P_1 and P_2 are true. To prove P_3 by the ordinary induction process, we would show that P_2 imples P_3. However, all that we want is a proof that P_3 is true, and it may be the case that P_3 is a consequence of P_1, or of a combination of P_1 and P_2. More generally, if it has been shown that P_1, P_2, ..., P_n are all true, and if it is possible to prove that the truth of P_{n+1} is a consequence of some, or possibly all, of the statements P_1, P_2, ..., P_n, then we can assert that P_1, P_2, ..., P_n, P_{n+1} are all true, and we are ready to go on to the next statement in the sequence. If this can be done for every n, then it is possible to proceed along the sequence of statements, proving them one at a time. Eventually, any particular statement will be shown to be true. We can formulate this process as a revised principle of induction which, at the same time, takes advantage of the more general notation introduced in (2–3.1).

(2–3.2). Let r be an integer. Suppose that P_r, P_{r+1}, P_{r+2}, ... is a sequence of statements such that

    (a) P_r is true, and

    (b) for any $n \geq r$, if P_r, P_{r+1}, ..., P_n are all true, then P_{n+1} is true.

Then all of the statements P_r, P_{r+1}, P_{r+2}, ... are true.

A proof which is based on (2–3.2) is called a *course of values induction*. As in the case of ordinary induction, the proof of the first statement P_r of the sequence is called the *basis* of the induction, and the proof that the truth of $P_r, P_{r+1}, \ldots, P_n$ implies that P_{n+1} is true is called the *induction step*. For a course of values induction, the induction hypothesis is the assumption that $P_r, P_{r+1}, \ldots, P_n$ are true.

The conditions (a) and (b) of (2–3.2) can be combined into a single condition.

(2–3.3). Let r be an integer. Suppose that $P_r, P_{r+1}, P_{r+2}, \ldots$ is a sequence of statements such that for any $n \geq r$, if P_m is true for all m satisfying $r \leq m < n$, then P_n is true. Then all of the statements $P_r, P_{r+1}, P_{r+2}, \ldots$ are true.

The condition in (2–3.3) may seem ambiguous in the case where $n = r$, since it is impossible to have a natural number m satisfying $r \leq m < r$. But this simply means that the statement "P_m is true for all m satisfying $r \leq m < r$" is automatically satisfied (or, in mathematical terminology, "vacuously satisfied"). Thus, the condition, for case $n = r$, is just the requirement that P_r is true, which is condition (a) of (2–3.2).

The induction hypothesis for the form of the induction principle given by (2–3.3) is the assumption that all of the statements P_m with $r \leq m < n$ are true. This is different from the induction hypothesis in (2–3.2), where it is assumed that P_m holds for $r \leq m \leq n$, that is, for

$$r \leq m < n + 1.$$

Our discussion above shows that this shift from $n + 1$ to n is necessary in order that condition (a) of (2–3.2) can be included in the condition of (2–3.3). Of course, condition (b) of (2–3.2) is also included in (2–3.3), which is assumed to hold for all n (and therefore it holds if n is replaced by $n + 1$).

Course of values induction is frequently used in the study of natural numbers. In order to give an example, we introduce the important concept of a prime number. A *prime number* (or simply a *prime*) is a natural number greater than 1, which is not divisible by any natural number other than itself and 1. For example, 2, 3, 5, 7, 11, and 13 are primes, while 4, 6, 8, 9, 10, 12, 14, and 15 are not primes.

EXAMPLE 2. We will prove using a course of values induction that every natural number greater than 1 is divisible by a prime. Since $n = 2$ is the first natural number greater than one, we take $r = 2$ in (2–3.3). The sequence of statements to be proved is:

$$P_2: \text{2 is divisible by a prime,}$$
$$P_3: \text{3 is divisible by a prime,}$$
$$\vdots$$
$$P_n: \text{n is divisible by a prime.}$$
$$\vdots$$

Suppose that $n \geq 2$ and that P_m is true for all m satisfying $2 \leq m < n$. This is the induction hypothesis. If n is a prime, then P_n is true, since n is divisible by itself. Note that this observation covers the case $n = 2$, the basis of the induction. If n is not a prime, then n has a divisor s which is different from 1 and n. Thus $n = s \cdot t$, where $2 \leq s < n$. By the induction hypothesis, P_s is true. Therefore, s is divisible by some prime p, that is, $s = p \cdot k$ for some natural number k. But then $n = (p \cdot k) \cdot t = p \cdot (k \cdot t)$, which shows that n is divisible by the prime p. By (2–3.3), P_n is true for every natural number n.

It is not hard to show that the number s in this proof must be less than $n - 1$. Thus it would be impossible to carry out the proof using ordinary induction, since P_n is not a consequence of P_{n-1}, but rather P_n follows from P_s, where $s < n - 1$.

As another example of a course of values induction we will give the promised proof of Theorem 1–5.2. Actually, we will prove only half of this theorem, since the other half has a similar proof.

Proof of Theorem 1–5.2. The statement to be proved is this: if sets A_1, $A_2, \ldots, A_n$, are united in any way, two at a time, using each set at least once, then the resulting set is equal to $\cup(\{A_1, A_2, \ldots, A_n\})$.

There is a surprise in this proof. The induction variable is not n, as one might expect. Consider the particular set $(A_1 \cup A_2) \cup (A_3 \cup A_4)$. For this case

$$(A_1 \cup A_2) \cup (A_3 \cup A_4) = [\cup(S_1)] \cup [\cup(S_2)] = \cup(S),$$

where

$$S_1 = \{A_1, A_2\}, S_2 = \{A_3, A_4\}, \text{ and } S = S_1 \cup S_2 = \{A_1, A_2, A_3, A_4\}.$$

The first equality of this calculation depends on the observation of Example 2 of Section 1–5, that

$$A_1 \cup A_2 = \cup(\{A_1, A_2\}) = \cup(S_1), \quad A_3 \cup A_4 = \cup(\{A_3, A_4\}) = \cup(S_2);$$

the second equality follows from Theorem 1–5.3. Each of the equality signs in the calculation can be considered as a course of values induction

cases given above with the hope of finding a more exact statement of the theorem:

$$1^3 = 1 = 1^2,$$

$$1^3 + 2^3 = 9 = 3^2,$$

$$1^3 + 2^3 + 3^3 = 36 = 6^2,$$

$$1^3 + 2^3 + 3^3 + 4^3 = 100 = 10^2,$$

$$1^3 + 2^3 + 3^3 + 4^3 + 5^3 = 225 = 15^2.$$

The sequence of numbers 1, 3, 6, 10, 15 was encountered in the discussion of Example 1 of Section 2–1. They were the sums $1, 1 + 2, 1 + 2 + 3, 1 + 2 + 3 + 4$, and $1 + 2 + 3 + 4 + 5$. We proved that these sums can be expressed in the form $\frac{1}{2}n(n + 1)$. This observation suggests that a more complete statement than the original one is true, namely,

$$1^3 + 2^3 + 3^3 + \cdots + n^3 = [\tfrac{1}{2}n(n + 1)]^2.$$

This identity can be proved by a straightforward application of the principle of mathematical induction. We leave this task as an exercise for the reader.

Example 1 illustrates a surprising phenomenon in the technique of using mathematical induction. Proofs by induction often fail because the theorem to be proved has not been stated in a strong enough form. When the appropriate statement of the result is discovered, mathematical induction may work quite well. The reason that this happens is not hard to see. When the statement of a theorem is strengthened, we of course have more to prove. However, we also have more to work with, because the induction hypothesis is also strengthened. The problem is to strike the right balance between hypothesis and conclusion, so that the induction step can be taken.

Induction often works better if we make the problem more general. Moreover, the inductive method can sometimes be used to discover theorems. Our next example illustrates these facts.

EXAMPLE 2. Consider a square array of points with 10 points on each side (see Fig. 2–1). We define a path through the array of points to be a broken line segment starting at the lower left-hand dot, proceeding from dot to dot, moving either to the right or upward, and finally ending at the upper right-hand dot. One such path is shown in Fig. 2–1. The problem is to find the number of possible paths through the array. A more concrete formulation of this problem is to consider a person in the center of a large town, say at the corner of First Street and First Avenue. In how many ways can he drive to the corner of Tenth Street and Tenth Avenue, traveling by a route just 18 blocks in length? A little experimentation will convince the reader that the number of such paths is too large to count easily. One possible method of finding the desired number is to

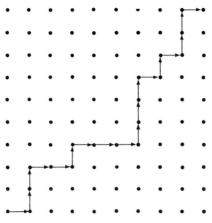

FIGURE 2–1

work up to it inductively. If the square has two dots on each side, as in Fig. 2–2, there are only two paths. We may hope to work up through squares with 3, 4, 5, . . . , 10 dots on each side. In fact, if s is any natural number, it should be possible to determine the number of paths through a square array with s dots along each side.

An even more general problem can be considered. How many paths are there through a rectangular array of points with r dots horizontally and s dots vertically? It may seem optimistic to try to solve this general problem when the particular case of a 10×10 square array is apparently not easy. However, here is a situation in which the general problem is more accessible to induction than the specific one.

Let $P_{r,s}$ denote the number of paths through an r by s rectangular array, where either $r > 1$ or $s > 1$. If $r = 1$ or $s = 1$, then the dots are in line (vertical or horizontal) and there is clearly only one path along the line of dots. In other words,

$$P_{1,r} = P_{s,1} = 1, \tag{2–6}$$

for all $r > 1$ and $s > 1$. If both r and s are larger than 1, then there are two possible starts for a path, either to the dot A immediately right of the lower left-hand dot, or to the dot B just above the initial one (see Fig. 2–3). Suppose

FIGURE 2–2

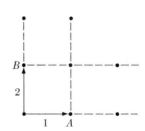

FIGURE 2–3

that the first move is to the right. We then have to follow a path from A to the upper right-hand corner. The number of such paths is just the number of paths through an $r - 1$ by s array, that is, $P_{r-1,s}$ in our notation. Similarly, if the first move is to point B, then there are $P_{r,s-1}$ ways to continue. Thus, since every path passing through A is different from every path passing through B,

$$P_{r,s} = P_{r-1,s} + P_{r,s-1}, \tag{2-7}$$

for $r > 1$ and $s > 1$. The relations (2–6) and (2–7) are similar to the identities (2–2) and (2–3) which determine the binomial coefficients.

This can be seen more easily by changing our notation. We restate (2–6) and (2–7) as

$$P_{1,n+1} = P_{n+1,1} = 1 \quad (n \geq 1), \tag{2-8}$$

$$P_{i+1,n-i+2} = P_{i,n-i+2} + P_{i+1,n-i+1} \quad (1 \leq i \leq n). \tag{2-9}$$

Now define

$$N_{k,l} = P_{k+1,l-k+1} \quad (0 \leq k \leq l). \tag{2-10}$$

Letting $k = 0, l = n$, and also $k = n, l = n$ in (2–10), we obtain

$$N_{0,n} = P_{1,n+1} = 1, \quad N_{n,n} = P_{n+1,1} = 1 \quad (n \geq 1),$$

which is (2–2). Similarly, (2–10) yields

$$N_{i,n+1} = P_{i+1,n-i+2}, N_{i-1,n} = P_{i,n-i+2}, N_{i,n} = P_{i+1,n-i+1}.$$

Then using (2–9), we have

$$N_{i,n+1} = P_{i+1,n-i+2} = P_{i,n-i+2} + P_{i+1,n-i+1}$$
$$= N_{i-1,n} + N_{i,n} \quad (1 \leq i \leq n),$$

which is (2–3). It was mentioned in Section 2–2 that the only solutions of (2–2) and (2–3) are the binomial coefficients. Therefore, $N_{k,l} = \binom{l}{k}$. Now let $k = r - 1, l = r + s - 2$. Then

$$\binom{r+s-2}{r-1} = N_{r-1,r+s-2} = P_{r,s}. \tag{2-11}$$

In the particular case of a square with s dots on a side, $r = s$ and the number of paths is

$$\binom{2s-2}{s-1} = \frac{(2s-2)!}{[(s-1)!]^2}. \tag{2-12}$$

By letting $s = 10$, we obtain the solution of the problem which was originally proposed; there are

$$\binom{18}{9} = \frac{18!}{(9!)^2} = 48{,}620$$

paths through the 10 by 10 array of dots. Thus, a person driving from First Avenue and First Street to Tenth Avenue and Tenth Street and back in our mythical city could do so every day of the year for more than 66 years without ever twice using exactly the same route in either direction.

In this example, we have used induction as a method of proof somewhat indirectly, namely, to show that $P_{r,s} = \binom{r+s-2}{r-1}$. This induction was actually carried out in Section 2–1. However, the method of setting up the problem (that is, obtaining a relation between $P_{r,s}$, $P_{r-1,s}$, and $P_{r,s-1}$) is clearly based on the principle of induction. Note that in order to apply this technique, it is necessary to generalize the original problem of finding the number of paths in a 10 by 10 array to the corresponding problem for a rectangular array of arbitrary size.

PROBLEMS

1. Carry out the proof of the identity

$$1^3 + 2^3 + 3^3 + \cdots + n^3 = [\tfrac{1}{2}n(n+1)]^2.$$

2. It is well known that the sum of the interior angles of a regular n-sided polygon is $(n-2)$ 180 degrees. Give a proof of this fact by first generalizing it to a suitable class of (not necessarily regular) polygons and then using induction. [*Hint:* Divide a regular polygon into two polygons with a smaller number of sides by drawing a line between two nonadjacent vertices. Then see what induction hypothesis is needed to carry through the induction step. You may use the fact that the sum of the interior angles of a triangle is 180°.]

3. Consider a triangular array of dots obtained from the s by s square array of Example 2 by deleting all dots above the diagonal line from the lower left-hand corner to the upper right-hand corner. Figure 2–4 illustrates the case $s = 5$. Define paths from the lower left-hand dot to the upper right-hand dot as before. What is the number of paths through the triangular array with 10 dots on the horizontal and vertical sides?

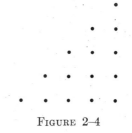

FIGURE 2–4

2–5 Inductive properties of the natural numbers.
There is a close relation between the principle of induction and the order properties of the natural numbers. Our purpose in this section is to describe this relationship.

We have spoken several times of a sequence $P_1, P_2, P_3, \ldots$ of statements, and later we will discuss arbitrary sequences of rational and real numbers. So far we have not given a complete definition of a sequence.

We have assumed that this notion has an intuitive meaning. When denoting a sequence by x_1, x_2, x_3, . . . , we are taking advantage of the obvious fact that the objects of any sequence can be labeled by the natural numbers. This observation can be used to define the concept of a sequence in any formal development of mathematics based on set theory and the axioms of the natural numbers. That is, a sequence is a correspondence between the natural numbers and the objects of a set

$$X = \{x_1, x_2, x_3, \ldots\},$$

where 1 corresponds to x_1, 2 corresponds to x_2, and so on. The objects x_1, x_2, x_3, . . . need not be distinct. For example, if 1 corresponds to 0, 2 corresponds to 1, 3 corresponds to 0, 4 corresponds to 1, etc., we obtain the sequence which is usually written 0, 1, 0, 1, ... The elements of the sequence are the members of the set X. This definition is precise, and it agrees with our intuitive notion of a sequence. Moreover, if sequences are defined in this way, then their properties, and in particular the principle of induction, can be derived from properties of the natural numbers. Let us see what property of the natural numbers it is that yields the principle of mathematical induction.

A careful examination of the discussion in Section 2–1 shows that the principle of induction depends on the fact that if one proceeds along a sequence of objects, from one to the next, then eventually any given element of the sequence will be reached. Applying this observation to the sequence 1, 2, 3, . . . of natural numbers in their usual order, we get the following statement.

(2–5.1). *Principle of induction for the natural numbers.* Let S be a set of natural numbers such that
    (a) $1 \in S$, and
    (b) if a natural number n is in S, then the next number $n + 1$ is in S.
Then S contains every natural number.

In the formal development of mathematics, (2–5.1) is usually taken as an axiom. The principle of induction is deduced from it easily. Let P_1, P_2, P_3, . . . be a sequence of statements indexed by the natural numbers. Let S be the set of all natural numbers n for which the corresponding statement P_n is true. Suppose that the sequence of statements satisfies the two conditions (a) and (b) of (2–1.1). Then by (2–1.1a), P_1 is true, so that by the definition of S, $1 \in S$. Thus S satisfies (2–5.1a). If $n \in S$, then by the definition of S, P_n is true, and therefore by (2–1.1b), P_{n+1} is true. Hence, $n + 1 \in S$. Thus S satisfies (2–5.1b). Consequently, according to (2–5.1), S contains every natural number. This means that every one of the statements P_1, P_2, P_3, . . . , P_n is true.

There is another important property related to the ordering of the natural numbers. Let A be a nonempty finite set of natural numbers. Then the elements of A can be listed in some way:

$$A = \{n_1, n_2, \ldots, n_k\}.$$

By successively examining the numbers in this list, it is possible to pick out a smallest one, that is, a number n_i which satisfies

$$n_i \leq n_1, n_i \leq n_2, \ldots, n_i \leq n_k.$$

Thus, A contains a smallest number. This same conclusion is reasonable even if A is infinite.

Suppose that A is any nonempty set of natural numbers. Since A is not empty, it is possible to select some element $a \in A$. Let $A_0 = \{n | n \in A, n \leq a\}$. Then A_0 consists of some, but not necessarily all, of the natural numbers $1, 2, 3, \ldots, a$. Therefore, A_0 contains only a finite number of elements, and it is not empty since $a \in A_0$. Thus A_0 has a smallest element. Call this smallest element m. By the definition of A_0, $m \in A$ and $m \leq a$. If $n \in A$, then either $n \in A_0$, or $n > a$. In the first case, $m \leq n$ because m is the smallest element of A_0. In the second case, we have $n > a \geq m$. Thus, m is the least element of A. In practice, it may be difficult to determine which numbers belong to A_0, and if the cardinality of A_0 is large (say $|A_0| = 10^{10^{10}}$), the process of selecting the smallest number m might take several lifetimes. However, A does have a least element, whether we can find it easily or not. This fact, which has important mathematical applications, can be stated as follows.

(2–5.2). *Well-ordering principle.* Let A be a nonempty set of natural numbers. Then A contains a smallest number m (that is, $m \in A$ and $m \leq n$ for all $n \in A$).

It is obvious that the conclusion of the well-ordering principle is not true if A is the empty set. There are two reasons for pointing this out. First, a common blunder in applying the principle is committed by failing to prove that the set to which it is applied is not empty. Second, the well-ordering principle is often used to show indirectly that some set A of natural numbers *is* empty. One assumes that A is not empty, so that the well-ordering principle can be used to infer that A contains a smallest number. Then, from the existence of this smallest number in A, some contradiction follows. Therefore, A must be empty. This method of proof can often be used instead of a course of values induction.

EXAMPLE 1. Using the well-ordering principle, we give a new proof of the fact that every natural number n greater than 1 is divisible by a prime number (originally proved in Example 2, Section 2–3, using course of values induction).

Let A be the set of all natural numbers n which are greater than one and not divisible by a prime. If A is empty, then every $n > 1$ is divisible by a prime, and this is what we wish to show. Hence, suppose that A is not empty. Then by the well-ordering principle, there is a smallest number $m \in A$. Since m belongs to A, it is not 1 and it is not divisible by a prime. In particular, m itself is not a prime. Therefore, m is divisible by some natural number k which is different from 1 and m. In particular, $k < m$, and $k \notin A$, since m is the smallest number in A. By the definition of A, this means that either $k = 1$, or k is divisible by a prime. However $k \neq 1$, so that k must be divisible by a prime p. Since p divides k and k divides m, it follows that p divides m. But this contradicts the fact that $m \in A$, since no number in A is divisible by a prime. Thus, the original assumption that A is not empty must be incorrect. That is, $A = \Phi$, which means that every natural number greater than one is divisible by a prime.

PROBLEMS

1. Show by examples that the well-ordering principle is not true for subsets of Z, Q, or R. [*Hint:* Give examples of nonempty sets which do not contain a smallest element.]

2. Show that the well-ordering principle is satisfied for subsets of the following sets.

    (a) $\{n \mid n \in Z, n \geq k\}$, where k is any integer

    (b) $\left\{ 1 - \dfrac{1}{n} \,\middle|\, n \in N \right\}$

    (c) $\left\{ 1 - \dfrac{1}{n} \,\middle|\, n \in N \right\} \cup \left\{ 2 - \dfrac{1}{n} \,\middle|\, n \in N \right\}$

    (d) $\left\{ k - \dfrac{1}{n} \,\middle|\, n \in N, k \in N \right\}$

3. Show by a method similar to the derivation of (2–1.1) from (2–5.1) that the generalized induction principle (2–3.3) can be deduced from the well-ordering principle (2–5.2).

4. Show that if m and n are any two natural numbers, then at least one of the following is true.

    (a) $m = n$
    (b) there is a natural number k such that $m = n + k$
    (c) there is a natural number l such that $n = m + l$

[*Hint:* Let S be the set of all natural numbers m such that for all n either (a), (b), or (c) is satisfied. Note that 1 is in S. Show that condition (b) of (2–5.1) is also satisfied.]

5. Show that (2–5.1) is a consequence of (2–5.2).

6. Give an inductive proof of the sequence of statements P_1, P_2, P_3, . . . , where P_n is the assertion: if A is a set of natural numbers and if $n \in A$, then A contains a smallest element.

7. Show by the well-ordering principle that every nonempty finite set of natural numbers has a largest element.

*2–6 Inductive definitions. As the reader probably realizes, definitions are an important part of mathematics. Often an inductive process is used to formulate a mathematical definition. Definitions of this sort are called *inductive*, or *recursive*.

EXAMPLE 1. Let x be a real number. Then the nth power of x is defined for all n as the product of x with itself n times. However, a more precise definition of x^n is formulated inductively by means of two requirements:

$$x^1 = x, \qquad x^{n+1} = (x^n) \cdot x.$$

EXAMPLE 2. Many important sequences are defined recursively. We cite as an example the Fibonacci sequence:

$$u_1 = 1, u_2 = 1, u_3 = 2, u_4 = 3, u_5 = 5, u_6 = 8, u_7 = 13, \ldots.$$

This sequence is defined by the inductive conditions

$$u_1 = u_2 = 1, \qquad u_{n+1} = u_n + u_{n-1} \qquad \text{(for } n \geq 2\text{)}.$$

EXAMPLE 3. Often informal definitions are given for objects which should properly be defined by induction. For example, the sum $S_n = 1 + 2 + \cdots + (n - 1) + n$ of the first n natural numbers was introduced informally in Section 2–1. The inductive definition of this sum is given by the conditions $S_1 = 1$, $S_{n+1} = S_n + (n + 1)$. A proof by mathematical induction would establish the identity $S_n = \frac{1}{2}n(n + 1)$ in the same way as before.

An inductive definition consists of two parts:

(1) conditions C_1, C_2, . . . , C_k, such that C_1 determines a unique object O_1, C_2 determines a unique object O_2, . . . , C_k determines a unique object O_k;

(2) a condition K, which for any natural number $n \geq k$, determines a unique object O_{n+1} in terms of O_1, O_2, . . . , O_n.

In Example 1, O_n is the number x^n which is obtained by taking the nth power of x. In this example, $k = 1$, and the condition C_1 is the equality $x^1 = x$. The condition K is the equality $x^{n+1} = (x^n) \cdot x$. In Example 2, O_n is the nth term of the Fibonacci sequence. Here, $k = 2$, C_1 is the condition $u_1 = 1$, C_2 is the condition $u_2 = 1$, and K is the condition

$$u_{n+1} = u_n + u_{n-1}, \qquad n \geq 2.$$

It is important to show that inductive definitions give uniquely determined objects O_n for every natural number n. That is, we would like to know that there exists a sequence $O_1, O_2, \ldots, O_n, \ldots$ of objects such that O_n satisfies C_n for every $n \leq k$, and O_n satisfies K for $n > k$, and that if $O_1', O_2', \ldots, O_n', \ldots$ is any sequence of objects such that O_n' satisfies C_n for $n \leq k$, and O_n' satisfies K for $n > k$, then $O_1' = O_1$, $O_2' = O_2, \ldots$, $O_n' = O_n \ldots$. This can be proved using the induction principle for the natural numbers (2–5.1).

THEOREM 2–6.1. Suppose that $C_1, C_2, \ldots, C_k$, and K are conditions having the properties stated in (1) and (2) above. Then there is a unique sequence $O_1, O_2, \ldots, O_n, \ldots$ of objects such that O_n satisfies C_n for $n \leq k$, and O_n satisfies K for $n > k$.

Proof. Let S be the set of all natural numbers m such that there are unique objects $O_1, O_2, \ldots, O_m$ with the properties that for $n \leq m$ and $n \leq k$, O_n satisfies C_n, and for $k < n \leq m$, O_n satisfies K (provided $m > k$). Then $1, 2, \ldots$, and k are in S, since by (1), conditions C_1, $C_2, \ldots, C_k$, respectively, determine unique objects $O_1, O_2, \ldots, O_k$. Suppose that some $m \geq k$ belongs to S. Then by (2), there is a unique object O_{m+1} satisfying K. Therefore there are unique objects $O_1, O_2, \ldots, O_m$, O_{m+1} such that $O_n(n \leq m + 1)$ satisfies C_n for $n \leq k$, and O_n satisfies K for $n > k$. Thus $m + 1 \in S$. Hence, S satisfies the conditions of (2–5.1), and therefore every natural number is in S. This means that there is a unique sequence $O_1, O_2, \ldots, O_n, \ldots$ of objects such that O_n satisfies C_n for $n \leq k$, and O_n satisfies K for $n > k$.

As one might expect, if objects O_n are defined inductively, then mathematical induction is an important tool for establishing the properties of these objects. We illustrate this fact by obtaining an estimate of the size of the Fibonacci numbers.

Let a be a positive real number satisfying $1 + a = a^2$. Then a is a solution of the equation $x^2 - x - 1 = 0$. By the formula for the roots of a quadratic equation, the solutions of this equation are $\frac{1}{2}(1 + \sqrt{5})$ and $\frac{1}{2}(1 - \sqrt{5})$. Of the solutions, only the first is positive. Thus, $a = \frac{1}{2}(1 + \sqrt{5})$. In particular, $a > 1$. Hence, $u_1 = 1 < a$ and $u_2 = 1 < a < a^2$. Make the induction hypothesis that $u_m < a^m$ for all

$m \leq n$. Then

$$u_{n+1} = u_n + u_{n-1} < a^n + a^{n-1} = a^{n-1}(1 + a) = a^{n-1}a^2 = a^{n+1}.$$

Thus by the principle of induction we conclude that $u_n < a^n$, for all n.

Note that although we do not know an explicit formula for the number u_n, we can nevertheless find some of its properties. This is typical of objects which are defined inductively.

PROBLEMS

1. Using the inductive definition of Example 1, prove that

$$x^m x^n = x^{m+n}, \qquad (x^m)^n = x^{mn}, \qquad (xy)^n = x^n y^n,$$

and if $0 < x < y$, then $0 < x^n < y^n$.

2. Give an inductive definition for the sums in Problems 1(a), 2(a), 3(a), and 4(a) of Section 2–1.

3. Give an inductive definition of $n!$

4. Give an inductive definition of nx (the operation of adding x to itself n times), and prove that this is the same as the operation of multiplying x by n.

5. List the first 50 terms of the Fibonacci sequence.

6. Show that no two consecutive terms of the Fibonacci sequence are divisible by the same natural number greater than one.

7. In the Fibonacci sequence $u_1, u_2, \ldots, u_n \ldots$, show that u_n is even if n is a multiple of 3 and that u_n is odd otherwise.

8. In the Fibonacci sequence $u_1, u_2, \ldots, u_n, \ldots$, show that for all n, $a^n < u_{n+2}$, where $a = \frac{1}{2}(1 + \sqrt{5})$.

9. Let $a = \frac{1}{2}(1 + \sqrt{5})$ and $b = \frac{1}{2}(1 - \sqrt{5})$. Prove that if u_n is the nth term of the Fibonacci sequence, then $u_n = (1/\sqrt{5})(a^n - b^n)$.

10. Let the sequence $v_1, v_2, v_3, \ldots$ be defined inductively by

$$v_1 = 1, \qquad v_2 = 3, \qquad v_{n+1} = v_n + v_{n-1}, \qquad n \geq 2.$$

List the first 25 terms of this sequence. Show by induction that for any natural numbers m and n, $2u_{m+v} = u_m v_n + u_n v_m$, where $u_1, u_2, \ldots, u_n, \ldots$ is the Fibonacci sequence.

CHAPTER 3

THE NATURAL NUMBERS

3–1 The definition of numbers. If you were to ask a person with an average education to define mathematics, his answer might be "the science of numbers." Although this definition does not convey much information, it would be hard to find a more concise description of mathematics. Almost all of mathematics is concerned directly or indirectly with ordinary numbers. For this reason, it is important to examine carefully the concept of number, a notion which up to now has been taken for granted.

What are numbers? This is a question of concern to both mathematicians and philosophers. Many answers have been given, but none can be considered to be final. However, 19th century mathematical research has shown that the common number systems (the integers, rational numbers, real numbers, and complex numbers) can all be constructed from the natural numbers. The question "What are numbers?" is therefore replaced by the apparently simpler problem "What are natural numbers?"

In this chapter, we will discuss the natural numbers. In later chapters, the integers, rational numbers, real numbers, and complex numbers will be studied in turn. We will concentrate on the basic properties of each number system, and discuss the extent to which these properties determine the system. The intuitive idea of the various kinds of numbers which students develop in school will be critically examined. Finally, we will indicate the processes by which the integers are formally constructed from the natural numbers, the rational numbers are obtained from the integers, the real numbers are defined from the rationals, and the complex numbers are constructed from the real numbers. It is important for advanced mathematics students to go through the constructions of these number systems in detail, but students at an elementary level will find the process long and tedious. It is better for beginners to concentrate on understanding the definitions and why they are made. The text which follows aims to present a guide toward such understanding. A complete development of the number systems will be given in the form of problems, and interested students are invited to work out the details for themselves.

The concept of a natural number was developed over a period of many centuries as a tool for counting the objects in sets. That is, the natural numbers were introduced as labels to designate the property shared by sets of equal cardinality (in the sense introduced by Cantor, see Section 1–2). Thus, when two traders of ancient Egypt agreed to exchange three camels for seven wives, it was essential that both understood how many items he would have to give up and how many he would receive. This understanding could be achieved, for example, by means of "counters," that is, collections of stones from which sets of small cardinality might be formed in the palm of the hand.

From very early times, numbers have been treated as concrete objects, rather than the names of properties of sets. In fact, this fictitious viewpoint was essential for the creation and development of mathematics. It was not until the 19th century that mathematicians started wondering how to justify the existence of numbers. One of the earliest attempts to define the natural numbers as objects was made by the German mathematician Gottlob Frege (1848–1925) in a book on the foundations of arithmetic, published in 1893. Basing his work on Cantor's set theory, Frege defined *the cardinal number* of a set A to be the class of all sets which are equivalent to A by Cantor's definition of equivalence (see Definition 1–2.3). According to Frege's definition, the cardinal number of $\{0, 1\}$ is the class of all sets $\{a_1, a_2\}$, where a_1 and a_2 are distinct objects. Similarly, the cardinal number of $\{I, II, III\}$ is the class of all sets $\{a_1, a_2, a_3\}$, where a_1, a_2, and a_3 are distinct elements. The natural numbers are defined to be the *cardinal numbers of finite sets*. Thus, the number "2" is a set, namely, the set of all pairs of distinct objects. Frege's definition of the natural numbers is therefore based on two concepts: the notion of a finite set, and the definition of the cardinal number of an arbitrary set.

In Section 1–2, it was taken for granted that the natural numbers existed, and that their properties were well known. Thus, it made sense in Definition 1–2.2 to define a set to be finite if it was equivalent to $\{1, 2, \ldots, n\}$ for some natural number n. This definition cannot be used if the natural numbers are defined as in Frege's program, using the concept of a finite set. This difficulty can be avoided by defining a set A to be finite if and only if there is no one-to-one correspondence between A and a proper subset* of A.

It turned out that there was a more serious flaw in the second notion which enters into Frege's definition of the natural numbers. Unless handled with great care, the concept of the class of all sets which are equivalent to a given set A leads to perplexing logical contradictions. Exactly how much care is needed to avoid these contradictions is somewhat uncertain even now. Thus, the definition of the cardinal number of an arbitrary set which Frege used is unacceptable, and therefore so is his construction of the natural numbers.

---

* It is possible to give a convincing argument that this definition of a finite set agrees with the intuitive idea of such a set. For example, see *The Foundations of Mathematics* by R. L. Wilder, pp. 62–71. Wiley (1952), New York.

A more satisfactory definition of the natural numbers was given by John von Neumann (1903–1957) in 1923. von Neumann observed that any standard sequence of sets, containing what we would intuitively recognize as 1, 2, 3, 4, . . . elements, respectively, can be adopted as the sequence of natural numbers. He showed that a convenient choice for this standard sequence is

$$1 = \{\Phi\},$$

$$2 = \{\Phi, \{\Phi\}\} = \{\Phi, 1\},$$

$$3 = \{\Phi, \{\Phi\}, \{\Phi, \{\Phi\}\}\} = \{\Phi, 1, 2\},$$

$$4 = \{\Phi, \{\Phi\}, \{\Phi, \{\Phi\}\}, \{\Phi, \{\Phi\}, \{\Phi, \{\Phi\}\}\}\} = \{\Phi, 1, 2, 3\},$$

. . .

These particular sets* are now usually called *finite ordinal numbers*. The elements of each such ordinal number n are the empty set, and all ordinal numbers which precede n. Usually, the number 0 (zero) is included among the ordinal numbers. If this is done, then according to von Neumann's definition, 0 would have to be the empty set, since Φ is the only set which contains no elements. With this convention, the definition of finite ordinal numbers is very natural: n is the set of all ordinal numbers which precede it. In this book, we will consider 0 to be an ordinal number, but *not* a natural number. This convention simplifies certain statements concerning the arithmetic of N, for example, the cancellation law of multiplication.

In order to develop some of von Neumann's theory of the natural numbers, we must give an exact definition of these objects. The method by which the natural numbers can be generated is clear:

$$n = \{\Phi, 1, 2, \ldots, n - 1\},$$

and

$$n + 1 = \{\Phi, 1, 2, \ldots, n - 1, n\}$$
$$= \{\Phi, 1, 2, \ldots, n - 1\} \cup \{n\} = n \cup \{n\}.$$

Starting with $1 = \{\Phi\}$, we obtain successively

$$2 = 1 \cup \{1\} = \{\Phi\} \cup \{1\} = \{\Phi, 1\} = \{\Phi, \{\Phi\}\},$$

$$3 = 2 \cup \{2\} = \{\Phi, 1\} \cup \{2\} = \{\Phi, 1, 2\} = \{\Phi, \{\Phi\}, \{\Phi, \{\Phi\}\}\},$$

and so on. Every natural number is ultimately obtained by this process.

---

* The reader should remember the convention discussed in Section 1–1 that an object a is to be distinguished from the set $\{a\}$ whose only element is a. Thus, $1 = \{\Phi\} \neq \Phi$, and $2 = \{\Phi, \{\Phi\}\} \neq \{\Phi, \Phi\} = \{\Phi\} = 1$, etc.

DEFINITION 3–1.1. (a) $\{\Phi\}$ is a natural number.

(b) If n is a set which is a natural number, then $n \cup \{n\}$ is a natural number.

(c) The natural numbers are just those sets which are obtained by repeated application of the rules (a) and (b).

Henceforth, the term "natural number" will refer to the sets defined in Definition 3–1.1. Of course, the familiar symbols 1, 2, 3, . . . will be used to denote the respective sets

$$\{\Phi\}, \qquad \{\Phi, \{\Phi\}\}, \qquad \{\Phi, \{\Phi\}, \{\Phi, \{\Phi\}\}\}, \ldots .$$

We will use lower-case letters to represent natural numbers, even though this violates the custom of denoting sets by capital letters. As usual, the symbol N will stand for the set of all natural numbers.

Our definition of the natural numbers may at first seem strange to the reader. However, the use of this definition requires very little readjustment in our way of thinking about natural numbers. The theorems and definitions which have been given in Chapters 1 and 2 are all sensible and correct when the term "natural number" is interpreted according to Definition 3–1.1. As an example, let us consider the principle of induction (2–5.1). It is convenient to introduce the following notation. If n is a natural number, define

$$S(n) = n \cup \{n\}.$$

Intuitively, $S(n)$ denotes the "successor" of n, that is, $n + 1$. With this notation, the induction principle can be stated in the following form.

(3–1.2). If A is a set of natural numbers such that

(a) $1 \in A$, and

(b) if $n \in A$, then $S(n) \in A$,

then A contains every natural number.

This principle is virtually a restatement of Definition 3–1.1(c). Indeed, the conditions (a) and (b) in (3–1.2) state that $\{\Phi\}$ belongs to A, and if n is in A, then $n \cup \{n\}$ belongs to A. In particular, any set which is obtained by repeated application of the (a) and (b) in Definition 3–1.1 must also belong to A. Therefore, according to Definition 3–1.1(c), every natural number is in A.

The fact that each natural number n is a set which contains what we instinctively think of as n elements often makes it possible to simplify the statements of definitions and theorems. For example, Definition 1–2.2 (of a set X having cardinality n) is intuitively equivalent to the statement that there is a one-to-one correspondence between X and n.

(3–1.3). If n is any natural number and X is a set, then $|X| = n$ if (and only if) X is equivalent to n.

Because it is intuitively sound and better suited than Definition 1–2.2 for the development of the theory of the natural numbers from Definition 3–1.1, we will use (3–1.3) as our definition of a set having cardinality n. As in Definition 1–2.2, a set X will be called *finite* if either $X = \Phi$, or there is a natural number n such that X is equivalent to n.

Although it would be contrary to our intuition, it is not inconceivable that a set X might be equivalent to two different natural numbers m and n. This would imply that there is a one-to-one correspondence between m and n. Fortunately, it is possible to show that if a one-to-one correspondence between natural numbers m and n exists, then $m = n$ (see Problem 19). Consequently, it makes sense to say that *the* cardinal number of the set X is n if X is equivalent to n, and to define $|X|$ to be this unique number. In other words, (3–1.3) is meaningful.

As a set, each natural number n is equivalent to itself. Therefore, according to (3–1.3), $|n| = n$, for every natural number n.

If X is any finite, nonempty set, then X is equivalent to $|X|$. In fact, for X to be nonempty and finite means by definition that there is a natural number n such that X is equivalent to n. Then by (3–1.3), $|X| = n$. Hence, X is equivalent to $|X|$. This observation leads to the following useful fact. If X and Y are two finite nonempty sets, then X is equivalent to Y if and only if $|X| = |Y|$. To prove this statement, suppose first that X and Y are equivalent. Since Y is equivalent to $|Y|$, it follows from (1–2.4c) that X is equivalent to $|Y|$. Therefore, taking n in (3–1.3) to be the natural number $|Y|$, we obtain $|X| = |Y|$. To prove the converse statement, suppose that $|X| = |Y|$. Since X is equivalent to $|X|$, and Y is equivalent to $|Y|$ (and $|X| = |Y|$), it follows from (1–2.4c) that X is equivalent to Y.

Many results follow from Definition 3–1.1 and (3–1.2). In particular, we cite the following.

(3–1.4). 1 is a natural number.

(3–1.5). If n is a natural number, then $S(n)$ is a natural number.

(3–1.6). There is no natural number n such that $1 = S(n)$.

(3–1.7). If m and n are natural numbers such that $S(m) = S(n)$, then $m = n$.

The statements (3–1.4) and (3–1.5) are reformulations of Definition 3–1.1(a) and (b), respectively, using the notation 1 instead of $\{\Phi\}$ and $S(n)$ instead of $n \cup \{n\}$. The proofs of (3–1.6) and (3–1.7) are easy, and we leave them as exercises for the reader (see Problems 4 and 6).

The statements (3–1.2), (3–1.4), (3–1.5), (3–1.6), and (3–1.7) are called *Peano's axioms*, because it was shown in 1889 by the Italian mathematician Guiseppi Peano (1858–1932) that the whole theory of the natural numbers can be developed from these statements. In Peano's development of arithmetic, the natural numbers constitute a set N of undefined objects, with a distinguished element 1. It is assumed that an operation is defined on N which corresponds intuitively to the process of passing from a natural number n to its successor $S(n)$. Finally, it is assumed that Peano's axioms are satisfied. From these few axioms, it is possible to define addition and multiplication in N, and show that these operations have their familiar properties. This axiomatic development of the natural numbers is carried out in several textbooks, in which a construction of the number systems is given. However, we will not use Peano's definition of the operations in N. When the natural numbers are defined as in Definition 3–1.1, the addition and multiplication operations have useful meanings in terms of the operations of set theory.

PROBLEMS

1. According to Frege's definition, what is the cardinal number of the empty set?

2. Write in full the sets which are 5 and 6 in von Neumann's definition of the natural numbers.

3. Prove that if $n \in N$, then $\Phi \in n$; thus, no natural number is the empty set. [*Hint:* Let $A = \{n \in N | \Phi \in n\}$. Use (3–1.2) to show that $A = N$.]

4. Show that if $n \in N$, then $n \notin 1$, so that $1 \neq S(n)$.

5. Prove that if $m \in n$, then $m \subseteq n$. [*Hint:* Let $A = \{n \in N|$ either $m \notin n$, or $m \subseteq n\}$. Use (3–1.2) to show that $A = N$.]

6. Prove (3–1.7).

The following problems lead to some of the most important properties of the natural numbers. Several of the assertions made in this section and a number of the unproved statements in the next two sections occur among these problems. The reader with limited mathematical background will probably have difficulty proving some of the statements in Problems 7 through 19, even though hints are supplied in many cases. Such students are advised to read the problems, and try to see what they mean (keeping in mind that the set n is $\{\Phi, 1, 2, \ldots, n-1\}$), without attempting to do all of them. However, Problems 7 through 19 should be worked in the order in which they appear, because many of them depend on the preceding ones.

7. Prove that $n \notin n$ for all natural numbers n. [*Hint:* Let $A = \{n \in N | n \notin n\}$. Use (3–1.2) to prove that $A = N$.]

8. Prove that if $m \in n$, then $m \subset n$.

9. Prove that for every natural number n, either $n = 1$, or $1 \in n$.

10. Prove that for all natural numbers n, either $n = 1$, or $n = S(k)$ for some $k \in N$.

11. Show that if $m \in n$, then either $S(m) = n$, or else $S(m) \in n$. [*Hint:* Let $A = \{n \in N|$ for all $m \in n$, either $S(m) = n$, or else $S(m) \in n\}$. Prove that $A = N$.]

12. Show that for all m and n, either $m \in n$, $m = n$, or $n \in m$. [*Hint:* Let $A = \{n \in N|$ for all m, either $m \in n$, $m = n$, or $n \in m\}$. Prove that $A = N$.]

13. Prove that for all m and n, either $m \subset n$, $m = n$, or $n \subset m$.

14. Prove that $m \subset n$ if and only if $m \in n$.

15. Prove that $m \subset n$ if and only if $S(m) \subset S(n)$.

16. Show that if n is a natural number, and X is a proper nonempty subset of n, then there exists $m \in N$ such that $m \subset n$ and $|X| = m$. [*Hint:* Let A be the set of all n for which the statement is true. Show that $1 \in A$. Suppose that $n \in A$. To prove that $S(n) \in A$, suppose that $\Phi \subset X \subset S(n) = n \cup \{n\}$. Let $Y = X \cap n$. Show that the statement of the problem is true for $S(n)$ and X in each of the following cases: $Y = \Phi$, $Y = n$, $\Phi \subset Y \subset n$ and $n \notin X$, $\Phi \subset Y \subset n$ and $n \in X$.]

17. Prove that if X is a subset of a finite set Y, then X is finite, and moreover, if $X \subset Y$, then $|X| \subset |Y|$.

18. (a) Show that if X is a finite set and z is any element, then $X \cup \{z\}$ is finite.

(b) Prove that if X and Y are finite sets, then $X \cup Y$ is finite. [*Hint:* Let $A = \{m \in N|$ if X is a finite set and $|Y| = m$, then $X \cup Y$ is finite$\}$. Use (3–1.2) to prove that $A = N$.]

19. (a) Prove that if $n \in N$ and $1 \subset n$, then there is no one-to-one correspondence between 1 and n.

(b) Show that if $m \in N$ and $n \in N$ are such that there is a one-to-one correspondence between $S(m)$ and $S(n)$, then there is a one-to-one correspondence between m and n. [*Hint:* Let $r \leftrightarrow s$ be a one-to-one correspondence between $S(m)$ and $S(n)$. If $m \in S(m)$ corresponds to $n \in S(n)$, then $r \leftrightarrow s$ is a one-to-one correspondence between m and n, also. If m does not correspond to n, show that the given correspondence can be modified to obtain a one-to-one correspondence between m and n.]

(c) Prove that if m and n are natural numbers such that m and n are equivalent, then $m = n$. [*Hint:* Let $A = \{m \in N|$ for all $n \in N$, if $m \subset n$, then m and n are not equivalent$\}$. Use Problem 19(a) and (b), and (3–1.2) to show that $A = N$. The statement (c) then follows from the result of Problem 13.]

3–2 Operations with the natural numbers. Once people began to think of the natural numbers as concrete objects, it was found that these objects could be combined in useful ways. Thus, if a set A contains 2 elements and a set B, which is disjoint from A, contains 3 elements, then the union $A \cup B$ invariably contains 5 elements. The process of forming the union

$A \cup B$ of disjoint sets gives rise to the abstract operation which we call addition: $2 + 3 = 5$.

The definition of addition can be stated very simply.

DEFINITION 3–2.1. Let m and n be natural numbers. Let X and Y be sets such that

(a) $|X| = m$, $|Y| = n$, and

(b) $X \cap Y = \Phi$.

Then the *sum* of m and n is the natural number $|X \cup Y|$.

The sum of m and n is denoted by $m + n$. The process which associates with each pair m and n of natural numbers their sum $m + n$ is the binary operation called *addition*. The fact that every pair of natural numbers has a unique sum is expressed by saying that the natural numbers are *closed under addition*.

In order to see that 3–2.1 is a valid definition, we must show that it provides a rule by which any two natural numbers can be combined to produce a unique third natural number. This is accomplished by proving the following statements.

(1) For any natural numbers m and n, there exist sets X and Y which satisfy (a) and (b).

(2) If X and Y are sets satisfying (a) and (b), then $X \cup Y$ is finite, that is, there is a natural number k such that $|X \cup Y| = k$.

(3) The natural number $|X \cup Y|$ is the same for all pairs X, Y of sets satisfying (a) and (b).

It is clear that (1) and (2) guarantee that each pair of natural numbers has a sum, and (3) insures the fact that this sum is unique.

To prove (1), we must define two sets X and Y which satisfy (a) and (b). There are many ways in which this can be done. We can, for example, use the following construction. Let X be the product set $m \times \{1\}$, and let $Y = n \times \{2\}$. Then

$$j \leftrightarrow \langle j, 1 \rangle, \qquad j \in m,$$
$$k \leftrightarrow \langle k, 2 \rangle, \qquad k \in n,$$

are one-to-one correspondences between m and $m \times \{1\}$ and n and $n \times \{2\}$, respectively. Therefore, X is equivalent to m and Y is equivalent to n. Thus, by (3–1.3), (a) is satisfied. Suppose that (b) is not satisfied, that is, $X \cap Y \neq \Phi$. Then there would be some $j \in m$ and $k \in n$ such that

$$\langle j, 1 \rangle = \langle k, 2 \rangle.$$

By Definition 1–3.1, this implies in particular that $1 = 2$, that is, $\{\Phi\} = \{\Phi, \{\Phi\}\}$. Since this is clearly false, it follows that $X \cap Y = \Phi$.

The proof of (2) is based on (3–1.2), and it will not be given (see Problem 18, Section 3–1). Statement (3) is a consequence of the following result from set theory.

(3–2.2). If X, X', Y, and Y' are sets such that
    (a) X is equivalent to X' and Y is equivalent to Y', and
    (b) $X \cap Y = \Phi$ and $X' \cap Y' = \Phi$,
then $X \cup Y$ is equivalent to $X' \cup Y'$.

Proof. Since X and X' are equivalent, there is a one-to-one correspondence $x \leftrightarrow x'$ between X and X'. Similarly, there is a one-to-one correspondence $y \leftrightarrow y'$ between Y and Y'. The required one-to-one correspondence between $X \cup Y$ and $X' \cup Y'$ is obtained by combining the given correspondences $x \leftrightarrow x'$ and $y \leftrightarrow y'$. Since $X \cap Y = \Phi$ and $X' \cap Y' = \Phi$, the resulting combination is a one-to-one correspondence. Figure 3–1 below illustrates this proof. As an exercise, the reader can use (3–2.2) to prove (3).

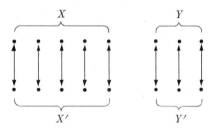

FIGURE 3–1

The following fact is an immediate consequence of Definition 3–2.1.

(3–2.3). If X and Y are disjoint, finite, nonempty sets, then

$$|X \cup Y| = |X| + |Y|.$$

The basic rules of addition are the following familiar statements.

(3–2.4). *Properties of Addition.* Let k, m, and n be natural numbers. Then
    (a) $k + (m + n) = (k + m) + n$;
    (b) $m + n = n + m$;
    (c) if $k + n = m + n$, then $k = m$.

Statement (a) is the *associative law of addition*, (b) is the *commutative law of addition*, and (c) is the *cancellation law of addition*.

The properties (a) and (b) are easily seen to follow from the corresponding associative and commutative laws for set unions. For example, if X

and Y are disjoint sets such that $|X| = m$ and $|Y| = n$, then by Definition 3–2.1, $m + n = |X \cup Y|$ and $n + m = |Y \cup X|$. Since $X \cup Y = Y \cup X$, it follows that $m + n = n + m$. The proof of (c) will be given in the next section.

Before turning our attention to the operation of multiplication, we will prove that the "successor" of each natural number is obtained by adding 1 to the number:

(3–2.5) $S(n) = n + 1$.

Proof. Let $X = n \times \{1\}$, and let $Y = \{\Phi\} \times \{2\} = \{\langle \Phi, 2 \rangle\}$. Then, as in the proof of statement (1) following Definition 3–2.1,

$$k \leftrightarrow \langle k, 1 \rangle, \qquad k \in n, \qquad \text{and} \qquad \Phi \leftrightarrow \langle \Phi, 2 \rangle$$

are one-to-one correspondences between n and X and $1 = \{\Phi\}$ and Y, respectively. Therefore, $|X| = n$ and $|Y| = 1$. Moreover, $X \cap Y = \Phi$ as before. Hence, by Definition 3–2.1, $|X \cup Y| = n + 1$. On the other hand, the correspondence

$$k \leftrightarrow \langle k, 1 \rangle, \qquad \text{for } k \in n, \qquad n \leftrightarrow \langle \Phi, 2 \rangle$$

is one-to-one between $n \cup \{n\} = S(n)$ and $X \cup Y$. Thus, $X \cup Y$ is equivalent to the natural number $S(n)$, that is, $|X \cup Y| = S(n)$. Therefore, $S(n) = |X \cup Y| = n + 1$.

Like addition, multiplication of natural numbers is a binary operation under which the set of natural numbers is closed. That is, if we are given natural numbers m and n, the operation of multiplication yields a unique natural number which is called the *product* of m and n, and is usually denoted by* mn or $m \cdot n$. In this book, both the notations mn and $m \cdot n$ will be used.

The multiplication of natural numbers is often defined to be the process of repeated addition. For a given natural number n, we obtain the product $2 \cdot n$ by adding $n + n$, the product $3 \cdot n$ by adding $(n + n) + n$ [or $n + (n + n)$, since by (3–2.4a), addition is associative]. In general, the product $m \cdot n$ is found by adding $n + n + \cdots + n$, where there are m terms in the sum. The familiar terminology "m times n" is a literal expression of the idea that multiplication is repeated addition. This definition is meaningful for specific products such as $2 \cdot n$ and $3 \cdot n$. However, in the definition of $m \cdot n$ for an arbitrary natural number m, the statement

---

* The symbol $m \times n$ is also frequently used to denote the product of m and n. However, in our notation, $m \times n$ stands for the set product of m and n considered as sets.

"there are m terms in the sum $n + n + \cdots + n$" is vague. The difficulty in this definition can be corrected by defining multiplication by the conditions

(a) $1 \cdot n = n$,

(b) $S(m) \cdot n = m \cdot n + n$,

and using (3–1.2) to prove that $m \cdot n$ is a uniquely defined natural number for each pair of natural numbers m and n.

An alternative definition of multiplication, based on the concept of the product of two sets, is better suited to our discussion in which the operations of the natural numbers are related to operations with sets. The following example shows that such a definition is reasonable.

EXAMPLE 1. The seats in theaters are usually labeled by letters corresponding to the rows, and by numbers corresponding to the positions of the seats in each row. Suppose that a theater has 26 rows, each of which contains 50 seats. Then each seat is labeled by an ordered pair consisting of a letter of the alphabet and a number from 1 to 50. Consequently, there is a one-to-one correspondence between the seats in the theater and the set $A \times L$, where $A = \{a, b, c, \ldots, z\}$, and $L = \{1, 2, 3, \ldots, 50\}$. Therefore the number of seats in the theater is exactly the cardinal number $|A \times L|$ of the product set $A \times L$. On the other hand, we know very well that the number of seats can be determined by multiplying the number of rows by the number of seats in each row. That is, $|A \times L| = |A| \cdot |L|$.

DEFINITION 3–2.6. Let m and n be natural numbers and X and Y be sets such that $|X| = m$ and $|Y| = n$. Then the *product* of m and n is defined to be the natural number $|X \times Y|$.

The process which associates with each pair m and n of natural numbers their product $m \cdot n$ is called *multiplication*.

As in the case of Definition 3–2.1, this definition needs some justification. In Definition 3–2.6, the existence of sets X and Y which satisfy $|X| = m$ and $|Y| = n$ is clear. Indeed, the sets m and n themselves satisfy $|m| = m$ and $|n| = n$. Two facts must be proved.

(1) If X and Y are sets such that $|X| = m$ and $|Y| = n$, then $X \times Y$ is finite, that is, there is a natural number k such that $|X \times Y| = k$.

(2) The natural number $|X \times Y|$ is the same for all pairs X, Y of sets satisfying $|X| = m$ and $|Y| = n$.

The result (1) is obtained by using (3–1.2), and as before the details will not be given (see Problem 6 in this section). Statement (2) is a consequence of the following result concerning set products.

(3–2.7). If X, X', Y, and Y' are sets such that X is equivalent to X' and Y is equivalent to Y', then $X \times Y$ is equivalent to $X' \times Y'$.

Proof. Since X is equivalent to X', there is a one-to-one correspondence $x \leftrightarrow x'$ between X and X'. Similarly, there is a one-to-one correspondence $y \leftrightarrow y'$ between Y and Y'. The required one-to-one correspondence between $X \times Y$ and $X' \times Y'$ is

$$\langle x, y \rangle \leftrightarrow \langle x', y' \rangle.$$

The following important theorem follows easily from Definition 3–2.6.

THEOREM 3–2.8. If X and Y are finite nonempty sets, then

$$|X \times Y| = |X| \cdot |Y|.$$

Proof. Since X and Y are finite nonempty sets, there exist natural numbers m and n such that X is equivalent to m, and Y is equivalent to n. By Definition 3–1.3, this means that $|X| = m$ and $|Y| = n$. Therefore,

$$|X \times Y| = m \cdot n = |X| \cdot |Y|$$

by Definition 3–2.6.

Multiplication has the following properties.

(3–2.9). *Properties of multiplication.* Let k, m, and n be any natural numbers. Then

(a) $k \cdot (m \cdot n) = (k \cdot m) \cdot n$;
(b) $m \cdot n = n \cdot m$;
(c) if $k \cdot n = m \cdot n$, then $k = m$;
(d) $1 \cdot n = n$;
(e) $k \cdot (m + n) = k \cdot m + k \cdot n$.

Parts (a), (b), and (c) of (3–2.9) correspond exactly to the three properties of addition given in (3–2.4). Thus, we say that multiplication is associative, commutative, and satisfies the cancellation law. The fact that the number 1 is an *identity element* for multiplication is stated in (d). The two basic operations are connected by the equality (e), which is called the *distributive law of multiplication with respect to addition.* Note that (b) and (d) imply $n \cdot 1 = n$, and (b) and (e) imply the "right-hand" distributive law $(m + n) \cdot k = m \cdot k + n \cdot k$.

The identities (a), (b), (d), and (e) are proved using the definitions of multiplication and addition, together with some simple results of set theory; the property (c) will be proved in the next section. Let X, Y, and

W be sets such that $|X| = k$, $|Y| = m$, and $|W| = n$. Then by Theorem 3–2.8,

$$k \cdot (m \cdot n) = |X| \cdot (|Y| \cdot |W|) = |X| \cdot |Y \times W| = |X \times (Y \times W)|.$$

Similarly,
$$(k \cdot m) \cdot n = |(X \times Y) \times W|.$$

Since $X \times (Y \times W)$ is equivalent to $(X \times Y) \times W$ by Theorem 1–3.3(b), and these are finite nonempty sets, it follows that $|X \times (Y \times W)| = |(X \times Y) \times W|$. Therefore, $k \cdot (m \cdot n) = (k \cdot m) \cdot n$. The identity (3–2.9b) is a direct consequence of Theorem 1–3.3(a):

$$m \cdot n = |Y \times W| = |W \times Y| = n \cdot m.$$

To prove (3–2.9d), we use the facts that $|\{\Phi\}| = 1$, and that $\langle \Phi, w \rangle \leftrightarrow w$, for $w \in W$ is a one-to-one correspondence between $\{\Phi\} \times W$ and W. Therefore,
$$1 \cdot n = |\{\Phi\} \times W| = |W| = n.$$

The proof of (3–2.9e) is based on the following result from set theory, which we leave for the reader to prove.

(3–2.10). Let X, Y, and W be any sets. Then

$$X \times (Y \cup W) = (X \times Y) \cup (X \times W).$$

For the application of (3–2.10) to the proof of (3–2.9e), let X, Y, and W be any sets such that $|X| = k$, $|Y| = m$, $|W| = n$, and $Y \cap W = \Phi$. Then it is clear that $(X \times Y) \cap (X \times W) = \Phi$. Hence, by (3–2.3), Theorem 3–2.8, and (3–2.10), $k \cdot m + k \cdot n = |X \times Y| + |X \times W| = |(X \times Y) \cup (X \times W)| = |X \times (Y \cup W)| = |X| \cdot |Y \cup W| = k \cdot (m + n)$.

PROBLEMS

1. Use (3–2.2) to prove the statement (3) following Definition 3–2.1.

2. Assuming that addition corresponds to set union and that multiplication corresponds to set intersection, which of the laws (3–2.4) and (3–2.9) have analogues for sets, and which of the identities of Theorem 1–4.3 have analogues in the arithmetic of natural numbers?

3. Write the proof (3–2.4a) in full.

4. If m and n are natural numbers, what is $|m \cup n|$ and $|m \cap n|$?

5. Prove (3–2.10).

6. Prove by induction (3–1.2) on the cardinal number of Y that if X and Y are finite sets, then $X \times Y$ is finite. [*Hint:* Use (3–2.10) and Problem 18, Section 3–1.]

3–3 The ordering of the natural numbers. Probably the most important property of the natural numbers is their ordering. Just the act of counting presents the natural numbers in a definite sequence: one, two, three, four, and so on. It is this ordering of the numbers that most children learn long before they can add or multiply.

In the development of the natural numbers based on Definition 3–1.1, the ordering is defined very simply.

DEFINITION 3–3.1. If m and n are natural numbers, then m is said to be *less than* n if $m \subset n$.

As is customary, we will write $m < n$ or $n > m$ if m is less than n. According to Definition 3–3.1 and the result of Problem 14, Section 3–1, the three conditions

$$m < n, \qquad m \subset n, \qquad m \in n$$

are equivalent.

In Section 2–5, we discussed one important aspect of the ordering of the natural numbers, namely the well-ordering principle (2–5.2). Here we point out some of the more elementary properties of order.

(3–3.2). *Properties of order.* Let k, m, and n be any natural numbers. Then
- (a) either $m < n$, $m = n$, or $n < m$, and it is impossible for more than one of these relations to be satisfied by a given pair m and n of natural numbers;
- (b) if $k < m$ and $m < n$, then $k < n$;
- (c) if $k < m$, then $k + n < m + n$;
- (d) if $k < m$, then $k \cdot n < m \cdot n$.

By the definition of $<$, the property (3–3.2a) is equivalent to the statement that exactly one of the relations $m \subset n$, $m = n$, $n \subset m$ is satisfied. It is clear from the definition of set theoretical inclusion that at most one of these relations holds. The fact that at least one of the relations is satisfied was stated as Problem 13, Section 3–1, and we will not prove this result. The assertion (3–3.2b) is the same as the statement that if $k \subset m$ and $m \subset n$, then $k \subset n$, and this is clearly true. In order to prove part (c), choose sets X, Y, and W such that

$$|X| = k, \qquad |Y| = m, \qquad |W| = n, \qquad (3\text{–}1)$$

and

$$X \subset Y \qquad \text{and} \qquad Y \cap W = \Phi. \qquad (3\text{–}2)$$

This can be done in the same way that sets were constructed for the proof of statement (1) following Definition 3–2.1. Then by Definition 3–2.1, $k + n = |X \cup W|$, and $m + n = |Y \cup W|$. (Note that $Y \cap W = \Phi$ implies $X \cap W = \Phi$.) It follows from (3–2) that $X \cup W \subset Y \cup W$. Using the result of Problem 17, Section 3–1, $X \cup W \subset Y \cup W$ implies $|X \cup W| \subset |Y \cup W|$. Therefore, using Definition 3–3.1, we have $k + n = |X \cup W| < |Y \cup W| = m + n$. The proof of (3–3.2d) is similar, and we leave it as an exercise for the reader.

The cancellation laws of addition and multiplication, (3–2.4c) and (3–2.9c), can be deduced from (3–3.2). It is necessary to show that if k, m, and n are natural numbers, then

(1) $k + n = m + n$ implies $k = m$, and

(2) $k \cdot n = m \cdot n$ implies $k = m$.

We prove the contrapositives of these implications (see the Introduction). Suppose that $k \neq m$. Then by (3–3.2a), either $k < m$, or $m < k$. Suppose that $k < m$. By (3–3.2c) and (d), $k + n < m + n$ and $k \cdot n < m \cdot n$. Therefore, $k + n \neq m + n$ and $k \cdot n \neq m \cdot n$. If $m < k$, the proof is similar.

There is a useful relation between the ordering and addition of natural numbers.

THEOREM 3–3.3. Let m and n be natural numbers. Then $m < n$ if and only if there is a natural number k such that $n = k + m$.

That is, if $n = k + m$, then $m < n$, and conversely, if $m < n$, it is possible to find a number k such that $n = k + m$. Intuitively, (3–3.3) is evident. The natural number k is obtained by counting the numbers in the sequence

$$m + 1, \qquad m + 2, \qquad \ldots, \qquad n.$$

A formal proof of Theorem 3–3.3 could be given by means of induction on m. To carry this out, it is necessary to use the results given in several of the problems in Section 3–1. We will leave this task to the reader who is interested in working out the details of the theory (see Problem 5).

It is easy to see that the number k which occurs in Theorem 3–3.3 is unique. Indeed, if $n = k + m$ and $n = k' + m$, then $k + m = k' + m$, so that by the cancellation law (3–2.4c), $k = k'$.

DEFINITION 3–3.4. Let m and n be natural numbers such that $m < n$. The unique number k satisfying $n = k + m$ is called the *difference* of n and m.

The usual notation to designate the difference of n and m is $n - m$. The operation which associates with the pair m and n of natural numbers (satisfying $m < n$) their difference $n - m$ is called *subtraction*. If m is not less than n, then it is impossible to form the difference $n - m$ and still remain within the system of natural numbers. That is, the natural numbers are *not* closed with respect to subtraction. One of the reasons for enlarging the system of natural numbers to the integers is to make subtraction of any two numbers possible. Subtraction satisfies the following identities.

(3–3.5). Let j, k, m, and n be natural numbers such that $j < k$ and $m < n$. Then

(a) $(k - j) + (n - m) = (k + n) - (j + n)$;

(b) $(k - j) \cdot (n - m) = (k \cdot n + j \cdot m) - (j \cdot n + k \cdot m)$;

(c) $(k + n) - (k + m) = n - m$;

(d) $k \cdot (n - m) = (k \cdot n) - (k \cdot m)$.

The proofs of all of these identities are based on the same observation. Suppose that x, y, and z are natural numbers. Then $y < x$, and z is equal to the difference $x - y$ if and only if $z + y = x$. In fact, if $z + y = x$, then $y < x$ by Theorem 3–3.3, and $z = x - y$ by Definition 3–3.4. Conversely, if $y < x$ and $z = x - y$, then $z + y = x$ by Definition 3–3.4. We now use this fact to prove (3–3.5b). In this case, $x = k \cdot n + j \cdot m$, $y = j \cdot n + k \cdot m$, and $z = (k - j) \cdot (n - m)$. Note that since $j < k$ and $m < n$, the differences $k - j$ and $n - m$ are natural numbers, so that $z = (k - j) \cdot (n - m)$ is a natural number. We must prove that $x = z + y$, that is,

$$k \cdot n + j \cdot m = (k - j) \cdot (n - m) + (j \cdot n + k \cdot m).$$

Since $n = (n - m) + m$, it follows that $j \cdot n = j \cdot [(n - m) + m] = j \cdot (n - m) + j \cdot m$. Consequently, by (3–2.4) and (3–2.9),

$$
\begin{aligned}
(k - j) \cdot (n - m) + (j \cdot n + k \cdot m) &= (k - j) \cdot (n - m) \\
&\quad + [(j \cdot (n - m) + j \cdot m) + k \cdot m] \\
&= [(k - j) \cdot (n - m) + j \cdot (n - m)] + (j \cdot m + k \cdot m) \\
&= [((k - j) + j) \cdot (n - m)] + (k \cdot m + j \cdot m) \\
&= k \cdot (n - m) + (k \cdot m + j \cdot m) \\
&= [k \cdot (n - m) + k \cdot m] + j \cdot m \\
&= k \cdot [(n - m) + m] + j \cdot m \\
&= k \cdot n + j \cdot m.
\end{aligned}
$$

We leave the proof of the remaining parts of (3–3.5) as an exercise for the reader.

PROBLEMS

1. Use the result of Problem 17, Section 3–1, to show that if Y is a finite set, and $X \subset Y$, then $|X| < |Y|$.

2. Prove (3–3.2d).

3. Show that if k, m, and n are natural numbers, then (a) $k + n < m + n$ implies $k < m$, and (b) $k \cdot n < m \cdot n$ implies $k < m$.

4. Use (and cite) the necessary results from the problems of Section 3–1 to prove that the following conditions on a natural number are equivalent. However, do not use Theorem 3–3.3.

    (a) $n \neq 1$
    (b) $n > 1$
    (c) There is a $k \in N$ such that $n = S(k)$.
    (d) There is a $k \in N$ such that $n = k + 1$.
    (e) There is a $k \in N$ and a $j \in N$ such that $n = k + j$.
    (f) There is a $k \in N$ such that $n > k$.

5. Using ordinary mathematical induction, together with the results of Problem 4, prove the following two statements (for all m).

    (a) For all natural numbers n, if $m < n$, then there is a natural number k such that $n = k + m$.
    (b) For all natural numbers n, if there is a natural number k such that $n = k + m$, then $m < n$.

6. Show that if $j < k$ and $m < n$ (where j, k, m, and n are natural numbers), then $j + m < k + n$ and $j \cdot m < k \cdot n$.

7. Prove (3–3.5a, c, d).

8. Show that if $k - n = m - n$, then $k = m$.

9. Let k, m, and n be natural numbers. Prove the following.

    (a) If $m < n$, then $(n + k) - m = (n - m) + k$.
    (b) If $n < m < k$, then $n + (k - m) = k - (m - n)$.
    (c) If $n < k < m < n + k$, then $n - (m - k) = (n + k) - m$
        $= k - (m - n)$.
    (d) If $n + k < m$, then $(m - k) - n = (m - n) - k = m - (n + k)$.

CHAPTER 4

THE INTEGERS

4–1 Construction of the integers. The average American student first encounters the integers in elementary algebra, where he learns that the integers consist of the natural numbers, zero, and the negative numbers (the negatives of the natural numbers). He learns by rote the rules for adding and multiplying these numbers and some identities which addition and multiplication satisfy. If given the opportunity to use this knowledge, he may remember these rules, but the chances are good that he will never ask why the integers are defined as they are, or why they satisfy their familiar rules of operation. Our purpose in this section is to explore these questions.

As far as historical research has determined, the negative numbers and zero were introduced by the Hindu mathematicians of India in the sixth or seventh century A.D. The increasing importance of commerce in India at that time stimulated this invention. The natural numbers could be used to measure fixed quantities of money or merchandise, but business transactions involved changes of these quantities, i.e., increases or decreases. Instead of dealing with receipt and payment as different kinds of exchanges, it was found that both transactions could be treated at once if the amount of money or goods received was denoted by an ordinary natural number, and the amount paid out was represented by a negative number. This idea is useful mainly because the effect of consecutive transactions can be obtained by the operation which we know as addition of integers. For example, if the receipt of five coins is followed by the payment of ten coins, the net result is the same as the payment of five coins. In symbolic form, this equivalence is expressed by the formula

$$5 + (-10) = -5.$$

The interpretation of consecutive exchanges as a single exchange also requires the consideration of transactions which involve no change of money or goods. These are of course represented by the number zero. For instance, a receipt of 5 coins followed by payment of 5 coins has the same effect as "breaking even":

$$5 + (-5) = 0.$$

The integers and their operations are of course very familiar in our modern society. The application of the integers to represent exchanges of money is also commonplace. However, before the sixth century, negative numbers were unknown, and zero was used only as a symbol to distinguish between numbers such as 102 and 12. The invention of these new numbers and the definition of addition and multiplication of the integers to satisfy the needs of commerce must be considered to be among the greatest advances of civilization.

Informally, the set Z of all integers consists of (1) all natural numbers, (2) an object called zero and denoted by 0, which is different from all natural numbers, and (3) for each natural number n, an object denoted by $-n$, which is different from all natural numbers and zero, and such that if m and n are two different natural numbers, then $-m$ and $-n$ are different objects. These objects are called the negative numbers.

It is not very important what the objects called "integers" really are. In fact, there are several ways to construct the system of integers from the natural numbers, and the different constructions lead to different answers to the question "What are the specific objects called integers?" Of course, all of these constructions lead to systems which are essentially* the same. When the natural numbers are defined to be the finite ordinal numbers in von Neumann's sense (Definition 3–1.1), then a convenient choice for zero is the empty set Φ, and the negative numbers can be defined as

$$-n = \{n\}, \qquad n = 1, 2, 3, \ldots .$$

DEFINITION 4–1.1. The set Z of all *integers* is

$$\{\{n\} \,|\, n \in N\} \;\cup\; \{\Phi\} \;\cup\; N.$$

Thus, the integers are the following sets:
  (a) all natural numbers:

$$\{\Phi\}, \qquad \{\Phi, \{\Phi\}\}, \qquad \{\Phi, \{\Phi\}, \{\Phi, \{\Phi\}\}\}, \qquad \ldots ,$$

  (b) zero: Φ, and
  (c) the negative numbers:

$$\{\{\Phi\}\}, \qquad \{\{\Phi, \{\Phi\}\}\}, \qquad \{\{\Phi, \{\Phi\}, \{\Phi,\{\Phi\}\}\}\}, \qquad \ldots .$$

As usual the symbol 0 will denote zero ($=\Phi$) and $-1, -2, -3, \ldots,$ $-n, \ldots$ will stand for $\{1\}, \{2\}, \{3\}, \ldots, \{n\}, \ldots$ respectively. It is easy to see that the set Z of Definition 4–1.1 satisfies the conditions (1), (2), and (3) of the informal description of Z given above. In particular, all of

---

* The systems obtained by the various constructions are isomorphic (from the Greek word meaning "of the same form"). The mathematical meaning of the term isomorphic will be explained in Section 4–2.

the objects in the list

$$\ldots, \quad \{3\}, \quad \{2\}, \quad \{1\}, \quad \Phi, \quad 1, \quad 2, \quad 3, \quad \ldots$$

are different.

The operations of addition, multiplication, and negation are responsible for the usefulness and importance of the integers. Addition and multiplication are extensions of the corresponding operations in the system of natural numbers, but negation has no counterpart in N. The definition of negation is suggested when we think of the set of integers in the usual order,

$$\ldots, \quad -3, \quad -2, \quad -1, \quad 0, \quad 1, \quad 2, \quad 3, \quad \ldots,$$

consisting of the natural numbers, and a mirror-image copy of these numbers (the negative numbers), linked together by the number zero. *Negation* is the process of passing from an integer a to its mirror-image.

DEFINITION 4–1.2. *Negation.* Let m be any natural number. Then
   (a) $-m = \{m\}$,
   (b) $-\{m\} = m$,
   (c) $-0 = 0$.

Once the meaning of Definition 4–1.2 is understood, the notation $-m$ for the negative numbers can be used without fear of trouble, since in fact $-m$ stands for $\{m\}$, whether we think of $-$ as the negation operation symbol, or simply as the usual sign to denote negative numbers.* If parts (a) and (b) of Definition 4–1.2 are combined, we obtain the familiar *rule of double negation:*

$$-(-m) = m.$$

The addition operation in the integers is surprisingly complicated.

DEFINITION 4–1.3. *Addition.* Let m and n be any natural numbers. Then
   (a) $m + n$ is defined as in N;
   (b) $(-m) + (-n) = -(m + n)$;
   (c) $m + (-n) = (-n) + m = \begin{cases} m - n & \text{if } n < m, \\ 0 & \text{if } m = n, \\ -(n - m) & \text{if } m < n; \end{cases}$
   (d) $m + 0 = 0 + m = m$;
   (e) $(-m) + 0 = 0 + (-m) = -m$;
   (f) $0 + 0 = 0$.

---

* The minus sign is also used to denote the binary operation of subtraction, as, for example, in expressions like $3 - 1$. When used in this way, the symbol "$-$" always occurs between two number symbols; when "$-$" denotes the operation of negation, it is never preceded by a number symbol.

This definition of addition is open to criticism on the grounds that it is cumbersome and difficult to use in proving the important properties of addition. To avoid such a complicated definition of addition, and an almost equally unwieldy definition of multiplication, mathematicians have devised another way of constructing Z from N. This construction employs three important new mathematical concepts: equivalence relation, equivalence class, and partition of a set. The introduction and study of these notions represents a considerable digression from our program of constructing the fundamental number system Z (see Section 6–4). We have therefore chosen to adopt Definition 4–1.3 as the definition of addition in Z. The rules of this definition provide an effective method of performing addition in Z, and they *can* be used to prove the main properties of addition.

(4–1.4). *Properties of addition.* Let a, b, and c be integers. Then
    (a) $a + b = b + a$;
    (b) $a + (b + c) = (a + b) + c$;
    (c) $a + 0 = a$;
    (d) $a + (-a) = 0$.

Actually, (4–1.4a, c, d) can be obtained very easily from Definitions 4–1.3, 4–1.2, and the properties of addition for the natural numbers (3–2.4). It is the proof of the associative law (4–1.4b) which requires the checking of a discouragingly large number of different cases.

EXAMPLE 1. We will prove the commutative law (4–1.4a). There are nine possible cases to examine. Let m and n be any natural numbers.
    (1) $m + n = n + m$, by (3–2.4);
    (2) $m + (-n) = (-n) + m$, by Definition 4–1.3(c);
    (3) $m + 0 = 0 + m$, by Definition 4–1.3(d);
    (4) $(-m) + n = n + (-m)$, by Definition 4–1.3(c);
    (5) $(-m) + (-n) = -(m + n) = -(n + m) = (-n) + (-m)$, by Definition 4–1.3(b) and (3–2.4);
    (6) $(-m) + 0 = 0 + (-m)$, by Definition 4–1.3(e);
    (7) $0 + n = n + 0$, by Definition 4–1.3(d);
    (8) $0 + (-n) = (-n) + 0$, by Definition 4–1.3(e);
    (9) $0 + 0 = 0 + 0$.

Of course, cases (2) and (4), cases (3) and (7), and cases (6) and (8) are really the same, so that one case of each of these pairs could be omitted.

EXAMPLE 2. There are 27 main cases to consider in the proof of (4–1.4b). These are obtained by letting a, b, and c take all combinations of natural numbers, negative numbers, or zeros. However, because of Definition 4–1.3(c), it is necessary to break some of these main cases into subcases. For example, suppose that k, m, and n are natural numbers, and that we wish to prove

$$(-k) + (m + n) = [(-k) + m] + n.$$

This identity has a different meaning in each of five subcases.

(1) If $k < m$, then it is necessary to show $(m + n) - k = (m - k) + n$.

(2) If $k = m$, then it is necessary to show $(m + n) - m = 0 + n$.

(3) If $m < k < m + n$, then it is necessary to show $(m + n) - k = n - (k - m)$.

(4) If $k = m + n$, then it is necessary to show $0 = [-((m + n) - m)] + n$.

(5) If $k > m + n$, then it is necessary to show $-[k - (m + n)] = -[(k - m) - n]$.

The desired identities in each of these cases can be proved using Definition 4–1.3 and the results of Problem 9, Section 3–3.

By considering the interpretation of the integers as measures of variation (increase or decrease), it is possible to find a rational basis for Definition 4–1.3 and for the properties of addition (4–1.4). Let us examine a specific example. Suppose that the integer a represents the change in the number of gallons of water in a certain reservoir during a given day. For instance, if the amount of water in the reservoir increased by 15,000 gallons during the day, then $a = 15,000$, whereas if it decreases by 15,000 gallons, then $a = -15,000$. Let b represent the change in the number of gallons of water in the reservoir during the next day. Then $a + b$ represents the change of volume of water in the reservoir (measured in number of gallons of water) during the two day period. If both a and b represent increases, then a and b are natural numbers, and our physical interpretation of addition agrees for natural numbers with the usual definition of addition in N. These facts are so familiar that they would probably be accepted without question. However, for the sake of our discussion, we could use this physical description as the definition of the addition of integers. Quite possibly the rules of addition were originally obtained in this way.

In terms of this example, the properties of addition (4–1.4) can be interpreted as statements of commonplace observations. The commutative law $a + b = b + a$ means that a change of amount a in one day, followed by a change of amount b the next day, produces the same result in the two-day period as a change of amount b on the first day, followed by a change of amount a on the second day. The associative law $a + (b + c) = (a + b) + c$ is even more evident, since the two sides of this identity simply represent two different ways of looking at the result of the changes on three consecutive days. The identities $a + 0 = a$ and $a + (-a) = 0$ have similar interpretations.

If m is a natural number, and a is an integer, then we can informally define the *product* $m \cdot a$ to be the integer which is obtained by adding a to itself m times. For example, $1 \cdot a = a$, $2 \cdot a = a + a$, $3 \cdot a = (a + a) + a$. This definition is both natural and useful. If a is a natural number, then $m \cdot a$ is the same as the product of m and a, obtained from Definition 3–2.6. If $a = 0$, then $m \cdot a = 0$, as the reader can show by induction on m. If $a = -n$, then $m \cdot a = -(m \cdot n)$. In fact,

$$1 \cdot (-n) = -n = -(1 \cdot n),$$
$$2 \cdot (-n) = (-n) + (-n) = -(n + n) = -(2 \cdot n),$$
$$3 \cdot (-n) = 2 \cdot (-n) + (-n) = [-(2 \cdot n)] + (-n)$$
$$= -(2 \cdot n + n) = -(3 \cdot n), \text{ etc.}$$

It is convenient to extend the definition of products so that any two integers can be multiplied together. This means that we must define $0 \cdot c$ and $(-m) \cdot c$ for an arbitrary integer c and natural number m. If the multiplication of integers is to satisfy the distributive law

$$(a + b) \cdot c = a \cdot c + b \cdot c,$$

then there is only one way in which these products can be defined. In fact, using this distributive law and (4–1.4), we obtain

$$0 \cdot c = 0 \cdot c + 0 = 0 \cdot c + [(0 \cdot c) + (-(0 \cdot c))]$$
$$= (0 \cdot c + 0 \cdot c) + [-(0 \cdot c)]$$
$$= (0 + 0) \cdot c + [-(0 \cdot c)] = 0 \cdot c + [-(0 \cdot c)] = 0.$$

Also,

$$(-m) \cdot c = (-m) \cdot c + 0 = (-m) \cdot c + [(m \cdot c) + (-(m \cdot c))]$$
$$= [(-m) \cdot c + m \cdot c] + [-(m \cdot c)]$$
$$= [(-m) + m] \cdot c + [-(m \cdot c)] = 0 \cdot c + [-(m \cdot c)]$$
$$= 0 + [-(m \cdot c)] = -(m \cdot c).$$

Thus, we are led to the well-known rules for multiplying integers. These will be adopted as the formal definition of multiplication.

DEFINITION 4–1.5. *Multiplication.* Let m and n be any natural numbers. Then

(a) $m \cdot n$ is defined as in N;

(b) $(-m) \cdot (-n) = m \cdot n$;

(c) $(-m) \cdot n = n \cdot (-m) = -(m \cdot n)$;

(d) $m \cdot 0 = 0 \cdot m = 0$;

(e) $(-m) \cdot 0 = 0 \cdot (-m) = 0$;

(f) $0 \cdot 0 = 0$.

From Definitions 4–1.5 and 4–1.3, and the properties of addition and multiplication of the natural numbers (3–2.4) and (3–2.9), it is possible to deduce the familiar properties of multiplication of the integers. The proofs are elementary, but tedious because they require the examination of numerous cases.

(4–1.6). *Properties of multiplication.* Let a, b, and c be integers. Then
(a) $a \cdot b = b \cdot a$;
(b) $(a \cdot b) \cdot c = a \cdot (b \cdot c)$;
(c) if $a \cdot c = b \cdot c$, then either $a = b$ or $c = 0$;
(d) $a \cdot 1 = a$;
(e) $a \cdot (b + c) = (a \cdot b) + (a \cdot c)$.

With the exception of the cancellation law (c), the properties of multiplication of integers (4–1.6) are identical with the properties of multiplication of the natural numbers given in (3–2.9). Since $a \cdot 0 = b \cdot 0 = 0$ for all integers a and b, the statement (3–2.9c) is not true for the integers. However (4–1.6c) shows that 0 is the only integer which cannot be cancelled.

PROBLEMS

1. Show that all of the sets in the list

$$\ldots, \quad \{3\}, \quad \{2\}, \quad \{1\}, \quad \Phi, \quad 1, \quad 2, \quad 3, \quad \ldots$$

are different.

2. Using Definition 4–1.3, prove that $a + 0 = a$ and $a + (-a) = 0$ for any integer a.

3. Let the integers be considered to measure amounts of change. Give an interpretation of the operation of negation and interpret the identity $a + (-a) = 0$.

4. Show by induction on m that $m \cdot 0 = 0$ (where m is a natural number, and $m \cdot 0$ is the result of adding 0 to itself m times).

5. Using Definition 4–1.5 and the properties of multiplication of the natural numbers (3–2.9), prove the laws $a \cdot b = b \cdot a$, $a \cdot (b \cdot c) = (a \cdot b) \cdot c$, and $a \cdot 1 = a$.

6. Using Definitions 4–1.2 and 4–1.5, prove that for any integers a and b, $(-a) \cdot b = a \cdot (-b) = -(a \cdot b)$, and $(-a) \cdot (-b) = a \cdot b$.

7. Using Definitions 4–1.3 and 4–1.5, the properties of addition and multiplication of the natural numbers (3–2.4) and (3–2.9), (3–3.5), and (4–1.4a, c, d), prove the distributive law $a \cdot (b + c) = (a \cdot b) + (a \cdot c)$ for the integers. [*Hints:* (a) Prove the law in the cases where at least one of a, b, or c is zero. (First show from Definition 4–1.5 that $d \cdot 0 = 0 \cdot d = 0$ for all $d \in Z$.) (b) Enumerate

the eight possible cases in which none of a, b, and c is zero. (c) Consider the cases

$$k \cdot [m + (-n)] = k \cdot m + k \cdot (-n),$$

$$(-k) \cdot [m + (-n)] = (-k) \cdot m + (-k) \cdot (-n)$$

separately, and state the meaning of these identities in each of the three sub-cases $m < n$, $m = n$, $m > n$. (d) Prove these cases (see 3–3.5). (e) Prove all other cases, either directly or by reducing them to the cases treated in (d).]

8. Using Definition 4–1.5, prove that if c and d are integers, and $c \neq 0$, $d \neq 0$, then $c \cdot d \neq 0$. Using this fact together with the distributive law (4–1.6e) and the result of Problem 6, prove (4–1.6c).

9. Prove the associative law of addition $a + (b + c) = (a + b) + c$. [Hints: (a) Use (4–1.4c) to prove the law in all cases in which at least one of a, b, or c is zero. (b) Enumerate the eight possible cases in which none of a, b, or c is zero. (c) Prove that $(-1) \cdot a = -a$, and use this fact together with the distributive law to reduce these eight cases to the three cases: (i) $k + (m + n) = (k + m) + n$, (ii) $(-k) + (m + n) = [(-k) + m] + n$, and (iii) $k + [(-m) + n] = [k + (-m)] + n$. (d) Complete the proof outlined in Example 2 of case (ii). (e) Give the proof of case (iii).]

4–2 Rings. Starting with the properties of addition and multiplication given in (4–1.4) and (4–1.6), it is possible to develop many useful facts about the integers. However, as the reader may have noticed, the system of rational numbers and the real number system also satisfy the identities listed in (4–1.4) and (4–1.6). Therefore, if we prove a theorem about the integers using only the facts contained in (4–1.4) and (4–1.6), the same theorem should be true for the rational numbers and real numbers. There is one trouble with this useful observation. In order to carry a theorem which has been stated and proved for the integers over to the real or rational numbers, it is necessary to examine the proof of the theorem to be sure that it uses only properties which can be deduced from (4–1.4) and (4–1.6). Mathematicians have solved this problem by a simple but power-ful idea. They have introduced a new term, "integral domain," to describe all systems on which are defined two operations (*called* addition and multiplication) satisfying all of the laws given in (4–1.4) and (4–1.6). Then, if a theorem can be deduced from the properties listed in (4–1.4) and (4–1.6), it is a theorem about integral domains, meaning that it is true for every system which satisfies (4–1.4) and (4–1.6). In particular, it is true for the integers, rational numbers, and real numbers.

In this section, we deal with systems which are defined by a set of axioms, without concern for the nature of the particular systems under considera-tion. Such a viewpoint is called *abstract*. There are several advantages (other than the possible economy of being able to treat many systems at once) to be gained by an abstract approach to mathematics. One of them is that in working with an axiomatically defined object, rather than a specific one, there is an economy of ideas and concepts. All of the super-fluous notions and facts are thrown away, and our concentration is focused on the essential features of the object which we are studying.

The abstract axiomatic approach to problems and theories has become a dominant feature of modern mathematics. Moreover this viewpoint is gaining importance in physical and social sciences. Anyone who wants to know what is current in science, particularly mathematics, must become acquainted with abstraction.

Instead of considering integral domains immediately, we introduce a more general concept.

DEFINITION 4–2.1. A *ring* is a set A on which are defined two binary operations $x + y$ and $x \cdot y$ (called *addition* and *multiplication*), and a unary operation $-x$ (called *negation*), such that A contains among its elements a particular one 0 (called the *zero** of A), and the following identities hold for all x, y, and z in A:

(a) $x + y = y + x$;
(b) $x + (y + z) = (x + y) + z$;
(c) $x + 0 = x$;
(d) $x + (-x) = 0$;
(e) $x \cdot (y \cdot z) = (x \cdot y) \cdot z$;
(f) $x \cdot (y + z) = (x \cdot y) + (x \cdot z)$;
(g) $(x + y) \cdot z = (x \cdot z) + (y \cdot z)$.

It must be strongly emphasized that in the definition of a ring A, nothing is assumed about the nature of the elements of A. Any collection of objects for which operations $x + y$, $x \cdot y$, and $-x$ are defined satisfying (a) through (g) is eligible to be called a ring. Moreover, although the operations of a ring are called "addition," "multiplication," and "nega-tion," they need not at all resemble the familiar operations of addition, multiplication, and negation of numbers. The only requirement is that there are definitions which, for every x and y in A, determine the ele-ments represented by $x + y$, $x \cdot y$, and $-x$. It should also be remembered that a ring is determined not by its elements alone, but by the elements, together with the operations of addition, multiplication, and negation. There are important examples of different rings having the same set of elements.

---

* The use of the symbol 0 to represent the zero in every ring is a long-standing mathematical tradition. There are instances in which this convention might cause confusion, but they are rare.

EXAMPLE 1. The number systems Z (the integers), Q (the rational numbers), and R (the real numbers), with their familiar operations, are all rings. In fact, as we have already observed, these systems are integral domains, that is, they satisfy the laws given in (4–1.4) and (4–1.6). It is easy to see that (4–1.6a) and (4–1.6e) together imply Definition 4–2.1(g), so that any integral domain is a ring.

EXAMPLE 2. The set $\{2a | a \in Z\}$ of all even integers is a ring, again with the familiar operations.

EXAMPLE 3. Let $A = \{a, 0\}$. Define

(a) $a + a = 0, a + 0 = a, 0 + a = a, 0 + 0 = 0$;
(b) $a \cdot a = a, a \cdot 0 = 0, 0 \cdot a = 0, 0 \cdot 0 = 0$;
(c) $-0 = 0, -a = a$.

Then A is a ring. The symbols a and 0 may be interpreted in this example as representing the properties of an integer being odd or even. However, such an interpretation has no bearing on the question of A being a ring.

EXAMPLE 4. Let $A = P(S)$, the set of all subsets of a set S. For $X \in A$ and $Y \in A$ (that is, X and Y are any subsets of S), define

$$X + Y = (X \cap Y^c) \cup (X^c \cap Y); \qquad X \cdot Y = X \cap Y; \qquad -X = X.$$

Then with these operations, A is a ring. More generally, if A is any collection of subsets of S such that if X and Y are in A, then $X \cup Y$ and $X \cap Y^c$ are in A, then A is a ring with respect to these operations. These are the collections which we called rings of sets in Section 1–6. The fact that these collections form a ring justifies the terminology "ring of sets."

The reader should verify that Examples 3 and 4 are rings as we claim (see Problem 14, Section 1–4).

It should be noted that the commutative law of multiplication, $x \cdot y = y \cdot x$, is not postulated for rings. If a ring satisfies the identity $x \cdot y = y \cdot x$, then it is called *commutative*. There are important examples of rings which are not commutative, one of which will be given in Chapter 10.

Because the commutative law for multiplication is omitted from the postulates for a ring, it is necessary to state both distributive laws, $x \cdot (y + z) = x \cdot y + x \cdot z$ and $(x + y) \cdot z = x \cdot z + y \cdot z$. If the ring is commutative, then either of these laws can be deduced from the other. For example, $(x + y) \cdot z = z \cdot (x + y) = z \cdot x + z \cdot y = x \cdot z + y \cdot z$.

THEOREM 4–2.2. Let A be a ring, and let $x \in A$. Then $0 + x = x$ and $(-x) + x = 0$.

THEOREM 4–2.3. Let A be a ring and let x, y, and z be any elements of A.
   (a) If $x + z = y + z$, then $x = y$.
   (b) If $z + x = z + y$, then $x = y$.

We leave the proof of Theorem 4–2.2 as an exercise for the reader. To prove Theorem 4–2.3(a), suppose that $x + z = y + z$. Then, by Definition 4–2.1(b), (c), and (d), $x = x + 0 = x + [z + (-z)] = (x + z) + (-z) = (y + z) + (-z) = y + [z + (-z)] = y + 0 = y$. The implication (b) follows from (a) and the commutative law, 4–2.1(a).

THEOREM 4–2.4. Let A be a ring, and let x and y be elements of A. Then

(a) $-(-x) = x$;
(b) $(-x) + (-y) = -(x + y)$;
(c) $x \cdot 0 = 0 \cdot x = 0$;
(d) $(-x) \cdot y = x \cdot (-y) = -(x \cdot y)$;
(e) $(-x) \cdot (-y) = x \cdot y$.

It is not hard to prove the identities of Theorem 4–2.4 for the integers by the direct use of Definitions 4–1.2, 4–1.3, and 4–1.5. It is significant however that the proof for general rings is simpler and more elegant.

To prove (a), note that by Definition 4–2.1(a) and (d),

$$x + (-x) = 0 = (-x) + [-(-x)] = [-(-x)] + (-x).$$

Thus, by Theorem 4–2.3, $x = -(-x)$.

The proof of (b) also uses the cancellation law, Theorem 4–2.3. By Definition 4–2.1(a), (b), (c), (d), and Theorem 4–2.2, we obtain $(x + y) + [(-x) + (-y)] = (y + x) + [(-x) + (-y)] = y + [x + ((-x) + (-y))] = y + [(x + (-x)) + (-y)] = y + [0 + (-y)] = y + (-y) = 0 = (x + y) + [-(x + y)]$. Thus, $(-x) + (-y) = -(x + y)$.

By Definition 4–2.1(c), $0 + 0 = 0$. Therefore $x \cdot 0 + 0 = x \cdot 0 = x \cdot (0 + 0) = (x \cdot 0) + (x \cdot 0)$ by Definition 4–2.1(f) and (c). Using Theorem 4–2.3, we obtain $x \cdot 0 = 0$. Similarly, $0 \cdot x = 0$. This proves (c).

To prove (d), use the distributive law, Definition 4–2.1(f) and (g), together with the result just proved, and the cancellation law, Theorem 4–2.3. For instance, $x \cdot y + (-x) \cdot y = [x + (-x)] \cdot y = 0 \cdot y = 0 = (x \cdot y) + [-(x \cdot y)]$ by Definition 4–2.1 and (c). Therefore, $(-x) \cdot y = -(x \cdot y)$ by Theorem 4–2.3.

The final statement (e) of Theorem 4–2.4 is obtained by two applications of part (d), together with (a): $(-x) \cdot (-y) = -[x \cdot (-y)] = -[-(x \cdot y)] = x \cdot y$.

From a mathematician's viewpoint, the advantage of the integers over the natural numbers is that the integers are closed under subtraction. That is, if a and b are any integers, then it is always possible to find an integer x which is a solution of

$$a + x = b.$$

As a matter of fact, subtraction is always possible in any ring.

THEOREM 4–2.5. Let A be a ring. Let $x \in A$ and $y \in A$. Then there is one and only one element $z \in A$ satisfying $y + z = x$, namely $z = x + (-y)$.

Proof. Let $z = x + (-y)$. Then $y + z = y + [x + (-y)] = y + [(-y) + x] = [y + (-y)] + x = 0 + x = x + 0 = x$, by the first four laws of Definition 4–2.1. Therefore, $z = x + (-y)$ is a solution of $y + z = x$. On the other hand, if z is a solution of $y + z = x$, then $x + (-y) = (y + z) + (-y) = (z + y) + (-y) = z + [y + (-y)] = z + 0 = z$. Hence, $z = x + (-y)$ is the *unique* solution of $y + z = x$.

It is customary to use the subtraction notation $x - y$ to denote the solution of the equation $y + z = x$ in an arbitrary ring. That is,

$$x - y = x + (-y). \tag{4–1}$$

The postulates for rings can be given using the binary operation of subtraction instead of the unary operation of negation. [Definition 4–2.1(c) and (d) are replaced by the single identity $y + (x - y) = x$.] However, Definition 4–2.1 is more familiar and convenient.

As we have pointed out in Example 1, the systems Z and Q of integers and rational numbers are rings. Also, Z is a subset of Q. However, more can be said: the operations of addition, negation, and multiplication in Q of the elements belonging to Z agree with the usual operations for the integers. In the study of rings, this situation occurs frequently enough to justify the introduction of a special term to describe it.

DEFINITION 4–2.6. Let A be a ring. A nonempty subset B of A is called a *subring* of A if for every x and y in B (not necessarily different) the sum $x + y$, the negative $-x$, and the product $x \cdot y$ all belong to B.

Since $x \in B$, $y \in B$ implies that $x \in A$ and $y \in A$, the sum $x + y$, negative $-x$, and product $x \cdot y$ always exist as elements of A. The condition that B be a subring is merely the added assumption that these elements are in B and not just A. If B is a subring of A, then the operations of A, applied to B, can be considered as operations on B. The set B with the operations which it inherits from A forms a ring because the identities of Definition 4–2.1 are automatically satisfied in B, so that the term *subring* is justified. In speaking of a subring B of A, it is customary to think of B as a ring with the operations on B agreeing with the operations of A.

EXAMPLE 5. Let $B = \{a/2^n | a \in Z, n = 0, 1, 2, \ldots\}$. Then B is a subring of Q.

EXAMPLE 6. Let $C = \{a/2 | a \in Z\}$. Then $C \subseteq Q$, but C is not a subring of Q, since, for example, $\frac{1}{4} = \frac{1}{2} \cdot \frac{1}{2}$ is a product of elements of C, but $\frac{1}{4} \notin C$.

EXAMPLE 7. As we have noted, Z is a subring of Q. However, N is not a subring of Z, nor of Q, because if $n \in N$, then $-n \notin N$.

The concept of isomorphism, which was mentioned in Section 3–3 for general mathematical systems, is very important in the theory of abstract rings.

DEFINITION 4–2.7. Let A and B be rings. Then A is *isomorphic* to B if there is a one-to-one correspondence $x \leftrightarrow x'$ between the elements of A and B, such that sums, products, and negatives are preserved by the correspondence. That is, if $x \leftrightarrow x'$ and $y \leftrightarrow y'$, then

$$x + y \leftrightarrow x' + y', \qquad x \cdot y \leftrightarrow x' \cdot y', \qquad \text{and} \qquad -x \leftrightarrow -(x').$$

If a ring A is isomorphic to a ring B, then any property of A which can be expressed in terms of the operations of addition, multiplication, and negation is also a property of B, and vice versa. For instance, suppose that A is a commutative ring which is isomorphic to the ring B. Let x' and y' be any elements of B. Then there exist elements x and y in A such that $x \leftrightarrow x'$ and $y \leftrightarrow y'$ by the given isomorphism. Moreover, $x \cdot y \leftrightarrow x' \cdot y'$ and $y \cdot x \leftrightarrow y' \cdot x'$. Since $x \cdot y = y \cdot x$ in A, and the correspondence is one-to-one, we have $x' \cdot y' = y' \cdot x'$ in B. Thus, B is a commutative ring, since x' and y' were arbitrary elements of B. The meaning of Definition 4–2.7 is that isomorphic rings are indistinguishable in every way which has to do with the fact that they are rings, even though A and B may be different as sets.

EXAMPLE 8. Let $M = \{\langle a, a \rangle | a \in Z\}$. Define addition, multiplication, and negation* in M by the rules

$$\langle a, a \rangle \oplus \langle b, b \rangle = \langle a + b, a + b \rangle,$$

$$\langle a, a \rangle \odot \langle b, b \rangle = \langle a \cdot b, a \cdot b \rangle,$$

$$\ominus \langle a, a \rangle = \langle -a, -a \rangle,$$

---

* The symbols used to denote addition, multiplication, and negation in a ring are usually $+$, $\cdot$, and $-$. When discussing two different rings at the same time, it may be confusing to denote the corresponding operations by the same symbols (although this was done in Definition 4–2.7). In this case, we will sometimes use $\oplus$, $\odot$, and $\ominus$ to represent the operations in one of the rings, and the usual symbols to denote the operations in the other ring.

where $+$, $\cdot$, and $-$ denote the ordinary operations in Z. It can easily be verified that the operations $\oplus$, $\odot$, and $\ominus$ in M satisfy the conditions of Definition 4–2.1, so that M is a ring. The correspondence $\langle a, a \rangle \leftrightarrow a$ is a one-to-one correspondence between the elements of M and Z, which is an isomorphism. For example,

$$\langle a, a \rangle \leftrightarrow a, \qquad \langle b, b \rangle \leftrightarrow b,$$

and

$$\langle a, a \rangle \oplus \langle b, b \rangle = \langle a + b, a + b \rangle \leftrightarrow a + b.$$

The reader can check that multiplication and negation are also preserved by this correspondence.

EXAMPLE 9. The rings Z and R are not isomorphic. In fact, we will show in Section 7–3 that R is not denumerable. Since Z is denumerable (see Section 1–2, Example 3), there cannot be any one-to-one correspondence between Z and R. For the same reason, Q and R are not isomorphic.

EXAMPLE 10. The rings Z and Q are not isomorphic. Of course there are one-to-one correspondences between Z and Q (see Section 1–2, Example 5, for instance), but none of these are isomorphisms. To prove this statement, suppose that there is an isomorphism between Z and Q. Let r be the rational number corresponding to the integer 1:

$$1 \leftrightarrow r.$$

Now let a be the integer corresponding to the rational number $r/2$:

$$a \leftrightarrow r/2.$$

Since any isomorphism preserves sums, the correspondence $a \leftrightarrow r/2$ added to itself gives

$$2a = a + a \leftrightarrow r/2 + r/2 = r.$$

Thus $1 \leftrightarrow r$ and $2a \leftrightarrow r$, so that $1 = 2a$. However no integer a satisfies $2a = 1$. This contradiction shows that Z cannot be isomorphic to Q.

EXAMPLE 11. Let S be a set with one element. Let $B = P(S)$, with the operations defined as in Example 4. Then the ring B is isomorphic to the ring A described in Example 3. The correspondence is given by $S \leftrightarrow a$ and $\Phi \leftrightarrow 0$.

EXAMPLE 12. Let S and T be two finite sets with the same number of elements. Then the rings $A = P(S)$ and $B = P(T)$, with the operations defined in Example 4, are isomorphic.

PROBLEMS

1. Let $A = \{\langle m, n \rangle \mid m \in Z, n \in Z\}$. Define

$$\langle m_1, n_1 \rangle + \langle m_2, n_2 \rangle = \langle m_1 + m_2, n_1 + n_2 \rangle,$$
$$\langle m_1, n_1 \rangle \cdot \langle m_2, n_2 \rangle = \langle m_1 m_2, n_1 n_2 \rangle,$$
$$-\langle m, n \rangle = \langle -m, -n \rangle.$$

Show that with these operations, A is a ring. What is the zero element of this ring? Show that in A, it is possible to find two nonzero elements whose product is zero.

2. Let $B = \{\langle m, n \rangle \mid m \in Z, n \in Z\}$. Define

$$\langle m_1, n_1 \rangle + \langle m_2, n_2 \rangle = \langle m_1 + m_2, n_1 + n_2 \rangle,$$
$$\langle m_1, n_1 \rangle \cdot \langle m_2, n_2 \rangle = \langle m_1 m_2 - n_1 n_2, m_1 n_2 + m_2 n_1 \rangle,$$
$$-\langle m, n \rangle = \langle -m, -n \rangle.$$

Show that with these operations, B is a ring.

3. Let $A = \{x, y\}$ (a set consisting of two distinct symbols). Define

$$x + x = x, \qquad x + y = y, \qquad y + x = y, \qquad y + y = x.$$

Find all possible ways in which negation and multiplication can be defined on A in order that it will be a ring.

4. Verify that Examples 3 and 4 are rings.

5. Show that there is one and essentially only one ring which contains one element.

6. Show that if $x + y = x$ in a ring, then $y = 0$.

7. Prove the following identities in any ring.
(a) $(x + y) - z = (x - z) + y = x + (y - z) = x - (z - y)$
(b) $x - (y + z) = (x - y) - z$
(c) $x \cdot (y - z) = x \cdot y - x \cdot z$

8. Show that if B is a subring of a ring A, then $0 \in B$.

9. Show that a nonempty subset B of a ring A is a subring of A if and only if $x \in B$ and $y \in B$ implies that $x - y \in B$ and $x \cdot y \in B$.

10. Prove the assertion in Example 5.

11. Show that if B is a subring of A, and if C is a subring of B, then C is a subring of A.

12. Verify that M, in Example 8, is a ring. Complete the proof that the given correspondence is an isomorphism between M and Z.

13. Prove the statements made in Examples 11 and 12.

14. Show that the ring Z of all integers is *not* isomorphic to the ring of all even integers.

15. Prove that if A, B, and C are rings such that A is isomorphic to B, and B is isomorphic to C, then A is isomorphic to C.

16. Let A be a nonempty set on which are defined three binary operations $x + y$, $x \cdot y$, and $x - y$, satisfying the parts (a), (b), (e), (f), (g) of Definition 4–2.1, and the law $y + (x - y) = x$. Do not assume the existence of a zero or negation in A.

(a) Prove the following for elements u, v, w, x, and y of A. [*Hint:* Use part (3) in the proofs of (4), (5), (6), and (7).]

    (1) If $y = (u - v) + (v - u)$, then $u + y = u$ and $v + y = v$.

    (2) If $u + w = v + w$ for some element w, then $u + x = v + x$ for all x.

    (3) If $u + w = v + w$, then $u = v$.

    (4) $u + v = w$ if and only if $v = w - u$.

    (5) $(x + y) - y = x$

    (6) $y + (x - x) = y$

    (7) $x - x = y - y$

(b) Show that by suitably defining the element 0, and the operation of negation, A becomes a ring in the sense of Definition 4–2.1.

17. Show that if $x - y$ is suitably defined in a ring A, then the law $y + (x - y) = x$ is satisfied in A. This result combined with Problem 16(b) shows that the postulate set consisting of (a), (b), (e), (f), (g) of Definition 4–2.1, and the condition $y + (x - y) = x$, is equivalent to Definition 4–2.1 for a ring.

4–3 Generalized sums and products. The purpose of this section is to investigate the consequences and generalizations of the associative, commutative, and distributive laws of addition and multiplication in rings:

$$x + (y + z) = (x + y) + z; \qquad\qquad (4\text{--}2)$$

$$x + y = y + x; \qquad\qquad (4\text{--}3)$$

$$x \cdot (y \cdot z) = (x \cdot y) \cdot z; \qquad\qquad (4\text{--}4)$$

$$x \cdot y = y \cdot x; \qquad\qquad (4\text{--}5)$$

$$x \cdot (y + z) = x \cdot y + x \cdot z. \qquad\qquad (4\text{--}6)$$

These laws are satisfied in the systems of natural numbers, integers, rational numbers, real numbers, complex numbers, and indeed in any commutative ring. Thus our results have a wide range of applicability. Moreover, the study of this section will give the reader a chance to become better acquainted with the abstract approach to mathematics.

The fact that multiplication and addition are binary operations means that numbers are always added and multiplied two at a time. However, everyone is familiar with expressions like $2 + 5 + 1$. Because ordinary addition satisfies the associative law, (4–2), it does not matter whether we add 2 and 5 and then add 1, or add 2 to the sum of 5 and 1. Consequently, the expression $2 + 5 + 1$ makes sense, even though it does not indicate which two of the numbers are to be added first. In general, the expression

$$a_1 + a_2 + \cdots + a_n$$

indicates the result of adding the n numbers, $a_1, a_2, \ldots, a_n$ in any way, two at a time. The fact that the result does not depend on how the terms of the sum are associated can be proved by induction, using (4–2), in a way which is similar to the proof of Theorem 1–5.2 given in Section 2–3. This result is called the general associative law.

There is a convenient notation which is used to indicate the sum of several numbers. It is the expression $\sum_{i=1}^{n} a_i$, standing for $a_1 + a_2 + \cdots + a_n$. We read $\sum_{i=1}^{n} a_i$ as "the sum of the a_i from $i = 1$ to $i = n$." A sum with a single term is provided for by adopting the convention that $\sum_{i=1}^{1} a_i = a_1$. The symbol $\sum$ is called the *summation sign*. The letter i in the expression $\sum_{i=1}^{n} a_i$ is called the *index of summation*. Another choice for the index of summation does not change the sum. Thus,

$$\sum_{i=1}^{n} a_i, \quad \sum_{j=1}^{n} a_j, \quad \sum_{\alpha=1}^{n} a_\alpha$$

are the same, since they are all abbreviations of

$$a_1 + a_2 + \cdots + a_n.$$

Variations of the summation notation such as $\sum_{i=0}^{n} a_i$, $\sum_{i=k}^{n} a_i$, and $\sum_{i=1}^{n+1} a_i$ are self-explanatory.

EXAMPLE 1. $\sum_{i=1}^{5} 2^i = 2 + 2^2 + 2^3 + 2^4 + 2^5 = 62.$

EXAMPLE 2. $\sum_{j=1}^{1000} j = 1 + 2 + \cdots + 1000 = 500500.$

EXAMPLE 3. $\sum_{i=1}^{5} a_i + \sum_{i=6}^{10} a_i = \sum_{i=1}^{10} a_i.$

EXAMPLE 4. $\sum_{r=1}^{n} r a_r = a_1 + 2a_2 + \cdots + n a_n.$

EXAMPLE 5. $\sum_{j=1}^{n} 2 = \overbrace{2 + 2 + \cdots + 2}^{n \text{ terms}} = 2n.$

It is easy to show that the commutative law of addition, (4–3), can be extended to sums with any number of terms. Using the notation for sums which we have just introduced, the "general commutative law" can be stated as follows.

(4–3.1) Let $a_1, a_2, \ldots, a_n$ be any numbers. Let $i_1, i_2, \ldots, i_n$ be any rearrangement of the indices $1, 2, \ldots, n$. Then

$$\sum_{j=1}^{n} a_{i_j} = \sum_{i=1}^{n} a_i.$$

For example, if $i_1 = 4$, $i_2 = 2$, $i_3 = 1$, $i_4 = 3$, then $\sum_{j=1}^{4} a_{i_j} = a_4 + a_2 + a_1 + a_3 = a_1 + a_2 + a_3 + a_4 = \sum_{i=1}^{4} a_i.$

Proof. The proof of (4–3.1) is by induction on n. If $n = 1$, there is nothing to prove. Note that one and only one of the numbers $a_{i_1}, a_{i_2}, \ldots,$ a_{i_n} is a_n. Suppose that a_{i_k} is a_n. Then by the general associative law and (4–3)

$$\sum_{j=1}^{n} a_{ij} = a_{i_1} + a_{i_2} + \cdots + a_{i_{k-1}} + a_{i_k} + a_{i_{k+1}} + \cdots + a_{i_n}$$

$$= (a_{i_1} + a_{i_2} + \cdots + a_{i_{k-1}}) + (a_{i_k} + (a_{i_{k+1}} + \cdots + a_{i_n}))$$

$$= (a_{i_1} + a_{i_2} + \cdots + a_{i_{k-1}}) + ((a_{i_{k+1}} + \cdots + a_{i_n}) + a_{i_k})$$

$$= ((a_{i_1} + a_{i_2} + \cdots + a_{i_{k-1}}) + (a_{i_{k+1}} + \cdots + a_{i_n})) + a_{i_k}$$

$$= (a_{i_1} + a_{i_2} + \cdots + a_{i_{k-1}} + a_{i_{k+1}} + \cdots + a_{i_n}) + a_n.$$

Since n does not occur in the list $i_1, i_2, \ldots, i_{k-1}, i_{k+1}, \ldots, i_n$, this finite sequence is simply a rearrangement of $a_1, a_2, \ldots, a_{n-1}$. Therefore, the induction hypothesis yields

$$a_{i_1} + a_{i_2} + \cdots + a_{i_{k-1}} + a_{i_{k+1}} + \cdots + a_{i_n} = a_1 + a_2 + \cdots + a_{n-1}.$$

Consequently,

$$\sum_{j=1}^{n} a_{ij} = (a_1 + a_2 + \cdots + a_{n-1}) + a_n = \sum_{i=1}^{n} a_i.$$

An important special case of the general commutative law occurs when we consider sums of sums:

$$\sum_{i=1}^{n} \sum_{j=1}^{m} a_{i,j}.$$

In this expression, we have a doubly indexed set of numbers $a_{i,j}$, where i ranges from 1 to n and j ranges from 1 to m. We first sum over j (for each i) and then add the resulting sums. For example,

$$\sum_{i=1}^{3} \sum_{j=1}^{4} a_{i,j} = \sum_{i=1}^{3} (a_{i,1} + a_{i,2} + a_{i,3} + a_{i,4})$$

$$= (a_{1,1} + a_{1,2} + a_{1,3} + a_{1,4}) + (a_{2,1} + a_{2,2} + a_{2,3} + a_{2,4})$$

$$+ (a_{3,1} + a_{3,2} + a_{3,3} + a_{3,4}).$$

According to the general commutative law, (4–3.1), we can write

$$\sum_{i=1}^{n} \sum_{j=1}^{m} a_{i,j} = \sum_{j=1}^{m} \sum_{i=1}^{n} a_{i,j}.$$

This equality expresses the fact that if the numbers $a_{i,j}$ are written in a rectangular array

$$
\begin{array}{cccc|c}
a_{1,1} & a_{1,2} & \cdots & a_{1,m} & \displaystyle\sum_{j=1}^{m} a_{1,j} \\[2em]
a_{2,1} & a_{2,2} & \cdots & a_{2,m} & \displaystyle\sum_{j=1}^{m} a_{2,j} \\[1em]
\vdots & \vdots & & \vdots & \displaystyle\sum_{j=1}^{m} a_{n,j} \\[1em]
a_{n,1} & a_{n,2} & \cdots & a_{n,m} & \\[2em]
\hline
\displaystyle\sum_{i=1}^{n} a_{i,1} & \displaystyle\sum_{i=1}^{n} a_{i,2} & \cdots & \displaystyle\sum_{i=1}^{n} a_{i,m} &
\end{array}
$$

and if the terms in each row are added, and then these sums added, the result will be the same as if the terms in each column are added and then the totals of the columns are added.

EXAMPLE 6. Let $a_{i,j} = \binom{i}{j}$ if $0 \leq j \leq i \leq n$ and $a_{i,j} = 0$ if $0 \leq i < j \leq n$. Then by formula (1–2) which gives the sum of the binomial coefficients,

$$
\sum_{j=0}^{n}\sum_{i=j}^{n}\binom{i}{j} = \sum_{j=0}^{n}\sum_{i=0}^{n} a_{i,j} = \sum_{i=0}^{n}\sum_{j=0}^{n} a_{i,j}
$$

$$
= \sum_{i=0}^{n}\sum_{j=0}^{i}\binom{i}{j} = \sum_{i=0}^{n} 2^{i} = 2^{n+1} - 1.
$$

The associative and commutative laws of multiplication, (4–4) and (4–5), can be generalized to show that the product of n numbers $a_1, a_2, \ldots, a_n$ does not depend on the grouping or order of the numbers in the product. Thus, for example,

$$
(a_1 \cdot a_2) \cdot (a_3 \cdot a_4) = a_4 \cdot [(a_1 \cdot a_3) \cdot a_2] = [(a_3 \cdot a_1) \cdot a_2] \cdot a_4.
$$

This justifies the use of the expression

$$
a_1 \cdot a_2 \cdot \cdots \cdot a_n
$$

to denote the product of the n numbers $a_1, a_2, \ldots, a_n$. There is also a useful notation for products which is similar to the $\sum$ notation for sums.

This consists of using the expression

$$\prod_{i=1}^{n} a_i$$

to stand for the product $a_1 \cdot a_2 \cdot \cdots \cdot a_n$. The expression $\prod_{i=1}^{n} a_i$ is read "the product of the a_i from $i = 1$ to $i = n$." The symbol $\prod$ is called the *product sign*.

EXAMPLE 7. $\prod_{i=1}^{6} 4^i = 4 \cdot 4^2 \cdot 4^3 \cdot 4^4 \cdot 4^5 \cdot 4^6 = 4^{21}$.

EXAMPLE 8. $\prod_{j=1}^{n} j = n!$.

EXAMPLE 9. $(\prod_{i=1}^{n} a_i)(\prod_{i=n+1}^{n+k} a_i) = \prod_{i=1}^{n+k} a_i$.

EXAMPLE 10. $\prod_{j=1}^{2} (\sum_{i=1}^{2} a_i)^i = \prod_{j=1}^{2} (a_1 + a_2)^i = (a_1 + a_2) \cdot (a_1 + a_2)^2$
$= (a_1 + a_2)^3$.

There is a useful generalization of the distributive law, (4–6).   Let $a_1, a_2, \ldots, a_n$, and $b_1, b_2, \ldots, b_m$ be any numbers.   Then

$$\left(\sum_{i=1}^{n} a_i\right)\left(\sum_{j=1}^{m} b_j\right) = \sum_{i=1}^{n} \sum_{j=1}^{m} a_i \cdot b_j. \tag{4–7}$$

We leave the proof of this identity as a problem for the reader.

As we observed in Section 4–1, it is possible to define the product $n \cdot a$ for a natural number n and an integer a in terms of the addition of integers. This remark can be generalized to arbitrary rings.

DEFINITION 4–3.2.   Let x be an element of the ring A.   Define

$$nx = \underbrace{x + x + \cdots + x}_{n \text{ summands}},$$

if n is a natural number, $0x = 0$,*

$$(-n)x = n(-x) = \underbrace{(-x) + (-x) + \cdots + (-x)}_{n \text{ summands}},$$

if n is a natural number.

---

* The symbol 0 is used here with two different meanings. The 0 on the left is the integer 0 (that is, Φ), while on the right, 0 stands for the zero of the ring.

On the basis of Definition 4–3.2, we can speak of ax where $a \in Z$ and x is an element of any ring. The generalized commutative, associative, and distributive laws of addition can be specialized to obtain the following result.

THEOREM 4–3.3. Let x and y be any elements of the ring A. Let a and b be arbitrary integers. Then

(a) $ax + bx = (a + b)x$;

(b) $a(bx) = (ab)x$;

(c) $a(x + y) = ax + ay$;

(d) $a(x \cdot y) = (ax) \cdot y = x \cdot (ay)$;

(e) $1x = x$;

(f) $a0 = 0$;

(g) $a(-x) = (-a)x$.

We leave the proof of this result as an exercise for the reader.

PROBLEMS

1. Using (4–2), prove that

$$[(a_1 + a_2) + a_3] + a_4 = a_1 + [(a_2 + a_3) + a_4].$$

2. Determine the following sums and products.

(a) $\displaystyle\sum_{j=1}^{5} (j^2 + j + 1), \qquad \prod_{j=1}^{5} (j^2 + j + 1)$

(b) $\displaystyle\sum_{i=1}^{n} i \quad$ (see Section 2–1)

(c) $\displaystyle\sum_{i=50}^{100} i^2$

(d) $\displaystyle\prod_{j=1}^{20} 2^{(2j-1)}$

3. Write the following sums and products in terms of the $\sum$ and $\prod$ notation.

(a) $1^6 - 2^6 + 3^6 - \cdots + (-1)^{n-1} n^6$

(b) $\dfrac{1}{1 \cdot 2 \cdot 3} + \dfrac{1}{2 \cdot 3 \cdot 4} + \dfrac{1}{3 \cdot 4 \cdot 5} + \cdots + \dfrac{1}{n(n + 1)(n + 2)}$

(c) $(1 + t)(1 + t^2)(1 + t^4) \cdots (1 + t^{2^{n-1}})$

(d) $(k + 1) \cdot (k + 2) \cdot \cdots \cdot n$

(e) $1 + nt + \dfrac{n(n - 1)}{2} t^2 + \dfrac{n(n - 1)(n - 2)}{2 \cdot 3} t^3 + \cdots + nt^{n-1} + t^n$

4. Find the sum in Problem 3(b) by noting that

$$\frac{1}{j(j+1)(j+2)} = \frac{1}{2}\left[\frac{1}{j(j+1)} - \frac{1}{(j+1)(j+2)}\right].$$

5. Let $a_i = a$ for $i = 1, 2, \ldots, n$. Show that

$$\sum_{i=1}^{n} a_i = na, \qquad \prod_{i=1}^{n} a_i = a^n.$$

6. Prove the following by mathematical induction.

(a) $\quad a\sum_{j=1}^{m} b_j = \sum_{j=1}^{m} ab_j$

(b) $\quad \left(\sum_{i=1}^{n} a_i\right)\left(\sum_{j=1}^{m} b_j\right) = \sum_{i=1}^{n}\sum_{j=1}^{m} a_i b_j$

7. Evaluate the following double sums.

(a) $\displaystyle\sum_{i=1}^{n}\sum_{j=1}^{m} i\cdot j$ (b) $\displaystyle\sum_{i=1}^{n}\sum_{j=1}^{m} i^2 2^j$ (c) $\displaystyle\sum_{i=1}^{n}\sum_{j=1}^{m} a^i b^j$

8. Is

$$\prod_{i=1}^{n}\prod_{j=1}^{m} a_{i,j} = \prod_{j=1}^{m}\prod_{i=1}^{n} a_{i,j}$$

true in general? Justify your answer.

9. Is

$$\prod_{i=1}^{n}\sum_{j=1}^{m} a_{i,j} = \sum_{j=1}^{n}\prod_{i=1}^{n} a_{i,j}$$

true in general? Justify your answer.

10. Show that

$$\prod_{i=1}^{n} t^{a_i} = t^{\sum_{i=1}^{n} a_i}.$$

11. Define $a_{i,j} = \binom{i}{j}t^j$ for $0 \le j \le i \le n$ and $a_{i,j} = 0$ for $0 \le i < j \le n$
By suitably interpreting the identity

$$\sum_{i=0}^{n}\sum_{j=0}^{n} a_{i,j} = \sum_{j=0}^{n}\sum_{i=0}^{n} a_{i,j},$$

show that $\binom{j}{j} + \binom{j+1}{j} + \cdots + \binom{n}{j} = \binom{n+1}{j+1}$.

12. Prove Theorem 4–3.3.

4-4 Integral domains. As we observed in Section 4–2, the integers satisfy three identities which do not occur in the definition of a ring. This section is concerned with some very simple consequences of these special properties.

DEFINITION 4–4.1. Let A be a ring. An element $e \in A$ is called an *identity* for A, or an *identity element* of A, if

$$e \cdot x = x \cdot e = x,$$

for all $x \in A$.

THEOREM 4–4.2. A ring can have at most one identity element.

Because of this theorem, we may speak of *the* identity element of A. It is clear from (4–1.6) (d) and (a) that the ring Z of all integers has 1 as its identity element. It is common practice to denote the identity element of any ring by the symbol 1. This might cause confusion, but usually it does not.

The proof of Theorem 4–4.2 is easy. Suppose that e and e' are both identity elements of A. That is, $e \cdot x = x \cdot e = x$ and $e' \cdot y = y \cdot e' = y$ for all x and y in A. In particular, if we let $x = e'$ and $y = e$, we get $e \cdot e' = e \cdot x = x = e'$ and $e \cdot e' = y \cdot e' = y = e$. Thus, $e = e \cdot e' = e'$.

If a ring A contains an identity element 1, then by Theorem 4–2.4, $(-1) \cdot x = -(1 \cdot x) = -x$. Similarly, $x \cdot (-1) = -x$. That is, the operation of negation is the same as multiplication (on either side) by the element -1. This fact is very familiar for the integers, rational, and real numbers, so that the reader may not be surprised to find that it is a property of rings in general. We will use the identity

$$(-1) \cdot x = x \cdot (-1) = -x$$

frequently, and without further discussion.

If a ring contains at least one element x different from 0, then 0 cannot be an identity element, since $0 \cdot x = 0 \neq x$. Thus the only ring in which zero is an identity element is the ring containing only the element 0.

DEFINITION 4–4.3. An *integral domain* is a commutative ring A with an identity element different from zero, such that the following cancellation law is satisfied in A: if x, y, and z are elements of A such that $x \cdot z = y \cdot z$, then either $x = y$, or $z = 0$.

As we have observed, the rings of integers, rational numbers, and real numbers are all integral domains. There is a way to determine whether a commutative ring satisfies the cancellation law. This test is most conveniently stated, using a new notion.

DEFINITION 4–4.4. Let A be a commutative ring. An element $z \in A$ is called a *divisor of zero* if for some $x \neq 0$ in A, $x \cdot z = 0$. If z is a divisor of zero and $z \neq 0$, then z is called a *proper divisor of zero*.

It is evident from Theorem 4–2.4(c) that if A contains at least one element different from zero, then 0 is a divisor of zero. However, an integral domain has no proper divisors of zero.

THEOREM 4–4.5. Let A be a commutative ring with an identity element different from zero. Then A is an integral domain if and only if A contains no proper divisors of zero.

Proof. Suppose that A is an integral domain. We wish to prove that A has no proper divisors of zero. Suppose that z is a divisor of zero. Then there is an $x \neq 0$ in A such that $x \cdot z = 0$. By Theorem 4–2.4(c), $0 \cdot z = 0$. Thus, $x \cdot z = 0 \cdot z$. By the cancellation law, either $x = 0$, or $z = 0$. However, by assumption, $x \neq 0$. Thus $z = 0$. In other words, 0 is the only divisor of zero in A. That is, A contains no proper divisors of zero. The proof of the converse depends on the distributive law. Suppose that A has no proper divisors of zero. Since A is commutative and has an identity element not equal to 0, it is only necessary to show that A satisfies the cancellation law. Assume that x, y, and z are elements of A satisfying $x \cdot z = y \cdot z$. Then

$$[x + (-y)] \cdot z = x \cdot z + (-y) \cdot z = y \cdot z + [-(y \cdot z)] = 0,$$

by Definition 4–2.1(f) and Theorem 4–2.4. Thus, by Definition 4–4.4, either $x + (-y) = 0$, or else z is a divisor of zero. Since we are assuming that A contains no divisors of zero except 0 (that is, no proper divisors of zero), it follows that either $x + (-y) = 0$, or $z = 0$. If $x + (-y) = 0$, than $x = y$. Thus, either $x = y$, or $z = 0$. This shows that A satisfies the cancellation law.

Some of the most interesting problems in the study of the integers are concerned with divisibility. In fact, a large part of the theory of numbers is devoted to the divisibility properties of the integers and the natural numbers. Most of the next chapter deals with this topic.

In the integers, x divides y if there is an integer z such that $y = z \cdot x$. This definition makes sense in an arbitrary ring A, but the notion "x divides y" is not very useful unless A is an integral domain.

DEFINITION 4–4.6. Let A be an integral domain. Let x and y be elements of A. Then x *divides* y in A (or y *is divisible by* x in A, or x *is a factor of* y in A), if there is a $z \in A$ such that $y = z \cdot x$.

It is important to note that the notion of divisibility depends not only on the elements x and y, but also on the integral domain under consideration. For example, 2 divides 3 in Q, but not in Z. Usually, however, discussions involving divisibility are restricted to elements of a fixed integral domain. In this case, the terminology "x divides y" and "y is divisible by x," and the notation

$$x \mid y \text{ if } x \text{ divides } y,$$

$$x \nmid y \text{ if } x \text{ does not divide } y$$

can be used without danger of confusion. For example, in the next chapter, the notion of "divisibility" and the symbolism $a \mid b$ will always refer to divisibility in the ring Z of all integers.

The reader can easily verify the following facts.

THEOREM 4–4.7. Let A be any integral domain. Then for elements x, y, z, u, v of A,

    (a) if $x \mid y$ and $y \mid z$, then $x \mid z$;

    (b) if $x \mid y$ and $x \mid z$, then $x \mid (y + z)$;

    (c) if $x \mid y$, then $x \cdot z \mid y \cdot z$;

    (d) $x \mid x \cdot y$;

    (e) if $x \mid y$ and $x \mid z$, then $x \mid (u \cdot y + v \cdot z)$;

    (f) $x \mid 0$, $1 \mid x$, $-1 \mid x$;

    (g) if $0 \mid x$, then $x = 0$.

If $x \mid y$ and $y \mid x$, then by definition, elements z and w exist in A such that $x = z \cdot y$, $y = w \cdot x$. Hence, $1 \cdot x = x = z \cdot (w \cdot x) = (z \cdot w) \cdot x$. If $x \neq 0$, this implies by Definition 4–4.3 that $z \cdot w = 1$. In the ring of integers it is easy to see from Definition 4–1.5 and (3–3.2) that the condition $z \cdot w = 1$ can be satisfied only if $z = w = 1$, or if $z = w = -1$. Therefore, either $x = y$, or $x = -y$. The same conclusion is obtained if $x = 0$, since $y = w \cdot x = w \cdot 0 = 0$. Thus, we obtain the following result for integers.

THEOREM 4–4.8. Let x and y be integers. Suppose that x divides y and y divides x in Z. Then either $x = y$, or $x = -y$.

Of course, if $x = y$, or if $x = -y$, then $x \mid y$ and $y \mid x$ in *any* integral domain. If $y = x \cdot z$ and $y = x \cdot w$ in an integral domain A, then $x \cdot z = x \cdot w$. Hence, if $x \neq 0$, then $z = w$. This observation justifies the following definition.

DEFINITION 4–4.9. Let A be an integral domain. Let x and y be elements of A such that x divides y in A, and $x \neq 0$. Then the unique element z such that

$$y = x \cdot z$$

is called the *quotient* of y and x, and it is denoted by

$$y/x \quad \text{or} \quad \frac{y}{x}.$$

PROBLEMS

1. Show that the ring of Example 2, Section 4–2, does not have an identity. Show that the rings of Examples 3 and 4 do have identities.

2. State which of the following rings are not integral domains and give your reasons.
   (a) The ring of all rational numbers.
   (b) The ring of Example 2, Section 4–2.
   (c) The ring of Example 3, Section 4–2.
   (d) The ring of Example 4, Section 4–2.
   (e) The ring of Problem 1, Section 4–2.

3. Give an example of an integral domain which contains exactly two elements.

4. Prove Theorem 4–4.7.

5. If x and y are rational numbers, what are the conditions for x to divide y in Q?

6. Using Definition 4–1.5 and (3–3.2), show that in the ring Z, the condition $z \cdot w = 1$ can be satisfied only if $z = w = 1$ or $z = w = -1$.

7. Let $A = \{\langle x, y \rangle | x \in Z, y \in Z\}$. Define

$$\langle x_1, y_1 \rangle + \langle x_2, y_2 \rangle = \langle x_1 + x_2, y_1 + y_2 \rangle,$$

$$\langle x_1, y_1 \rangle \cdot \langle x_2, y_2 \rangle = \langle x_1 x_2 - y_1 y_2, x_1 y_2 + x_2 y_1 \rangle,$$

$$-\langle x, y \rangle = \langle -x, -y \rangle.$$

Show that A is an integral domain. Show that $\langle x_1, y_1 \rangle$ divides $\langle x_2, y_2 \rangle$ in A if and only if $x_1^2 + y_1^2$ divides both $x_1 x_2 + y_1 y_2$ and $x_1 y_2 - x_2 y_1$ in Z.

8. Let A be an integral domain containing elements x, y, and z. Prove the following facts.
   (a) If $z|x$ and $z|y$, then $x/z + y/z = (x + y)/z$.
   (b) If $z|x$, then $y \cdot (x/z) = (y \cdot x)/z$.
   (c) If $y|z$ and $x|(z/y)$, then $(x \cdot y)|z$, and $z/(x \cdot y) = (z/y)/x$.

9. Show that if B is a subring of an integral domain A, and if B contains the identity element of A, then B is an integral domain.

10. Let A be a ring with the identity element e. Show that $B = \{ae|a \in Z\}$ is a subring of A. (See Definition 4–3.2 and Theorem 4–3.3.)

11. Let A be an integral domain. Show that if B is a ring which is isomorphic to A, then B is also an integral domain.

4–5 The ordering of the integers. Since the ordering of the natural numbers is of such great importance in mathematics, it is not surprising that we would want to define a similar order relation on the integers. The way in which this is done is familiar. The ordering in Z is given by

$$\cdots < -3 < -2 < -1 < 0 < 1 < 2 < 3 < \cdots. \qquad (4\text{–}8)$$

But why order Z in this way? For example, why not define

$$0 < -1 < -2 < \cdots < 1 < 2 < 3 < \cdots ?$$

The answer is that the ordering (4–8) is the only really useful one. If an ordering is to be defined on Z, it should agree on N with the usual ordering, and it should satisfy as many of the basic conditions listed in (3–3.2) as possible. In particular, such an ordering should at least have the property that addition of the integer c to each of the integers a and b does not change the order relation between them. That is,

$$\text{if } a < b, \text{ then } a + c < b + c. \qquad (4\text{–}9)$$

The fact is that the only ordering of Z which agrees on N with the usual order relation, and which satisfies (4–9), is the familiar one given by (4–8). This assertion is not hard to prove. Suppose that $<$ is such an order relation defined on A. If m and n are natural numbers and $m < n$, then (4–9) implies

$$-n = m + [(-m) + (-n)] < n + [(-m) + (-n)] = -m.$$

Also, if $m \in N$, then $1 < m + 1$, so that

$$0 = 1 + (-1) < (m + 1) + (-1) = m.$$

Consequently,

$$-m = 0 + (-m) < m + (-m) = 0.$$

Thus, our order relation agrees with (4–8).

It is possible to describe the ordering of Z given by (4–8) in a convenient way.

DEFINITION 4–5.1. Let a and b be integers. Then a is *less than* b (or b is *greater than* a) if $b - a \in N$. In this case, we write $a < b$ (or $b > a$).

In other words, $a < b$ if and only if there is a natural number m such that $b = a + m$. It follows in particular that Definition 4–5.1 agrees with the usual ordering of N. (See Definition 3–3.4.)

THEOREM 4–5.2. Let a, b, and c be any integers. Then
  (a) either $a < b$, $a = b$, or $b < a$, and it is impossible for more than one of these relations to be satisfied by a given pair a, b of integers;
  (b) if $a < b$, and $b < c$, then $a < c$;
  (c) if $a < b$, then $a + c < b + c$;
  (d) if $a < b$ and $c > 0$, then $a \cdot c < b \cdot c$.

These statements are easily derived from the properties of the integers and the natural numbers. For instance, if c is any integer, then by Definitions 4–1.1 and 4–1.2 exactly one of the following holds true: $c \in N$, $c = 0$, $-c \in N$. Applying this remark to $c = b - a$, it follows that either $b - a \in N$, $b - a = 0$, or $-(b - a) = a - b \in N$. Thus, by Definition 4–5.1, either $a < b$, $a = b$, or $b < a$.

The condition $c > 0$ is obviously essential for Theorem 4–5.2(d) to be true. We point this out because neglecting to check this condition is a frequent source of error in algebraic manipulations involving inequalities.

It is possible to derive most of the useful properties of the ordering of the ring Z from Theorem 4–5.2 (a), (b), (c), and (d). As we will show later, the rational numbers and the real numbers also have orderings which satisfy these laws. Thus, any theorems which can be proved using only the properties of rings and the laws given in Theorem 4–5.2 will also be true for Q and for R. By introducing the abstract notion of an ordered integral domain, we can cover all of these cases at once.

DEFINITION 4–5.3. Let A be an integral domain. Suppose that an order relation (written $x < y$ or $y > x$) is defined on A satisfying the conditions of Theorem 4–5.2. That is, if x, y, and z are elements of A, then
  (a) either $x < y$, $x = y$, or $y < x$, and it is impossible for more than one of these relations to be satisfied by a given pair x, y of elements of A;
  (b) if $x < y$ and $y < z$, then $x < z$;
  (c) if $x < y$, then $x + z < y + z$;
  (d) if $x < y$, and $z > 0$, then $x \cdot z < y \cdot z$.
Then, A is called an *ordered integral domain*.

By Theorem 4–5.2, Z is an ordered integral domain. As we remarked above, the number systems Q and R are also ordered integral domains so that all definitions and theorems concerning ordered integral domains apply to each of the rings Z, Q, and R.

THEOREM 4–5.4. Let A be an ordered integral domain. Let x, y, z, and w be any elements of A. Then

(a) if $x < y$ and $z < w$, then $x + z < y + w$;
(b) if $x > 0$ and $y > 0$, then $x + y > 0$;
(c) if $x > 0$ and $y > 0$, then $x \cdot y > 0$.

Proof. If $x < y$, then $x + z < y + z$ by Definition 4–5.3(c). Also, if $z < w$, then $y + z < y + w$ by Definition 4–5.3(c) and the commutativity of addition. Thus, by Definition 4–5.3(b), if $x < y$ and $z < w$, then $x + z < y + w$. This proves (a). The statement (b) is a special case of (a), and the statement (c) is a special case of Definition 4–5.3(d), using Theorem 4–2.4(c).

THEOREM 4–5.5. Let A be an ordered integral domain. Let x, y, and z be any elements of A. Then

(a) if $x < y$, then $-y < -x$;
(b) if $x < y$ and $z < 0$, then $y \cdot z < x \cdot z$;
(c) if $x < 0$ and $y < 0$, then $x \cdot y > 0$;
(d) if $x \neq 0$, then $x^2 > 0$;
(e) $1 > 0$.

Proof. (a) By Definition 4–5.3(c), $-y = x + [(-x) + (-y)] < y + [(-x) + (-y)] = -x$. (b) If $z < 0$, then $0 < -z$ by (a). Thus, by Theorem 4–2.4 and Definition 4–5.3(d), $-(x \cdot z) = x \cdot (-z) < y \cdot (-z) = -(y \cdot z)$. Hence, $y \cdot z = -[-(y \cdot z)] < -[-(x \cdot z)] = x \cdot z$. (c) This statement is obtained from (b) by taking y to be 0 and z to be y. (d) If $x \neq 0$, then either $x > 0$, or $x < 0$. If $x > 0$, then $x^2 > 0$ by Theorem 4–5.4(c). If $x < 0$, then $x^2 > 0$ by (c). (e) By Definition 4–4.3, $1 \neq 0$. Thus, by (d), $1 = 1^2 > 0$.

It follows from Theorem 4–5.5(e) that not every integral domain can have defined on it an order relation satisfying the conditions of Definition 4–5.3, since there exist integral domains A which satisfy the condition $1 + 1 = 0$ (see Example 3, Section 4–2). If such an A could be made into an ordered integral domain by an order relation $<$, then $0 < 1$. Consequently $1 = 0 + 1 < 1 + 1 = 0$. This contradicts Definition 4–5.3(a).

In any ordered integral domain A, the elements of the set

$$P = \{x \in A \,|\, x > 0\}$$

are called the *positive* elements, and the elements of the set

$$M = \{x \in A \,|\, x < 0\}$$

are called the *negative* elements.

If $x \in P$ and $y \in P$, then by Theorem 4–5.4, $x + y \in P$ and $x \cdot y \in P$. Moreover, for any $x \in A$, either $x > 0$, $x = 0$, or $x < 0$. That is, any element of A is either positive, zero, or negative. This remark explains why an element x of an ordered integral domain is called *nonnegative* if either $x > 0$, or $x = 0$. By Definition 4–5.1, an integer a is positive if and only if $a = a - 0$ is in N. For this reason, the natural numbers, when regarded as elements of Z, are often called positive integers.

PROBLEMS

1. Prove Theorem 4–5.2(a), (c), and (d).

2. Let P be the set of all positive elements of an ordered integral domain A. Let M be the set of negative elements of A. Then $A = P \cup \{0\} \cup M$, where the sets P, $\{0\}$, and M are pairwise disjoint. Justify this statement.

3. Let A be an ordered integral domain with P as its set of positive elements. Show that $x < y$ in A if and only if $y - x \in P$.

4. Let A be an integral domain. Let P be a subset of A which satisfies the following conditions:

    (a) if $x \in P$ and $y \in P$, then $x + y \in P$ and $x \cdot y \in P$;
    (b) if $x \in A$ and $x \neq 0$, then either $x \in P$, or $-x \in P$;
    (c) $0 \notin P$.

Define $x < y$ if $y - x \in P$. Prove that $<$ is an order relation which makes A an ordered integral domain.

5. The analogue for multiplication of Theorem 4–5.4(a) is:

$$\text{if } x < y \text{ and } z < w, \text{ then } x \cdot z < y \cdot w.$$

Give an example to show that this is false. Find conditions on x, y, z, and w that will guarantee that $x \cdot z < y \cdot w$.

6. Show that it is impossible to define an ordering of the integral domain given in Problem 2, Section 4–2, so that it becomes an ordered integral domain. [*Hint:* Find an element $x \neq 0$ such that $x^2 < 0$.]

7. Let A be an ordered integral domain. Suppose that $u \in A$, and m is a natural number. Prove the following statements.

    (a) If m is odd, then the equation $x^m = u$ has either one solution x in A, or else no solution in A. Give examples for the case $A = Z$ to show that both of these possibilities can occur.
    (b) If m is even, and $u > 0$, then the equation $x^m = u$ has either two solutions in A, or else no solution in A. Give examples for the case $A = Z$ to show that both of these possibilities can occur.
    (c) If m is even, and $u = 0$, then $x = 0$ is the only solution of $x^m = u$.
    (d) If m is even, and $u < 0$, then $x^m = u$ has no solution in A.

4–6 Properties of order. Some of the most important concepts encountered in the calculus are defined in terms of the order relation of the real numbers. Many of these notions can be studied profitably in the abstract setting of ordered integral domains.

DEFINITION 4–6.1. Let A be any ordered integral domain. Then $x \leq y$ (or $y \geq x$) means that either $x < y$, or $x = y$. The relations $x < y$ and $x \leq y$ are called inequalities.

THEOREM 4–6.2. Let A be any ordered integral domain. Let x, y, z, and w be arbitrary elements of A.
   (a) If $x < y$ and $y \leq z$, or if $x \leq y$ and $y < z$, then $x < z$.
   (b) If $x \leq y$ and $y \leq z$, then $x \leq z$.
   (c) If $x \leq y$ and $y \leq x$, then $x = y$.
   (d) Either $x \leq y$, or $y \leq x$.
   (e) Exactly one of the relations $x \leq y$, $y < x$ is satisfied.
   (f) If $x < y$ and $z \leq w$, or if $x \leq y$ and $z < w$, then $x + z < y + w$.
   (g) If $x \leq y$ and $z \leq w$, then $x + z \leq y + w$.
   (h) If $x \leq y$ and $z \geq 0$, then $x \cdot z \leq y \cdot z$.
   (i) If $x \leq y$ and $z \leq 0$, then $y \cdot z \leq x \cdot z$.
   (j) For all x, $x^2 \geq 0$.

Proof. The proof of this theorem is routine. For example, if $x < y$ and $y \leq z$, then either $x < y$ and $y < z$, or $x < y$ and $y = z$. In the first case, $x < z$ by Definition 4–5.3(b). In the second case, $x < z$, since $x < y = z$. This proves the first part of (a). To prove the first part of (f), suppose that $x < y$ and $z \leq w$. If $z = w$, then $x + z < y + w$, since $x + z < y + z$ by Definition 4–5.3(c). If $z < w$, then $x + z < y + w$ by Theorem 4–5.4(a). We leave the remaining statements for the reader to prove.

It is common practice to write sequences of inequalities and equalities. For example,

$$x < y = z \leq w < u$$

is an abbreviation for $x < y$, $y = z$, $z \leq w$, and $w < u$. Usually all of the inequalities in such a sequence are directed in the same way, from small to large, or from large to small. It then follows from Theorem 4–6.2 that the inequalities obtained by omitting part of the sequence are valid. In the above example, we get $x < z$, $x < w$, $x < u$, $y \leq w$, $y < u$, and $z < u$.

Frequently sets are defined by means of inequalities. By using the laws given in Theorem 4–6.2, it is often possible to simplify the descriptions of these sets.

EXAMPLE 1. Determine $\{x \in R | x^2 + x \leq 2\}$. The condition $x^2 + x \leq 2$ is equivalent to $(x + 2)(x - 1) = x^2 + x - 2 \leq 2 - 2 = 0$. The product $(x + 2)(x - 1)$ is positive if $x + 2$ and $x - 1$ have the same sign (either positive or negative). Therefore, the product $(x + 2)(x - 1)$ will be ≤ 0 if and only if $x + 2$ and $x - 1$ have opposite signs, or one of these factors is zero. Since $x - 1 < x + 2$, it follows that $(x + 2)(x - 1) \leq 0$ is equivalent to $x - 1 \leq 0 \leq x + 2$. Consequently, $x^2 + x \leq 2$ if and only if $x \leq 1$ and $-2 \leq x$. Therefore,

$$\{x \in R | x^2 + x \leq 2\} = \{x \in R | -2 \leq x \leq 1\}.$$

DEFINITION 4–6.3. Let A be any ordered integral domain. Let S be a nonempty subset of A. An element x in A is called the *smallest* (or *least*, or *minimum*) element of S if $x \in S$ and $x \leq y$ for all $y \in S$. An element z in A is called the *largest* (or *greatest*, or *maximum*) element of S if $z \in S$ and $y \leq z$ for all $y \in S$. The smallest element of S (if it exists) is denoted by min S and the largest element of S (if it exists) is denoted by max S.

EXAMPLE 2. Min $\{x \in R | x \geq 0\} = 0$, max $\{x \in R | x \geq 0\}$ does not exist, min $\{x \in R | x > 0\}$ does not exist, min $\{x \in Z | x > 0\} = 1$, max $\{x \in Z | x > 0\}$ does not exist.

Generally, a nonempty set need not have either a smallest or a largest element. For example, it is easy to see that if $S = A$, then neither min S nor max S exists. However, if S is finite, the situation is different.

THEOREM 4–6.4. Let S be a nonempty finite subset of an ordered integral domain. Then S has a smallest element and a largest element.

Proof. The proof is by induction on the number of elements in S. Let

$$S = \{x_1, x_2, \ldots, x_n\}.$$

If $n = 1$, then x_1 is both the largest and the smallest element of S. Suppose that $n > 1$ and that every set containing fewer than n elements has a largest element and a smallest element. Let

$$T = \{x_1, x_2, \ldots, x_{n-1}\}.$$

By assumption, T has a smallest element x_i. Then by Theorem 4–6.2, either $x_i \leq x_n$, in which case x_i is the smallest element of S, or $x_n < x_i$, in which case x_n is the smallest element of S. Similarly, S contains a largest element. This completes the proof of the induction step and proves the theorem.

THEOREM 4–6.5. Let A be an ordered integral domain. Let $x_1, x_2, \ldots,$ x_n, and y be any elements of A.

(a) $\min \{x_1, x_2, \ldots, x_n\} + y = \min \{x_1 + y, x_2 + y, \ldots, x_n + y\},$
      $\max \{x_1, x_2, \ldots, x_n\} + y = \max \{x_1 + y, x_2 + y, \ldots, x_n + y\}.$

(b) If $y \geq 0$, then

$$y \cdot \min \{x_1, x_2, \ldots, x_n\} = \min \{y \cdot x_1, y \cdot x_2, \ldots, y \cdot x_n\},$$

and

$$y \cdot \max \{x_1, x_2, \ldots, x_n\} = \max \{y \cdot x_1, y \cdot x_2, \ldots, y \cdot x_n\}.$$

(c) If $y \leq 0$, then

$$y \cdot \min \{x_1, x_2, \ldots, x_n\} = \max \{y \cdot x_1, y \cdot x_2, \ldots, y \cdot x_n\},$$

and

$$y \cdot \max \{x_1, x_2, \ldots, x_n\} = \min \{y \cdot x_1, y \cdot x_2, \ldots, y \cdot x_n\}.$$

Proof. Let x_i be the smallest of the elements $x_1, x_2, \ldots, x_n$. Then $\min \{x_1, x_2, \ldots, x_n\} = x_i$, and $x_i \leq x_1, x_i \leq x_2, \ldots, x_i \leq x_n$. For any y, $x_i + y \leq x_1 + y$, $x_i + y \leq x_2 + y$, $\ldots$, $x_i + y \leq x_n + y$. Thus, since $x_i + y$ occurs among the numbers $x_1 + y, x_2 + y, \ldots, x_n + y$, it follows that

$$\min \{x_1 + y, x_2 + y, \ldots, x_n + y\} = x_i + y = \min \{x_1, x_2, \ldots, x_n\} + y.$$

This proves the first part of (a). If $y \geq 0$, then by Theorem 4–6.2(h),

$$y \cdot x_i \leq y \cdot x_1, y \cdot x_i \leq y \cdot x_2, \ldots, y \cdot x_i \leq y \cdot x_n.$$

Thus, as before,

$$\min \{y \cdot x_1, y \cdot x_2, \ldots, y \cdot x_n\} = y \cdot x_i = y \cdot \min \{x_1, x_2, \ldots, x_n\}.$$

This proves the first part of (b). If $y \leq 0$, then by Theorem 4–6.2(i),

$$y \cdot x_i \geq y \cdot x_1, y \cdot x_i \geq y \cdot x_2, \ldots, y \cdot x_i \geq y \cdot x_n.$$

Hence

$$\max \{y \cdot x_1, y \cdot x_2, \ldots, y \cdot x_n\} = y \cdot x_i = y \cdot \min \{x_1, x_2, \ldots, x_n\}.$$

This proves the first part of (c). The second statement of each part of the theorem is proved in a way which is similar to the proof of the first statement.

DEFINITION 4–6.6. Let A be an ordered integral domain. Suppose that $x \in A$. The *absolute value* of x, denoted* by $|x|$, is defined to be

$$|x| = \max \{x, -x\}.$$

In other words, $|x| = x$ if $x \geq 0$ and $|x| = -x$ if $x \leq 0$. Thus, in the integers for example,

$$|27| = 27, \qquad |-6| = 6, \qquad |0| = 0.$$

THEOREM 4–6.7. Let A be an ordered integral domain, and let x and y be arbitrary elements of A.

(a) $|x| \geq 0$; moreover, $|x| = 0$ only if $x = 0$.

(b) If $x > 0$, then $|y| \leq x$ if and only if $-x \leq y \leq x$.

(c) $|x + y| \leq |x| + |y|$.

(d) $|x \cdot y| = |x| \cdot |y|$.

(e) $x + |x| \geq 0$.

Proof. (a) If $x \neq 0$, then either $x > 0$, or $-x > 0$. Hence,

$$\max \{x, -x\} > 0.$$

(b) If $|y| \leq x$, then $\max \{y, -y\} \leq x$. Thus, $y \leq x$ and $-y \leq x$. By Theorem 4–6.2(i), $-y \leq x$ implies $-x \leq y$. Thus, $-x \leq y \leq x$. Conversely, if $-x \leq y$ and $y \leq x$, then $-y \leq x$ and $y \leq x$. Therefore, $|y| = \max \{y, -y\} \leq x$.   (c) $|x| \leq |x|$ and $|y| \leq |y|$.   Hence, by (b), $-|x| \leq x \leq |x|$ and $-|y| \leq y \leq |y|$. Therefore, by Theorem 4–6.2(g), $-(|x| + |y|) \leq x + y \leq |x| + |y|$.   Consequently, by (b), $|x + y| \leq |x| + |y|$.   (d) If $x \geq 0$ and $y \geq 0$, then $x \cdot y \geq 0$, so that $|x \cdot y| = x \cdot y = |x| \cdot |y|$. If $x \geq 0$, $y \leq 0$, then $x \cdot y \leq 0$. In this case, $|x \cdot y| = -(x \cdot y) = x \cdot (-y) = |x| \cdot |y|$.   The case $x \leq 0$, $y \geq 0$ is similar. Finally, if $x \leq 0$, $y \leq 0$, then $x \cdot y \geq 0$, and therefore $|x \cdot y| = x \cdot y = (-x) \cdot (-y) = |x| \cdot |y|$.   (e) By Definition 4–6.6 and Theorem 4–6.5(a),

$$|x| + x = \max \{x, -x\} + x = \max \{x + x, -x + x\}$$
$$= \max \{2x, 0\} \geq 0.$$

Problems involving algebraic manipulation of absolute values occur often in analysis. Sometimes Theorem 4–6.7 can be used to solve them.

---

* It might be expected that the use of vertical bars to denote both absolute value and the cardinality of a set would be confusing. However, both notations are standard and the double meaning causes no confusion.

EXAMPLE 3. Determine $\{x \in R | |x^2 - 4x| \leq 1\}$. By Theorem 4–6.7(b), $|x^2 - 4x| \leq 1$ is equivalent to $-1 \leq x^2 - 4x \leq 1$. These inequalities hold if and only if $3 = -1 + 4 \leq x^2 - 4x + 4 \leq 1 + 4 = 5$. Thus, x belongs to the set $\{x \in R \, | |x^2 - 4x| \leq 1\}$ if and only if

$$3 \leq (x - 2)^2 \leq 5.$$

If $\sqrt{3}$ and $\sqrt{5}$ denote the (positive) square roots of 3 and 5, then this inequality can be written in the form

$$(\sqrt{3})^2 \leq (x - 2)^2 \leq (\sqrt{5})^2.$$

It follows that $|x^2 - 4x| \leq 1$ if and only if either

$$\sqrt{3} \leq x - 2 \leq \sqrt{5}, \quad \text{or} \quad -\sqrt{5} \leq x - 2 \leq -\sqrt{3}$$

(see Problem 3 below). Hence,

$$\{x \in R | |x^2 - 4x| \leq 1\} = \{x \in R | 2 + \sqrt{3} \leq x \leq 2 + \sqrt{5}\}$$
$$\cup \{x \in R | 2 - \sqrt{5} \leq x \leq 2 - \sqrt{3}\}.$$

PROBLEMS

1. Complete the proof of Theorem 4–6.2.

2. Let A be an ordered integral domain. Prove the following properties of A.
   (a) If $0 \leq x < y$ and $0 \leq z < w$, then $x \cdot z < y \cdot w$.
   (b) If $0 \leq x \leq y$ and $0 \leq z \leq w$, then $x \cdot z \leq y \cdot w$.
   (c) If $0 \leq x < y$, then $x^n < y^n$ for all $n \in N$.
   (d) If $0 \leq x \leq y$, then $x^n \leq y^n$ for all $n \in N$.
   (e) If $x < y$, then $z - y < z - x$.
   (f) If $x \leq y$, then $z - y \leq z - x$.
   (g) If $x \leq y$, then $-y \leq -x$.

3. (a) Prove that if u, v, and x are elements of an ordered integral domain such that $0 \leq u \leq v$, then $u^2 \leq x^2 \leq v^2$ if and only if either

$$u \leq x \leq v, \quad \text{or} \quad -v \leq x \leq -u.$$

Show that if $0 \leq u \leq v$, then $u^2 < x^2 < v^2$ if and only if either

$$u < x < v, \quad \text{or} \quad -v < x < -u.$$

(b) Generalize this result from squares to arbitrary exponents.

4. Let A be an ordered integral domain. Prove the following properties of the elements of A.
   (a) $2xy \leq x^2 + y^2$
   (b) If $x \neq y$, then $2xy < x^2 + y^2$.
   (c) $(xy + zw)^2 \leq (x^2 + z^2)(y^2 + w^2)$
   　　[*Hint:* Show that $[(x^2 + z^2)(y^2 + w^2) - (xy + zw)^2] \geq 0$.]

5. Determine the following sets of real numbers.
   (a) $\{x \in R | 4x - 12 > 0\}$
   (b) $\{x \in R | 9 - 3x < 0\}$
   (c) $\{x \in R | 2x + 1 < 4x - 7\}$
   (d) $\{x \in R | (-\frac{1}{3})(3 - x) \leq (\frac{1}{4})(x + 4)\}$
   (e) $\{x \in R | 9x^2 < 25\}$
   (f) $\{x \in R | 7x^2 > 63\}$
   (g) $\{x \in R | (x - 1)(x + 2) < 0\}$
   (h) $\{x \in R | (x - 1)(x - 3) > 0\}$
   (i) $\{x \in R | (x - 1)(x + 2) < 0\}$
   (j) $\{x \in R | x^2 + x > 6\}$
   (k) $\{x \in R | x^2 + x - 6 < 6\}$
   (l) $\{x \in R | (x + 1)(x - 2)(x - 3) < 0\}$
   (m) $\{x \in R | (x - 3)(x + 1)(x - 2) > 0\}$
   (n) $\{x \in R | x^3 - x + 3 > 3\}$

6. Prove the second half of each statement in Theorem 4–6.5.

7. Show that if A is an ordered integral domain, then max A and min A do not exist. What does this imply about finite integral domains?

8. Let A be an ordered integral domain. Suppose S and T are finite non-empty subsets of A. Show that
   (a) max $S \cup T$ = max $\{$max S, max $T\}$.
   (b) min $S \cup T$ = min $\{$min S, min $T\}$.

9. Let A be an ordered integral domain. Suppose that x, y, and z are arbitrary elements of A. Prove the following facts.
   (a) $|-x| = |x|$
   (b) $|x^2| = x^2$
   (c) $|x + y + z| \leq |x| + |y| + |z|$
   (d) $|x| - |y| \leq |x - y| \leq |x| + |y|$
   (e) If $z > 0$, then $|x - y| < z$ if and only if

$$y - z < x < y + z.$$

   (f) If x divides y in A, then $|x|$ divides $|y|$ in A, and $|y/x| = |y|/|x|$.

10. Determine the following sets of real numbers.
   (a) $\{x \in R | |2x + 1| < 3\}$ (b) $\{x \in R | |1 - x| < 2\}$
   (c) $\{x \in R | 2|x - 1| < 3\}$ (d) $\{x \in R | |2x + 4| \leq 2\}$
   (e) $\{x \in R | |x - 1| > 0\}$ (f) $\{x \in R | |x - 3| > 4\}$
   (g) $\{x \in R | |x^2 - 2x| < 1\}$ (h) $\{x \in R | |4x - x^2| \leq 4\}$
                    (i) $\{x \in R | |x^2 - 2x| > 3\}$

CHAPTER 5

ELEMENTARY NUMBER THEORY

5-1 The division algorithm. In this chapter we will develop some useful and interesting results concerning the natural numbers and the integers. Our study can be viewed as a brief introduction to the theory of numbers, one of the oldest and most respected branches of pure mathematics. We begin with a discussion of the familiar process of long division and some of its consequences.

If a and b are integers, and if $a \neq 0$, then it is possible to "divide a into b" obtaining a quotient q and a remainder r. The exact statement of this fact is called the *division algorithm*. It is a basic result of considerable importance in number theory.

THEOREM 5-1.1. *Division algorithm.* Let a and b be integers, with $a \neq 0$. Then there exist unique integers q and r such that

$$b = aq + r,$$

where $0 \leq r < |a|$.

Proof. There are two things to prove. We must show that integers q and r exist which satisfy

$$b = aq + r, \qquad 0 \leq r < |a|,$$

and that there is just one pair of integers q and r which satisfy these conditions.

First we present the existence proof. Consider the set S of all nonnegative integers of the form $b - ax$, $x \in Z$. We wish to apply the well-ordering principle (2-5.2) to the set S. It is first necessary to prove that S is nonempty. Since $a \neq 0$, either $a \geq 1$ or $a \leq -1$. If $a \geq 1$, then $a|b| \geq |b|$, and

$$b - a(-|b|) = b + a|b| \geq b + |b| \geq 0.$$

Thus, if $x = -|b|$, then $b - ax \in S$. If $a \leq -1$, then $-a|b| \geq |b|$, and

$$b - a|b| \geq b + |b| \geq 0.$$

In this case, $b - ax \in S$, when $x = |b|$. By the well-ordering principle, S contains a smallest number r. Let q be the value of x such that $b - ax = r$.

That is, $b - aq = r$, $r \geq 0$. We will prove that $r < |a|$. Suppose that $a \geq 1$. Then

$$b - a(q + 1) = b - aq - a < b - aq = r.$$

Since r is the smallest number in S, it follows that $b - a(q + 1)$ is not a member of S. Since $b - a(q + 1)$ is of the form $b - ax$, and since S consists of all nonnegative integers of this form, the only possible reason for $b - a(q + 1)$ not to be in S is that $b - a(q + 1)$ is negative. Hence,

$$r = b - aq = b - a(q + 1) + a < a = |a|.$$

If $a \leq -1$, then

$$b - a(q - 1) = b - aq + a < b - aq = r.$$

Thus, by the argument we have just given, $b - a(q - 1) < 0$. Therefore,

$$r = b - aq = b - a(q - 1) - a < -a = |a|.$$

In both of the possible cases $a \geq 1$, $a \leq -1$, we obtain $r < |a|$.

To prove uniqueness, suppose that

$$b = aq + r,$$

where $0 \leq r < |a|$, and

$$b = aq' + r',$$

where $0 \leq r' < |a|$. Then $aq + r = aq' + r'$. Thus, $a(q - q') = r' - r$. Taking absolute values, we obtain $|a| \, |q - q'| = |r' - r|$. By adding the inequalities $-|a| < -r \leq 0$ and $0 \leq r' < |a|$, it follows that $-|a| < r' - r < |a|$. Therefore, by Theorem 4–6.7, $|r' - r| < |a|$. Hence, $|a| \, |q - q'| < |a|$, so that $|q - q'| < 1$. Since q and q' are integers, so is $|q - q'|$. Moreover $0 \leq |q - q'| < 1$. Hence, $|q - q'| = 0$, and therefore $q = q'$. Consequently, $r = r'$.

In the expression $b = aq + r$, q is called the *quotient* and r the *remainder* in the division of b by a. If $r = 0$, then a divides b in Z, and in this case $q = b/a$.

The division algorithm can be generalized to obtain an important theorem on the representation of natural numbers. The proof of this generalization uses the following simple fact.

(5–1.2). If $a > 1$ and $b > 0$ in Theorem 5–1.1, then $b > q \geq 0$.

Proof. Assume that $q < 0$. Then $-q > 0$, and therefore $-q \geq 1$. Hence, $a(-q) \geq a > r$. Adding aq to both sides of this inequality, we obtain

$$0 > aq + r = b > 0,$$

which is a contradiction. Consequently $q \geq 0$. If $q = 0$, then obviously $b > q \geq 0$. If $q > 0$, then since $a > 1$, we have $aq > q$. Therefore

$$b = aq + r \geq aq > q \geq 0.$$

This proves (5–1.2).

THEOREM 5–1.3. Let a be a natural number greater than 1. Then every natural number n can be uniquely represented in the form

$$n = r_k a^k + r_{k-1} a^{k-1} + \cdots + r_1 a + r_0,$$

where k is some nonnegative integer and $r_0, r_1, \ldots, r_k$ are nonnegative integers less than a.

Proof. The proof is by course of values induction on n (see 2–3.3). Assume that every natural number $m < n$ can be represented uniquely in the form

$$r_k a^k + r_{k-1} a^{k-1} + \cdots + r_1 a + r_0,$$

where $r_0, r_1, \ldots, r_k$ are nonnegative integers less than a. By the division algorithm, there are unique integers q and r such that

$$n = qa + r, \qquad 0 \leq r < |a| = a.$$

By (5–1.2), $n > q \geq 0$. If $q = 0$, then $n = r$ is the required unique representation (with $k = 0, r_0 = r$). Of course this is the case when $n = 1$.

Assume now that $q > 0$, that is, $n \geq a$. Then q is a natural number less than n, so that the induction hypothesis applies to q. Thus, there is a unique representation

$$q = r_k a^k + r_{k-1} a^{k-1} + \cdots + r_1 a + r_0, \qquad 0 \leq r_i < a.$$

Using this representation of q, we obtain

$$n = qa + r = r_k a^{k+1} + r_{k-1} a^k + \cdots + r_1 a^2 + r_0 a + r.$$

With a change of notation, this is an expression for n in the required form. To prove that this representation of n is unique, suppose that

$$n = s_j a^j + s_{j-1} a^{j-1} + \cdots + s_1 a + s_0,$$

where j is a nonnegative integer, and $s_0, s_1, \ldots, s_j$ are nonnegative integers less than a. Because $n \geq a$, it follows that $j \geq 1$, and

$$n = qa + r = (s_j a^{j-1} + s_{j-1} a^{j-2} + \cdots + s_1)a + s_0.$$

Since $0 \leq s_0 < a$, the uniqueness of q and r implies that $s_0 = r$ and

$$q = s_j a^{j-1} + s_{j-1} a^{j-2} + \cdots + s_1.$$

Finally, it follows from the uniqueness of the expression

$$q = r_k a^k + r_{k-1} a^{k-1} + \cdots + r_0$$

that $j - 1 = k$, $s_j = r_k$, $s_{j-1} = r_{k-1}, \ldots,$ and $s_1 = r_0$.

In the particular case $a = 10$, this theorem is merely a formal statement of the well-known fact that every natural number can be represented in decimal notation. In fact, when we write an expression such as

$$27931016,$$

we are using a standard abbreviation for the number

$$2 \cdot 10000000 + 7 \cdot 1000000 + 9 \cdot 100000 + 3 \cdot 10000 + 1 \cdot 1000$$
$$+ 0 \cdot 100 + 1 \cdot 10 + 6 = 2 \cdot 10^7 + 7 \cdot 10^6 + 9 \cdot 10^5$$
$$+ 3 \cdot 10^4 + 1 \cdot 10^3 + 0 \cdot 10^2 + 1 \cdot 10 + 6.$$

The fact that every natural number admits a unique representation of this form is usually taken for granted. By Theorem 5–1.3, such an assumption is justified. In fact, we have proved that it is not necessary to use powers of 10 for such a representation. Any natural number $a > 1$ will do just as well.

In an expression

$$n = r_k a^k + r_{k-1} a^{k-1} + \cdots + r_1 a + r_0, \qquad 0 \leq r_i < a,$$

the number a is called the *base*, or *radix*, of the representation. As in the case of the decimal system, it is convenient to abbreviate

$$r_k a^k + r_{k-1} a^{k-1} + \cdots + r_1 a + r_0 \qquad \text{to} \qquad r_k r_{k-1} \ldots r_1 r_0.$$

For this notation to be unambiguous, it is necessary to have individual symbols representing each of the numbers $0, 1, \ldots, a - 1$. If $a \leq 10$, then the customary digits can be used. For example, every number is expressible with the base 5, using the coefficients 0, 1, 2, 3, and 4. Thus, 1411301 represents $1 \cdot 5^6 + 4 \cdot 5^5 + 1 \cdot 5^4 + 1 \cdot 5^3 + 3 \cdot 5^2 + 0 \cdot 5 + 1$.

If $a > 10$, then new symbols must be introduced for the numbers which are written in the decimal notation as $10, 11, \ldots, a - 1$. (Clearly, the use of 10, 11, etc., would be confusing.) A frequently used base is 12. The scheme for representing numbers to the base 12 is called the *duodecimal* system. The letters A and B are often employed to denote 10 and 11, respectively, in the duodecimal system. For instance,

$$7A1B0 \text{ represents } 7 \cdot 12^4 + 10 \cdot 12^3 + 1 \cdot 12^2 + 11 \cdot 12 + 0.$$

In representing numbers to bases other than 10, we must be careful that the base being used is clearly understood. If there is a possibility of confusion, the base is usually indicated as a subscript. Thus,

$$(124)_7 = 1 \cdot 7^2 + 2 \cdot 7 + 4 = (67)_{10},$$
$$(124)_5 = 1 \cdot 5^2 + 2 \cdot 5 + 4 = (39)_{10},$$
$$(124)_{12} = 1 \cdot 12^2 + 2 \cdot 12 + 4 = (172)_{10}.$$

The reader will find that with a little practice he can do elementary arithmetic with numbers expressed to bases other than 10. The methods used are the usual ones.

EXAMPLE 1. Let 413204, 223001 be numbers written to the base 5. Then

```
      4 1 3 2 0 4
    + 2 2 3 0 0 1
    ─────────────
    1 1 4 1 2 1 0

      4 1 3 2 0 4
    × 2 2 3 0 0 1
    ─────────────
        4 1 3 2 0 4
        0 0 0 0 0
        0 0 0 0 0
    2 3 0 0 1 2 2
  1 3 3 1 4 1 3
  1 3 3 1 4 1 3
  ───────────────────
  2 0 4 3 1 2 0 2 0 2 0 4
```

The magnitudes of numbers expressed to any base can be compared in the same familiar way that decimal numbers are compared. For example,

$$(111)_3 < (222)_3, \qquad (132)_5 < (141)_5,$$
$$(11)_2 < (100)_2, \quad \text{and} \quad (A99)_{12} < (B00)_{12}.$$

The rule used to compare two numbers is a simple one, but the general statement of it is somewhat involved.

THEOREM 5–1.4. Let a be a natural number greater than 1. Suppose that n and m are natural numbers represented to the base a. Then $n < m$ if and only if either n has fewer digits than m or n and m have the same number of digits, and at the first place from the left where the digits of n and m differ, the digit in n is less than the corresponding digit in m.

The proof is left as an exercise for the reader (see Problem 9 below).

In the *binary system* of enumeration, each number is represented to the base 2. Thus, a binary number is written as a series of zeros and ones. For example,

$$(101101001)_2 = 1 \cdot 2^8 + 0 \cdot 2^7 + 1 \cdot 2^6 + 1 \cdot 2^5 + 0 \cdot 2^4 + 1 \cdot 2^3$$
$$+ 0 \cdot 2^2 + 0 \cdot 2 + 1 = (361)_{10}.$$

Many large-scale digital computers operate with numbers in binary form. There are two reasons for this. First, the operations of addition and multiplication are particularly simple in the binary system. Second, most of the basic components (switches, relays, diodes, rectifiers) of digital computers are bistable devices, that is, they are always in one of two states, which conveniently correspond to the digits 0 and 1 in the representation of a binary number.

The binary system of enumeration has other important uses in mathematics.

EXAMPLE 2. For the case $a = 2$, Theorem 5–1.3 can be stated as follows: every natural number n can be uniquely represented in the form

$$n = 2^{k_1} + 2^{k_2} + \cdots + 2^{k_r},$$

where $k_1 > k_2 > \cdots > k_r \geq 0$. Thus,

$$\{k_1, k_2, \ldots, k_r\} \leftrightarrow 2^{k_1} + 2^{k_2} + \cdots + 2^{k_r}$$

is a one-to-one correspondence between the set of all finite subsets of $\{0, 1, 2, \ldots\}$ and N. Since the set of all finite subsets of any denumerable set has the same cardinality as the set of all finite subsets of $\{0, 1, 2, \ldots\}$ (see Problem 14, Section 1–3), we obtain a useful theorem.

The set of all finite subsets of a denumerable set is denumerable.

EXAMPLE 3. The binary number system can be used to obtain a winning strategy for *Nim*, an ancient game, which originated in China. Nim is played by two contestants, using three piles of counters. The contestants alternately pick up any number of counters from one of the three piles. On each play they must take at least one counter, and the counters chosen can come only from a single pile. The winner is the player who takes the last counter.

From a mathematical standpoint, the game is completely described by specifying the numbers l, m, and n of counters in each of the piles at the beginning of each play. Thus, a sample game might be represented by

$$(12, 7, 18) \rightarrow (6, 7, 18) \rightarrow (6, 7, 3) \rightarrow (3, 7, 3) \rightarrow (3, 2, 3) \rightarrow (1, 2, 3)$$
$$\rightarrow (1, 2, 2) \rightarrow (1, 2, 1) \rightarrow (1, 0, 1) \rightarrow (1, 0, 0) \rightarrow (0, 0, 0).$$

We say that a triple (l, m, n) of nonnegative integers describes a "position" of the game.

Let (l, m, n) be any position. Write l, m, and n in binary form.

$$l = e_k 2^k + e_{k-1} 2^{k-1} + \cdots + e_0, \qquad e_i = 0 \text{ or } 1,$$
$$m = f_k 2^k + f_{k-1} 2^{k-1} + \cdots + f_0, \qquad f_i = 0 \text{ or } 1,$$
$$n = g_k 2^k + g_{k-1} 2^{k-1} + \cdots + g_0, \qquad g_i = 0 \text{ or } 1.$$

We call this position "unfavorable" if each of the sums

$$e_k + f_k + g_k, \qquad e_{k-1} + f_{k-1} + g_{k-1}, \qquad \ldots, \qquad e_0 + f_0 + g_0$$

is even. Otherwise, the position is "favorable." In particular $(0, 0, 0)$ is unfavorable. It is easy to see that if (l, m, n) is unfavorable, then any position (l', m, n) with $l' < l$, or (l, m', n) with $m' < m$, or (l, m, n') with $n' < n$ is favorable. Suppose that the counters are removed from the first pile. Then $l' < l$, so that when l' is written in binary form

$$l' = e_k' 2^k + e_{k-1}' 2^{k-1} + \cdots + e_0',$$

at least one of the binary digits e_i' is different from the corresponding e_i in the representation of l. Since e_i and e_i' are either 0 or 1, we have $e_i' = e_i + 1$ if $e_i = 0$, and $e_i' = e_i - 1$ if $e_i = 1$. Therefore,

$$e_i' + f_i + g_i = e_i + f_i + g_i \pm 1.$$

The fact that (l, m, n) is an unfavorable position means that $e_i + f_i + g_i$ is even. Consequently $e_i' + f_i + g_i$ is odd, and the position (l', m, n) is favorable. In particular, an unfavorable position can never lead to $(0, 0, 0)$; hence no player can finish the game from an unfavorable position. Thus, a good strategy is to remove enough counters from some pile so that the opponent is left in an unfavorable position. Of course, if (l, m, n) is unfavorable, this is impossible. But if (l, m, n) is favorable, then by reducing one of l, m, or n, an unfavorable position results. This can be done in the following way. Suppose that j is the largest number such that $e_j + f_j + g_j$ is odd, that is, $e_k + f_k + g_k$, $e_{k-1} + f_{k-1} + g_{k-1}$, $\ldots, e_{j+1} + f_{j+1} + g_{j+1}$ are even, but $e_j + f_j + g_j$ is odd. By the definition of a favorable position, such a j exists. Then either $e_j = 1$, $f_j = 1$, or $g_j = 1$, since otherwise $e_j + f_j + g_j = 0$. For the sake of definiteness, suppose that $e_j = 1$. Define for each i

$$e'_i = e_i \quad \text{if} \quad e_i + f_i + g_i \quad \text{is even,}$$

$$e'_i = 1 - e_i \quad \text{if} \quad e_i + f_i + g_i \quad \text{is odd.}$$

In particular, $e'_i = e_i$ for $i > j$ and $e'_j = 0 < e_j$. Let

$$l' = e'_k 2^k + e'_{k-1} 2^{k-1} + \cdots + e'_0.$$

Then $l' < l$ by Theorem 5–1.4 and for all i,

$$e'_i + f_i + g_i = e_i + f_i + g_i$$

if $e_i + f_i + g_i$ is even,

$$e'_i + f_i + g_i = 1 - e_i + f_i + g_i = 1 + (e_i + f_i + g_i) - 2e_i$$

if $e_i + f_i + g_i$ is odd. Consequently, (l', m, n) is unfavorable. To illustrate this procedure, suppose that

$$l = 27, \qquad m = 55, \qquad n = 34.$$

Then

$$l = 0 \cdot 2^5 + 1 \cdot 2^4 + 1 \cdot 2^3 + 0 \cdot 2^2 + 1 \cdot 2 + 1,$$

$$m = 1 \cdot 2^5 + 1 \cdot 2^4 + 0 \cdot 2^3 + 1 \cdot 2^2 + 1 \cdot 2 + 1,$$

$$n = 1 \cdot 2^5 + 0 \cdot 2^4 + 0 \cdot 2^3 + 0 \cdot 2^2 + 1 \cdot 2 + 0;$$

$$e_5 + f_5 + g_5 = 0 + 1 + 1 = 2, \qquad e_4 + f_4 + g_4 = 1 + 1 + 0 = 2,$$

$$e_3 + f_3 + g_3 = 1 + 0 + 0 = 1, \qquad e_2 + f_2 + g_2 = 0 + 1 + 0 = 1,$$

$$e_1 + f_1 + g_1 = 1 + 1 + 1 = 3, \qquad e_0 + f_0 + g_0 = 1 + 1 + 0 = 2.$$

Thus, (l, m, n) is favorable. Using the procedure which we outlined above, we can obtain an unfavorable position (l', m, n), where

$$l' = 0 \cdot 2^5 + 1 \cdot 2^4 + 0 \cdot 2^3 + 1 \cdot 2^2 + 0 \cdot 2 + 1 = 21.$$

That is, the appropriate strategy is to remove 6 counters from the pile containing 27. The other player will then be faced with an unfavorable position, so that whatever he does leads to a new favorable position. In this way, the player who finds himself with a favorable position can always keep his opponent in an unfavorable position and win the game. In particular, if the initial position is favorable, the player with the first move can always win, provided that he knows the method which we have described. If he does not know this strategy, there is a good chance that one of his moves will lead to a favorable position for his opponent, since usually there are more favorable than unfavorable positions.

Problems

1. Using long division, find the quotient and remainder in the division of b by a, where a and b are as follows.

(a) $a = 212$, $b = 3111$ (b) $a = -2164$, $b = 6411037$
(c) $a = 2164$, $b = -6411037$ (d) $a = 121$, $b = -36$
(e) $a = -121$, $b = -36$ (f) $a = 2^{10}$, $b = 3^{10}$

2. Write the following decimal numbers in the base 5 system of enumeration: 2, 21, 3116, 711096, 10^{10}.

3. Write the following decimal numbers in the base 12 system of enumeration: 4, 16, 3102, 999111.

4. Find the decimal expression for the following numbers:

$(21031)_4$, $(7A08B1)_{12}$, $(1010101010)_2$, $(185111034)_9$, $(30143014)_5$.

5. Convert the following numbers in the base 2 to the base 8:

1110111, 101001000100001, 111111111111111, 101101101101101101101101.

6. Carry out the following addition without converting to the base 10.

(a) $(12145)_6 + (51015)_6$ (b) $(111010111)_2 + (10101100)_2$
(c) $(1A1B21)_{12} + (ABAB11A)_{12}$ (d) $(140314)_5 + (2134114)_5$

7. Carry out the following multiplication without converting to the base 10.

(a) $(12145)_6 \cdot (51015)_6$
(b) $(111010111)_2 \cdot (10101100)_2$
(c) $(1A1B21)_{12} \cdot (ABAB11A)_{12}$
(d) $(140314)_5 \cdot (2134114)_5$

8. Let n be a natural number. Suppose that

$$2^k \le n < 2^{k+1}, \qquad k \in Z.$$

(a) Show that in the sequence of numbers 1, 2, 3, ..., n, no number other than 2^k is divisible by 2^k (in Z).

(b) Use the result of part (a) to prove

$$\sum_{j=1}^{n} \frac{1}{j} = \frac{a}{2^k \cdot b},$$

where $a \in N$, $b \in N$, and a and b are odd.

9. Let a be a natural number greater than 1.

(a) Show that if $n = r_k a^k + r_{k-1} a^{k-1} + \cdots + r_0$, where $0 \le r_i < a$, then $n < a^{k+1}$. [*Hint:* First show that $a^{k+1} - 1 = (a - 1)a^k + (a - 1)a^{k-1} + \cdots + (a - 1)$.]

(b) Use the result of (a) to prove Theorem 5–1.4.

5-2 Greatest common divisor. If a and b are any two integers, then an integer c is called a *common divisor* of a and b if $c|a$ and $c|b$. Several simple facts follow immediately from this definition. Since 1 is a divisor of every integer, 1 is a common divisor of any two integers a and b. Thus, the set of common divisors of two integers is nonempty. Every integer divides 0. Hence if $b = 0$, then the common divisors of a and b are just the divisors of a. In particular, if $a = b = 0$, every integer is a common divisor of a and b. In this case the set of common divisors of a and b is infinite. However, in every other case the set of common divisors of a and b is finite. Indeed, if $a \neq 0$ and $c|a$, then $a = w \cdot c$ for some nonzero integer w. Consequently, by Theorem 4–6.7, $|a| = |w| \cdot |c| \geq |c|$. Therefore, if $a \neq 0$ and if c is a common divisor of a and b, then $-|a| \leq c \leq |a|$. Obviously, there are only finitely many integers c satisfying $-|a| \leq c \leq |a|$. Similarly, if $b \neq 0$, then $-|b| \leq c \leq |b|$, and there are only finitely many integers c satisfying $-|b| \leq c \leq |b|$. Therefore, if either a or b (or both) is different from zero, then the set of common divisors of a and b is finite and nonempty. Thus, by Theorem 4–6.4, this set contains a largest integer. Since 1 is in the set of common divisors, this largest integer is positive, that is, it is a natural number.

DEFINITION 5–2.1. Let a and b be integers which are not both zero. The *greatest common divisor* of a and b is the largest integer in the set of all common divisors of a and b. The greatest common divisor of a and b is denoted by (a, b).

The expression "greatest common divisor" is often abbreviated g.c.d.

EXAMPLE 1. The common divisors of 12 and -30 are ± 1, ± 2, ± 3, ± 6. Therefore, the g.c.d. of 12 and -30 is 6.

Note that all of the common divisors of 12 and -30 divide the greatest common divisor. We will show that this is no coincidence, but rather is a fundamental property of the g.c.d.

THEOREM 5–2.2. Let a and b be integers which are not both zero.

(a) There exist integers u and v such that

$$(a, b) = ua + vb.$$

(b) Every common divisor of a and b divides (a, b).

Proof. If c is a common divisor of a and b, then c divides any number of the form $sa + tb$, where s and t are integers. Thus, statement (b) follows from the property (a). Let S be the set of all positive integers (natural numbers) which are of the form $sa + tb$, with s and t integers. Since a and b are not both zero, at least one of the integers

$$(+1) \cdot a + 0 \cdot b, \qquad (-1) \cdot a + 0 \cdot b,$$
$$0 \cdot a + (+1) \cdot b, \qquad 0 \cdot a + (-1) \cdot b$$

is positive and therefore belongs to S. By the well-ordering principle, S contains a smallest number d. By the definition of S, there are integers u and v such that

$$d = u \cdot a + v \cdot b.$$

As we noted above, every common divisor of a and b divides d, so that in particular $(a, b)|d$. Thus, $(a, b) \le d$. The proof will be finished if we show that $d \le (a, b)$. By the division algorithm,

$$a = q \cdot d + r,$$

where $0 \le r < d, r \in Z, q \in Z$. Therefore,

$$r = a - q \cdot d = (1 - q \cdot u)a + (-q \cdot v)b.$$

If r were positive, then $r \in S$, since r is of the form $sa + tb$. But $r < d$ and d is the smallest number in S. Therefore, r cannot be positive, that is, $r = 0$. Thus, $a = q \cdot d$, so that d divides a. Similarly, d divides b. Therefore, d is a common divisor of a and b. Since (a, b) is the greatest common divisor of a and b, $d \le (a, b)$. The two inequalities $(a, b) \le d$ and $d \le (a, b)$ imply that $(a, b) = d = ua + vb$.

Suppose that a and b are integers which are not both zero and d is an integer which satisfies the following conditions:

$$d|a \qquad \text{and} \qquad d|b. \tag{5–1}$$

If c is an integer such that $c|a$ and $c|b$, then $c|d$. $\qquad$ (5–2)

By (5–1), d is a common divisor of a and b. Therefore, by Theorem 5–2.2(b), $d|(a, b)$. Since $(a, b)|a$ and $(a, b)|b$, it follows from (5–2) that $(a, b)|d$. Thus, $d = \pm(a, b)$. In other words, the greatest common divisor of a and b is characterized up to its sign by the above conditions. In fact, these conditions together with the requirement that d be positive can be taken as the definition of the g.c.d. in Z. The importance of the conditions (5–1) and (5–2) lies in the fact that they make sense in an arbitrary integral domain, whereas Definition 5–2.1 depends not only on the ordering of Z, but also on the very special fact that a nonzero integer has only a finite number of divisors. Accordingly, if A is an integral domain and if a and b are elements of A which are not both zero, then an element $d \in A$ is called a *greatest common divisor* of a and b (in A) if d satisfies (5–1) and (5–2) [where in (5–2), c is an element of A]. Of course, in some integral domains, not every pair of elements has a greatest common divisor (see Probelm 14 below). Also, greatest common divisors in integral domains need not be unique. For example, in Q, if a and b are not both zero, then every nonzero rational number satisfies (5–1) and (5–2). We will use this generalized notion of a greatest common divisor in our discussion of polynomials in Chapter 9.

We will now derive some of the most useful properties of greatest common divisors. The first of these are simple consequences of Definition 5–2.1.

(5–2.3). Let a and b be integers which are not both zero. Then
   (a) $(a, b) \geq 1$;
   (b) $(a, b) = (b, a)$;
   (c) $(a, b) = (-a, b) = (a, -b) = (-a, -b) = (|a|, |b|)$;
   (d) $(a, b) = |a|$ if and only if $a|b$;
   (e) $(a, 0) = |a|$ (provided that $a \neq 0$).

Proof. The statement (c) becomes evident if we note that the set of common divisors of a and b is identical with the sets of common divisors of $-a$ and b, of a and $-b$, and of $-a$ and $-b$. To prove (d), suppose first that $(a, b) = |a|$. Then in particular $|a|$ is a divisor of b. Therefore, $a|b$. Conversely, if $a|b$, then any divisor of a is also a divisor of b. Thus, the common divisors of a and b are exactly the divisors of a. Note that $a \neq 0$, since $a = 0$ and $a|b$ implies $b = 0$, and we have assumed that a and b are not both zero. By the discussion preceding Definition 5–2.1, every divisor c of a satisfies $c \leq |a|$. Since $|a|$ divides a, it follows that $|a|$ is the largest divisor of a, and therefore $|a|$ is the g.c.d. of a and b. The remaining statements of (5–2.3) are easy to prove.

THEOREM 5–2.4.   Let a and b be integers which are not both zero. Suppose that c is a nonzero integer. Then

$$(ca, cb) = |c|(a, b).$$

Proof. Since (a, b) is a common divisor of a and b, and since $|c|$ divides c, it follows that $|c|(a, b)$ is a common divisor of ca and cb. Hence, by Theorem 5–2.2(b),

$$|c|(a, b) \text{ divides } (ca, cb).$$

On the other hand, by Theorem 5–2.2(a), there exist integers u and v such that $(a, b) = ua + vb$. Consequently,

$$|c|(a, b) = u|c|a + v|c|b = u'ca + v'cb,$$

where $u' = u$, $v' = v$ if $c > 0$, and $u' = -u$, $v' = -v$ if $c < 0$. Since (ca, cb) is a common divisor of ca and cb, it follows that

$$(ca, cb) \text{ divides } |c|(a, b).$$

Since both (ca, cb) and $|c|(a, b)$ are positive, and each divides the other, $(ca, cb) = |c|(a, b)$.

An immediate consequence of this theorem is the following.

THEOREM 5–2.5.   Let a and b be integers which are not both zero. Suppose that c is a common divisor of a and b. Then

$$(a/c, b/c) = (a, b)/|c|.$$

Note that since a and b are not both zero, and c divides both a and b, c cannot be zero. By Theorem 5–2.4,

$$(a, b) = (c \cdot a/c, c \cdot b/c) = |c|(a/c, b/c).$$

Any pair of integers a and b has -1 and 1 as common divisors. If these are the only common divisors, then a and b are said to be *relatively prime*. In other words, a and b are relatively prime if $(a, b) = 1$. For example, 2 and 5 are relatively prime, 9 and 16 are relatively prime, -27 and 35 are relatively prime, but 24 and 63 are not relatively prime since they have 3 as a common divisor.

We now obtain a result which is needed in the next section for the proof of the fundamental theorem of arithmetic.

THEOREM 5–2.6.   Suppose that a and b are relatively prime and a divides $b \cdot c$. Then a divides c.

Proof. Since $(a, b) = 1$, by Theorem 5–2.2(a) there are integers u and v such that

$$1 = ua + vb.$$

Multiplying this equation by c, we obtain

$$c = (ua)c + (vb)c.$$

Since a divides bc and a divides a, it follows that a divides $(uc)a + v(bc) = c$.

As we pointed out at the beginning of this section, any common divisor c of two nonzero integers a and b satisfies $c \leq \min \{|a|, |b|\}$. Thus, the problem of finding the g.c.d. of a and b can be solved by examining all of the natural numbers which are less than min $\{|a|, |b|\}$ to find the largest one which divides both a and b. However, unless a and b are small, this procedure is impractical. There is a very efficient process for determining the g.c.d. of two integers, using the division algorithm. This method was apparently discovered by Euclid, and is called the Euclidean algorithm.

If either a or b is zero, then (a, b) is obtained from (5–2.3e). Moreover, since $(a, b) = (|a|, |b|)$ by (5–2.3c), it is only necessary to consider positive integers, that is, natural numbers.

Let a and b be natural numbers. By the division algorithm,

$$a = bq_1 + r_1, \qquad 0 \le r_1 < b.$$

If $r_1 = 0$, then b divides a, $(a, b) = b$, and the process ends. If $r_1 \ne 0$, divide b by r_1, obtaining

$$b = r_1 q_2 + r_2, \qquad 0 \le r_2 < r_1 < b.$$

If $r_2 = 0$, the process ends. Otherwise, divide r_1 by r_2, and the division algorithm yields

$$r_1 = r_2 q_3 + r_3, \qquad 0 \le r_3 < r_2 < r_1 < b.$$

This process can be continued as long as a nonzero remainder is obtained. Since each new remainder is a nonnegative integer which is smaller than the preceding one, the sequence

$$b > r_1 > r_2 > r_3 > \cdots$$

must terminate with some $r_{n+1} = 0$. Thus, we have the following equations:

$$
\begin{aligned}
a &= bq_1 + r_1, \\
b &= r_1 q_2 + r_2, \\
r_1 &= r_2 q_3 + r_3, \\
r_2 &= r_3 q_4 + r_4, \\
&\ \vdots \\
r_{n-2} &= r_{n-1} q_n + r_n, \\
r_{n-1} &= r_n q_{n+1} + 0.
\end{aligned}
\qquad (5\text{-}3)
$$

We will show that r_n, the last nonzero remainder, is the g.c.d. of a and b.

By the equation $r_{n-1} = r_n q_{n+1}$, we see that $r_n | r_{n-1}$. Since $r_{n-2} = r_{n-1} q_n + r_n$, it follows that $r_n | r_{n-2}$. Continuing up the sequence of equations (5–3) we find that r_n divides each of the preceding remainders. Then since $b = r_1 q_2 + r_2$, it follows that $r_n | b$, and since $a = b q_1 + r_1$, it follows that $r_n | a$. Therefore, r_n is a common divisor of a and b. Suppose that c is any common divisor of a and b. Then $c | r_1$, since $r_1 = a - b q_1$. Consequently, $c | r_2$, since $r_2 = b - r_1 q_2$. Continuing down the sequence of equations (5–3), we find that $c | r_3$, $c | r_4$, ..., $c | r_n$. In particular, since $r_n \neq 0$, $c \leq |c| \leq |r_n| = r_n$. Thus, r_n is the g.c.d. of a and b.

EXAMPLE 2. Let $a = 24756$, $b = 6108$. We obtain the following equations:

$$24756 = 6108 \cdot 4 + 324, \qquad 6108 = 324 \cdot 18 + 276,$$
$$324 = 276 \cdot 1 + 48, \qquad 276 = 48 \cdot 5 + 36,$$
$$48 = 36 \cdot 1 + 12, \qquad 36 = 12 \cdot 3 + 0.$$

Therefore,

$$(24756, 6108) = 12.$$

It is possible to use equations (5–3) obtained in applying the Euclidean algorithm to determine not only the greatest common divisor d of any pair a and b of natural numbers, but also integers u and v such that

$$d = ua + vb.$$

The existence of such numbers was proved in Theorem 5–2.2(a), but that proof does not give a convenient method for finding the values of u and v. We illustrate the use of equations (5–3) to find u and v with the example $a = 24756$, $b = 6108$.

Write the equation $48 = 36 \cdot 1 + 12$ in the form $12 = 48 - 36 \cdot 1$. Now reorder the preceding equation of Example 2 to obtain $36 = 276 - 48 \cdot 5$. Substitute and collect:

$$12 = 48 - 36 \cdot 1 = 48 - (276 - 48 \cdot 5) \cdot 1 = 48 \cdot 6 - 276 \cdot 1.$$

Continue this process, using each of the equations obtained in the above example (except the last one, $36 = 12 \cdot 3 + 0$):

$$12 = 48 \cdot 6 - 276 \cdot 1 = (324 - 276 \cdot 1) \cdot 6 - 276 \cdot 1$$
$$= 324 \cdot 6 - 276 \cdot 7 = 324 \cdot 6 - (6108 - 324 \cdot 18) \cdot 7$$
$$= 324 \cdot 132 - 6108 \cdot 7 = (24756 - 6108 \cdot 4) \cdot 132 - 6108 \cdot 7$$
$$= 24756 \cdot 132 - 6108 \cdot 535 = (132)(24756) + (-535)(6108).$$

In general terms,

$$
\begin{aligned}
d = r_n &= r_{n-2} - r_{n-1}q_n = r_{n-2} - (r_{n-3} - r_{n-2}q_{n-1})q_n \\
&= r_{n-2}(1 + q_{n-1}q_n) - r_{n-3}q_n \\
&= (r_{n-4} - r_{n-3}q_{n-2})(1 + q_{n-1}q_n) - r_{n-3}q_n \\
&= r_{n-4}(1 + q_{n-1}q_n) - r_{n-3}(q_{n-2} + q_n + q_{n-2}q_{n-1}q_n) \\
&= \cdots .
\end{aligned}
$$

Continuing up the set of equations (5–3) in this way, we can eventually express r_n in terms of a and b.

It is possible to extend the definition of the greatest common divisor to collections of several integers. Thus, if $\{a_1, a_2, \ldots, a_n\}$ is any nonempty set of integers, we say that c is a *common divisor* of the integers in this set if $c|a_1, c|a_2, \ldots,$ and $c|a_n$. If not all of $a_1, a_2, \ldots, a_n$ are zero, then this collection has only a finite number of common divisors, and therefore there is a natural number d which is the *greatest common divisor* of $a_1, a_2, \ldots, a_n$. As before, the g.c.d. of $a_1, a_2, \ldots, a_n$ is denoted by $(a_1, a_2, \ldots, a_n)$. Note that if $n = 1$, then $(a_1) = |a_1|$. Further, if any $a_i = 0$, then $(a_1, a_2, \ldots, a_n) = (a_1, a_2, \ldots, a_{i-1}, a_{i+1}, \ldots, a_n)$, so that we may restrict our attention to sets of nonzero integers.

THEOREM 5–2.7. Let $a_1, a_2, \ldots, a_n$ be nonzero integers, where $n \geq 1$.
(a) There exist integers $u_1, u_2, \ldots, u_n$ such that

$$
(a_1, a_2, \ldots, a_n) = \sum_{i=1}^{n} u_n a_n.
$$

(b) Every common divisor of $a_1, a_2, \ldots, a_n$ divides $(a_1, a_2, \ldots, a_n)$.

The proof of this theorem is similar to the proof of Theorem 5–2.2, and we leave it as an exercise. A useful consequence of Theorem 5–2.7(b) is the following theorem.

THEOREM 5–2.8. Let $a_1, a_2, \ldots, a_n$ be nonzero integers, where $n \geq 2$. Then

$$
(a_1, a_2, \ldots, a_n) = (a_1, (a_2, \ldots, a_n)).
$$

Proof. If c is a common divisor of $a_1, a_2, \ldots, a_n$, then by Theorem 5–2.7(b), $c|a_1$ and $c|(a_2, \ldots, a_n)$. Thus, by Theorem 5–2.2(b), $c|(a_1, (a_2, \ldots, a_n))$. In particular, $(a_1, a_2, \ldots, a_n)|(a_1, (a_2, \ldots, a_n))$. Conversely, if c is a common divisor of a_1 and $(a_2, \ldots, a_n)$, then $c|a_1$ and $c|(a_2, \ldots, a_n)$. Therefore, c is a common divisor of $a_1, a_2, \ldots, a_n$, so that by Theorem 5–2.7(b), $c|(a_1, a_2, \ldots, a_n)$. In particular,

$$
(a_1, (a_2, \ldots, a_n))|(a_1, a_2, \ldots, a_n).
$$

Since $(a_1, a_2, \ldots, a_n)$ and $(a_1, (a_2, \ldots, a_n))$ are natural numbers, each of which divides the other, they are equal.

By using the Euclidean algorithm, together with Theorem 5–2.8, it is possible to determine the g.c.d. of any nonempty finite set of natural numbers. Moreover, Theorem 5–2.8 can also be used with induction to extend results on the greatest common divisor of two integers to theorems about any nonempty set of integers.

Let $a_1, a_2, \ldots, a_n$ be any nonzero integers. An integer c is called a *common multiple* of $a_1, a_2, \ldots, a_n$ if $a_1|c, a_2|c, \ldots$, and $a_n|c$. Evidently, $a_1 \cdot a_2 \cdot \cdots \cdot a_n$ and $-a_1 \cdot a_2 \cdot \cdots \cdot a_n$ are both common multiples of $a_1, a_2, \ldots, a_n$. At least one of these is positive. By the well-ordering property of the natural numbers, there exists a smallest positive integer c which is a common multiple of $a_1, a_2, \ldots, a_n$. This unique positive integer is called the *least common multiple* (or l.c.m.) of $a_1, a_2, \ldots, a_n$. The usual notation for the l.c.m. of $a_1, a_2, \ldots, a_n$ is $[a_1, a_2, \ldots, a_n]$. There is a close relationship between the g.c.d. and the l.c.m. In fact it is possible to prove that for any two nonzero integers a and b,

$$(a, b)[a, b] = |a|\,|b|$$

(see Problem 12 below).

PROBLEMS

1. In the following cases, find the g.c.d. (a, b), and express it in the form $ua + vb$.

   (a) $a = -121, b = 33$
   (b) $a = 543, b = -241$
   (c) $a = 78696, b = 19332$

2. Show that in the expression $(a, b) = ua + vb$, the integers u and v are not unique.

3. Find the following g.c.d.'s.

   (a) $(144, 90, -1512)$
   (b) $(1932, 476, -952, 504, -9261)$

4. Show that the integers a and b are relatively prime if and only if there exist integers u and v such that $ua + vb = 1$.

5. Show that any two consecutive integers are relatively prime.

6. Prove that any two successive terms of the Fibonacci sequence

$$1, 1, 2, 3, 5, 8, 13, 21, 34, \ldots$$

are relatively prime (see Section 2–6).

7. Prove Theorem 5–2.7.

8. Show that if $a_1, a_2, \ldots, a_n$ are nonzero integers $(n \geq 1)$, and if $c \neq 0$, then
$$(ca_1, ca_2, \ldots, ca_n) = |c|(a_1, a_2, \ldots, a_n).$$

9. Show that if a and b are integers which are not both zero, then $a/(a, b)$ and $b/(a, b)$ are relatively prime.

10. Let a, b, and c be nonzero integers. Prove the following result concerning least common multiples:
$$[ca, cb] = |c|[a, b].$$

11. Let a and b be nonzero integers which are relatively prime. Use Theorem 5–2.6 to show that
$$[a, b] = |a| \cdot |b|.$$

12. Using the results of Problems 9, 10, and 11, show that for any two nonzero integers a and b,
$$[a, b](a, b) = |a| \cdot |b|.$$

13. In equations (5–3), show that
   (a) $r_n \geq 1, r_{n-1} \geq 2r_n, r_{n-2} \geq r_{n-1} + r_n, r_{n-3} \geq r_{n-2} + r_{n-1}, \ldots,$
   $b \geq r_1 + r_2.$
   (b) Using this result, show that if $u_1, u_2, \ldots$ denote the terms 1, 1, 2, 3, 5, 8, $\ldots$ of the Fibonacci sequence, then
   $$r_n \geq u_2, r_{n-1} \geq u_3, r_{n-2} \geq u_4, \ldots, r_1 \geq u_{n+1}, b \geq u_{n+2}.$$
   (c) Show that if p is the number of digits in b, then the number $n + 1$ of steps in Euclid's algorithm is less than or equal to $5p$. [*Hint:* By (b) and Problem 8, Section 2–6,
   $$b > \left(\frac{1 + \sqrt{5}}{2}\right)^n.$$
   Thus,
   $$\left(\frac{1 + \sqrt{5}}{2}\right)^n < 10^p < \left(\frac{1 + \sqrt{5}}{2}\right)^{5p}.]$$

14. Let $A = \{m + n\sqrt{10} \mid m, n \in Z\}$. Prove the following.
   (a) A is an integral domain with the usual addition and multiplication of real numbers.
   (b) If $a + b\sqrt{10}$ divides $c + d\sqrt{10}$ in A, then $a^2 - 10b^2$ divides $c^2 - 10d^2$ in Z.
   (c) 2 and $4 + \sqrt{10}$ are both common divisors of 6 and $8 + 2\sqrt{10}$ in A.
   (d) If 2 divides $a + b\sqrt{10}$ in A, then $2|a$ and $2|b$ in Z.
   (e) If $4 + \sqrt{10}$ divides $2c + 2d\sqrt{10}$ in A, then $3|c^2 - 10d^2$ in Z.
   (f) If $2c + 2d\sqrt{10}$ divides 6 in A, then $c^2 - 10d^2|9$ in Z.
   (g) If $2c + 2d\sqrt{10}$ divides $8 + 2\sqrt{10}$ in A, then $c^2 - 10d^2|6$ in Z.

(h) Prove that there is no element $a + b\sqrt{10}$ in A which is a common divisor of 6 and $8 + 2\sqrt{10}$, and is divisible by both 2 and $4 + \sqrt{10}$ in A. [*Hint:* If such an $a + b\sqrt{10}$ exists, then by (d), (e), (f), and (g), we have $a + b\sqrt{10} = 2c + 2d\sqrt{10}$, where $c^2 - 10d^2 = \pm 3$. Now use the easily verified fact that the square of a natural number written in decimal form never ends with 3 or 7.]

5–3 The fundamental theorem of arithmetic. As the two preceding sections indicate, many questions considered in the study of the natural numbers are concerned with divisibility properties. That is, when will a number a divide a number b, if a and b are somehow related? As an example, we might be interested in conditions under which the natural number n divides the binomial coefficient $\binom{n}{i}$. One of the principal elementary tools in the study of divisibility problems is a theorem, called the fundamental theorem of arithmetic, which says that every natural number greater than 1 can be written in an essentially unique way as a product of prime numbers. The primes, which we discussed briefly in Section 2–3, can therefore be considered as the basic building blocks of all natural numbers.

DEFINITION 5–3.1. A natural number p is called a *prime* (or *prime number*) if $p \neq 1$, and p is not divisible by any natural number other than 1 or p. A natural number $n > 1$ which is not a prime is called *composite.*

For example, 2, 3, 5, 7, 11, 13, 17, and 19 are all of the primes less than 20, and 4, 6, 8, 9, 10, 12, 14, 15, 16, and 18 are all of the composite numbers less than 20. The number 1 is distinguished: it is neither prime nor composite. Following an old tradition, we will usually designate primes by the small latin letters p and q (sometimes with subscripts).

If p is a prime, and if a is any natural number, then the greatest common divisor (p, a) divides p, so that either $(p, a) = p$, or $(p, a) = 1$. If $(p, a) = p$, then p divides a (since it is the g.c.d. of p and a). Thus, either p divides a, or else p and a are relatively prime.

There are two parts of the fundamental theorem of arithmetic. The more elementary part states that every natural number greater than 1 can be written in some way as a product of primes. That is, if $n > 1$, then

$$n = \prod_{i=1}^{k} p_i,$$

where $p_1, p_2, \ldots, p_k$ are primes (not necessarily different). Of course, it may happen that $k = 1$, so that the product has only one factor. This result is easily proved by course of values induction on n [see (2–3.3)]. It is only necessary to show that if every natural number m, which satisfies $1 < m < n$, can be written as a product of primes, then n can be written as a product of primes. If n is itself a prime, there is nothing to prove. (This remark takes care of the basis for the induction when $n = 2$.) Otherwise, n is composite, and therefore $n = a \cdot b$, where neither a nor b is 1 or n. That is, $1 < a < n$ and $1 < b < n$. By the induction hypothesis,

$$a = \prod_{i=1}^{k} p_i \quad \text{and} \quad b = \prod_{j=1}^{l} q_j,$$

where the p_i and q_j are primes. Therefore,

$$n = a \cdot b = \prod_{i=1}^{k} p_i \cdot \prod_{j=1}^{l} q_j$$

is a product of primes.

The second part of the fundamental theorem of arithmetic is sometimes called the unique factorization theorem. It states that the expression of a natural number as a product of primes is unique, except for the order of the factors. This fact is also proved by induction. This time the induction is on the number k of prime factors in the expression of n as a product of primes. To begin with, however, we need a preliminary fact.

(5–3.2). If a prime p divides a product $a_1 a_2 \ldots a_k$, then p divides at least one of the factors a_i.

Proof. If $k = 1$, then the hypothesis is the same as the conclusion, so that there is nothing to prove. We may therefore make the induction hypothesis that if p divides a product of $k - 1$ ($k > 1$) natural numbers, then it divides at least one of the factors of this product. By assumption, p divides $a_1 a_2 \ldots a_k = (a_1 a_2 \ldots a_{k-1}) \cdot a_k$. As we remarked above, either $p|a_k$ or $(p, a_k) = 1$. If $(p, a_k) = 1$, then by Theorem 5–2.6, p divides $a_1 a_2 \ldots a_{k-1}$. In this case, the induction hypothesis yields $p|a_i$ for some i with $1 \le i \le k - 1$. This completes the proof of the induction step, and proves (5–3.2).

We can now complete the proof that factorization of a natural number n into a product of primes is unique. Suppose that

$$n = p_1 \cdot p_2 \cdot \cdots \cdot p_k = q_1 \cdot q_2 \cdot \cdots \cdot q_l,$$

where $p_1, p_2, \ldots, p_k$ and $q_1, q_2, \ldots, q_l$ are primes. If $k = 1$, then $n = p_1$ is a prime. Moreover, $q_1|p_1$ and $q_1 \ne 1$. Thus, by Definition 5–3.1, $q_1 = p_1$. If l were greater than 1, then $n = p_1 = q_1 \cdot (q_2 \cdot \cdots \cdot q_l)$. Since $q_2, \ldots, q_l$ are primes, $q_2 \cdot \cdots \cdot q_l \ne 1$, and $n = p_1$ is composite. This is a contradiction. Therefore, $l = 1$ and $n = p_1 = q_1$, which is the desired conclusion. This proves the basis step in the induction on k. We may therefore assume that $k > 1$. Our induction hypothesis is that if a natural number can be expressed as a product of less than k primes, then this expression is unique up to the order of the factors. That is, the number has no other representation, regardless of the number of factors. From the equality

$$p_1 \cdot p_2 \cdot \cdots \cdot p_k = q_1 \cdot q_2 \cdot \cdots \cdot q_l,$$

it follows that p_k divides $q_1 \cdot q_2 \cdot \cdots \cdot q_l$. By (5–3.2), p_k divides some q_i. Since q_i is a prime and $p_k \neq 1$, it follows that $p_k = q_i$. By canceling p_k, we obtain

$$p_1 \cdot p_2 \cdot \cdots \cdot p_{k-1} = q_1 \cdot q_2 \cdot \cdots \cdot q_{i-1} \cdot q_{i+1} \cdot \cdots \cdot q_l.$$

Now $p_1 \cdot p_2 \cdot \cdots \cdot p_{k-1}$ is a product of $k - 1$ primes, and by the induction hypothesis, the factors p_1, p_2, ..., p_{k-1} are equal to the factors q_1, q_2, ..., q_{i-1}, q_{i+1}, ..., q_l in some order. This completes the proof of the main result of this section, which can be stated as follows.

THEOREM 5–3.3.   *Fundamental theorem of arithmetic.*   Every natural number $n > 1$ can be written as a product of primes, and except for the order of the factors, the expression of n in this form is unique.

Of course, the primes which appear in the factorization of a natural number may be repeated. For example, $360 = 2 \cdot 2 \cdot 2 \cdot 3 \cdot 3 \cdot 5 = 2^3 \cdot 3^2 \cdot 5$. In writing a number as a product of primes, it is convenient to group together the repeated primes so that the number is expressed as a product of powers of distinct primes. Thus, each natural number greater than 1 has a unique expression

$$n = p_1^{e_1} \cdot p_2^{e_2} \cdot \cdots \cdot p_g^{e_g},$$

where p_1, p_2, ..., p_g are distinct prime numbers and the exponents e_i are natural numbers.

It is easy to see from Theorem 5–3.3 that the natural numbers which are divisors of $n = p_1^{e_1} p_2^{e_2} \ldots p_g^{e_g}$ are the numbers $p_1^{f_1} p_2^{f_2} \ldots p_g^{f_g}$ where $0 \le f_i \le e_i$. For instance, the divisors of $360 = 2^3 \cdot 3^2 \cdot 5$ are

$2^0 \cdot 3^0 \cdot 5^0 = 1,$	$2^1 \cdot 3^0 \cdot 5^0 = 2,$	$2^2 \cdot 3^0 \cdot 5^0 = 4,$	$2^3 \cdot 3^0 \cdot 5^0 = 8,$
$2^0 \cdot 3^1 \cdot 5^0 = 3,$	$2^1 \cdot 3^1 \cdot 5^0 = 6,$	$2^2 \cdot 3^1 \cdot 5^0 = 12,$	$2^3 \cdot 3^1 \cdot 5^0 = 24,$
$2^0 \cdot 3^2 \cdot 5^0 = 9,$	$2^1 \cdot 3^2 \cdot 5^0 = 18,$	$2^2 \cdot 3^2 \cdot 5^0 = 36,$	$2^3 \cdot 3^2 \cdot 5^0 = 72,$
$2^0 \cdot 3^0 \cdot 5^1 = 5,$	$2^1 \cdot 3^0 \cdot 5^1 = 10,$	$2^2 \cdot 3^0 \cdot 5^1 = 20,$	$2^3 \cdot 3^0 \cdot 5^1 = 40,$
$2^0 \cdot 3^1 \cdot 5^1 = 15,$	$2^1 \cdot 3^1 \cdot 5^1 = 30,$	$2^2 \cdot 3^1 \cdot 5^1 = 60,$	$2^3 \cdot 3^1 \cdot 5^1 = 120,$
$2^0 \cdot 3^2 \cdot 5^1 = 45,$	$2^1 \cdot 3^2 \cdot 5^1 = 90,$	$2^2 \cdot 3^2 \cdot 5^1 = 180,$	$2^3 \cdot 3^2 \cdot 5^1 = 360.$

Associated with any natural number $n > 1$ are two quantities of some interest. These are

$$\tau(n) = \text{number of divisors of } n,$$

and

$$\sigma(n) = \text{sum of all divisors of } n.$$

If we know the factorization of n into a product of powers of primes, it is possible to determine these quantities easily.

Suppose that

$$n = p_1^{e_1} p_2^{e_2} \ldots p_g^{e_g},$$

where $p_1, p_2, \ldots, p_g$ are distinct primes and $e_1, e_2, \ldots, e_g$ are natural numbers. If d is a divisor of n, then

$$d = p_1^{f_1} p_2^{f_2} \ldots p_g^{f_g},$$

where $0 \le f_i \le e_i$. By Theorem 5–3.3, different choices of the sequence $f_1, f_2, \ldots, f_g$ give rise to different divisors. Thus, $\tau(n)$ is the number of different sequences $f_1, f_2, \ldots, f_g$ with $0 \le f_i \le e_i$. It is easy to show (by induction on g, for example) that the number of such sequences is

$$(e_1 + 1)(e_2 + 1) \cdots (e_g + 1).$$

Thus, we obtain the following result.

(5–3.4) If $n = p_1^{e_1} p_2^{e_2} \ldots p_g^{e_g}$, where $p_1, p_2, \ldots, p_g$ are distinct primes, then

$$\tau(n) = (e_1 + 1)(e_2 + 1) \cdots (e_g + 1).$$

In order to evaluate $\sigma(n)$, consider the product

$$(1 + p_1 + p_1^2 + \cdots + p_1^{e_1})(1 + p_2 + p_2^2 + \cdots + p_2^{e_2})$$
$$\cdots (1 + p_g + p_g^2 + \cdots + p_g^{e_g}).$$

This product can be expanded as the sum of all products $p_1^{f_1} p_2^{f_2} \ldots p_g^{f_g}$, where $p_i^{f_i}$ is chosen from a summand of $1 + p_i + \cdots + p_i^{e_i}$. Thus, $0 \le f_i \le e_i$. Therefore, the expansion of this product is just the sum of all divisors of n, that is, $\sigma(n)$. Finally, since

$$1 + p_i + p_i^2 + \cdots + p_i^{e_i} = \frac{p_i^{e_i+1} - 1}{p_i - 1}$$

[see Problem 6(a), Section 2–1], we have proved

(5–3.5) If $n = p_1^{e_1} p_2^{e_2} \ldots p_g^{e_g}$, where $p_1, p_2, \ldots, p_g$ are distinct primes, then,

$$\sigma(n) = \prod_{i=1}^{g} \frac{p_i^{e_i+1} - 1}{p_i - 1}.$$

EXAMPLE 1. Let $n = 360 = 2^3 \cdot 3^2 \cdot 5$. Then

$$\tau(360) = (3+1)(2+1)(1+1) = 24,$$

$$\sigma(360) = \frac{2^4 - 1}{2 - 1} \cdot \frac{3^3 - 1}{3 - 1} \cdot \frac{5^2 - 1}{5 - 1} = 15 \cdot 13 \cdot 6 = 1170.$$

Another useful application of Theorem 5–3.3 is in finding the greatest common divisor and the least common multiple of a set of natural numbers. Let $\{a_1, a_2, \ldots, a_n\}$ be a set of natural numbers. Then each number a_i can be expressed as a product of powers of the same set of primes $p_1, p_2, \ldots, p_k$, if zero exponents are used. For example, consider $\{360, 105, 1078\}$. Here, $360 = 2^3 \cdot 3^2 \cdot 5^1 \cdot 7^0 \cdot 11^0$, $105 = 2^0 \cdot 3^1 \cdot 5^1 \cdot 7^1 \cdot 11^0$, $1078 = 2^1 \cdot 3^0 \cdot 5^0 \cdot 7^2 \cdot 11^1$. Naturally, any prime raised to the power zero is 1.

(5–3.6). Let $\{a_1, a_2, \ldots, a_n\}$ be a set of natural numbers, where

$$a_i = p_1^{e_{1i}} p_2^{e_{2i}} \ldots p_k^{e_{ki}}, \qquad e_{ji} \geq 0,$$

for $i = 1, 2, \ldots, n$ and $j = 1, 2, \ldots, k$. Then

(a) $(a_1, a_2, \ldots, a_n) = p_1^{f_1} p_2^{f_2} \ldots p_k^{f_k}$, where
$$f_j = \min \{e_{j1}, e_{j2}, \ldots, e_{jn}\};$$

(b) $[a_1, a_2, \ldots, a_n] = p_1^{g_1} p_2^{g_2} \ldots p_k^{g_k}$, where
$$g_j = \max \{e_{j1}, e_{j2}, \ldots, e_{jn}\}.$$

Proof. To prove (a), we note first that since

$$f_j = \min \{e_{j1}, e_{j2}, \ldots, e_{jn}\} \leq e_{ji}$$

for all i and j, then $p_1^{f_1} p_2^{f_2} \ldots p_k^{f_k}$ is a divisor of each a_i. On the other hand, a number which is a divisor of each a_i must be of the form $p_1^{h_1} p_2^{h_2} \ldots p_k^{h_k}$, where $h_j \leq e_{ji}$ for all i and j. Then $h_j \leq \min \{e_{j1}, e_{j2}, \ldots, e_{jn}\} = f_j$. Thus, $p_1^{h_1} p_2^{h_2} \ldots p_k^{h_k}$ divides $p_1^{f_1} p_2^{f_2} \ldots p_k^{f_k}$, so that $p_1^{f_1} p_2^{f_2} \ldots p_k^{f_k} = (a_1, a_2, \ldots, a_n)$. The proof of part (b) is similar and is left to the reader.

EXAMPLE 2. Find the g.c.d. and l.c.m. of the set of numbers $\{360, 105, 1078\}$. We have

$$360 = 2^3 \cdot 3^2 \cdot 5^1 \cdot 7^0 \cdot 11^0, \qquad 105 = 2^0 \cdot 3^1 \cdot 5^1 \cdot 7^1 \cdot 11^0,$$
$$1078 = 2^1 \cdot 3^0 \cdot 5^0 \cdot 7^2 \cdot 11^1,$$

and

$$\min \{3, 0, 1\} = 0, \quad \min \{2, 1, 0\} = 0, \quad \min \{1, 1, 0\} = 0,$$
$$\min \{0, 1, 2\} = 0, \quad \min \{0, 0, 1\} = 0.$$

Hence, $(360, 105, 1078) = 2^0 \cdot 3^0 \cdot 5^0 \cdot 7^0 \cdot 11^0 = 1$. We find

$$\max \{3, 0, 1\} = 3, \qquad \max \{2, 1, 0\} = 2, \qquad \max \{1, 1, 0\} = 1,$$

$$\max \{0, 1, 2\} = 2, \qquad \max \{0, 0, 1\} = 1.$$

Therefore, $[360, 105, 1078] = 2^3 \cdot 3^2 \cdot 5^1 \cdot 7^2 \cdot 11^1 = 194040$.

PROBLEMS

1. Express the following numbers as products of powers of distinct primes.
   (a) 100 (b) 1300 (c) 1960 (d) 109 (e) 713

2. Find the set of all divisors of each of the numbers in Problem 1.

3. Using (5–3.4) and (5–3.5), find $\tau(n)$ and $\sigma(n)$ for each of the numbers n in Problem 1. Check your results on $\sigma(n)$ by computing the sum of the divisors of n directly.

4. Use (5–3.6) to find the g.c.d. and l.c.m. of the following sets of integers.
   (a) $\{20, -15, 22, -10\}$ (b) $\{27, -18, 21, 45\}$
   (c) $\{168, 842, 252\}$ (d) $\{253, 690, 1127\}$

5. Use the fundamental theorem of arithmetic to determine the square roots of the following numbers with three decimal place accuracy. (a) 392 (b) 5780 (c) 122694
   [Note: $\sqrt{2} = 1.41421..., \sqrt{3} = 1.73205..., \sqrt{5} = 2.23607....$]

6. Prove in detail that if $d|n$ and $n = p_1^{e_1}p_2^{e_2} \ldots p_g^{e_g}$, then $d = p_1^{f_1}p_2^{f_2} \ldots p_g^{f_g}$, where $0 \leq f_i \leq e_i$.

7. Show that if the natural numbers a and b are relatively prime, then

$$\sigma(a \cdot b) = \sigma(a) \cdot \sigma(b).$$

8. For any natural number n, let $\sigma_k(n)$ be the sum of the kth powers of the divisors of n: $\sigma_k(n) = \sum_{d|n} d^k$, where the sum is over all natural numbers d which divide n.

   (a) Show that $\sigma_0(n) = \tau(n)$.
   (b) Show that if $n = p_1^{e_1}p_2^{e_2} \ldots p_g^{e_g}$, where $p_1, p_2, \ldots, p_g$ are distinct primes, then

$$\sigma_k(n) = \prod_{i=1}^{g} \left(\frac{p_i^{k(e_i+1)} - 1}{p_i^k - 1} \right).$$

   (c) Show that $\sigma_{-k}(n) = n^{-k}\sigma_k(n)$ both from the definition of $\sigma_k(n)$ and from the formula obtained in part (b).

9. Use the fundamental theorem of arithmetic to give a new proof of Theorem 5–2.4.

10. Use the fundamental theorem of arithmetic to show that for any natural numbers a and b,

$$(a, b)[a, b] = ab.$$

*5-4 More about primes. The fundamental theorem of arithmetic shows that the primes are of great importance in number theory. In this section we will consider some apparently simple questions about the set of all primes. Most of these questions will be left unanswered. Indeed, some of the simplest looking problems of the theory of prime numbers can be counted among the outstanding unsolved problems of mathematics.

Probably the first question which one would ask about prime numbers is: How can I tell when a natural number is a prime? It is always possible to test by long division whether or not a natural number a is divisible by a natural number b in the range $1 < b < a$. If a is not divisible by any such b, then a must be a prime. However, if a is large, then the amount of computation required to determine in this way whether a is a prime may be considerable. The labor can be reduced by using a simple property of composite numbers.

(5-4.1). Every composite number a is divisible by a prime $p \leq \sqrt{a}$.

Since a is composite, $a = b \cdot c$ where $b > 1$ and $c > 1$. Suppose that $b \leq c$. (One of the factors of a is less than or equal to the other one, and we can denote that factor by b.) Assume that $b > \sqrt{a}$. Then $c \geq b > \sqrt{a}$, so that $c > \sqrt{a}$. Therefore, $a = b \cdot c > \sqrt{a} \cdot \sqrt{a} = a$, which is impossible. Since the assumption that $b > \sqrt{a}$ led to a contradiction, we can conclude that $b \leq \sqrt{a}$. By Theorem 5-3.3 or Example 2, Section 2-3, b is divisible by a prime p. Hence $a = b \cdot c$ is divisible by p where $p \leq b \leq \sqrt{a}$.

To test whether a natural number a is a prime, it suffices by (5-4.1) to divide a by all primes which are not larger than $\sqrt{a}$. If each division has a nonzero remainder, then a is a prime. For example, consider $a = 787$. Since $28^2 = 784$ and $29^2 = 841$, $28 < \sqrt{787} < 29$. The primes which are not larger than $\sqrt{787}$ are 2, 3, 5, 7, 11, 13, 17, 19, and 23. By trial we find that 787 is not divisible by any of these primes. Therefore, by (5-4.1), 787 is a prime.

The first tables of prime numbers were compiled by a simple process based on (5-4.1). This method "sifts" the composite numbers from the sequence of all natural numbers which are less than or equal to some fixed natural number. The process is credited to the Greek mathematician Eratosthenes (276-194 B.C.).

Suppose that we wish to find all primes ≤ 100. By (5-4.1), every composite number ≤ 100 is divisible by a prime $p \leq \sqrt{100} = 10$. Therefore, the primes ≤ 100 are those numbers which are not proper multiples of 2, 3, 5, and 7. Thus, if we let the multiples of 2, 3, 5, and 7 fall through a sieve which contains the first hundred natural numbers, the primes will be left. This process, the sieve of Eratosthenes, is illustrated in Fig. 5-1.

```
 1   [2]  [3]   4̸   [5]   6̸  [7]    8̸    9̸   10̸
[11] 12̸ [13]  14̸  1̵5̵  16̸ [17]  18̸  [19]  20̸
2̵1̵  22̸ [23]  24̸  2̵5̵  26̸  2̵7̵  28̸  [29]  30̸
[31] 32̸ 3̵3̵  34̸  3̵5̵  36̸ [37]  38̸  3̵9̵  40̸
[41] 42̸ [43]  44̸  4̵5̵  46̸ [47]  48̸  4̵9̵  50̸
5̵1̵  52̸ [53]  54̸  5̵5̵  56̸  5̵7̵  58̸  [59]  60̸
[61] 62̸ 6̵3̵  64̸  6̵5̵  66̸ [67]  68̸  6̵9̵  70̸
[71] 72̸ [73]  74̸  7̵5̵  76̸  7̵7̵  78̸  [79]  80̸
8̵1̵  82̸ [83]  84̸  8̵5̵  86̸  8̵7̵  88̸  [89]  90̸
9̵1̵  92̸ 9̵3̵  94̸  9̵5̵  96̸ [97]  98̸  9̵9̵  100̸
```

FIGURE 5–1

Knowing the primes $\leq 100 = \sqrt{10{,}000}$ we can use this method for finding the primes $\leq 10{,}000$, and so forth. There are various refinements to the sieve of Eratosthenes which cut down the labor involved in compiling tables of primes. Moreover at the present time, this computation can be done by automatic computing machines. A complete list of all the primes among the first 11,000,000 natural numbers has been obtained by the sieve method.

Note that in our table of primes, the primes thin out as the numbers get larger. There are 15 primes ≤ 50 and 10 primes between 50 and 100. A natural question to ask is whether the primes stop somewhere in the sequence of natural numbers, that is, is there a largest prime? Euclid* answered this question in the negative.

THEOREM 5–4.2. There are infinitely many primes.

Proof. Euclid's proof of this fact is a proof by contradiction. Suppose that the number of primes is finite. Then all of the primes can be written down in order of increasing size,

$$2 < 3 < 5 < \cdots < q < p,$$

where p is the largest prime. The natural number

$$n = (2 \cdot 3 \cdot 5 \cdot \cdots \cdot q \cdot p) + 1,$$

---

* Most people think of Euclid as a geometer. Actually, Euclid's contributions to the subject of geometry seem to be slight. The familiar geometrical portions of Euclid's *Elements* are mainly compilations of the work of other geometers. However, Euclid's contributions to number theory were of the highest significance. Theorem 5–4.2 is rightly considered to be one of the fine gems of mathematical science.

which is the product of all of the primes plus 1, is not divisible by any prime in our list. This is true, since the remainder on dividing n by any one of these primes is $1 \neq 0$. For example, if we divide n by 5, we obtain

$$n = 5 \cdot (2 \cdot 3 \cdot 7 \cdot \cdots \cdot q \cdot p) + 1.$$

But by Theorem 5–3.3 (or by Example 2, Section 2–3), every natural number greater than 1 is divisible by a prime. Therefore, n is divisible by a prime which is not in our list of all of the primes. This is a contradiction. Hence our assumption that there is only a finite number of primes is false, and Theorem 5–4.2 is true.

Although Euclid showed over 2200 years ago that the set of primes is infinite, a closely related problem remains unsettled. If p and $p + 2$ are both primes, then they are said to form a *prime pair*. For example, 5 and 7, 11 and 13, 17 and 19, 29 and 31 are prime pairs. The largest known prime pair seems to be 1,000,000,009,649 and 1,000,000,009,651. There is strong evidence to support the conjecture that the number of prime pairs is infinite. However, no proof has been found for this statement.

Very little regularity is found in the occurrence of primes in the sequence of natural numbers. On the one hand, the difference between consecutive primes can probably be as small as two infinitely often. On the other hand, there are arbitrarily large gaps between consecutive primes. For if n is any natural number, then the numbers

$$n! + 2, \qquad n! + 3, \qquad \ldots, \qquad n! + n$$

are all composite. In fact $n! + 2 = (1 \cdot 2 \cdot 3 \cdot \cdots \cdot n) + 2$ is divisible by 2, $n! + 3$ is divisible by 3, and so forth. Therefore, if p is the largest prime less than $n! + 2$, and q is the next largest prime, then $q - p \geq n$.

The irregular occurrence of the primes makes it seem unlikely that there is any simple expression for the number of primes less than the natural number n. However, studies of tables of primes indicate that the number of primes less than n is *approximately* equal to $n/\log n$. (Here $\log n$ represents the natural logarithm of n; hence $\log n = c \cdot \log_{10} n$, where $c = 2.302585\ldots$ and $\log_{10} n$ is the usual logarithm to the base 10.) The fact that the ratio of the number of primes less than n to the quantity $n/\log n$ approaches 1 as n gets large is one of the most important results in the theory of prime numbers. It is known as the *prime number theorem*. This theorem was conjectured by several mathematicians in the late eighteenth century, but over a hundred years of mathematical development was required before it could be proved.

Even though the set of all primes is irregularly distributed among the natural numbers, it might be hoped that a subset of the primes could be obtained by some simple formula. Pierre de Fermat (1601–1665), the founder of modern number theory and one of the great mathematicians of all time, observed that for $n = 0, 1, 2, 3$, and 4, the quantity

$$F_n = 2^{2^n} + 1$$

is a prime, and he conjectured that this might be the case for all n. However, it was found in 1732 that F_5 is composite:

$$
\begin{aligned}
F_5 &= 2^{32} + 1 = 16 \cdot 2^{28} + 1 = (641 - 5^4) \cdot 2^{28} + 1 \\
&= 641 \cdot 2^{28} - (5 \cdot 2^7)^4 + 1 \\
&= 641 \cdot 2^{28} - (641 - 1)^4 + 1 \\
&= 641 \cdot (2^{28} - 641^3 + 4 \cdot 641^2 - 6 \cdot 641 + 4) \\
&= 641 \cdot 6700417.
\end{aligned}
$$

None of the *Fermat numbers* F_n has been found to be a prime for $n > 4$, and in fact F_n has been shown to be composite for 28 values of n. Nevertheless, the Fermat numbers have numerous interesting properties.

A related class of numbers from which one might hope to obtain primes is given by the formula

$$M_p = 2^p - 1, \qquad p \text{ a prime.}$$

These are called *Mersenne numbers* after a rather undistinguished French mathematician Marin Mersenne (1588–1648), who asserted in 1644 that M_p is a prime for $p = 2, 3, 5, 7, 13, 17, 19, 31, 67, 127$, and 257, and is composite for all other p less than 257. It has since been shown that Mersenne's statement was incorrect: M_{67} and M_{257} are not primes, and M_{61}, M_{89}, and M_{107} are not composite. There is an efficient method for testing whether certain Mersenne numbers are primes. This test has been used (with the aid of an automatic digital computer) to find the largest known prime M_{2281}, a number with 686 digits. It is not known, however, whether there are infinitely many Mersenne primes.

There are two apparent ways to generalize the Mersenne numbers: replace 2 by an arbitrary natural number $a > 1$, and drop the restriction that the exponent p be a prime. Neither of these generalizations leads to new primes, however.

THEOREM 5–4.3. Let a and n be natural numbers greater than 1. Suppose that $k = a^n - 1$ is a prime. Then $a = 2$ and n is a prime.

Proof. If $a > 2$, then $k = a^n - 1 = (a - 1)(a^{n-1} + a^{n-2} + \cdots + 1)$ has a proper divisor $a - 1$ which is larger than 1. This contradicts the assumption that k is a prime. Hence, $a = 2$. If $n = r \cdot s$, where $r > 1$

and $s > 1$, then $k = 2^{r \cdot s} - 1 = b^s - 1$, where $b = 2^r > 2$. As we have just seen, this implies that k is composite. Thus, n is a prime.

The Mersenne primes are closely connected with a class of numbers which greatly interested the ancient Greeks: the so called perfect numbers. A *perfect number* is a natural number which is equal to the sum of its proper divisors, that is, the sum of all of the divisors except the number itself. For example, $6 = 1 + 2 + 3$ and $496 = 2^4 \cdot 31 = 1 + 2 + 4 + 8 + 16 + 31 + 62 + 124 + 248$ are perfect numbers. Since $\sigma(n)$ is the sum of all of the divisors of n, including n, n is a perfect number if and only if $\sigma(n) = 2n$. From Euclid's time a rule has been known for determining all even perfect numbers.

THEOREM 5-4.4. A number of the form

$$2^{p-1}(2^p - 1),$$

where p and $2^p - 1$ are primes, is a perfect number. Conversely, if n is an even perfect number, then n is of this form.

Proof. If $n = 2^{p-1}(2^p - 1)$, where p and $2^p - 1$ are primes, then by (5-3.5),

$$\sigma(n) = \frac{2^p - 1}{2 - 1} \cdot \frac{(2^p - 1)^2 - 1}{(2^p - 1) - 1} = (2^p - 1) \cdot \frac{2^{2p} - 2 \cdot 2^p}{2^p - 2}$$

$$= (2^p - 1) \cdot \frac{2^p(2^p - 2)}{(2^p - 2)}$$

$$= (2^p - 1) \cdot 2^p = 2[2^{p-1}(2^p - 1)] = 2n.$$

Hence, n is a perfect number.

Conversely, suppose that $\sigma(n) = 2n$, where n is even. Since n is even, $n = 2^l \cdot k$ where $l > 0$ and k is odd. Therefore, $\sigma(n) = \sigma(2^l) \cdot \sigma(k)$ (see Problem 7, Section 5-3), and

$$2^{l+1} \cdot k = 2(2^l \cdot k) = 2n = \sigma(n) = \sigma(2^l) \cdot \sigma(k) = \frac{2^{l+1} - 1}{2 - 1} \cdot \sigma(k)$$

$$= (2^{l+1} - 1) \cdot \sigma(k).$$

Since 2 is the only prime dividing 2^{l+1}, and $2^{l+1} - 1$ is odd, it follows that 2^{l+1} and $2^{l+1} - 1$ are relatively prime. In view of the equality

$$2^{l+1} \cdot k = (2^{l+1} - 1) \cdot \sigma(k),$$

Theorem 5-2.5 implies that $(2^{l+1} - 1)$ divides k. Thus,

$$k = (2^{l+1} - 1) \cdot m \quad \text{and} \quad \sigma(k) = 2^{l+1} \cdot m.$$

Now m and k are divisors of k and

$$m + k = m + (2^{l+1} - 1) \cdot m = m(1 + 2^{l+1} - 1)$$
$$= m \cdot 2^{l+1} = \sigma(k).$$

Thus, the sum of all of the divisors of k is the sum of the two divisors m and k. Hence, k has only two divisors. This implies that $m = 1$ and k is a prime. Moreover $k = 2^{l+1} - 1$. Thus,

$$n = 2^l(2^{l+1} - 1) = 2^{(l+1)-1}(2^{l+1} - 1),$$

where $k = 2^{l+1} - 1$ is a prime. By Theorem 5–4.3, $l + 1$ must also be a prime p. Therefore,

$$n = 2^{p-1}(2^p - 1),$$

where p and $2^p - 1$ are primes.

Whether there are any odd perfect numbers is another unsolved problem in number theory. Results have been obtained which show that if an odd perfect number exists, it must be larger than 2,200,000,000,000.

PROBLEMS

1. Determine which of the following natural numbers are primes and justify your answer. (a) 503 (b) 943 (c) 1511 (d) $2^{13} - 1$ (e) 899

2. Use the sieve of Eratosthenes to compile a table of primes less than 300.

3. Prove that the only prime triple (that is, three consecutive primes of the form p, $p + 2$, $p + 4$) is 3, 5, 7.

4. Show that 28 is a perfect number.

5. Show that 33,550,336 is a perfect number.

6. Show that 2,096,128 is not a perfect number.

7. (a) Prove that if $m < n$, then F_m divides $F_n - 2$ (where F_m and F_n are the Fermat numbers $2^{2^m} + 1$ and $2^{2^n} + 1$).
   (b) Show that if $m \neq n$, then F_m and F_n are relatively prime.
   (c) Use the result of (b) to give a new proof of Euclid's Theorem 5–4.2.

8. Show that if n is a natural number and if $k = 2^n + 1$ is a prime, then n is a power of 2.

9. (a) Prove that the product of natural numbers which are all of the form $3x + 1$ is a number which is again of this form.
   (b) Use this remark to prove that there are infinitely many primes of the form $3x + 2$, that is, that the infinite sequence 5, 8, 11, 14, 17, ... of natural numbers contains infinitely many primes. [*Hint:* Proceed as in the proof of

Theorem 5–4.2. Suppose that there is only a finite number of primes of the form $3x + 2$. List them all:

$$5, 11, 17, \ldots, p,$$

where p is the largest such prime. Show that the number

$$n = 3(5 \cdot 11 \cdot 17 \cdot \ldots \cdot p) - 1$$

is divisible only by primes of the form $3x + 1$, but n itself is not of this form, contrary to (a).]

*5–5 Applications of the fundamental theorem of arithmetic. The importance of the fundamental theorem of arithmetic can hardly be overestimated. This fact can be appreciated after some applications of the theorem are examined. In this section, we will present four different applications. Numerous others will appear later in the book.

Gödel numbering. Any scheme which associates a natural number with each sentence, or sequence of sentences, in some language in such a way that different expressions are associated with different numbers is called a Gödel numbering of the language (after the mathematician Kurt Gödel, who used such a numbering to prove important results in mathematical logic). One of the ways in which this can be done depends on the fundamental theorem of arithmetic and the fact that there are infinitely many prime numbers (Theorem 5–4.2).

Nearly all expressions in the English language can be written using 38 symbols and a space marker. The symbols are the 26 letters of the alphabet, the period, question mark, exclamation point, comma, colon, semicolon, hyphen, apostrophe, two parentheses, and two quotation marks. Associate the numbers 1 to 38 with these symbols in the given order, that is,

1	2	3	...	26	27	28	...	37	38
↕	↕	↕		↕	↕	↕		↕	↕
A	B	C		Z	.	?		"	" .

Associate zero with the space symbol. Let $p_1, p_2, p_3, p_4, \ldots$ denote the sequence of all primes in the order of increasing size. That is, $p_1 = 2$, $p_2 = 3$, $p_3 = 5$, $p_4 = 7, \ldots$. It is now possible to define a Gödel numbering of the English language by associating with the expression

$$s_1 \quad s_2 \quad s_3 \quad \ldots \quad s_n$$

(where the s_i are either one of the 38 symbols listed above, or else a space marker) the number

$$p_1^{e_1} p_2^{e_2} p_3^{e_3} \ldots p_n^{e_n},$$

where e_i is the integer from 0 to 38 which corresponds to s_i. For example, the number associated with the expression

GEORGE WASHINGTON

is

$$2^7 \cdot 3^5 \cdot 5^{15} \cdot 7^{18} \cdot 11^7 \cdot 13^5 \cdot 17^0 \cdot 19^{24} \cdot 23^1 \cdot 29^{19} \cdot 31^8 \cdot 37^9 \cdot 41^{14} \cdot$$
$$43^7 \cdot 47^{20} \cdot 53^{15} \cdot 59^{14}.$$

Since there are infinitely many primes, this scheme associates numbers with expressions of any length. Of course, the numbers involved may be very large. The number associated with the expression GEORGE WASHING-TON has more than 250 decimal digits. Nevertheless, even the text of a book such as the King James version of the bible (written in capitals, and with numbers written out) has a uniquely associated number. It is theorectically possible to determine any expression from the knowledge of its corresponding number. For example, the number

$$1,502,353,522,541,760,000$$

factors to

$$2^9 \cdot 3^0 \cdot 5^4 \cdot 7^{15},$$

and therefore

I DO

is the expression from which it is obtained. Different expressions must correspond to different numbers, since by the fundamental theorem of arithmetic, two different products of primes cannot be equal to the same natural number. Thus, our scheme satisfies the requirements for a Gödel numbering of the English language.

The scheme for constructing a Gödel numbering which we have presented is not very practical, since the numbers involved are usually very large. However, when applied to formal mathematical languages, the method has important theoretical consequences for logicians and philosophers.

A cardinal number problem revisited. In Section 1–2, we showed that the set F of all fractions a/b (where a and b are natural numbers) has the same cardinality as N, the set of natural numbers. We will now use the fundamental theorem of arithmetic to give another proof of this fact, that is, to establish a one-to-one correspondence between N and F. First, define a one-to-one correspondence between the set of all nonnegative integers and the set of all integers in such a way that 0 corresponds to 0. Any such correspondence will do, but to be specific, let

$$
\begin{array}{cccccccc}
0 & 1 & 2 & 3 & 4 & & 2n-1 & 2n \\
\updownarrow & \updownarrow & \updownarrow & \updownarrow & \updownarrow & \cdots & \updownarrow & \updownarrow & \cdots \\
0 & -1 & 1 & -2 & 2 & & -n & n
\end{array}
\tag{5-4}
$$

For each nonnegative integer e, let $\bar{e}$ stand for the mate of e under this correspondence. For example,

$$\bar{0} = 0, \quad \bar{1} = -1, \quad \bar{2} = 1, \quad \ldots, \quad \overline{2n-1} = -n, \quad \overline{2n} = n.$$

THEOREM 5-5.1. With each natural number

$$a = p_1^{e_1} p_2^{e_2} \ldots p_g^{e_g},$$

where $p_1, p_2, \ldots, p_g$ are distinct primes and $e_1, e_2, \ldots, e_g$ are nonnegative integers, associate the fraction

$$r = p_1^{\overline{e_1}} p_2^{\overline{e_2}} \ldots p_g^{\overline{e_g}}.$$

Then the association $a \leftrightarrow r$ is a one-to-one correspondence between N and F.

Before discussing the proof of this theorem, let us compare the correspondence between N and F given by Theorem 5-5.1 with the correspondence defined in Section 1-2. We see immediately that they are different. For example, with the definition given in Theorem 5-5.1,

$$
\begin{array}{ccccccccccccccccc}
1 & 2 & 3 & 4 & 5 & 6 & 7 & 8 & 9 & 10 & 11 & 12 & 13 & 14 & 15 & 16 & 17 \\
\updownarrow & \updownarrow & \updownarrow & \updownarrow & \updownarrow & \updownarrow & \updownarrow & \updownarrow & \updownarrow & \updownarrow & \updownarrow & \updownarrow & \updownarrow & \updownarrow & \updownarrow & \updownarrow & \updownarrow \\
1 & \frac{1}{2} & \frac{1}{3} & 2 & \frac{1}{5} & \frac{1}{6} & \frac{1}{7} & \frac{1}{4} & 3 & \frac{1}{10} & \frac{1}{11} & \frac{2}{3} & \frac{1}{13} & \frac{1}{14} & \frac{1}{15} & 4 & \frac{1}{17}
\end{array}
$$

which bears no resemblance to the correspondence given in Section 1-2. The correspondence of Section 1-2 was defined in rather vague terms. We gave no rule stating what fraction would correspond to a specific natural number n. Instead, it was pointed out how one could, with sufficient patience, find the fraction corresponding to any particular n. For large values of n, the method would not be practical. For example, to find the fraction corresponding to 90,000,000 would be a long, tedious job. On the other hand, the correspondence given by Theorem 5-5.1 is much more explicit. To apply the rule, the only requirement is that we be able to factor the natural number a into its prime factors. For example, the number $90,000,000 = 2^7 \cdot 3^2 \cdot 5^7$ corresponds to $2^{-4} \cdot 3 \cdot 5^{-4} = 3/10,000$. For a mathematician, the correspondence defined in Theorem 5-5.1 is much more satisfying than the vague directions laid down in Section 1-2. Nevertheless, he would admit, perhaps reluctantly, that the discussion in Section 1–2 proves just as effectively that the set F is denumerable.

The proof of Theorem 5–5.1 is based on a generalization of the fundamental theorem of arithmetic.

THEOREM 5–5.2. The positive rational numbers r can be expressed in the form

$$r = p_1^{x_1} p_2^{x_2} \ldots p_g^{x_g},$$

where $p_1, p_2, \ldots, p_g$ are distinct primes and $x_1, x_2, \ldots, x_g$ are integers. Moreover, this representation is unique, except for the order of the factors and the occurrence of primes with exponent zero.

This theorem is an almost immediate consequence of Theorem 5–3.3, and the fact that every positive rational number r has a unique representation a/b in "lowest terms," that is, with a and b natural numbers which are relatively prime. We leave to the reader the chore of supplying a detailed proof.

Theorem 5–5.1 can now be easily proved by reinterpreting Theorem 5–3.3 and 5–5.2. For this purpose, let $p_1, p_2, p_3, p_4, \ldots$ denote the sequence of all primes in increasing order. Thus, $p_1 = 2$, $p_2 = 3$, $p_3 = 5$, $p_4 = 7$, ... Then by Theorem 5–3.3, each natural number a can be written

$$a = p_1^{e_1} p_2^{e_2} \ldots p_g^{e_g},$$

where now $e_1, e_2, \ldots, e_g$ are nonnegative integers, and g is some sufficiently large number. The number of factors in the expression is not uniquely determined because we can always multiply by primes to the zero power. Thus,

$$10 = 2^1 \cdot 3^0 \cdot 5^1 \cdot 7^0 \cdot 11^0 \cdot 13^0.$$

However, the number a determines, and is determined by, the sequence of exponents $e_1, e_2, \ldots, e_g$. By adjoining an infinite number of zeros, we do achieve complete uniqueness. In other words, there is a one-to-one correspondence between the natural numbers and the infinite sequence of nonnegative integers

$$(e_1, e_2, e_3, \ldots, e_g, e_{g+1}, e_{g+2}, \ldots),$$

which are zero from some point on (that is, for sufficiently large g, $e_{g+1} = 0$, $e_{g+2} = 0, \ldots$). The uniqueness statement in the fundamental theorem of arithmetic tells us that the correspondence

$$a = p_1^{e_1} p_2^{e_2} \ldots p_g^{e_g} \leftrightarrow (e_1, e_2, \ldots, e_g, 0, 0, \ldots)$$

is one-to-one.

In exactly the same way, there exists, by Theorem 5–5.2, a one-to-one correspondence between the set F of all positive rational numbers and the set of all sequences

$$(x_1, x_2, \ldots, x_g, x_{g+1}, x_{g+2}, \ldots)$$

of integers with the property that $x_{g+1} = 0$, $x_{g+2} = 0$, $\ldots$ from some point on. The correspondence is

$$r = p_1^{x_1} p_2^{x_2} \ldots p_g^{x_g} \leftrightarrow (x_1, x_2, \ldots, x_g, 0, 0, \ldots).$$

We now have two sets of infinite sequences: the set J of all

$$(e_1, e_2, \ldots, e_g, \ldots),$$

where the e_i are nonnegative integers which are zero from some point on, and the set K of all $(x_1, x_2, \ldots, x_g, \ldots)$, where the x_i are integers which are zero from some point on. The one-to-one correspondence $e \leftrightarrow \bar{e}$ given by (5–4) clearly determines a one-to-one correspondence between J and K:

$$(e_1, e_2, \ldots, e_g, \ldots) \leftrightarrow (\bar{e}_1, \bar{e}_2, \ldots, \bar{e}_g, \ldots).$$

If all of these one-to-one correspondences are combined, we obtain

$$p_1^{e_1} p_2^{e_2} \ldots p_g^{e_g} \leftrightarrow (e_1, e_2, \ldots, e_g, 0, \ldots) \leftrightarrow (\bar{e}_1, \bar{e}_2, \ldots, \bar{e}_g, 0, \ldots)$$
$$\leftrightarrow p_1^{\bar{e}_1} p_2^{\bar{e}_2} \ldots p_g^{\bar{e}_g},$$

which is the correspondence described in Theorem 5–5.1.

A Diophantine problem. It is well known that there are right triangles whose sides have integral length. The best known example is the 3, 4, 5 right triangle with bases of length 3 and 4, and hypotenuse of length 5. Somewhat less well known is the right triangle with sides of length 5, 12, and 13. Since the length c of the hypotenuse of a right triangle is related to the lengths a and b of the sides by the Pythagorean formula

$$c^2 = a^2 + b^2, \tag{5–5}$$

the problem of finding all right triangles with sides of integral length is equivalent to finding all natural numbers a, b, and c which satisfy (5–5).

An equation such as (5–5) involving powers of unknown quantities with integral coefficients is called a Diophantine equation (after the ancient Greek mathematician Diophantus). For example, $a + b = 2$, $a^2 - 5b^2 = 1$, $a^2 + ab + b^2 = 5c^2$, and $a^4 + b^4 = c^2$ are all Diophantine equations. The problem of finding all integral solutions of a Diophantine equation, or a system of Diophantine equations, is called a *Diophantine problem.*

Using the fundamental theorem of arithmetic, it is possible to obtain the complete solution of (5–5). First note that if r, s, and t are natural numbers, with $r > s$, and if we let

$$a = (r^2 - s^2)t, \qquad b = 2rst, \qquad c = (r^2 + s^2)t, \qquad (5\text{–}6)$$

then

$$\begin{aligned} a^2 + b^2 &= (r^2 - s^2)^2 t^2 + 4r^2 s^2 t^2 = r^4 t^2 - 2r^2 s^2 t^2 + s^4 t^2 + 4r^2 s^2 t^2 \\ &= r^4 t^2 + 2r^2 s^2 t^2 + s^4 t^2 = (r^2 + s^2)^2 t^2 = c^2. \end{aligned}$$

Therefore, (5–6) gives a large family of solutions of (5–5). We will show that every solution of (5–5) with a, b, and c natural numbers is of the form (5–6) (or a similar form with a and b interchanged) for suitable natural numbers r, s, and t. The proof is based on the following useful consequence of the fundamental theorem of arithmetic.

THEOREM 5–5.3. Suppose that a and b are natural numbers which are relatively prime, and $ab = c^n$ for some natural number c. Then $a = a_1^n$, $b = b_1^n$, where a_1 and b_1 are natural numbers.

Proof. Let

$$a = p_1^{e_1} \ldots p_g^{e_g}, \qquad b = q_1^{f_1} \ldots q_h^{f_h},$$

where $p_1, \ldots, p_g$ are distinct primes, $q_1, \ldots, q_h$ are distinct primes, and the exponents $e_1, \ldots, e_g$ and $f_1, \ldots, f_h$ are all positive. Then the p_i must be different from all q_j, since otherwise a and b would have a common prime factor, contrary to the assumption that they are relatively prime. Let

$$c = r_1^{m_1} \ldots r_k^{m_k},$$

where $r_1, \ldots, r_k$ are distinct primes and $m_1, \ldots, m_k$ are positive exponents. Then the condition $ab = c^n$ can be written

$$p_1^{e_1} \ldots p_g^{e_g} q_1^{f_1} \ldots q_h^{f_h} = r_1^{nm_1} \ldots r_k^{nm_k}.$$

By Theorem 5–3.3, it follows that the primes $r_1, \ldots r_k$ must be $p_1, \ldots, p_g$, $q_1, \ldots, q_h$ in some order, and that $e_1, \ldots, e_g, f_1, \ldots, f_h$ are the corresponding exponents $nm_1, \ldots, nm_k$. Thus, each e_i and f_j is divisible by n, that is, $e_1/n, \ldots, e_g/n, f_1/n, \ldots, f_h/n$ are all natural numbers. Let

$$a_1 = p_1^{e_1/n} \ldots p_g^{e_g/n}, \qquad b_1 = q_1^{f_1/n} \ldots q_h^{f_h/n}.$$

Then $a = a_1^n$, $b = b_1^n$.

We now return to the problem of finding all natural number solutions of (5–5). Suppose that a, b, and c are natural numbers which satisfy (5–5).

Let t be the greatest common divisor of a, b, and c. Then a/t, b/t, and c/t are natural numbers with no prime factor in common which satisfy

$$\left(\frac{a}{t}\right)^2 + \left(\frac{b}{t}\right)^2 = \left(\frac{c}{t}\right)^2.$$

We will show that a/t, b/t, and c/t have the form $r^2 - s^2$, $2rs$, and $r^2 + s^2$, respectively, or else $2rs$, $r^2 - s^2$, and $r^2 + s^2$, respectively. Let $x = a/t$, $y = b/t$, and $z = c/t$. Then

$$x^2 + y^2 = z^2, \tag{5–7}$$

where no prime divides any two of these natural numbers, that is, each pair of the numbers x, y, z are relatively prime. For example, if $p|x$ and $p|z$, then p divides $z^2 - x^2 = y^2$. Thus, by (5–3.2), $p|y$. But this is a contradiction, since x, y, and z have no prime factor in common. Since x and y are relatively prime, they cannot both be even. Suppose they are both odd. Then we could write $x = 1 + 2m$, $y = 1 + 2n$, with m and n nonnegative integers. Consequently

$$x^2 = 1 + 4m(m + 1), \qquad y^2 = 1 + 4n(n + 1),$$

and

$$z^2 = x^2 + y^2 = 2 + 4[m(m + 1) + n(n + 1)].$$

This implies that z is even, say $z = 2l$. Then $z^2 = 4l^2$, so that

$$2 = 4l^2 - 4[m(m + 1) + n(n + 1)].$$

This is clearly impossible. Therefore, one of x or y is even, while the other is odd. Suppose that x is odd and y is even. Then z is odd, so that $z - x$ and $z + x$ are even. That is, $\frac{1}{2}(z - x)$ and $\frac{1}{2}(z + x)$ are integers. Moreover, they are relatively prime, since if a prime p divides $\frac{1}{2}(z - x)$ and $\frac{1}{2}(z + x)$, then p divides $\frac{1}{2}(z + x) + \frac{1}{2}(z - x) = z$ and $\frac{1}{2}(z + x) - \frac{1}{2}(z - x) = x$. But this is impossible, since x and z are relatively prime. By (5–7),

$$\tfrac{1}{2}(z + x) \cdot \tfrac{1}{2}(z - x) = \tfrac{1}{4}(z^2 - x^2) = \tfrac{1}{4}y^2 = (\tfrac{1}{2}y)^2,$$

where $\frac{1}{2}y$ is a natural number, since y is even. By Theorem 5–5.3, $\frac{1}{2}(z + x)$ and $\frac{1}{2}(z - x)$ are squares, that is, there exist natural numbers r and s such that

$$\tfrac{1}{2}(z + x) = r^2, \qquad \tfrac{1}{2}(z - x) = s^2.$$

Consequently, $z = r^2 + s^2$, $x = r^2 - s^2$, and

$$y = (z^2 - x^2)^{1/2} = [(r^2 + s^2)^2 - (r^2 - s^2)^2]^{1/2} = (4r^2s^2)^{1/2} = 2rs.$$

Since $r^2 - s^2 = x$, a natural number, we have $r^2 > s^2$. Therefore, $r > s$. In the case that x is even and y is odd, a similar argument shows that $x = 2rs$, $y = r^2 - s^2$, and $z = r^2 + s^2$. Thus, we have proved the following theorem.

THEOREM 5–5.4.   Every solution in natural numbers a, b, c of the equation

$$a^2 + b^2 = c^2$$

is obtained from natural numbers r, s, and t, with $r > s$, by letting

(a) $a = (r^2 - s^2)t,$ $b = 2rst,$ $c = (r^2 + s^2)t,$

or else

(b) $a = 2rst,$ $b = (r^2 - s^2)t,$ $c = (r^2 + s^2)t.$

Moreover, for every such choice of r, s, and t, the natural numbers a, b, and c, defined by (a) or (b), satisfy $a^2 + b^2 = c^2$.

The Fermat conjecture.   In his copy of the *Arithmetic* of Diophantus, Fermat jotted down a number of marginal notes. Among these notes was the following statement, which is sometimes known as the "great Fermat theorem."

"A cube, however, cannot be split into two cubes or a biquadrate into two biquadrates, and in general no power beyond the second can be split into two similar powers. I have discovered a truly wonderful proof of this proposition but the margin is too small to contain it."

In other words, Fermat asserted that if $n > 2$, then there are no natural numbers a, b, and c which satisfy

$$a^n + b^n = c^n.$$

After 300 years no proof has been found for Fermat's assertion, even though it has been proved for all values of n up to about 7000. However, the attempts to prove Fermat's statement have led to mathematical theories of major importance. The great Fermat theorem is an instance (and there are numerous others) of an unproved conjecture whose most important contribution to the development of mathematics has been the challenge of discovering its proof.

It is possible to use Theorems 5–5.4 and 5–5.3 to prove the Fermat conjecture in the case $n = 4$. In fact, we will prove that there are no natural numbers a, b, and c such that $a^4 + b^4 = c^2$. This certainly implies that $a^4 + b^4 = c^4 = (c^2)^2$ has no solution in N. First note a useful consequence of Theorem 5–5.4, which the reader should be able to prove for himself.

(5–5.5). If a, b, and c are natural numbers which have no common prime factor and satisfy $a^2 + b^2 = c^2$, then
(a) c is odd;
(b) either a is even and b is odd, or vice versa;
(c) if a is even,

$$a = 2rs, \qquad b = r^2 - s^2, \qquad c = r^2 + s^2,$$

where r and s are relatively prime natural numbers and $r > s$.

Now suppose that the equation $x^4 + y^4 = z^2$ can be satisfied by some natural numbers. Then the set of all natural numbers z for which there exist natural numbers x and y, such that $x^4 + y^4 = z^2$, is not empty. Consequently, by the well-ordering principle, this set contains a smallest number c. Let a and b be corresponding natural numbers such that $a^4 + b^4 = c^2$. We will obtain a contradiction by showing that there is a natural number t smaller than c such that $t^2 = x^4 + y^4$ for some natural numbers x and y. This will show that our original assumption that a solution exists is false.

If a and b had a common prime factor p, then $p^4 | c^2$. Thus, by the fundamental theorem of arithmetic, $p^2 | c$, and therefore $(a/p)^4 + (b/p)^4 = (c/p^2)^2$. Since $c/p^2 < c$, this contradicts the assumption that c is the smallest of the natural numbers z for which $z^2 = x^4 + y^4$ has a solution. Consequently, a and b are relatively prime. This implies that a^2, b^2, and c have no common prime factor, so that (5–5.5) applies to the equation $(a^2)^2 + (b^2)^2 = c^2$. We obtain that either a^2 or b^2 is even, and assuming that a^2 is even, we have

$$a^2 = 2rs, \qquad b^2 = r^2 - s^2, \qquad c = r^2 + s^2,$$

where r and s are relatively prime natural numbers and $r > s$. Since r and s are relatively prime, it follows that s, b, and r in the equation $s^2 + b^2 = r^2$ have no prime factor in common. Thus, by (5–5.5a), applied to the equation $s^2 + b^2 = r^2$, r is odd. However, a^2 is even, so that a is even. Thus, 4 divides $a^2 = 2rs$, and consequently $2 | rs$. Since r is odd, s must be even, and we have

$$\left(\frac{a}{2}\right)^2 = r \cdot \left(\frac{s}{2}\right).$$

Since $(r, s) = 1$, it follows that r and $s/2$ are relatively prime. Consequently, by Theorem 5–5.3, the equation $(a/2)^2 = r \cdot (s/2)$ implies that r and $s/2$ are squares:

$$r = t^2, \qquad \frac{s}{2} = u^2, \qquad t \in N, \qquad u \in N.$$

Now apply (5–5.5) to the equation $s^2 + b^2 = r^2$ again. Since s is even, we can write

$$s = 2vw, \qquad b = v^2 - w^2, \qquad r = v^2 + w^2,$$

where v and w are relatively prime natural numbers. Hence,

$$vw = \frac{s}{2} = u^2.$$

By Theorem 5–5.3, it follows that

$$v = x^2, \qquad w = y^2$$

for some natural numbers x and y. Combining these equalities with the equations $r = t^2$ and $r = v^2 + w^2$, we obtain

$$t^2 = x^4 + y^4.$$

Moreover, $t \leq t^2 = r \leq r^2 < r^2 + s^2 = c$. Thus, we have arrived at the promised contradiction, and proved the following result.

THEOREM 5–5.6.   There are no natural numbers a, b, and c which satisfy $a^4 + b^4 = c^2$. In particular, the equation $x^4 + y^4 = z^4$ has no solution in natural numbers.

The reader should reexamine the proof of this theorem, noting the following aspects of it.

(1) The main step of the proof is to show that the existence of one triple $\langle x_1, y_1, z_1 \rangle$ of natural numbers satisfying $x_1^4 + y_1^4 = z_1^2$ leads to another triple $\langle x_2, y_2, z_2 \rangle$ satisfying $x_2^4 + y_2^4 = z_2^2$ with $z_2 < z_1$. Repeating the argument would lead to a sequence of triples $\langle x_n, y_n, z_n \rangle$, $n = 1, 2, 3, \ldots$, with $x_n^4 + y_n^4 = z_n^2$ and $z_1 > z_2 > z_3 > \ldots$. This sequence of inequalities is impossible by the well-ordering principle, and therefore proves that the existence of the original triple $\langle x_1, y_1, z_1 \rangle$ is impossible. (Actually, it was convenient for our argument to use the well-ordering principle at the beginning of the proof.) This technique of proof is common in number theory. It is called the "method of infinite descent." The reader may recall that this method was used to establish the Euclidean algorithm in Section 5–2.

(2) The main step of the proof is carried out by two applications of (5–5.5) and two applications of Theorem 5–5.3. Remembering this observation and the general method of proof, the reader should be able to reconstruct the argument without the help of the book.

(3) The method of proof which we used would not suffice to show directly that the equation $x^4 + y^4 = z^4$ has no solutions in N. The generalization

to $x^4 + y^4 = z^2$ is essential to the success of our proof. This is another instance of the situation discussed in Section 2–4, where induction fails in the proof of a certain theorem, but is successful in proving a stronger result. In the case of Theorem 5–5.6, induction occurs as an application of the well-ordering principle.

(4) It is an immediate consequence of Theorem 5–5.6 that no equation of the form

$$x^{4l} + y^{4m} = x^{2n}$$

has a solution $x = a$, $y = b$, $z = c$, with $a \in N$, $b \in N$, $c \in N$. Indeed, if such a solution exists, then a^l, b^m, c^n is a solution of $x^4 + y^4 = z^2$. In particular, if 4 divides n, then the Fermat equation $x^n + y^n = z^n$ has no solution in N.

PROBLEMS

1. Using the Gödel numbering of the English language which was defined in this section, find the Gödel numbers (in factored form) of the following expressions. (a) ALGEBRA (b) U.S.A. (c) DON'T GIVE UP THE SHIP!

2. Give the proof of Theorem 5–5.2.

3. Let a and b be any natural numbers. Show that integers r and s exist such that $rs = (a, b)$, $(a/r, b/s) = 1$.

4. Let a be a natural number. Let s^2 be the largest square dividing a. Show that if d^2 is a square dividing a, then $d|s$.

5. Suppose that $(a, b) = 1$, $(c, d) = 1$, and $ab = cd$. Show that integers r, s, t, and u exist, each pair of which are relatively prime, such that

$$a = rs, \qquad b = tu, \qquad c = rt, \qquad d = su.$$

6. Show that if p is a prime, and if $1 \le i < p$, then p divides the binomial coefficient $\binom{p}{i}$.

7. Show that every solution in natural numbers of the Diophantine equation

$$a^2 + 2b^2 = c^2$$

is given by

$$a = \pm(r^2 - 2s^2)t, \qquad b = 2rst, \qquad c = (r^2 + 2s^2)t$$

[or $a = 2rst$, $b = \pm(r^2 - 2s^2)t$, $c = (r^2 + 2s^2)t$], where r, s, and t are natural numbers.

5–6 Congruences.

Many interesting problems and numerous theoretical questions in number theory are concerned with properties of the remainder obtained by dividing an integer by a fixed natural number m. For example, if the first of July falls on Sunday, then what will be the day of the week on which the first of September falls? Since July and August each have 31 days, the answer is that the first of September falls r days after Sunday, where r is the remainder obtained on dividing $31 + 31$ by 7, namely, $r = 6$, and the day is Saturday. Another example is the following problem: a certain chemical reaction requires 100 hours; if it is desirable to complete the reaction at 8:00 A.M., at what time of day should it be started? The answer is r hours before 8:00 A.M., where r is the remainder obtained on dividing 100 by 24, that is, 4:00 A.M. A property of remainders which was needed for the solution of Problem 9, Section 5–4, is the fact that if the natural number a leaves the remainder 1 on division by 3, then the same is true for every power of a.

The study of many such problems involving remainders is simplified by the systematic use of a concept which was introduced by the great German mathematician Carl Friedrich Gauss (1777–1855).

DEFINITION 5–6.1. Let m be a natural number. An integer a is *congruent modulo m* to an integer b if $a - b$ is divisible by m in the ring of integers. It is customary to write

$$a \equiv b \pmod{m}$$

to indicate that a is congruent to b modulo m. The relation $a \equiv b \pmod{m}$ is called a *congruence*, and m is called the *modulus* of the congruence.

By the definition of congruence, every pair a, b of integers are congruent modulo 1. Thus, congruence with the modulus 1 is not very interesting. Congruence modulo 2 has a familiar meaning: $a \equiv b \pmod{2}$ if and only if a and b have the same parity; that is, either a and b are both even, or they are both odd.

The connection between the remainders on division by m and congruence with the modulus m is seen from the following fact.

THEOREM 5–6.2. Let m be a natural number. Then each integer is congruent modulo m to one and only one of the numbers 0, 1, 2, . . . , $m - 1$.

This theorem is an immediate consequence of the division algorithm. If a is any integer and m is a natural number, then there are unique integers q and r, with $0 \le r < m$, such that $a = qm + r$. Thus, there is a unique number r among the numbers 0, 1, 2, . . . , $m - 1$ such that $a - r$ is divisible by m. By Definition 5–6.1, this means that a is congruent modulo m to one and only one of the numbers 0, 1, 2, . . . , $m - 1$.

It is clear that an integer a is divisible by a natural number m if and only if $a \equiv 0 \pmod{m}$. Moreover, $a \equiv b \pmod{m}$ is equivalent to the statement that $a - b \equiv 0 \pmod{m}$. Thus, the notion of congruence is apparently only a variation of the concept of divisibility. It is therefore surprising that this notion is so useful. The usefulness is partly explained by the fact that congruence has many of the familiar properties of ordinary equality, so that manipulations with congruences are similar to the computations of elementary algebra.

THEOREM 5–6.3. Let m be a natural number and let a, b, c, and d be integers. Then

(a) $a \equiv a \pmod{m}$;

(b) if $a \equiv b \pmod{m}$, then $b \equiv a \pmod{m}$;

(c) if $a \equiv b \pmod{m}$ and $b \equiv c \pmod{m}$, then $a \equiv c \pmod{m}$;

(d) if $a \equiv b \pmod{m}$ and $c \equiv d \pmod{m}$, then
$a + c \equiv b + d \pmod{m}$ and $a - c \equiv b - d \pmod{m}$;

(e) if $a \equiv b \pmod{m}$ and $c \equiv d \pmod{m}$, then $ac \equiv bd \pmod{m}$;

(f) if $a \equiv b \pmod{m}$, then $ca \equiv cb \pmod{m}$;

(g) if $a \equiv b \pmod{m}$, then $a^n \equiv b^n \pmod{m}$ for any natural number n.

The properties (a), (b), and (c) follow easily from Definition 5–6.1. To prove (d), suppose that $a \equiv b \pmod{m}$ and $c \equiv d \pmod{m}$. Then by Definition 5–6.1, $a - b = km$ and $c - d = lm$ for some integers k and l. Thus,

$$(a + c) - (b + d) = (a - b) + (c - d) = km + lm = (k + l)m$$

and

$$(a - c) - (b - d) = (a - b) - (c - d) = km - lm = (k - l)m.$$

Therefore, the differences $(a + c) - (b + d)$ and $(a - c) - (b - d)$ are both divisible by m. By Definition 5–6.1, $a + c \equiv b + d \pmod{m}$ and $a - c \equiv b - d \pmod{m}$. The statement (e) is proved similarly. Using the same notation as in the proof of (d), we have

$$
\begin{aligned}
ac - bd &= (a - b)(c - d) + ad + bc - 2bd \\
&= (a - b)(c - d) + d(a - b) + b(c - d) \\
&= (km)(lm) + d(km) + b(lm) \\
&= (klm + dk + bl)m.
\end{aligned}
$$

Property (f) is an immediate consequence of (e) and the fact that $c \equiv c \pmod{m}$ by (a). Property (g) is obtained by successively applying (e) to the congruence $a \equiv b \pmod{m}$. Using the given congruence twice, (e) implies $a^2 \equiv b^2 \pmod{m}$. Using $a \equiv b \pmod{m}$ and $a^2 \equiv b^2 \pmod{m}$,

(e) gives $a^3 \equiv b^3 \pmod{m}$, and so forth. Of course, this argument can be formalized by induction.

The "transitive law," Theorem 5–6.3(c), and the "reflexive law," Theorem 5–6.3(a), justify the use of sequences of equalities and congruences. For example,

$$a \equiv b = c \equiv d = e \pmod{m}$$

is a convenient abbreviation for $a \equiv b \pmod{m}$, $b = c$, $c \equiv d \pmod{m}$, and $d = e$. By (a) and (c), the congruences obtained by omitting one or more quantities from this sequence are valid: $a \equiv c \pmod{m}$, $a \equiv d \pmod{m}$, $a \equiv e \pmod{m}$, $b \equiv d \pmod{m}$, $b \equiv e \pmod{m}$, and $c \equiv e \pmod{m}$.

It is a consequence of Theorem 5–6.3 that in a congruence with modulus m which involves sums and differences of products, any integer in the congruence can be replaced by any other integer to which it is congruent modulo m. For example, if $ab^3 - 2abc \equiv 5d^2 \pmod{m}$, and if $b \equiv e$ $\pmod{m}$, then $ae^3 - 2aec \equiv 5d^2 \pmod{m}$. In fact by (g), $b^3 \equiv e^3 \pmod{m}$. Using (f), we obtain $ab^3 \equiv ae^3 \pmod{m}$. Similarly, $2abc \equiv 2aec \pmod{m}$. By (d), $ab^3 - 2abc \equiv ae^3 - 2aec \pmod{m}$. Finally, employing (c), we find $ae^3 - 2aec \equiv 5d^2 \pmod{m}$.

Even the simple properties of congruence given in Theorem 5–6.3 have useful applications.

EXAMPLE 1. Let us find the remainder obtained on dividing the sum

$$1^{10} + 2^{10} + 3^{10} + \cdots + 100^{10}$$

by 7. By Theorem 5–6.3,

$$1^{10} + 2^{10} + 3^{10} + \cdots + 100^{10} \equiv$$
$$1^{10} + 2^{10} + \cdots + 6^{10} + 0^{10} +$$
$$1^{10} + 2^{10} + \cdots + 6^{10} + 0^{10} +$$

$$\cdots$$

$$1^{10} + 2^{10} + \cdots + 6^{10} + 0^{10} + 99^{10} + 100^{10} \pmod{7},$$

where this sum contains 14 occurrences of the blocks $1^{10} + 2^{10} + \cdots + 6^{10} + 0^{10}$ (since $14 \cdot 7 = 98$). Thus,

$$1^{10} + 2^{10} + 3^{10} + \cdots + 100^{10} \equiv 14 \cdot (1^{10} + 2^{10} + \cdots + 6^{10}) + 1^{10} + 2^{10}$$
$$\equiv 1^{10} + 2^{10} = 1 + (32)^2$$
$$\equiv 1 + 4^2 = 17 \equiv 3 \pmod{7}.$$

Consequently, the remainder obtained on dividing the sum $1^{10} + 2^{10} + 3^{10} + \cdots + 100^{10}$ by 7 is 3.

EXAMPLE 2. A well-known property of natural numbers written in decimal notation is that such a number is divisible by 9 if and only if the sum of its digits is divisible by 9. The basis for this useful fact is the observation that if

$$n = r_k 10^k + r_{k-1} 10^{k-1} + \cdots + r_1 10 + r_0,$$

where $0 \le r_i < 10$, then since $10 \equiv 1 \pmod 9$,

$$n \equiv r_k + r_{k-1} + \cdots + r_1 + r_0 \pmod 9.$$

That is, any natural number is congruent modulo 9 to the sum of its digits. In particular, n is divisible by 9 if and only if the sum of the digits of n is divisible by 9. Note that the process of adding digits can be repeated to obtain the remainder on division of a number by 9. For instance,

$$77815 \equiv 7 + 7 + 8 + 1 + 5 = 28 \equiv 2 + 8 = 10 \equiv 1 + 0 = 1 \pmod 9.$$

One of the simplest and most familiar methods of checking the addition of a column of numbers is based on this observation. The process is called "casting out nines." It consists of summing the digits of each number in the column, adding these sums, and comparing the result with the number which is obtained by summing the digits of the number which is supposed to be the sum of the given numbers. If the two numbers being compared are not congruent modulo 9, then there is an error. For example:

$$
\begin{array}{rl}
2165 & \equiv 14 \\
3082 & \equiv 13 \\
7165 & \equiv 19 \\
11011 & \equiv 4 \\
35171 & \equiv 17 \\
\underline{1022} & \equiv \underline{5} \\
59616 & \quad 72 \equiv 7 + 2 \equiv 0 \pmod 9 \\
& \equiv 27 \equiv 2 + 7 \equiv 0 \pmod 9
\end{array}
$$

Of course, this check is not infallible, but it is easy to apply. It is left to the reader to show that this method can also be used to check multiplication.

The following theorem gives some of the most useful relations between congruences with different moduli.

THEOREM 5–6.4.
  (a) If $a \equiv b \pmod m$, then $la \equiv lb \pmod{lm}$.
  (b) If $a \equiv b \pmod m$ and $l \mid m$, then $a \equiv b \pmod l$.
  (c) If $a \equiv b \pmod m$ and d is a common divisor of a, b, and m, then $a/d \equiv b/d \pmod{m/d}$.
  (d) If $ca \equiv cb \pmod m$, then $a \equiv b \pmod{m/(c, m)}$.

(e) If $a \equiv b \pmod{m_1}$ and $c \equiv d \pmod{m_2}$,
then $a + c \equiv b + d \pmod{(m_1, m_2)}$, $a - c \equiv b - d \pmod{(m_1, m_2)}$,
and $ac \equiv bd \pmod{(m_1, m_2)}$.

(f) If $a \equiv b \pmod{m_1}$, $a \equiv b \pmod{m_2}$, $\ldots$, $a \equiv b \pmod{m_k}$, then
$a \equiv b \pmod{n}$, where n is the least common multiple of m_1, m_2,
$\ldots$, m_k.

The reader will find that (a), (b), and (c) are straightforward consequences of Definition 5–6.1. Property (d) is the cancellation law for congruences. To prove (d), we first note that since (c, m) is a common divisor of ca, cb, and m, by (c) we have $ca/(c, m) \equiv cb/(c, m) \pmod{m/(c, m)}$. This means that $m/(c, m)$ divides $[c/(c, m)](a - b)$. But $m/(c, m)$ and $c/(c, m)$ are relatively prime. Therefore, by Theorem 5–2.6, $m/(c, m)$ divides $(a - b)$. That is, $a \equiv b \pmod{m/(c, m)}$, proving (d). In order to prove (e), we observe that $a \equiv b \pmod{(m_1, m_2)}$ and $c \equiv d \pmod{(m_1, m_2)}$ by (b), since $(m_1, m_2) | m_1$ and $(m_1, m_2) | m_2$. The conclusion follows from Theorem 5–6.3 (d) and (e). By Definition 5–6.1, the hypothesis of (f) is equivalent to the statement that $m_1 | (a - b)$, $m_2 | (a - b)$, $\ldots$, and $m_k | (a - b)$. Therefore, by (5–3.6b) the least common multiple n of m_1, m_2, $\ldots$, m_k divides $a - b$. In other words, $a \equiv b \pmod{n}$.

PROBLEMS

1. Show that every integer is congruent modulo 7 to exactly one of the following numbers: 291, 7, 54, 31, 36, 20, 765.

2. Find the remainders on dividing 3^{60} by 7, 15, and 31. [*Hint:* Write $60 = 2^5 + 2^4 + 2^3 + 2^2$, so that $3^{60} = 3^{32}3^{16}3^83^4$.]

3. Prove (a), (b), and (c) of Theorem 5–6.3.

4. Prove that if $a \equiv b \pmod{m}$, then $(a, m) = (b, m)$.

5. Show that the method of "casting out nines" can be used to check multiplication of natural numbers.

6. Use the fact that $10 \equiv -1 \pmod{11}$ and $10^2 \equiv 1 \pmod{11}$ to discover a rule for divisibility of a natural number (written in decimal notation) by 11.

7. Discover a method of "casting out sixes" as a check for addition and multiplication for natural numbers written in the base 7 notation.

8. Prove (a), (b), and (c) of Theorem 5–6.4.

9. Find the remainder obtained for the following divisions.
   (a) $1^5 + 2^5 + 3^5 + \cdots + 1080^5$ divided by 14.
   (b) $1 + 2! + 3! + 4! + \cdots + (10^{10})!$ divided by 24.
   (c) $\binom{3}{0} + \binom{4}{1} + \binom{5}{2} + \cdots + \binom{102}{99}$ divided by 7.

5–7 Linear congruences. The linear equation $ax = b$, where a and b are integers, has a solution which is an integer if and only if a divides b. In fact, this statement is just the definition of divisibility. This section is concerned with the analogous problem of solving the linear congruence

$$ax \equiv b \pmod{m}.$$

Linear congruences occur in a variety of practical problems.

EXAMPLE 1. A synodic month (the period of time between two consecutive appearances of a full moon) is approximately $29\frac{1}{2}$ days. If a full moon occurs at a certain time on Monday evening, how many synodic months later will the full moon occur at approximately the same time on Wednesday evening? If we measure time in terms of half days, the synodic month is 59 half days in length and a week is 14 half days long. After x synodic months beyond the occurrence of the full moon, $59x$ half days have elapsed, and a full moon occurs again. If we divide $59x$ by 14 obtaining a remainder r, then this full moon occurs r half days after Monday evening. Since Wednesday is 4 half days after Monday, the x which solves our problem is the smallest positive integral solution of the congruence

$$59x \equiv 4 \pmod{14}.$$

Since $59 \equiv 3 \pmod{14}$, this congruence is equivalent to

$$3x \equiv 4 \pmod{14}.$$

By trial, we find that $x = 6$ is the smallest positive solution of this congruence.

To understand more clearly the nature of the solutions of linear congruences, let us examine a particular example. Consider the congruence

$$3x \equiv 2 \pmod{5}.$$

Substituting $x = 1, 2, 3, \ldots, 20$, we find that among these numbers only $x = 4$, $x = 9$, $x = 14$, and $x = 19$ satisfy the congruence. Note that these numbers are all congruent modulo 5. This suggests that all integers x which are congruent to 4 modulo 5, and only these numbers, are solutions of $3x \equiv 2 \pmod{5}$.

By checking more values of x we could gather additional evidence for our guess. However, this is unnecessary, since the conjecture is easy to prove. First, if $x \equiv 4 \pmod{5}$, then by Theorem 5–6.3, $3x \equiv 3 \cdot 4 = 12 \equiv 2 \pmod{5}$. Thus every such x is a solution. Next we must show that these are the only solutions. If x is any solution, then

$$3x \equiv 2 \equiv 3 \cdot 4 \pmod{5}.$$

Since 3 is relatively prime to 5, it follows from Theorem 5–6.4(d) that $x \equiv 4 \pmod 5$. The result that x satisfies $3x \equiv 2 \pmod 5$ if and only if $x \equiv 4 \pmod 5$ provides a complete solution of the linear congruence $3x \equiv 2 \pmod 5$.

In order to describe the solutions of linear congruences in general, we introduce a new concept. By Theorem 5–6.2, every integer is congruent modulo m to one and only one of the numbers $0, 1, 2, \ldots, m - 1$. Thus the set Z of all integers is divided into disjoint subsets $X_0, X_1, X_2, \ldots, X_{m-1}$ where

$$X_r = \{x \in Z \mid x \equiv r \pmod m\}.$$

The sets $X_0, X_1, X_2, \ldots, X_{m-1}$ are called *congruence classes modulo m* (or *residue classes modulo m*). For example, if $m = 2$, X_0 is the set of all even integers and X_1 is the set of all odd integers. If $m = 4$, $X_0 = \{4k \mid k \in Z\}$, $X_1 = \{4k + 1 \mid k \in Z\}$, $X_2 = \{4k + 2 \mid k \in Z\}$, and $X_3 = \{4k + 3 \mid k \in Z\}$.

If the integers x and y are in the same congruence class X_r modulo m, then $x \equiv r \pmod m$ and $y \equiv r \pmod m$. Therefore, by Theorem 5–6.3(b) and (c), $x \equiv y \pmod m$. Conversely, if $x \equiv y \pmod m$ and $y \in X_r$, then $x \equiv y \equiv r \pmod m$, so that $x \in X_r$. Thus, two integers x and y are in the same congruence class modulo m if and only if $x \equiv y \pmod m$.

As in the example discussed above, if x is a solution of the congruence

$$ax \equiv b \pmod m,$$

and if $y \equiv x \pmod m$, then by Theorem 5–6.3,

$$ay \equiv ax \equiv b \pmod m.$$

Thus, if x is a solution of $ax \equiv b \pmod m$, then every member of the congruence class which contains x is also a solution of the congruence. In the example $3x \equiv 2 \pmod 5$, every element of the congruence class X_4 is a solution of the congruence. In fact, the solutions of $3x \equiv 2 \pmod 5$ are *exactly* the integers which belong to X_4. However, it may happen that a linear congruence modulo m has solutions belonging to more than one congruence class modulo m. For example,

$$2x \equiv 6 \pmod{12}$$

has the solutions 3 and 9, and therefore every element in either of the two congruence classes X_3 and X_9 is a solution of this congruence. On the other hand, some linear congruences have no solutions. For instance,

$$2x \equiv 1 \pmod 6$$

cannot be satisfied by any integer x, since $2x - 1$ is always odd and therefore not divisible by 6.

These remarks suggest that a linear congruence

$$ax \equiv b \pmod{m}$$

is effectively solved if we obtain a representative set of solutions

$$\{r_1, r_2, \ldots, r_k\} \quad \text{(possibly empty)},$$

where $0 \le r_i \le m - 1$ and $r_i \ne r_j$ for $i \ne j$ (which implies that the r_i
belong to different congruence classes), such that every solution of
$ax \equiv b \pmod{m}$ is a member of the congruence class of some r_i. If
$ax \equiv b \pmod{m}$ has such a representative set of solutions $\{r_1, r_2, \ldots, r_k\}$,
then this congruence is said to have exactly k *incongruent solutions modulo*
m. In particular, if $k = 1$, that is, all solutions belong to the same congruence class, then we say that the congruence has a *unique solution modulo*
m. This is the case for the congruence $3x \equiv 2 \pmod{5}$.

If m is not very large, it is possible to obtain the representative set of
solutions by testing each of the numbers $0, 1, 2, \ldots, m - 1$ to see which
of them satisfy $ax \equiv b \pmod{m}$. However, this procedure is impractical
for large values of m. Fortunately, it is possible to prove general theorems
which give a complete solution for any linear congruence.

THEOREM 5-7.1. If $(a, m) = 1$, the congruence $ax \equiv b \pmod{m}$ has a
unique solution modulo m.

Proof. By Theorem 5-2.2(a), there exist integers u and v such that
$ua + vm = 1$. Multiplying by b, we obtain

$$bua + bvm = b, \quad \text{or} \quad a(bu) - b = (-bv)m.$$

By Definition 5-6.1, $a(bu) \equiv b \pmod{m}$, so that $x = bu$ is a solution of
the given congruence. Suppose that r is any solution of $ax \equiv b \pmod{m}$.
Then

$$ar \equiv b \equiv a(bu) \pmod{m}.$$

Since $(a, m) = 1$, we can use the cancelation law for congruences, Theorem 5-6.4(d), to cancel a and obtain

$$r \equiv bu \pmod{m}.$$

Thus, any solution of the given congruence is congruent modulo m to the
solution $x = bu$, so that $ax \equiv b \pmod{m}$ has a unique solution modulo m.
Note that u can be found by using the Euclidean algorithm, explained in
Section 5-2.

Now consider the general linear congruence.

THEOREM 5-7.2. The congruence $ax \equiv b \pmod{m}$ has a solution if and only if (a, m) divides b. If (a, m) divides b, the congruence has exactly (a, m) incongruent solutions modulo m.

Proof. If the congruence $ax \equiv b \pmod{m}$ has a solution r, then $ar - b = lm$, or $ar - lm = b$, for some integer l. Since (a, m) is a common divisor of a and m, (a, m) divides b. Conversely, if (a, m) divides b, then we can consider the congruence

$$\frac{a}{(a, m)} x \equiv \frac{b}{(a, m)} \left(\mathrm{mod}\ \frac{m}{(a, m)} \right). \tag{5-8}$$

Since $a/(a, m)$ and $m/(a, m)$ are relatively prime, (5-8) has a solution s by Theorem 5-7.1. Then $as \equiv b \pmod{m}$ by Theorem 5-6.4(a), so that s is a solution of $ax \equiv b \pmod{m}$. In fact, any solution of (5-8) is a solution of the given congruence.

If the condition $(a, m)|b$ is satisfied, then the congruence (5-8) has a solution s satisfying $0 \le s < m/(a, m)$. Define for $j = 0, 1, \ldots, (a, m) - 1$,

$$s_j = s + \frac{jm}{(a, m)}. \tag{5-9}$$

Then $s_j \equiv s \left(\mathrm{mod}\ m/(a, m) \right)$, so that s_j is a solution of (5-8), and therefore of $ax \equiv b \pmod{m}$. Moreover, since

$$0 \le s_0 < s_1 < s_2 < \cdots < s_{(a,m)-1} < m,$$

it follows that if $0 \le i < j \le (a, m) - 1$, then s_i is not congruent to s_j modulo m. We will show that

$$\{s_0, s_1, s_2, \ldots, s_{(a,m)-1}\} \tag{5-10}$$

is a representative set of solutions of the congruence $ax \equiv b \pmod{m}$. That is, every integer t satisfying $at \equiv b \pmod{m}$ is congruent modulo m to s_r for some r. By Theorem 5-6.4(c), $at \equiv b \pmod{m}$ implies that t is a solution of (5-8). Therefore, $t \equiv s \left(\mathrm{mod}\ m/(a, m) \right)$ by Theorem 5-7.1. That is,

$$t = s + l[m/(a, m)]$$

for some integer l. By the division algorithm, $l = q(a, m) + r$, where $0 \le r \le (a, m) - 1$. Thus,

$$t = s + \frac{rm}{(a, m)} + qm = s_r + qm \equiv s_r \pmod{m}.$$

EXAMPLE 2. Solve the congruence $15x \equiv 20 \pmod{35}$. Since $(15, 35) = 5$, and $5|20$, the congruence has 5 solutions which are incongruent modulo 35. These are obtained by first solving $3x \equiv 4 \pmod 7$. We find the solution $x = 6$. Then a representative set of solutions of $15x \equiv 20 \pmod{35}$ is obtained from (5–9) and (5–10). These are

$$6, \qquad 6 + 7 = 13, \qquad 6 + 14 = 20, \qquad 6 + 21 = 27, \qquad 6 + 28 = 34.$$

For $(a, m) = 1$, the congruence $ax \equiv b \pmod m$ can be solved as in Theorem 5–7.1 using the Euclidean algorithm. This is probably the best method if the numbers a and b are large. If these numbers are small, the congruence can often be solved more easily by trial, or by using the properties of congruences given in Theorem 5–6.3.

EXAMPLE 3. Solve $3x \equiv 4 \pmod 7$. If x is a solution, then $6x \equiv 8 \pmod 7$, so that $-x \equiv 1 \pmod 7$, and $x \equiv -1 \equiv 6 \pmod 7$. Suppose that we wish to solve $5x \equiv 9 \pmod{13}$. If x is a solution, then $18x \equiv 9 \pmod{13}$, and therefore $2x \equiv 1 \pmod{13}$; consequently, $14x \equiv 7 \pmod{13}$, and $x \equiv 7 \pmod{13}$. As a final example, if x is a solution of $5x \equiv 11 \pmod{17}$, then $5x \equiv 45 \pmod{17}$; hence $x \equiv 9 \pmod{17}$.

There is an important application of Theorem 5–7.1 to the construction of sets of orthogonal Latin squares. A *Latin square of side m* is an arrangement of m distinct symbols in m^2 subsquares of a square, in such a way that every row and every column contains each symbol exactly once. It is immaterial what symbols are used, but it is convenient to let them be the number symbols $0, 1, 2, \ldots, m - 1$. As an example,

0	1	2
2	0	1
1	2	0

is a Latin square of side 3. Two Latin squares of the same size are called *orthogonal* if, when one is superposed on the other, every ordered pair of symbols occurs exactly once in the resulting square. For instance

0	1	2
2	0	1
1	2	0

0	1	2
1	2	0
2	0	1

TABLE 5–1

$r(0)$	$r(1)$	$r(2)$	$\cdots$	$r(p-1)$
$r(k)$	$r(1+k)$	$r(2+k)$	$\cdots$	$r(p-1+k)$
$r(2k)$	$r(1+2k)$	$r(2+2k)$	$\cdots$	$r(p-1+2k)$
$\cdot$ $\cdot$ $\cdot$	$\cdot$ $\cdot$ $\cdot$	$\cdot$ $\cdot$ $\cdot$	$\cdots$ $\cdots$ $\cdots$	$\cdot$ $\cdot$ $\cdot$
$r((p-1)k)$	$r(1+(p-1)k)$	$r(2+(p-1)k)$	$\cdots$	$r(p-1+(p-1)k)$

are orthogonal Latin squares, since when one is superposed on the other we have

0, 0	1, 1	2, 2
2, 1	0, 2	1, 0
1, 2	2, 0	0, 1

For centuries, amateur and professional mathematicians have found Latin squares interesting. In recent years the study of pairs of orthogonal Latin squares has taken a serious turn, because of the discovery that such pairs have important applications in algebra, geometry, and applied statistics.

Let p be a prime. For any integer a, let $r(a)$ be the remainder on dividing a by p. That is, $0 \le r(a) < p$, and $a \equiv r(a) \pmod{p}$. For $0 < k < p$, define a Latin square (which we designate by L_k) as in Table 5–1. In other words, the number in the ith row and jth column of L_k is

$$r((j-1)+(i-1)k).$$

To show that L_k is a Latin square, it is necessary to prove that if $0 \le b < p$, then b occurs in every row of L_k and in every column of L_k. Consider the ith row. Then $b-(i-1)k \equiv c \pmod{p}$ for some c satisfying $0 \le c \le p-1$. Let $j = c+1$. Then

$$(j-1)+(i-1)k \equiv b \pmod{p}.$$

Thus,

$$r((j-1)+(i-1)k) = b.$$

Therefore, b occurs as the jth entry of the ith row. Now examine the jth column. Since $0 < k < p$ and p is a prime, it follows that $(k, p) = 1$.

Hence by Theorem 5–7.1, there is an integer d such that

$$kd \equiv b - (j - 1) \pmod{p}.$$

We can select d so that $0 \leq d \leq p - 1$. Define $i = d + 1$. Then

$$(j - 1) + (i - 1)k = (j - 1) + kd \equiv b \pmod{p}.$$

Consequently, $r((j - 1) + (i - 1)k) = b$, so that b is the ith entry of the jth column in L_k. Thus, we have shown that each row and column contains each of the numbers $0, 1, \ldots, p - 1$ at least once. Since there are only p entries in each row and column, it follows that the rows and columns cannot contain these symbols more than once. Therefore, L_k is a Latin square.

We wish to show now that if $0 < k < k' < p$, then the squares L_k and $L_{k'}$ are orthogonal. For this, we have to prove that if $0 \leq a \leq p - 1$ and $0 \leq b \leq p - 1$, there are natural numbers i and j such that $1 \leq i \leq p$, $1 \leq j \leq p$, and $r((j - 1) + (i - 1)k) = a$, $r((j - 1) + (i - 1)k') = b$. This is clearly equivalent to the problem of solving the congruences

$$(j - 1) + (i - 1)k \equiv a \pmod{p},$$
$$(j - 1) + (i - 1)k' \equiv b \pmod{p}$$

for i and j. Subtracting these congruences, we obtain the condition

$$(i - 1)(k' - k) \equiv b - a \pmod{p},$$

which can be written in the form

$$(k' - k)i \equiv (b - a) + (k' - k) \pmod{p}.$$

Since $0 < k' - k < p$ and p is a prime, it follows from Theorem 5–7.1 that this congruence has a solution i such that $1 \leq i \leq p$. Choose j so that $1 \leq j \leq p$ and

$$j - 1 \equiv a - (i - 1)k \pmod{p}.$$

Then by construction, $j - 1$ and $i - 1$ satisfy the congruence $(j - 1) + (i - 1)k \equiv a \pmod{p}$. However, these values of $j - 1$ and $i - 1$ also satisfy the congruence $(j - 1) + (i - 1)k' \equiv b \pmod{p}$. In fact,

$$j - 1 + (i - 1)k' \equiv a - (i - 1)k + (i - 1)k'$$
$$= a + (i - 1)(k' - k) \equiv b \pmod{p}.$$

This proves that L_k and $L_{k'}$ are orthogonal. Note that we have constructed a set of $p - 1$ Latin squares, each pair of which is orthogonal.

Many problems in number theory require the simultaneous solution of systems of congruences. We will prove a famous and important theorem about such congruences. This result was known to Chinese mathematicians as early as 250 A.D., and for this reason it is usually called the *Chinese remainder theorem*.

THEOREM 5–7.3. Let $m_1, m_2, \ldots, m_k$ be natural numbers such that $(m_i, m_j) = 1$ if $i \neq j$. Then if $b_1, b_2, \ldots, b_k$ are any integers, there exists an integer x such that

$$x \equiv b_1 \pmod{m_1}, \quad x \equiv b_2 \pmod{m_2}, \quad \ldots, \quad x \equiv b_k \pmod{m_k}.$$

Moreover, x is unique modulo $m_1 m_2 \ldots m_k$.

Proof. Let $n_i = m_1 m_2 \ldots m_{i-1} m_{i+1} \ldots m_k$. Then $(n_i, m_i) = 1$ since $(m_i, m_j) = 1$ if $i \neq j$. Consequently, by Theorem 5–7.1, there is an integer t_i such that $n_i t_i \equiv b_i \pmod{m_i}$. Let

$$x = n_1 t_1 + n_2 t_2 + \cdots + n_k t_k.$$

Then $x \equiv n_i t_i \equiv b_i \pmod{m_i}$, since if $j \neq i$, then $m_i | n_j$, and consequently $n_j t_j \equiv 0 \pmod{m_i}$. Thus, x is a simultaneous solution of the given system of congruences. If y also satisfies $y \equiv b_1 \pmod{m_1}$, $y \equiv b_2 \pmod{m_2}, \ldots, y \equiv b_k \pmod{m_k}$, then $x \equiv y \pmod{m_1}$, $x \equiv y \pmod{m_2}, \ldots, x \equiv y \pmod{m_k}$. Therefore by Theorem 5–6.4(f), $x \equiv y \pmod{m}$, where m is the least common multiple of $\{m_1, m_2, \ldots, m_k\}$. But since these integers have no common prime factors, their least common multiple is $m_1 m_2 \ldots m_k$.

PROBLEMS

1. Give the representative set of solutions for each of the following linear congruences.
   (a) $362x \equiv 236 \pmod{24}$
   (b) $55x \equiv 5 \pmod{31}$
   (c) $84x \equiv 96 \pmod{7}$
   (d) $36x \equiv 6 \pmod{21}$
   (e) $270x \equiv 30 \pmod{150}$

2. Let p be a prime. Show that if $p \nmid a$, then the congruence $ax \equiv b \pmod{p}$ has a unique solution modulo p.

3. Find the solutions of the following systems of congruences.
   (a) $x \equiv 5 \pmod{6}$, $x \equiv 7 \pmod{11}$
   (b) $x \equiv 1 \pmod{2}$, $x \equiv 0 \pmod{3}$, $x \equiv 2 \pmod{5}$
   (c) $x \equiv 21 \pmod{29}$, $x \equiv 5 \pmod{30}$, $x \equiv 24 \pmod{31}$

4. Let a, b, and c be integers and let m be a natural number. Suppose that $(c, m) = 1$.

(a) Prove that the congruence $ax \equiv b \pmod{m}$ is equivalent to the congruence $cax \equiv cb \pmod{m}$, that is, every solution of $ax \equiv b \pmod{m}$ is a solution of $cax \equiv cb \pmod{m}$, and conversely.

(b) Suppose, in addition, that $(a, m) = 1$. Prove that the congruence $ax \equiv b \pmod{m}$ is equivalent to the congruence $x \equiv b' \pmod{m}$ for some integer b'.

5. Let m_1, m_2, $\ldots$, m_k be natural numbers such that $(m_i, m_j) = 1$ if $i \neq j$. Let a_1, a_2, $\ldots$, a_k and b_1, b_2, $\ldots$, b_k be integers. Prove that the system of congruences

$$a_1x \equiv b_1 \pmod{m_1}, \qquad a_2x \equiv b_2 \pmod{m_2}, \qquad \ldots, \qquad a_kx \equiv b_k \pmod{m_k}$$

has a solution if and only if

$$(a_1, m_1)|b_1, \qquad (a_2, m_2)|b_2, \qquad \ldots, \qquad (a_k, m_k)|b_k.$$

[*Hint:* Reduce the system of congruences to the form treated in Theorem 5–7.3 by using Problem 4(b), together with an argument similar to that given in the proof of Theorem 5–7.2.]

6. Determine which of the following systems of congruences have a solution, and when solutions exist, find at least one.

(a) $5x \equiv 1 \pmod{7}$, $22x \equiv 2 \pmod{6}$
(b) $8x \equiv 14 \pmod{24}$, $4x \equiv 1 \pmod{125}$
(c) $3^8x \equiv 3 \pmod{12}$, $50x \equiv 75 \pmod{125}$, $x \equiv 1000 \pmod{91}$
(d) $2^{33}x \equiv 10 \pmod{12}$, $73x \equiv 1 \pmod{219}$, $12x \equiv 4 \pmod{8}$

7. A band of 17 thieves stole a large sack of dollar bills. They tried to divide the bills evenly, but had three bills left over. Two of the thieves began to argue about the extra money, so one of them shot the other. The money was redistributed, but this time there were ten bills remaining. Again argument developed, and one more thief was shot. When the money was redistributed, there was none left over. What was the least possible amount of money which could have been stolen originally?

8. Construct a set of 4 Latin squares with 5 rows and 5 columns, such that each pair of the set is orthogonal.

*5–8 The theorems of Fermat and Euler. One of the oldest and most famous theorems in number theory was discovered by Fermat and communicated to a friend in 1640. The first published proof of Fermat's theorem, due to the Swiss mathematician Leonhard Euler (1707–1783), appeared almost a century later. Subsequently, a more general theorem was found by Euler. In this section we will discuss these classical results and some of their applications.

Fermat's theorem concerns congruences with prime moduli. These are important because many problems concerning congruences with composite modulus can be reduced to questions about congruences with prime modulus. We begin by noting a simple property of the binomial coefficients.

(5–8.1). If p is a prime and if i is an integer such that $0 < i < p$, then

$$\binom{p}{i} = \frac{p!}{i!(p-i)!} \equiv 0 \ (\text{mod } p).$$

We leave the proof of this fact as an exercise for the reader (see Problem 6, Section 5–5).

If p is a prime, and if a and b are any integers, then by the binomial theorem

$$(a+b)^p = a^p + \binom{p}{i} a^{p-1}b + \binom{p}{2} a^{p-2}b^2 + \cdots$$

$$+ \binom{p}{p-1} ab^{p-1} + b^p \equiv a^p + b^p \ (\text{mod } p),$$

since by (5–8.1), $\binom{p}{i}a^{p-i}b^i \equiv 0 \ (\text{mod } p)$ if $1 \le i \le p - 1$. Using mathematical induction, this observation can be generalized as follows.

(5–8.2). If p is a prime, and if $a_1, a_2, \ldots, a_n$ are any integers, then

$$(a_1 + a_2 + \cdots + a_n)^p \equiv a_1^p + a_2^p + \cdots + a_n^p \ (\text{mod } p).$$

Proof. If $n = 1$, then the assertion is that $a_1^p \equiv a_1^p \ (\text{mod } p)$, which is clearly valid. Assuming that the result holds for n, it follows from the remarks above that

$$[(a_1 + a_2 + \cdots + a_n) + a_{n+1}]^p \equiv (a_1 + a_2 + \cdots + a_n)^p + a_{n+1}^p$$

$$\equiv a_1^p + a_2^p + \cdots + a_n^p + a_{n+1}^p \ (\text{mod } p).$$

This proves the induction step.

If we let $a_1 = a_2 = \ldots = a_n = 1$ in (5–8.2), we obtain $n^p \equiv n \ (\text{mod } p)$. Also, if p is odd, and $a_1 = a_2 \ldots = a_n = -1$, then (5–8.2) specializes to $(-n)^p \equiv -n \ (\text{mod } p)$. This is also true if $p = 2$, since $-n \equiv n \ (\text{mod } 2)$. Obviously, $0^p \equiv 0 \ (\text{mod } p)$. Therefore, we have proved the following theorem.

THEOREM 5–8.3. If p is a prime, and if a is any integer, then

$$a^p \equiv a \ (\text{mod } p).$$

Although this theorem is obtained as a special case of (5–8.2), it is evident that (5–8.2) can be deduced easily from the theorem. The *"little theorem of Fermat"* is a slight variation of Theorem 5–8.3.

THEOREM 5–8.4. If p is a prime, and if a is any integer which is not divisible by p, then

$$a^{p-1} \equiv 1 \pmod{p}.$$

Proof. By Theorem 5–8.3, p divides $a(a^{p-1} - 1)$. Since p does not divide a, it must divide $a^{p-1} - 1$, by (5–3.2). Hence, $a^{p-1} \equiv 1 \pmod{p}$.

The method by which we have proved Theorem 5–8.4 is similar to Euler's first proof of this theorem. Some years later, Euler found a different way to prove Fermat's theorem. Using the ideas of this second proof, he was able to establish the more general result known as Euler's theorem. We will prove Euler's theorem by a method which was discovered about 50 years later. This proof is important because it introduces a technique which has many applications in number theory. The following definition is needed.

DEFINITION 5–8.5. Let m be a natural number. The *totient* of m is the number of nonnegative integers less than m which are relatively prime to m. The totient of m is usually denoted by $\varphi(m)$.

In other words, $\varphi(m)$ is the number of integers k such that $0 \leq k < m$ and $(k, m) = 1$. For example, $\varphi(1) = 1$, $\varphi(2) = 1$, $\varphi(3) = 2$, $\varphi(4) = 2$, $\varphi(5) = 4$, and $\varphi(6) = 2$. If p is a prime, then the numbers $1, 2, \ldots, p-1$ are all prime to p, so that $\varphi(p) = p - 1$.

THEOREM 5–8.6. *Euler's theorem.* If m is a natural number and a is an integer which is relatively prime to m, then

$$a^{\varphi(m)} \equiv 1 \pmod{m}.$$

Proof. To simplify notation, let t denote $\varphi(m)$. According to the definition of $\varphi(m)$, there are exactly t different natural numbers in the set $\{0, 1, 2, \ldots, m - 1\}$ which are relatively prime to m. Let these be designated as

$$k_1, \quad k_2, \quad \ldots, \quad k_t.$$

Consider the set of integers

$$ak_1, \quad ak_2, \quad \ldots, \quad ak_t.$$

By the division algorithm, we have for $i = 1, 2, \ldots, t$

$$ak_i = q_i m + r_i,$$

where q_i is an integer and $0 \le r_i < m$. Thus, $ak_i \equiv r_i \pmod{m}$. The main step of the proof consists of showing that the list of numbers r_1, r_2, ..., r_t is just a rearrangement of the sequence k_1, k_2, ..., k_t. We do this indirectly. First note that each r_i is relatively prime to m. In fact, if a prime p divides both m and r_i, then p also divides $q_i m + r_i = ak_i$. Thus, either $p|a$ or $p|k_i$. However, since $p|m$ and both a and k_i are relatively prime to m, p cannot divide either a or k_i. Therefore, $(r_i, m) = 1$. Since k_1, k_2, ..., k_t is the list of *all* integers k such that $0 \le k < m$ and $(k, m) = 1$, and since each r_i satisfies these conditions, it follows that each r_i must be equal to some k_n. If we can show that the numbers r_1, r_2, ..., r_t are all different, then our proof that $r_1, r_2, \ldots, r_t$ is a rearrangement of $k_1, k_2, \ldots, k_t$ will be complete. Suppose that $r_i = r_j$ for some $i \ne j$. Then subtracting the equations $ak_i = q_i m + r_i$ and $ak_j = q_j m + r_j$ gives

$$a(k_i - k_j) = (q_i - q_j)m.$$

Therefore, $m|a(k_i - k_j)$. Since a is prime to m, it follows from Theorem 5–2.6 that $m|(k_i - k_j)$. However, $i \ne j$ implies $k_i \ne k_j$, and $0 \le k_i, k_j < m$ yields $-m < k_i - k_j < m$. Hence, $0 < |k_i - k_j| < m$. Therefore, m cannot divide $k_i - k_j$. This contradiction proves that the numbers r_1, r_2, ..., r_t are all different, and that the list $r_1, r_2, \ldots, r_t$ is the same (in possibly different order) as $k_1, k_2, \ldots, k_t$. In particular, by the commutative law of multiplication,

$$r_1 \cdot r_2 \cdot \cdots \cdot r_t = k_1 \cdot k_2 \cdot \cdots \cdot k_t.$$

Consequently, since $ak_i \equiv r_i \pmod{m}$,

$$k_1 \cdot k_2 \cdot \cdots \cdot k_t = r_1 \cdot r_2 \cdot \cdots \cdot r_t \equiv (ak_1) \cdot (ak_2) \cdot \cdots \cdot (ak_t)$$
$$= a^t \cdot (k_1 \cdot k_2 \cdot \cdots \cdot k_t) \pmod{m}.$$

It only remains to observe that the product $k_1 \cdot k_2 \cdots \cdot k_t$ can be cancelled from each side of this congruence. In fact, no prime factor of m divides any of the integers $k_1, k_2, \ldots, k_t$ since these numbers are relatively prime to m. Thus, m has no prime factor in common with the product $k_1 \cdot k_2 \cdot \cdots \cdot k_t$. That is, $(k_1 \cdot k_2 \cdot \cdots \cdot k_t, m) = 1$, and the cancellation is permissible by (5–6.4d). Thus, $1 \equiv a^t = a^{\varphi(m)} \pmod{m}$.

This proof can be illustrated by carrying it out in a particular numerical case. Let $m = 14$. Then the integers in the range from 0 to 13 which are relatively prime to 14 are 1, 3, 5, 9, 11, and 13. These can be taken as the numbers $k_1, k_2, \ldots, k_t$ in the proof of Theorem 5–8.6. In this example,

$t = \varphi(14) = 6$. Let $a = -5$. Then the numbers ak_i are

$$(-5) \cdot 1 \ = -5, \qquad (-5) \cdot 3 \ = -15, \qquad (-5) \cdot 5 \ = -25,$$
$$(-5) \cdot 9 = -45, \qquad (-5) \cdot 11 = -55, \qquad (-5) \cdot 13 = -65.$$

The division algorithm gives

$$(-5) \cdot 1 \ = (-1) \cdot 14 + 9, \qquad (-5) \cdot 3 \ = (-2) \cdot 14 + 13,$$
$$(-5) \cdot 5 \ = (-2) \cdot 14 + 3, \qquad (-5) \cdot 9 \ = (-4) \cdot 14 + 11,$$
$$(-5) \cdot 11 = (-4) \cdot 14 + 1, \qquad (-5) \cdot 13 = (-5) \cdot 14 + 5.$$

Therefore in our special case, the numbers $r_1, r_2, \ldots, r_t$ occurring in the proof of Theorem 5–8.6 are 9, 13, 3, 11, 1, and 5. This agrees with the general result that $r_1, r_2, \ldots, r_t$ is a rearrangement of $k_1, k_2, \ldots, k_t$. To conclude the illustration, note that

$$1 \cdot 3 \cdot 5 \cdot 9 \cdot 11 \cdot 13 = 9 \cdot 13 \cdot 3 \cdot 11 \cdot 1 \cdot 5$$
$$\equiv [(-5) \cdot 1][(-5) \cdot 3][(-5) \cdot 5][(-5) \cdot 9][(-5) \cdot 11][(-5) \cdot 13]$$
$$= (-5)^6 (1 \cdot 3 \cdot 5 \cdot 9 \cdot 11 \cdot 13) \ (\text{mod } 14).$$

Since $1 \cdot 3 \cdot 5 \cdot 9 \cdot 11 \cdot 13$ is relatively prime to 14, it follows that

$$(-5)^6 \equiv 1 \ (\text{mod } 14).$$

If the natural number m in Euler's theorem is a prime p, then $\varphi(m) = \varphi(p) = p - 1$, and the theorem asserts that if $(a, p) = 1$, then $a^{p-1} \equiv 1 \ (\text{mod } p)$. This is exactly the statement of Fermat's theorem.

In order to use Euler's theorem, it is necessary to know the value of the totient $\varphi(m)$. For small values of m, $\varphi(m)$ can be obtained by counting the numbers from 0 to $m - 1$ which are relatively prime to m. However, if m is large, this procedure is impractical. Fortunately there is a convenient formula for $\varphi(m)$.

THEOREM 5–8.7. If m is a natural number different from 1, and if $m = p_1^{e_1} p_2^{e_2} \ldots p_g^{e_g}$, where $p_1, p_2, \ldots, p_g$ are distinct primes, and the exponents $e_1, e_2, \ldots, e_g$ are positive, then

$$\varphi(m) = m \cdot (1 - 1/p_1) \cdot (1 - 1/p_2) \cdot \cdots \cdot (1 - 1/p_g).$$

We will not give a proof of this theorem (however, see Problems 14, 15, and 16 below).

Euler's theorem has numerous applications. For example, it provides another method of solving linear congruences of the type discussed in

Theorem 5–7.1:

$$ax \equiv b \ (\text{mod } m), \qquad \text{where} \quad (a, m) = 1.$$

Indeed, if we let $x = a^{\varphi(m)-1} \cdot b$, then

$$ax = a \cdot a^{\varphi(m)-1} \cdot b = a^{\varphi(m)} \cdot b \equiv 1 \cdot b = b \ (\text{mod } m).$$

EXAMPLE 1. Consider the congruence

$$15x \equiv 6 \ (\text{mod } 22).$$

We have $\varphi(22) = \varphi(2 \cdot 11) = 1 \cdot 10 = 10$. Then $6 \cdot 15^9$ is a solution of the congruence. , Since $15^2 = 225 \equiv 5 \ (\text{mod } 22)$, $15^4 \equiv 5^2 \equiv 3 \ (\text{mod } 22)$, $15^8 \equiv 3^2 = 9 \ (\text{mod } 22)$, $6 \cdot 15^9 \equiv 6 \cdot 15 \cdot 9 = 90 \cdot 9 \equiv 2 \cdot 9 = 18 \ (\text{mod } 22)$. Therefore, $x = 18$ is the smallest nonnegative solution of the congruence. This method of solving linear congruences is very often not the easiest. If $15x \equiv 6 \ (\text{mod } 22)$, then $5x \equiv 2 \equiv 90 \ (\text{mod } 22)$, and $x \equiv 18 \ (\text{mod } 22)$.

Another application of Euler's theorem is the reduction of large powers of a number modulo m.

EXAMPLE 2. Suppose that we wish to find the least nonnegative integer to which 5^{221} is congruent modulo 18. Since $\varphi(18) = 6$ and $(5, 18) = 1$, Euler's theorem yields $5^6 \equiv 1 \ (\text{mod } 18)$. Since $221 = 36 \cdot 6 + 5$, we obtain

$$5^{221} = 5^{36 \cdot 6 + 5} = (5^6)^{36} 5^5 \equiv 5^5 \ (\text{mod } 18).$$

Finally, $5^2 \equiv 7 \ (\text{mod } 18)$, $5^4 \equiv 49 \equiv 13 \ (\text{mod } 18)$, and $5^5 \equiv 5 \cdot 13 = 65 \equiv 11 \ (\text{mod } 18)$. Thus, 11 is the least nonnegative integer to which 5^{221} is congruent modulo 18.

EXAMPLE 3. What are the last two decimals of the number 3^{119}? This is equivalent to the problem of finding the least nonnegative integer to which 3^{119} is congruent modulo 100. Since $(3, 100) = 1$ and $\varphi(100) = \varphi(2^2 \cdot 5^2) = 40$, we have $3^{40} \equiv 1 \ (\text{mod } 100)$. Thus, $(3^{40})^3 = 3 \cdot 3^{119} \equiv 1 \ (\text{mod } 100)$. Consequently, by Theorem 5–7.1, $3^{119} \equiv r \ (\text{mod } 100)$, where r is any solution of $3x \equiv 1 \ (\text{mod } 100)$. Since $100 = 33 \cdot 3 + 1$, we obtain $1 \equiv 3 \cdot (-33) \equiv 3 \cdot 67 \ (\text{mod } 100)$. Hence, $3^{119} \equiv 67 \ (\text{mod } 100)$, so that the last two decimal digits of 3^{119} are 67.

DEFINITION 5–8.8. Let m be a natural number and let a be an integer such that $(a, m) = 1$. The *order of a modulo m* (or the *exponent* to which

a belongs modulo m) is the smallest natural number d such that

$$a^d \equiv 1 \ (\mathrm{mod}\ m).$$

By Theorem 5–8.6, the set of all natural numbers n such that $a^n \equiv 1 \ (\mathrm{mod}\ m)$ is nonempty, since in fact $\varphi(m)$ belongs to this set. Therefore, d is well defined and $d \leq \varphi(m)$. It is clear from Definition 5–8.8 and Theorem 5–6.3 that if $a \equiv b \ (\mathrm{mod}\ m)$, then a and b have the same order modulo m.

THEOREM 5–8.9. Let d be the order of the integer a modulo m. If $a^n \equiv 1 \ (\mathrm{mod}\ m)$, then $d|n$. In particular, $d|\varphi(m)$.

Proof. By the division algorithm, $n = qd + r$, where q is a nonnegative integer and $0 \leq r < d$. Consequently,

$$a^r \equiv a^r(a^d)^q = a^{qd+r} = a^n \equiv 1 \ (\mathrm{mod}\ m).$$

Since d is the smallest positive exponent such that $a^d \equiv 1 \ (\mathrm{mod}\ m)$, it follows that $r = 0$. That is, $d|n$. The last statement of the theorem is a consequence of Theorem 5–8.6.

It is possible to find the order modulo m of an integer a by trial, provided that m is small. For example, if m is 5, then $\varphi(m) = 4$, and the numbers which are relatively prime to m are 1, 2, 3, and 4. If d is the order of a modulo 5, then $d|4$, by Theorem 5–8.9. Hence, $d = 1$, 2, or 4. Clearly, 1 belongs to the exponent 1. Also,

$$2^2 = 4 \equiv -1 \ (\mathrm{mod}\ 5),$$
$$3^2 = 9 \equiv -1 \ (\mathrm{mod}\ 5),$$
$$4^2 = 16 \equiv 1 \ (\mathrm{mod}\ 5).$$

Thus, 4 belongs to the exponent 2, while 2 and 3 belong to the exponent 4 modulo 5. The problem of finding the order of a modulo m can be difficult if a and m are large.

By Theorem 5–8.9, the largest possible order of an integer modulo m is $\varphi(m)$. If the integer a is relatively prime to m and a belongs to the exponent $\varphi(m)$ modulo m, then a is called a *primitive root modulo m*. For example, 2 and 3 are primitive roots modulo 5. It is possible to prove that if m is a prime, then there are exactly $\varphi(\varphi(m))$ primitive roots modulo m among the natural numbers 1, 2, $\ldots$, $m-1$. However, if m is composite, there may not be any primitive roots for this modulus. For example, every odd integer belongs to one of the exponents 1, 2, or 4 modulo 16, and $\varphi(16) = 8$.

An amusing application of Theorem 5–8.9 concerns the perfect shuffling of cards. Consider a deck of $2m$ cards. Let the cards of the deck be numbered from top to bottom: $1, 2, 3, \ldots, m, m + 1, \ldots, 2m$. The deck is split into two equal piles, the first pile consisting of the cards $1, 2, 3, \ldots, m$ in order, and the second pile consisting of the cards $m + 1, m + 2, \ldots, 2m$ in order. A perfect shuffle results if the cards are shuffled together from the bottom up, alternating a card from each pile, and beginning with the first pile. After a perfect shuffle, the arrangement of the cards will be changed from $1, 2, 3, \ldots, m, m + 1, \ldots, 2m$ to $m + 1, 1, m + 2, 2, \ldots, 2m, m$. A card numbered $1, 2, \ldots, m$ which was in position i before the perfect shuffle is in position $2i$ after the shuffle. A card numbered $m + 1, m + 2, \ldots, 2m$ which was in position i before the shuffle is in position $2i - (2m + 1)$ afterwards. Note that for $1 \leq i \leq m$,

$$2i = 0 \cdot (2m + 1) + 2i, \qquad 0 < 2i < 2m + 1;$$

while for $m + 1 \leq i \leq 2m$,

$$2i = 1 \cdot (2m + 1) + [2i - (2m + 1)],$$
$$0 < 2i - (2m + 1) < 2m + 1.$$

Thus, in every case the ith card goes into position r_1, where r_1 is the remainder obtained on dividing $2i$ by $2m + 1$. Hence,

$$r_1 \equiv 2i \;(\text{mod } 2m + 1).$$

A second perfect shuffle will send a card which is now in position r_1 into position r_2, where

$$r_2 \equiv 2r_1 \equiv 2 \cdot 2i = 2^2 \cdot i \;(\text{mod } 2m + 1).$$

In general, after n perfect shuffles, the ith card will be in position r_n, where

$$r_n \equiv 2^n \cdot i \;(\text{mod } 2m + 1).$$

The question now arises: what is the least number of perfect shuffles required to return a deck of $2m$ cards to its original order? The answer is plainly the smallest positive integer n satisfying

$$i = r_n \equiv 2^n \cdot i \;(\text{mod } 2m + 1)$$

for $i = 1, 2, 3, \ldots, m, m + 1, \ldots, 2m$. Since this congruence must hold in particular for $i = 1$, it is necessary that

$$2^n \equiv 1 \;(\text{mod } 2m + 1).$$

On the other hand, if this latter congruence is satisfied, then

$$i \equiv 2^n \cdot i \pmod{2m + 1}$$

for every i, by Theorem 5–6.3(f). Thus, the positive integer which is the answer to the problem is the order of 2 modulo $2m + 1$. [Note that Definition 5–8.8 applies since $(2, 2m + 1) = 1$.]

Suppose now that we are considering an ordinary deck of 52 cards. Then $m = 26$, and $2m + 1 = 53$. By Theorem 5–8.9, the order of 2 modulo 53 is a divisor of $\varphi(53) = 52$. That is, the order of 2 is one of the numbers 2, 4, 13, 26, or 52. Clearly 2^2 and 2^4 are not congruent to 1 modulo 53. Also, $2^6 = 64 \equiv 11 \pmod{53}$, $2^{12} \equiv 121 \equiv 15 \pmod{53}$, and therefore $2^{13} \equiv 30 \pmod{53}$. Finally, $2^{26} = (2^{13})^2 \equiv 30^2 = 900 = 53 \cdot 17 - 1 \equiv -1 \pmod{53}$. Thus, the order of 2 modulo 53 is 52. Consequently, it follows from our general result that 52 perfect shuffles are required to return an ordinary card deck to its original order.

PROBLEMS

1. Solve the following linear congruences, using Euler's theorem.
   (a) $68x \equiv 13 \pmod{19}$ (b) $50x \equiv -21 \pmod{33}$
   (c) $2^{691}x \equiv 11 \pmod{9}$ (d) $11x \equiv 25 \pmod{12}$

2. Find the last three decimal digits of the following numbers: 3^{25000}, 7^{1610}, 9^{9999}.

3. Find the last two decimal digits of 9^{9^9}.

4. Prove that for every natural number a, a and a^5 have the same final decimal digit.

5. Show that if p is an odd prime which does not divide the integer a, then either

$$a^{(p-1)/2} \equiv 1 \pmod{p}, \quad \text{or} \quad a^{(p-1)/2} \equiv -1 \pmod{p}.$$

6. Find $\varphi(m)$ for $m = 1, 2, 7, 8, 9, 10, 12$, and 16 by listing the numbers k which satisfy $0 \le k < m$, and $(k, m) = 1$.

7. Illustrate the proof of Euler's theorem, Theorem 5–8.6, for the particular case $m = 15$, $a = 4$.

8. (a) Find the order modulo 16 of the numbers 1, 3, 5, 7, 9, 11, 13, and 15.
   (b) Find the order modulo 15 of the numbers 1, 2, 4, 7, 8, 11, 13, and 14.

9. Let p be a prime, let e be a positive exponent, and let a and b be integers such that $a \equiv b \pmod{p^e}$. Prove that $a^p \equiv b^p \pmod{p^{e+1}}$. [Hint: Write $a = b + cp^e$, $c \in Z$, and expand $a^p = (b + cp^e)^p$ by the binomial theorem.]

10. Show that if a is an odd number, then

$$a^{2^n} \equiv 1 \pmod{2^{n+2}}$$

for every natural number n. What does this imply about the existence of primitive roots modulo powers of 2?

11. Using the result of Problem 9, deduce the following case of Euler's theorem from Fermat's theorem. Let p be a prime, let e be a positive exponent, and let a be an integer which is not divisible by p. Then

$$a^{(p-1)p^{e-1}} \equiv 1 \pmod{p^e}.$$

12. How many perfect shuffles are required to return a deck of 46 cards to their original order? How many for a deck of 22 cards?

13. Suppose that p is a prime and that a is a primitive root modulo p.

(a) Show that

$$1^n + 2^n + \cdots + (p-1)^n \equiv 1 + a^n + a^{2n} + \cdots + a^{(p-2)n} \pmod{p}.$$

(b) Use (a) to prove that if $(p-1) \nmid n$, then

$$1^n + 2^n + \cdots + (p-1)^n \equiv 0 \pmod{p}.$$

(c) Show that if $(p-1) \mid n$, then

$$1^n + 2^n + \cdots + (p-1)^n \equiv -1 \pmod{p}.$$

(d) Determine $1^n + 2^n + \cdots + 52^n \pmod{53}$ for all n.

The following three problems lead to a proof of Theorem 5–8.7. Accordingly, this theorem should not be used to prove any of the statements in these problems.

14. Let p be a prime and let e be a positive exponent. Prove that

$$\varphi(p^e) = p^e - p^{e-1} = p^e(1 - 1/p).$$

[*Hint:* First show that the number of integers k such that $0 \le k < p^e$ and $p \mid k$ is p^{e-1}.]

15. Let m and n be natural numbers which are relatively prime. Let $r_1, r_2, \ldots, r_u$ be all of the different integers r such that $0 \le r < m$, and $(r, m) = 1$, and let $s_1, s_2, \ldots, s_v$ be all of the different integers s such that $0 \le s < n$, and $(s, n) = 1$.

(a) Show that for any integers a and b, if $c = ma + nb$, then $(c, mn) = 1$ if and only if $(a, n) = 1$ and $(b, m) = 1$.

(b) Show that if $ms_i + nr_j \equiv ms_k + nr_l \pmod{mn}$, then $i = k$ and $j = l$.

(c) Show that if c is an integer such that $(c, mn) = 1$, then for some i and j,

$$c \equiv ms_i + nr_j \pmod{mn}.$$

(d) Prove that $\varphi(mn) = \varphi(m) \cdot \varphi(n)$. [*Hint:* Using (a), (b), and (c), show that for each integer k such that $0 \leq k < mn$ and $(k, mn) = 1$, there is exactly one pair $\langle i, j \rangle$ of indices such that

$$k \equiv ms_i + nr_j \pmod{mn},$$

and every pair $\langle i, j \rangle$ occurs this way.]

16. Using the results of Problems 14 and 15, prove Theorem 5–8.7.

CHAPTER 6

THE RATIONAL NUMBERS

6–1 Basic properties of the rational numbers. The positive rational fractions were used by some of the earliest civilizations on earth long before negative numbers were introduced. There are records which indicate that the Babylonians employed symbols for the fractions $\frac{1}{2}$, $\frac{1}{3}$, and $\frac{5}{6}$ as long ago as 2400 B.C. Before 1650 B.C., the Egyptians devised a curious system of representing certain fractions as sums of reciprocals of distinct natural numbers. For example,

$$\tfrac{2}{7} = \tfrac{1}{4} + \tfrac{1}{28}.$$

By the time Euclid wrote his *Elements* (about 300 B.C.), rational arithmetic had been developed to almost the same form that we know today. Of course, the negative rational numbers came later.

It is not surprising that the invention of fractions occurred early in the history of our culture. The use of numbers for measuring length must have developed naturally from their use as counting devices. If a trader wished to buy a certain amount of cloth, he had to have some way of giving the seller a description of how much cloth was wanted. A convenient measure was the number of arm lengths (approximately, the number of yards). With the need for more accuracy came the necessity of measuring fractional parts of unit lengths. A tailor who could make 3 robes from 10 yards of cloth would not want to buy 4 yards to make a single robe. He would need some way to express the length, $3\frac{1}{3}$ yards. Such needs must have led to the early invention of "rulers" and "yard sticks." Through the years, devices for measuring distance have progressed from the crude "measuring sticks" to the finest microscopic gauges.

Let us review the facts about rational numbers which are usually discussed in elementary algebra courses. As we have seen, the main reason for enlarging the ring of integers to the rational numbers is to make division by natural numbers possible. Thus, ideally the system Q of rational numbers should satisfy the following conditions.

(6–1.1). *Properties of Q.*

(a) Q is an ordered integral domain.

(b) Q contains Z as a subring. That is, $Z \subseteq Q$, and the ordering and the operations of addition, multiplication, and negation in Z agree with the ordering and operations in Q.

(c) If $a \in Z$ and $n \in N$, then the equation $nr = a$ has a solution $r \in Q$, that is, the quotient a/n exists in Q (see Definition 4–4.9).

(d) Every element r of Q is a quotient a/n for some $a \in Z$ and $n \in N$, that is, r satisfies $nr = a$ for some $n \in N$, $a \in Z$.

The property (d) implies that Q is the "smallest" system which satisfies the requirements (a), (b), and (c). This is stated more exactly in the following theorem.

THEOREM 6–1.2. Let A be an ordered integral domain containing the ring Z of all integers as a subring. Suppose that for each $a \in Z$ and $n \in N$, the quotient a/n exists in A. That is, A satisfies (a), (b), and (c) of (6–1.1). Let B be the set of all elements $r \in A$ which satisfy $nr = a$ for some $n \in N$ and $a \in Z$. Then B is a subring of A, and B satisfies (6–1.1a, b, c, d). Moreover, any ring which satisfies all of the conditions of (6–1.1) is isomorphic to B.

Since we will not use this theorem, its proof will be omitted.

The conditions (c) and (d) of (6–1.1) lead to the familiar method of representing all rational numbers. In fact, every rational number is a quotient

$$a/n, \qquad a \in Z, \qquad n \in N,$$

and conversely, for every $a \in Z$, $n \in N$, there is a rational number which is the quotient a/n. It should be remembered that a/n is no more than a way of designating a particular rational number. We think of a/n as the expression representing the solution of the equation $n \cdot x = a$; that is, a/n represents the number obtained from the division of a by n, just as $a \cdot n$ represents the number obtained by multiplying a and n. Of course, each rational number has infinitely many representations in this form. For example

$$\tfrac{1}{2}, \quad \tfrac{2}{4}, \quad \tfrac{3}{6}, \quad \cdots$$

all denote the same rational number.

The conditions (6–1.1) are the specifications which must be met by the system of rational numbers, and as we noted in Theorem 6–1.2, any two rings which satisfy these conditions are isomorphic. However, it is not immediately obvious that there is any system at all which satisfies (6–1.1). In Section 6–5, starting with N and Z, we will construct an ordered integral domain Q which does satisfy (6–1.1).

By using (6–1.1a, b), it is possible to discover the rules of operation for rational numbers, represented as quotients.

(6–1.3). *Rules of operation for rational numbers.* Let a and b be integers, and let m and n be natural numbers. Then
(a) $a/m = b/n$ if and only if $na = mb$;
(b) $a/m < b/n$ if and only if $na < mb$;
(c) $(a/m) + (b/n) = (na + mb)/mn$;
(d) $-(a/m) = (-a)/m$;
(e) $(a/m) \cdot (b/n) = (ab)/(mn)$.

Proof. Let r denote the rational number a/m, and let s represent b/n. That is, r and s are the unique rational numbers satisfying

$$mr = a, \qquad ns = b.$$

We first prove (a). Note that

$$mnr = na, \qquad mns = mb.$$

If $r = s$, then $mnr = mns$. Hence $na = mb$. Conversely, if $na = mb$, then $mnr = mns$. Since m and n are natural numbers, $mn \neq 0$, and by the cancellation law in an integral domain, $r = s$. The proof of (b) is similar to the proof of (a). If $r < s$, then $na = mnr < mns = mb$, since mn is positive in Z, and therefore also positive in Q. Conversely, if $na < mb$, then $mnr < mns$. This implies that $r < s$. For otherwise, $s \leq r$ and hence $mns \leq mnr$, by Theorem 4–6.2. The proofs of (c), (d), and (e) are very simple. Note that by Definition 4–2.1 and Theorem 4–2.4

$$(mn)(r + s) = mnr + mns = na + mb,$$
$$m(-r) = -(mr) = -a,$$
$$(mn)(rs) = (mr)(ns) = ab.$$

Thus, by Definition 4–4.9,

$$(a/m) + (b/n) = r + s = (na + mb)/mn,$$
$$-(a/m) = -r = (-a)/m,$$
$$(a/m) \cdot (b/n) = r \cdot s = (ab)/(mn).$$

Although the system of rational numbers is constructed in order to divide integers by natural numbers, it happens that this system enjoys the strongest possible divisibility property: if r and s are rational numbers, and if $r \neq 0$, then r divides s in Q. This fact is easily proved using the properties of Q given above. By (6–1.1), we can write $r = a/m$, $s = b/n$, where a and b are integers and m and n are natural numbers. Then it is well known that $s/r = mb/na$ is the required quotient. However, if a is negative, then na is not a natural number, and it does not follow from

(6–1.1c) that mb/na is in Q. This defect is easily corrected by noting that s/r can just as well be represented by mab/na^2, where a^2 is a positive integer, and consequently $na^2 \in N$. This is the idea involved in the proof of the important divisibility property, which we now formulate more carefully.

THEOREM 6–1.4. If r and s are rational numbers, and if $r \neq 0$, then r divides s in Q; that is, there is a rational number t such that $r \cdot t = s$.

Proof. By (6–1.1), we can write

$$r = \frac{a}{m}, \qquad s = \frac{b}{n},$$

where a and b are suitably chosen integers, and m and n are natural numbers. Thus, the rational numbers r and s satisfy

$$mr = a, \qquad ns = b.$$

Since $r \neq 0$, it follows that $a \neq 0$. Thus, by Theorem 4–5.5, a^2 is a positive integer. Therefore $na^2 \in N$. Evidently, $mab \in Z$. By (6–1.1c), there is a rational number t such that

$$na^2 t = mab.$$

Therefore,

$$(mna^2)rt = (mr)(na^2 t) = a(mab) = (ma^2)b = (ma^2)(ns) = (mna^2)s.$$

Since Q is an integral domain, and $mna^2 \in N$ (hence, $mna^2 \neq 0$), it follows that $rt = s$.

It should be noted that in several places in the above proof, we have used the fact that multiplication in Q of elements belonging to Z agrees with the usual multiplication in Z, that is, Z is a subring of Q.

PROBLEMS

1. Prove the cancellation law for quotients: if m and n are natural numbers and a is an integer, then $ma/mn = a/n$ in Q.

2. Prove that each positive rational number can be represented *uniquely* in the form m/n, where m and n are relatively prime natural numbers.

3. Prove that if $a \in Z$, then $a = an/n$ in Q for every $n \in N$.

4. The Farey series F_k of order k is the ascending sequence of rational fractions m/n, where $0 \leq m \leq n \leq k$ and $(m, n) = 1$. For instance, F_4 is $\frac{0}{1}, \frac{1}{4}, \frac{1}{3}, \frac{1}{2}, \frac{2}{3}, \frac{3}{4}, \frac{1}{1}$. Write the Farey series F_5 and F_6.

5. Prove that $a/m - b/n = (na - mb)/mn$ (where $a, b \in Z$, $m, n \in N$).

6. Prove that if r and s are rational numbers, then

$$(-r)/s = r/(-s) = -(r/s) \quad \text{and} \quad (-r)/(-s) = r/s.$$

7. Point out the places where the condition (6–1.1b) was used in the proof of Theorem 6–1.4.

8. Prove Theorem 6–1.2.

6–2 Fields. The theory of ordered integral domains developed in Chapter 4 can be applied to the ring Q of rational numbers. However, Q also satisfies the divisibility property, given in Theorem 6–1.4, which does not hold in all integral domains (for example, it is not satisfied in Z). It is to be expected that certain properties of the rational numbers are consequences of Theorem 6–1.4 (together with the other properties of integral domains). If this is so, then these properties will hold as well for any ordered integral domain which satisfies this divisibility condition. There are examples of such integral domains. For us, the most interesting one other than Q itself is the ring R of all real numbers. Thus, as in Section 4–2, it appears that by introducing a new abstract concept, we will be able to prove theorems in a general setting which will apply to a number of important special cases.

DEFINITION 6–2.1. A *field* is a commutative ring F such that
  (a) F contains at least one element different from 0;
  (b) if $x \in F$, $y \in F$, and $x \neq 0$, then there is an element $z \in F$ such that $x \cdot z = y$.

EXAMPLE 1. The rings Q and R are fields, as we have mentioned. So is the system C of all complex numbers. The ring of integers is not a field.

EXAMPLE 2. Let $F = \{0, a\}$, where $0 + 0 = 0$, $0 + a = a + 0 = a$, $a + a = 0; 0 \cdot 0 = a \cdot 0 = 0 \cdot a = 0$, $a \cdot a = a; -0 = 0, -a = a$. Then F is a field.

EXAMPLE 3. Let $F = \{0, 1, u, v\}$. Define addition and multiplication by the tables

+	0	1	u	v
0	0	1	u	v
1	1	0	v	u
u	u	v	0	1
v	v	u	1	0

·	0	1	u	v
0	0	0	0	0
1	0	1	u	v
u	0	u	v	1
v	0	v	1	u

Define $-x = x$ for $x = 0, 1, u,$ and v. Then F is a field, as the reader can easily verify.

The definition of a field does not explicitly require the existence of an identity element. However, it is not hard to show that every field does contain an identity. In fact a much stronger statement can be made.

THEOREM 6–2.2. Every field is an integral domain.

Proof. Suppose that F is a field. We first prove that F contains a nonzero identity element. Let x be any nonzero element of F. There is such an x by Definition 6–2.1(a). By Definition 6–2.1(b), there is an $e \in F$ such that $x \cdot e = x$. Since $x \neq 0$, it is evident that e cannot be 0. To prove that e is an identity element, it is only necessary to show that $y \cdot e = y$ for all $y \in F$. Note that since F is commutative, $e \cdot y = y \cdot e$ for all y. If y is any element of F, there exists $z \in F$ such that $x \cdot z = y$. Consequently, $y = x \cdot z = (x \cdot e) \cdot z = (e \cdot x) \cdot z = e \cdot (x \cdot z) = e \cdot y = y \cdot e$. Thus, e is a nonzero identity in F. To complete the proof of the theorem, it will now be enough (by Theorem 4–4.5) to prove that F has no proper divisors of zero. Suppose that y is a divisor of zero in F. That is, $x \cdot y = 0$ for some nonzero element x. By Definition 6–2.1(b), there is an element $w \in F$ such that $x \cdot w = e$, the identity of F. Consequently, $y = y \cdot e = y \cdot (x \cdot w) = (y \cdot x) \cdot w = (x \cdot y) \cdot w = 0 \cdot w = 0$. Thus, if y is a divisor of zero, then $y = 0$, that is, F contains no proper divisors of zero.

As we mentioned in Chapter 4, the identity element in any ring is usually denoted by 1. Of course, this custom is observed for fields in particular.

Since every field F is an integral domain, there is, for each $x \neq 0$ and y in F, only one $z \in F$ satisfying the equation $x \cdot z = y$. Thus, as in any integral domain, we can write z as the quotient y/x. The property which distinguishes fields from arbitrary integral domains is the fact that in a field the quotient y/x always exists when $x \neq 0$.

DEFINITION 6–2.3. Let F be a field. Let x be a nonzero element of F. The quotient $1/x$ is called the *inverse of x in F*, and is denoted by x^{-1}.

Thus, x^{-1} is the unique element satisfying $x \cdot x^{-1} = 1$. It should be emphasized that x^{-1} is *not defined* for $x = 0$. Moreover, if $x \neq 0$, then $x^{-1} \neq 0$.

THEOREM 6–2.4. Let $x, y, x_1, x_2, \ldots, x_n$ $(n \geq 1)$ be nonzero elements of a field F. Then

(a) $(x \cdot y)^{-1} = x^{-1} \cdot y^{-1}$;

(b) $(x_1 \cdot x_2 \cdot \cdots \cdot x_n)^{-1} = x_1^{-1} \cdot x_2^{-1} \cdot \cdots \cdot x_n^{-1}$;

(c) $(x^{-1})^{-1} = x$;

(d) $1^{-1} = 1$; $(-1)^{-1} = -1$.

Proof. The proofs of all of these statements [except (b), which can be obtained by induction from (a)] are based on the above observation about the uniqueness of the inverse, namely, if s and t are elements of F such that $s \cdot t = 1$, then $t = s^{-1}$. For example, to prove (a), let $s = x \cdot y$, $t = x^{-1} \cdot y^{-1}$. Then $s \cdot t = (x \cdot y) \cdot (x^{-1} \cdot t^{-1}) = (x \cdot x^{-1}) \cdot (y \cdot y^{-1}) = 1 \cdot 1 = 1$. Thus, $x^{-1} \cdot y^{-1} = t = s^{-1} = (x \cdot y)^{-1}$. The proof of (c) is similar. By definition of the inverse, $x \cdot x^{-1} = 1$. Thus, $x^{-1} \cdot x = 1$. Therefore, x is the inverse of x^{-1}. That is, $x = (x^{-1})^{-1}$. The proofs of (b) and (d) are left for the reader to complete.

Quotients can be expressed in terms of the inverse operation: if $x \neq 0$, then

$$\frac{y}{x} = x^{-1} \cdot y = y \cdot x^{-1}. \tag{6-1}$$

Indeed, $x \cdot (x^{-1} \cdot y) = (x \cdot x^{-1}) \cdot y = 1 \cdot y = y$. This observation is useful, because inverses are easier to manipulate than quotients.

DEFINITION 6–2.5. Let x be a nonzero element of the field F. Define x^n for natural numbers n by the inductive conditions

$$x^1 = x, \qquad x^{n+1} = x^n \cdot x.$$

Define $x^0 = 1$, and

$$x^{(-n)} = (x^{-1})^n.$$

For a natural number n, x^n is the product

$$\overbrace{x \cdot x \cdot \cdots \cdot x}^{n \text{ factors}}.$$

We have briefly discussed powers of real numbers in Section 2–6. The new concept which Definition 6–2.5 introduces is the idea of zero and negative exponents. That is, if x is a nonzero element of a field, then the object x^a is defined for every *integer* a.

(6–2.6). *Rules of exponents.* Let x and y be nonzero elements of a field F. Let a and b be arbitrary integers. Then
   (a) $x^a \cdot x^b = x^{a+b}$;
   (b) $(x^a)^b = x^{a \cdot b}$;
   (c) $(x \cdot y)^a = x^a \cdot y^a$;
   (d) $(x^{-1})^a = x^{(-a)}$;
   (e) $1^a = 1$.

The identities (d) and (e) are easy consequences of Definition 6–2.5. Also, if a and b are natural numbers, then the identities (a), (b), and (c) can be proved by induction on a (see Problem 1, Section 2–6). To extend these results to arbitrary integers involves a somewhat tedious checking of cases. As an illustration, let us consider the identity (a) for the case in which a is a positive integer and b is a negative integer. Then $a = n$ and $b = -m$, where n and m are natural numbers.

If $n > m$, then $n = (n - m) + m$. Hence,

$$x^a \cdot x^b = x^{(n-m)+m} \cdot x^{-m} = (x^{n-m} \cdot x^m) \cdot (x^{-1})^m$$
$$= x^{n-m} \cdot [x^m \cdot (x^{-1})^m] = x^{n-m} \cdot (x \cdot x^{-1})^m$$
$$= x^{n-m} \cdot 1^m = x^{n-m} = x^{a+b},$$

assuming that all of the identities above have been verified in the cases where a and b are natural numbers. If $n = m$, the proof is simpler:

$$x^a \cdot x^b = x^n \cdot x^{-n} = x^n \cdot (x^{-1})^n = (x \cdot x^{-1})^n$$
$$= 1^n = 1 = x^0 = x^{n-n} = x^{a+b}.$$

If $n < m$, then $m = (m - n) + n$ and

$$x^a \cdot x^b = x^n \cdot x^{-m} = x^n \cdot (x^{-1})^m = x^n \cdot [(x^{-1})^{m-n} \cdot (x^{-1})^n]$$
$$= [x^n \cdot (x^{-1})^n] \cdot (x^{-1})^{m-n} = (x \cdot x^{-1})^n \cdot (x^{-1})^{m-n}$$
$$= 1^n \cdot (x^{-1})^{m-n} = 1 \cdot (x^{-1})^{m-n} = (x^{-1})^{m-n}$$
$$= x^{-(m-n)} = x^{n-m} = x^{a+b}.$$

An ordered integral domain which satisfies Definition 6–2.1(b) is naturally called an *ordered field*. The most important examples of ordered fields are the systems of rational numbers and real numbers.

THEOREM 6–2.7. Let F be an ordered field. Let x and y be elements of F, and let a and b be integers.
  (a) If $x > 0$, then $x^{-1} > 0$; if $x < 0$, then $x^{-1} < 0$.
  (b) If $0 < x < y$, or $x < y < 0$, then $x^{-1} > y^{-1}$.
  (c) If $x > 0$, then $x^a > 0$; if $x < 0$ and a is odd, then $x^a < 0$; if $x < 0$ and a is even then $x^a > 0$.
  (d) If $0 < x < y$, and $a > 0$, then $x^a < y^a$; if $0 < x < y$, and $a < 0$, then $x^a > y^a$.
  (e) If $0 < x < 1$ and $a < b$, then $x^b < x^a$; if $1 < x$, and $a < b$, then $x^a < x^b$.

Proof. If $x > 0$, then $x^{-1} \neq 0$. Hence, either $x^{-1} > 0$, or $x^{-1} < 0$. If $x^{-1} < 0$, then $1 = x \cdot x^{-1} < 0$, which is false by Theorem 4–5.5. Thus, $x^{-1} > 0$. Similarly, if $x < 0$, then x^{-1} must also be < 0. Suppose that $0 < x < y$. Then x^{-1} and y^{-1} are positive. Assume that $x^{-1} \leq$

y^{-1}. Then $1 = x \cdot x^{-1} < y \cdot x^{-1} \leq y \cdot y^{-1} = 1$, which is a contradiction. Therefore, $y^{-1} < x^{-1}$. If $x < y < 0$, then $0 < -y < -x$. Hence, $(-x)^{-1} < (-y)^{-1}$. Therefore, $-(-y)^{-1} < -(-x)^{-1}$. However,

$$-(-y)^{-1} = (-1) \cdot (-y)^{-1} = (-1)^{-1} \cdot (-y)^{-1}$$
$$= [(-1) \cdot (-y)]^{-1} = y^{-1},$$

and similarly $-(-x)^{-1} = x^{-1}$. The remaining statements are left for the reader to prove.

EXAMPLE 4. Often problems of simplifying the description of sets of real or rational numbers involve inverses. The rules given in Theorem 6–2.7 are useful in solving such problems. Consider the set $\{x \in R | x + 2x^{-1} > 3\}$. If $x + 2x^{-1} > 3$, then $x \leq 0$ is impossible. Hence, $x + 2x^{-1} > 3$ if and only if $x > 0$ and $x(x + 2x^{-1}) > 3x$, that is $x^2 + 2 > 3x > 0$. This inequality holds if and only if $(x - 2)(x - 1) > 0$ and $x > 0$. Since $x > 0$, the product $(x - 2)(x - 1)$ is positive if and only if $0 < x < 1$ or $x > 2$. Hence,

$$\{x \in R | x + 2x^{-1} > 3\} = \{x \in R | 0 < x < 1\} \cup \{x \in R | x > 2\}.$$

PROBLEMS

1. Simplify the following expressions.
   (a) $(x^{-1} \cdot y^{-1})^{-1} \cdot (x^{-1})^{-1}$
   (b) $(x \cdot y \cdot z^{-1})^{-1} \cdot (x^{-1} \cdot y^{-1} \cdot z^{-1})$
   (c) $[(x^{-1}) \cdot y]^{-1} \cdot [x \cdot (y^{-1})]$

2. If A is a subring of a field F, and if $1 \in A$, does it follow that A is a field? An integral domain? Support your answer by examples or proofs.

3. Show that the systems in Examples 2 and 3 are fields.

4. Complete the proof of Theorem 6–2.4.

5. Prove by induction on n that if $x, x_1, x_2, \ldots, x_n$ are elements of a field F, and $a, a_1, a_2, \ldots, a_n$ are integers, then

   (a) $\displaystyle\prod_{i=1}^{n} x^{a_i} = x^{\sum_{i=1}^{n} a_i},$

   (b) $\displaystyle\prod_{i=1}^{n} (x_i)^a = \left(\prod_{i=1}^{n} x_i\right)^a.$

6. Simplify the following expressions.

   (a) $\displaystyle\prod_{k=1}^{n} x^{k^2}$ (b) $\displaystyle\prod_{k=1}^{n} x^{2^k}$ (c) $\displaystyle\prod_{k=-n}^{n} x^k$

7. Simplify the descriptions of the following sets.
  (a) $\{x \in R | x^{-1} > \frac{3}{4}\}$
  (b) $\{x \in R | x \geq (\frac{9}{16})x^{-1}\}$
  (c) $\{x \in R | x + x^{-1} \leq 2\}$.

8. Let F be an ordered field. Suppose that $x \in F$, $y \in F$, and $x \neq 0$. Show that
  (a) $|x^{-1}| = |x|^{-1}$,
  (b) $|x/y| = |x|/|y|$.

9. Let x, y, z, and w be elements of an ordered field. Suppose that $z \neq 0$ and $w \neq 0$. Prove the following.
  (a) If z and w have the same sign, then $x/z < y/w$ if and only if $xw < yz$.
  (b) If z and w have opposite sign, then $x/z < y/w$ if and only if $xw > yz$.

10. Prove Theorem 6–2.7(c), (d), and (e).

11. Prove Theorem 6–2.6 in detail.

12. Show that if A is a commutative ring with an identity element e such that for every $x \neq 0$ in A, there is an element $y \in A$ such that $x \cdot y = e$, then A is a field.

13. Prove that if F is a field, and if A is a ring which is isomorphic to F (see Definition 4–2.7), then A is a field.

6–3 The characteristic of integral domains and fields. The rules of exponents (6–2.6) resemble the identities listed in Theorem 4–3.3 for repeated sums. Indeed, the operation of forming powers of x is the multiplicative analogue of the additive operation ax defined in Definition 4–3.2. Recall that if $a = n$ is a natural number and x is an element of a ring, then

$$\overbrace{ax = x + x + \cdots + x}^{n \text{ summands}};$$

if $a = 0$, then $ax = 0$; if $a = -n$ is a negative integer, then

$$ax = n(-x) = \overbrace{(-x) + (-x) + \cdots + (-x)}^{n \text{ summands}}.$$

There is an important classification of integral domains and fields which is based on the operation ax.

THEOREM 6–3.1. Let A be an integral domain. Then exactly one of the following statements is true.
  (a) If $x \neq 0$ in A, then $nx \neq 0$ for all $n \in N$.
  (b) There is a unique prime p such that $px = 0$ for all $x \in A$, and if $nx = 0$ for $x \neq 0$, then p divides n in Z.

Proof. Suppose that $nx = 0$ for some $n \in N$ and $x \neq 0$. By the well-ordering principle for N, there is a smallest natural number p which has this property. That is, if $m < p$, $m \in N$, then $my \neq 0$ for all nonzero $y \in A$, but there is an $x \neq 0$ in A such that $px = 0$. Let e be the identity* of A. By Theorem 4–3.3, $(pe) \cdot x = p(e \cdot x) = px = 0$. Thus, since A is an integral domain and $x \neq 0$, we obtain $pe = 0$. Therefore, for any $y \in A$, $py = p(e \cdot y) = (pe) \cdot y = 0$. We next show that p is a prime. Suppose otherwise. Then there are natural numbers r and s such that $1 < r < p$, $1 < s < p$, and $p = r \cdot s$. Therefore, $(re) \cdot (se) = (rs)e^2 = pe = 0$. Since A is an integral domain, this implies that either $re = 0$ or $se = 0$. However, by its choice, p was the smallest natural number such that $pe = 0$. Thus, p must be a prime. It is clear that the prime p is unique. Finally, suppose that $nx = 0$ for some natural number n and $x \neq 0$ in A. If $p \nmid n$, then $(n, p) = 1$. Thus, integers a and b exist satisfying $an + bp = 1$. Therefore, by Theorem 4–3.3, $x = 1x = (an + bp)x = (an)x + (bp)x = a(nx) + b(px) = a0 + b0 = 0$. This contradiction shows that $p|n$. To review our proof, we have shown that if statement (a) is not true, then statement (b) is true. Therefore, either (a) is true or else (b) is true. Obviously both statements cannot be true for the same integral domain A.

DEFINITION 6–3.2. Let A be an integral domain. The *characteristic of A* is defined to be zero if A satisfies Theorem 6–3.1(a), and it is defined to be the prime p if A satisfies Theorem 6–3.1(b). We say that A is of *prime characteristic* if its characteristic is some prime p.

The characteristic of the rings of integers, the rational numbers, the real numbers, and the complex numbers is zero. In fact a more general result can be proved.

THEOREM 6–3.3. The characteristic of every ordered integral domain A is zero.

Proof. Suppose that $x > 0$ in A. Then $2x = x + x > 0 + x = x$, $3x = 2x + x > x + x = 2x$, and so on

$$0 < x < 2x < 3x < \ldots.$$

In particular $nx \neq 0$ for all $n \in N$. If $x < 0$, then $-x > 0$, and $-(nx) = n(-x) \neq 0$ for all $n \in N$. Therefore, $nx \neq 0$ for all $n \in N$ and $x \in A$. Consequently, Theorem 6–3.1(a) is satisfied, and the characteristic of A is zero.

---

*In order to avoid confusing the identity of A with the natural number 1, we do not follow the custom of denoting the identity of A by 1 in this proof.

The fields in Examples 2 and 3 of Section 6–2 have characteristic 2. It is possible to construct fields of arbitrary prime characteristic.

EXAMPLE 1. Let p be a prime. Define $Z_p = \{0, 1, 2, \ldots, p - 1\}$. Instead of the usual addition, negation, and multiplication of integers, define operations $\oplus$, $\ominus$, and $\odot$ by

$$a \oplus b = d,$$

where d is the unique integer such that $0 \leq d < p$, and $d \equiv a + b \pmod{p}$;

$$\ominus a = e,$$

where e is the unique integer such that $0 \leq e < p$, and $e \equiv -a \pmod{p}$;

$$a \odot b = f,$$

where f is the unique integer such that $0 \leq f < p$, and $f \equiv a \cdot b \pmod{p}$.

The fact that Z_p is a ring with respect to these operations is a consequence of the elementary properties of integers and the relation of congruence. For example, to prove that $(a \oplus b) \oplus c = a \oplus (b \oplus c)$, let $a + b \equiv d \pmod{p}$, where $0 \leq d < p$. Then $(a \oplus b) \oplus c = e$, where e is determined by the conditions $0 \leq e < p$ and $d + c \equiv e \pmod{p}$. Thus, $(a + b) + c \equiv e \pmod{p}$. In exactly the same way, $a \oplus (b \oplus c) = f$, where f is the integer determined by the conditions $0 \leq f < p$ and $a + (b + c) \equiv f \pmod{p}$. Since $(a + b) + b = a + (b + c)$, it follows that $e \equiv f \pmod{p}$. However, e and f satisfy $0 \leq e < p$ and $0 \leq f < p$. Thus, $e = f$, and consequently $a \oplus (b \oplus c) = (a \oplus b) \oplus c$. The other ring postulates are proved similarly. Note that Z_p is commutative and has 1 as an identity. These facts do not depend on p being a prime. However, the assumption that p is prime is needed to show that Z_p is a field. Suppose that $a \neq 0$ in Z_p. Then $0 < a < p$, so that p does not divide a. Thus, since p is prime $(a, p) = 1$. Consequently if $b \in Z_p$, there exists (by Theorem 5–7.2) an integer m such that $am \equiv b \pmod{p}$. Let c be the unique integer such that $0 \leq c < p$ and $m \equiv c \pmod{p}$. Then $c \in Z_p$, and $a \cdot c \equiv a \cdot m \equiv b \pmod{p}$. Since $0 \leq b < p$, it follows that $a \odot c = b$. Hence, by Definition 6–2.1, Z_p is a field. Our final observation concerning Z_p is that its characteristic is p. In fact

$$p1 = \underbrace{1 \oplus 1 \oplus \cdots \oplus 1}_{p \text{ summands}}$$

is the integer d such that $0 \leq d < p$ and

$$d \equiv \underbrace{1 + 1 + \cdots + 1}_{p \text{ summands}} = p \pmod{p}.$$

Thus, $p1 = 0$ in Z_p.

The fields Z_p, defined in the above example, are almost as important in mathematics as the fields Q and R. They connect the theory of numbers with the powerful methods of abstract algebra. In Chapter 9, we will see an example of how a rather simple theorem about abstract fields can be translated into an important result of number theory when it is specialized to a statement about Z_p. For the sake of future reference, we collect some useful facts about Z_p.

THEOREM 6–3.4. (a) The elements of Z_p are the integers $0, 1, 2, \ldots,$ $p - 1$.
(b) Z_p is a field with respect to the operations $\oplus$, $\ominus$, $\odot$.
(c) If a and b are elements of Z_p, then

$$a + b \equiv a \oplus b \pmod{p},$$

$$-a \equiv \ominus a \pmod{p},$$

$$a \cdot b \equiv a \odot b \pmod{p}.$$

PROBLEMS

1. Verify Theorem 6–3.4(c).

2. Complete the proof that Z_p is a commutative ring.

3. (a) Show that the field Z_2 is isomorphic to the field described in Example 2, Section 6–2. (b) Show that the field given in Example 3, Section 6–2, is not isomorphic to any of the fields Z_p.

4. Show that a field which has only a finite number of elements cannot have zero characteristic.

5. Let A be an integral domain of prime characteristic p. Show that for any x and y in A,
$$(x + y)^p = x^p + y^p.$$

6. Let A be an integral domain with identity element e. Let B be the subring of A consisting of all elements ae with $a \in Z$ (see Problem 10, Section 4–6).
(a) Show that if the characteristic of A is zero, then the correspondence

$$a \leftrightarrow ae$$

is an isomorphism between Z and B.
(b) Show that if the characteristic of A is the prime p, then the correspondence

$$0 \leftrightarrow 0, \quad 1 \leftrightarrow e, \quad 2 \leftrightarrow 2e, \ldots, \quad p - 1 \leftrightarrow (p - 1)e$$

is an isomorphism between Z_p and B.

6–4 Equivalence relations.   In Section 6–1, the system of rational numbers was described informally. Some basic properties of this system were listed in (6–1.1), and the consequences of these properties were discussed. We now face the problem of constructing the rational numbers. Our goal is to define a set of objects, operations of addition, negation, and multiplication, and an ordering of the objects, such that the conditions of (6–1.1) are satisfied. What the objects called rational numbers really are does not matter very much. They stand for different things in different applications. The important thing is to satisfy the conditions of (6–1.1). It is a fact (and not very difficult to prove) that any two systems which satisfy these conditions are isomorphic in the sense of Section 3–3. This remark explains why the problem of constructing the rational numbers is equivalent to the construction of a system which satisfies these conditions.

How should a set of objects which satisfies the conditions of (6–1.1) be defined? By (6–1.1d), each rational number can be represented by an expression a/m, where a represents an integer, m represents a natural number, and the solidus bar / is a punctuation mark which separates a and m. This describes the symbol for a rational number in a purely formal way, and points out the fact that a rational number is really determined by the pair of numbers a and m, written in a definite order. Therefore, the symbol $\langle a, m \rangle$, which denotes an ordered pair of numbers can be used to represent the rational number a/m. The set of all ordered pairs $\langle a, m \rangle$ with $a \in Z$ and $m \in N$ is a definite collection of objects. Our discussion suggests that this set of ordered pairs might be a likely candidate for the set Q of rational numbers. However, there is a difficulty with this choice for Q. It follows from (6–1.3) that different expressions a/m and b/n can represent the same rational number. For example, $\frac{1}{2} = \frac{3}{6} = \frac{21}{42}$. In fact, by (6–1.3a), $a/m = b/n$ if $na = mb$. Thus, in the collection of ordered pairs $\langle a, m \rangle$, we must agree to somehow identify the pairs $\langle a, m \rangle$ and $\langle b, n \rangle$ when $na = mb$. This identification procedure is based on the important concept of an equivalence relation. Although our immediate interest is the construction of the system of rational numbers, the methods which will be discussed in the present section are applicable to very general situations.

The term "relation" is familiar to almost everyone. Mathematicians use many particular relations such as inequalities of numbers, inclusions of sets, congruence of integers, and similarity of geometric figures. In addition to these specific examples, the general notion of a relation on a set is of great importance in mathematics.

DEFINITION 6–4.1.   Let S be any set.   A *relation on* S is a set T of ordered pairs $\langle x, y \rangle$ of elements of S.

At first, this definition seems to be far from the usual meaning of the term "relation." It would be less strange if we said that the relation "corresponds to" the set T of all ordered pairs $\langle x, y \rangle$ of elements of S which stand in the given relation. For example, the relation $<$ on the set of all integers corresponds to the set of all ordered pairs $\langle a, b \rangle$ which satisfy $a < b$ (or more explicitly, $b - a \in N$). The trouble is that there are relations on sets of objects which correspond to the same set of ordered pairs, but would be considered different by familiar standards.

Consider a set of three brothers, Jack, Jerry, and Jim. Suppose that Jack is 8 years old and 5 feet tall, Jerry is 5 years old and 4 feet tall, while Jim is 3 years old and 3 feet tall. Then the relations "is older than" and "is taller than" applied to this set both correspond to the following set of ordered pairs:

$$\{\langle \text{Jack, Jerry} \rangle, \langle \text{Jack, Jim} \rangle, \langle \text{Jerry, Jim} \rangle\}.$$

From a mathematician's standpoint, these two relations are the same even though the concepts "older" and "taller" would lead to different relations on another collection of people. Simplification is a characteristic of mathematics. Considering two relations to be identical if the corresponding sets of ordered pairs are the same is a typical example of simplifying a familiar concept so that it can be used with mathematical precision. This is the justification for Definition 6–4.1.

Although a relation is defined to be a set T of ordered pairs, it is often convenient to express the fact that a certain pair $\langle x, y \rangle$ belongs to T by writing $x < y$, $x \equiv y$, $x \cong y$, $x \sim y$, or $x \approx y$. That is, a symbol such as $\sim$ is associated with the relation T and if $\langle x, y \rangle \in T$ then we write

$$x \sim y,$$

and speak of the relation $\sim$ on S (meaning, of course, the relation T). The particular relations of congruence and inequality which we have considered in previous sections have all been defined and expressed in this way.

The most important and useful relations in mathematics satisfy certain special conditions. The equivalence relations which we will discuss in this section are defined to be relations which satisfy three particular conditions.

DEFINITION 6–4.2. Let S be a set. Let T be a relation on S. Then T is an *equivalence relation** if

    (a) $\langle x, x \rangle \in T$ for all $x \in S$;
    (b) if $\langle x, y \rangle \in T$, then $\langle y, x \rangle \in T$;
    (c) if $\langle x, y \rangle \in T$ and $\langle y, z \rangle \in T$, then $\langle x, z \rangle \in T$.

---

* This notion should not be confused with the concept of the "equivalence of two sets" which was introduced in Section 1–2. The relation of equivalence of sets defined in Definition 1–2.3 is a particular equivalence relation on the class of all sets.

If we write $x \sim y$ to stand for $\langle x, y \rangle \in T$, then the conditions (a), (b), and (c) take a more familiar form:

(a') $x \sim x$ for all $x \in S$;

(b') if $x \sim y$, then $y \sim x$;

(c') if $x \sim y$ and $y \sim z$, then $x \sim z$.

The condition (a) or its equivalent (a') is called the "reflexive law." The properties (b) and (b') are called the "law of symmetry," while (c) and (c') are called the "transitive law." Because of the transitive law, it makes sense to write a sequence of equivalences

$$a \sim b \sim c \sim d \sim e,$$

as we have done in the case of inequalities or congruences. Also, by the reflexivity, such a sequence can include equalities

$$a \sim b = c \sim d \sim e = f.$$

The convenience of writing sequences of equivalences and equalities is one reason why the notation $a \sim b$ is preferred to $\langle a, b \rangle \in T$.

EXAMPLE 1. Let S be any set. Let $T = \{\langle x, x \rangle | x \in S\}$. Then T is an equivalence relation on S. This equivalence relation is ordinary equality, since $\langle x, y \rangle \in T$ if and only if $x = y$.

EXAMPLE 2. Let m be a natural number. Let $T = \{\langle a, b \rangle | a \in Z, b \in Z, a \equiv b \pmod{m}\}$. Then T is the equivalence relation on the set Z of all integers (see Theorem 5–6.3), which was called "congruence modulo m" in Chapter 5.

EXAMPLE 3. Let S be the set of all ordered pairs $\langle m, n \rangle$ of natural numbers. Let T be the collection of all ordered pairs of ordered pairs $\langle \langle m, n \rangle, \langle k, l \rangle \rangle$ satisfying $m + l = n + k$. Then T is an equivalence relation on S.

EXAMPLE 4. Let S be the set of all ordered pairs $\langle a, m \rangle$ where $a \in Z$ and $m \in N$. Define T to be the set of all ordered pairs of ordered pairs

$$\langle \langle a, m \rangle, \langle b, n \rangle \rangle$$

such that $na = mb$. Then T is an equivalence relation on S. To prove the transitive law for example, suppose that

$$\langle \langle a, m \rangle, \langle b, n \rangle \rangle \in T \quad \text{and} \quad \langle \langle b, n \rangle, \langle c, k \rangle \rangle \in T.$$

Then $na = mb$ and $kb = nc$. Therefore, $nka = mkb = mnc = nmc$. Hence, by cancellation, $ka = mc$. Thus, by definition,

$$\langle \langle a, m \rangle, \langle c, k \rangle \rangle \in T.$$

The last example is the equivalence relation which will lead to the construction of the system Q of rational numbers. For convenience, we will use the symbol $\approx$ to denote this relation. That is, write

$$\langle a, m \rangle \approx \langle b, n \rangle \qquad \text{if} \qquad na = mb.$$

Example 3 is similar to Example 4. It is possible to use this equivalence relation to obtain a new construction of the integers from the natural numbers. The process is analogous to the construction of Q using the equivalence relation of Example 4, which will be given in the next section.

DEFINITION 6–4.3. Let S be a set and let $\sim$ be an equivalence relation on S. For $x \in S$, define

$$[x] = \{y \in S | x \sim y\}.$$

The set $[x]$ is called the *equivalence class* of the element x with respect to the equivalence relation $\sim$.

It should be remembered that the definition of $[x]$ depends on the equivalence relation $\sim$, although this fact is not indicated by the notation.

THEOREM 6–4.4. Let $\sim$ be an equivalence relation on a set S. Then
    (a) $x \in [x]$;
    (b) $[x] = [y]$ if and only if $x \sim y$;
    (c) if $y \in [x]$, then $[x] = [y]$;
    (d) for any $x \in S$ and $y \in S$, either $[x] = [y]$ or $[x] \cap [y] = \Phi$;
    (e) $S = \cup(\{[x] | x \in S\})$.

Proof. By Definition 6–4.2(a′), $x \sim x$. Thus by Definition 6–4.3, $x \in [x]$. To prove (b), suppose first that $[x] = [y]$. Then $y \in [y] = [x]$. Thus, by Definition 6–4.3, $x \sim y$. Conversely, suppose that $x \sim y$. If $z \in [y]$, then $y \sim z$. Therefore, by Definition 6–4.2, (c'), $x \sim z$. Hence, $z \in [x]$. This shows that $x \sim y$ implies $[y] \subseteq [x]$. Similarly, $y \sim x$ implies $[x] \subseteq [y]$. Consequently, since $y \sim x$ follows from $x \sim y$ by Definition 6–4.2(b′), we obtain $x \sim y$ implies $[x] = [y]$. This proves (b). If $y \in [x]$, then by Definition 6–4.3, $x \sim y$. Therefore, $[x] = [y]$ by what has just been shown. This proves (c). In order to obtain (d), assume that $[x] \cap [y] \neq \Phi$. Then there is a $z \in S$ such that $z \in [x]$ and $z \in [y]$. By the property (c) which we have just established, $[x] = [z] = [y]$. Finally (e) is evident because by Definition 6–4.3, $[x] \subseteq S$ for all x, so that $\cup(\{[x] | x \in S\}) \subseteq S$. On the other hand, by (a), if $y \in S$, then $y \in [y] \subseteq \cup(\{[x] | x \in S\})$. Hence, every element of S belongs to the union $\cup(\{[x] | x \in S\})$.

EXAMPLE 5. Let S be the set Z of all integers and let $\sim$ be the relation of congruence modulo m. Then for any $a \in Z$, it is easy to see that

$$[a] = \{a + b \cdot m | b = 0, \pm 1, \pm 2, \cdots\}.$$

Therefore there are exactly m distinct (and disjoint) equivalence classes; namely, $[0], [1], [2], \ldots, [m - 1]$. These are the sets which were denoted by $X_0, X_1, X_2, \ldots, X_{m-1}$ in Section 5–7.

EXAMPLE 6. Let S be the set of all ordered pairs of natural numbers, and let T be the equivalence relation on S which was defined in Example 3. If $\langle m, n \rangle \in S$, then

$$[\langle m, n \rangle] = \{\langle k, l \rangle | k - l = m - n\}.$$

Consequently, there is a one-to-one correspondence between the equivalence classes for this equivalence relation and the set of all integers; this correspondence is given by

$$[\langle m, n \rangle] \leftrightarrow m - n.$$

EXAMPLE 7. Let S be the set F of all ordered pairs $\langle a, m \rangle$ with $a \in Z$, $m \in N$. The equivalence classes of F with respect to the equivalence relation $\approx$ defined in Example 4 are

$$[\langle a, m \rangle] = \{\langle b, n \rangle | na = mb\}.$$

By (6–1.3a), $na = mb$ if and only if $a/m = b/n$. Thus, $[\langle a, m \rangle]$ consists of all pairs $\langle b, n \rangle$ such that $b/n = a/m$. Therefore, there is a one-to-one correspondence between these equivalence classes and the rational numbers as we know them informally. This remark is the key to the *formal* construction of Q: the rational numbers are defined to be the equivalence classes of elements of F with respect to $\approx$.

PROBLEMS

1. Find all relations on the set $\{0, 1\}$.

2. Find all equivalence relations on the set $\{0, 1, 2\}$.

3. Give examples of a relation on the set $\{0, 1, 2\}$ which satisfies the following conditions of Definition 6–4.2.

    (i) none of (a), (b), and (c)
    (ii) (a), but neither (b) nor (c)
    (iii) (b), but neither (a) nor (c)
    (iv) (c), but neither (a) nor (b)
    (v) (a) and (b), but not (c)
    (vi) (a) and (c), but not (b)
    (vii) (b) and (c), but not (a)

4. Show that the relations of Examples 3 and 4 are equivalence relations.

5. Let S be the set of all straight lines in the Euclidean plane. Let P_0 be a fixed point in the plane. Let l_0 be a fixed line in the plane. State which of the conditions (a), (b), or (c) of Definition 6–4.2 are satisfied by the following relations.

   (i) $l \sim m$ if l is parallel or equal to m
   (ii) $l \sim m$ if l is not parallel to m
   (iii) $l \sim m$ if l is perpendicular to m
   (iv) $l \sim m$ if l is perpendicular to m, or if l is parallel or equal to m
   (v) $l \sim m$ if l and m both pass through P_0
   (vi) $l \sim m$ if l and m intersect in a point on the line l_0
   (vii) $l \sim m$ if $l \neq m$

6. Verify directly that the equivalence classes of integers modulo m given in Example 5 satisfy the statements of Theorem 6–4.4.

7. Let S be the set of all natural numbers. Define $T = \{\langle m, n\rangle | n$ divides m^k for some k, and m divides n^j for some $j\}$. Show that T is an equivalence relation on S. What are the equivalence classes [1], [2], and [6] with respect to the equivalence relation T?

8. A *partition* P of a set S is a set of nonempty subsets of S such that

   (i) if $A \in P$, $B \in P$, and $A \neq B$, then $A \cap B = \Phi$;
   (ii) $\cup(P) = S$.

   (a) Show that if $\sim$ is an equivalence relation on S, then the set of all equivalence classes in S (with respect to the relation $\sim$) is a partition of S.
   (b) Suppose that P is a partition of S. Define $x \sim y$ if $x \in A$ and $y \in A$, where A is some set of P. Show that $\sim$ is an equivalence relation on S.

6–5 The construction of Q. Let F be the set of all ordered pairs $\langle a, m\rangle$, with $a \in Z$, $m \in N$.

DEFINITION 6–5.1. Let Q be the set of all equivalence classes $[\langle a, m\rangle]$ of F with respect to the equivalence relation $\approx$ defined by

$$\langle a, m\rangle \approx \langle b, n\rangle \quad \text{if} \quad na = mb.$$

The elements of Q are called *rational numbers*.

It is necessary now to introduce operations of addition, negation, and multiplication on the set Q defined above. The discussion of Example 7, Section 6–4, suggests that $[\langle a, m\rangle]$ should be interpreted as the quotient a/m. On the basis of this interpretation, the laws given in (6–1.3) motivate the definitions of the operations and the ordering in Q. For example, since $a/m + b/n = (na + mb)/mn$, it is natural to define

$$[\langle a, m\rangle] + [\langle b, n\rangle] = [\langle na + mb, mn\rangle]. \tag{6–2}$$

A little thought is required to see that this definition makes sense. Consider a particular example:

$$[\langle 1, 2 \rangle] = \{\langle 1, 2 \rangle, \langle 2, 4 \rangle, \langle 3, 6 \rangle, \langle 4, 8 \rangle, \ldots\},$$
$$[\langle 2, 3 \rangle] = \{\langle 2, 3 \rangle, \langle 4, 6 \rangle, \langle 6, 9 \rangle, \langle 8, 12 \rangle, \ldots\}.$$

According to (6–2),

$$[\langle 1, 2 \rangle] + [\langle 2, 3 \rangle] = [\langle 3 \cdot 1 + 2 \cdot 2, 2 \cdot 3 \rangle] = [\langle 7, 6 \rangle].$$

However, we also have, for example,

$$[\langle 1, 2 \rangle] = [\langle 3, 6 \rangle] \qquad \text{and} \qquad [\langle 2, 3 \rangle] = [\langle 4, 6 \rangle],$$

so that by (6–2),

$$[\langle 1, 2 \rangle] + [\langle 2, 3 \rangle] = [\langle 3, 6 \rangle] + [\langle 4, 6 \rangle] = [\langle 6 \cdot 3 + 4 \cdot 6, 6 \cdot 6 \rangle]$$
$$= [\langle 42, 36 \rangle].$$

Therefore, in order to justify (6–2), it is necessary to show that $[\langle 7, 6 \rangle] = [\langle 42, 36 \rangle]$. By Theorem 6–4.4, this condition is equivalent to

$$\langle 7, 6 \rangle \approx \langle 42, 36 \rangle,$$

which is easily verified from the definition of $\approx$. Of course, in order to justify (6–2) generally, we must work with expressions which involve arbitrary numbers. However, before proceeding with this calculation, let us formulate the exact definitions of the operations and the ordering in Q.

DEFINITION 6–5.2. Let r and s be elements of Q. That is, r and s are equivalence classes of ordered pairs, with respect to the relation $\approx$. Arbitrarily, select $\langle a, m \rangle \in r$ and $\langle b, n \rangle \in s$. Define
  (a) $r + s = [\langle na + mb, mn \rangle]$,
  (b) $-r = [\langle -a, m \rangle]$,
  (c) $r \cdot s = [\langle ab, mn \rangle]$,
  (d) $r < s$ if $na < mb$.

Frequently, as in this case, mathematical definitions are made to depend on an arbitrary choice of one or more things. Whenever this happens, it is necessary to show that the object being defined does not really depend on these initial choices. If this can be proved, then the object is said to be *well defined*.

The fact which must be proved in order to justify Definition 6–5.2 is that the equivalence classes $[\langle na + mb, mn \rangle]$, $[\langle -a, m \rangle]$, $[\langle ab, mn \rangle]$ and the condition $na < mb$ are the same for all choices of $\langle a, m \rangle \in r$ and $\langle b, n \rangle \in s$.

Suppose that $\langle a, m \rangle \in r$, $\langle a', m' \rangle \in r$, $\langle b, n \rangle \in s$, and $\langle b', n' \rangle \in s$. Then by Theorem 6–4.4,

$$\langle a, m \rangle \approx \langle a', m' \rangle \qquad \text{and} \qquad \langle b, n \rangle \approx \langle b', n' \rangle,$$

that is,

$$m'a = ma' \qquad \text{and} \qquad n'b = nb'.$$

What has to be shown is that

$$[\langle na + mb, mn \rangle] = [\langle n'a' + m'b', m'n' \rangle],$$
$$[\langle -a, m \rangle] = [\langle -a', m' \rangle],$$
$$[\langle ab, mn \rangle] = [\langle a'b', m'n' \rangle],$$

and

$$na < mb \qquad \text{if and only if} \qquad n'a' < m'b'.$$

By Theorem 6–4.4(b) and the definition of $\approx$, these conditions are equivalent to

$$m'n'(na + mb) = mn(n'a' + m'b'),$$
$$m'(-a) = m(-a'),$$
$$(m'n') \cdot (ab) = (mn) \cdot (a'b'),$$

and

$$na < mb \qquad \text{if and only if} \qquad n'a' < m'b'.$$

These results can easily be obtained from the relations $m'a = ma'$ and $n'b = nb'$. For example,

$$
\begin{aligned}
m'n'(na + mb) &= (n'n) \cdot (m'a) + (m'm) \cdot (n'b) \\
&= (n'n) \cdot (ma') + (m'm) \cdot (nb') \\
&= mn(n'a' + m'b').
\end{aligned}
$$

Also, if $na < mb$, then $m'n'na < m'n'mb$, since m' and n' are natural numbers. Thus, $n'nma' < m'mnb'$, or $(mn) \cdot (n'a') < (mn) \cdot (m'b')$. Therefore, $n'a' < m'b'$. In the same way, $n'a' < m'b'$ implies $na < mb$. The remaining identities are left for the reader to check.

THEOREM 6–5.3. The set Q defined in Definition 6–5.1, together with the operations and the ordering given by Definition 6–5.2 is an ordered integral domain.

Proof. The proof of this result is entirely straightforward, as the following sample indicates. Let r, s, and t be elements of Q, that is, equivalence classes of ordered pairs. We will prove the distributive law $(r + s) \cdot t = r \cdot t + s \cdot t$. Let $\langle a, m \rangle \in r$, $\langle b, n \rangle \in s$, and $\langle c, k \rangle \in t$. Then $(r + s) \cdot t = [\langle na + mb, mn \rangle] \cdot [\langle c, k \rangle]$. Note that $\langle na + mb, mn \rangle$ belongs to its equivalence class $[\langle na + mb, mn \rangle]$, so we may choose it to form the product $[\langle na + mb, mn \rangle] \cdot [\langle c, k \rangle]$. By Definition 6–5.2(c),

$$(r + s) \cdot t = [\langle (na + mb)c, mnk \rangle] = [\langle nac + mbc, mnk \rangle].$$

On the other hand,

$$\begin{aligned} r \cdot t + s \cdot t &= [\langle ac, mk \rangle] + [\langle bc, nk \rangle] \\ &= [\langle nkac + mkbc, mknk \rangle]. \end{aligned}$$

Finally, we observe that

$$\langle nac + mbc, mnk \rangle \approx \langle nkac + mkbc, mknk \rangle.$$

Indeed,

$$mknk(nac + mbc) = mnk(nkac + mkbc).$$

Thus, by Theorem 6–4.4, $(r + s) \cdot t = r \cdot t + s \cdot t$.

The construction of Q given in this section encounters the following problem: the set Q defined in Definition 6–5.1 does not contain the set Z of all integers. However, Q does contain the subset

$$Z' = \{[\langle a, 1 \rangle] | a \in Z\},$$

which has all the properties of Z. Indeed, by Definition 6–5.2,

$$\begin{aligned} [\langle a, 1 \rangle] + [\langle b, 1 \rangle] &= [\langle a + b, 1 \rangle], \\ -[\langle a, 1 \rangle] &= [\langle -a, 1 \rangle], \\ [\langle a, 1 \rangle] \cdot [\langle b, 1 \rangle] &= [\langle a \cdot b, 1 \rangle], \end{aligned} \tag{6–3}$$

and

$$[\langle a, 1 \rangle] < [\langle b, 1 \rangle] \qquad \text{if and only if } a < b.$$

Thus, Z' is a subring of Q. Moreover, the correspondence

$$a \leftrightarrow [\langle a, 1 \rangle]$$

is an isomorphism between Z and Z'. In fact, if $a \neq b$, then $1 \cdot a \neq 1 \cdot b$, so that $\langle a, 1 \rangle$ is not equivalent to $\langle b, 1 \rangle$ under the relation $\approx$. Hence, by Theorem 6–4.4, $[\langle a, 1 \rangle] \neq [\langle b, 1 \rangle]$. This proves that the correspondence is one-to-one. The other conditions required for an isomorphism are easily obtained from (6–3).

In order to satisfy condition (b) of (6–1.1), we will identify each equivalence class $[\langle a, 1 \rangle]$ with the corresponding integer a. That is, $[\langle a, 1 \rangle]$ will be considered as a new label for a. The process of identifying a ring A (or a more general mathematical system) with a subring B of another ring is used frequently in mathematical constructions. This is always possible if A is isomorphic to B, and if we are only concerned with properties which are consequences of the operations in A. Indeed, from this viewpoint, there is no real difference between A and B.

The identification of Z with Z' carries with it the identification of N with $N' = \{[\langle m, 1 \rangle] | m \in N\}$. Thus, we obtain $N \subset Z \subset Q$. It remains to show that (6–1.1c, d) are satisfied.

THEOREM 6–5.4. For any $a \in Z$ and $m \in N$,

$$[\langle m, 1 \rangle] \cdot [\langle a, m \rangle] = [\langle a, 1 \rangle].$$

Hence, $[\langle a, 1 \rangle]/[\langle m, 1 \rangle] = [\langle a, m \rangle]$.

Proof. Since $\langle m, 1 \rangle \in [\langle m, 1 \rangle]$ and $\langle a, m \rangle \in [\langle a, m \rangle]$, it follows from Definition 6–5.2 that

$$[\langle m, 1 \rangle] \cdot [\langle a, m \rangle] = [\langle ma, m \rangle].$$

By the definition of the relation $\approx$, $\langle ma, m \rangle \approx \langle a, 1 \rangle$. Thus, by Theorem 6–4.4(b), $[\langle ma, m \rangle] = [\langle a, 1 \rangle]$.

From this theorem and the identification of the integer a with the equivalence class $[\langle a, 1 \rangle]$, we obtain the result that Q satisfies (6–1.1c, d).

THEOREM 6–5.5. If $a \in Z$ and $m \in N$, then $[\langle m, 1 \rangle]$ divides $[\langle a, 1 \rangle]$ in Q. Moreover, every element of Q is of the form $[\langle a, 1 \rangle]/[\langle m, 1 \rangle]$ for some $a \in Z$ and $m \in N$.

PROBLEMS

1. Complete the proof that the operations of Definition 6–5.2(b) and (c) are well defined.

2. Complete the proof of Theorem 6–5.3.

3. Let A be a ring. Suppose that $\sim$ is an equivalence relation on A such that if $x \sim x'$ and $y \sim y'$, then $x + y \sim x' + y'$, $-x \sim -x'$, and $x \cdot y \sim x' \cdot y'$. Show that the set of equivalence classes of A form a ring with the definition $[x] + [y] = [x + y]$, $-[x] = [-x]$, and $[x] \cdot [y] = [x \cdot y]$.

4. Apply the construction outlined in Problem 3 to the ring Z with the equivalence relation of congruence modulo m. How many elements are there in the

resulting ring? Show that if m is a prime, then the ring obtained by this construction is a field which is isomorphic to Z_p.

5. Let S be the set of all ordered pairs $\langle m, n \rangle$ of natural numbers with the equivalence relation defined in Example 3, Section 6-4:

$$\langle k, l \rangle \sim \langle m, n \rangle \qquad \text{if} \qquad k + n = l + m.$$

Define

$$[\langle k, l \rangle] + [\langle m, n \rangle] = [\langle k + m, l + n \rangle],$$
$$-[\langle m, n \rangle] = [\langle n, m \rangle],$$
$$[\langle k, l \rangle] \cdot [\langle m, n \rangle] = [\langle km + ln, kn + lm \rangle],$$
$$[\langle k, l \rangle] < [\langle m, n \rangle] \qquad \text{if} \qquad k + n < m + l.$$

(a) Prove that these operations are well defined on the set Z' of equivalence classes of S, and that with these operations, Z' is an ordered integral domain.

(b) Show that the correspondence $[\langle m, n \rangle] \leftrightarrow m - n$ is an isomorphism between Z' and the ring Z of all integers.

CHAPTER 7

THE REAL NUMBERS

7–1 Development of the real numbers. It is correct to say that the real number system is the foundation on which modern mathematics is built. If all of the mathematical theories which depend on real numbers were to be wiped out, then mathematics, and more generally all physical science, would be set back 500 years. This is perhaps surprising, since rigorous construction of the real numbers is a relatively recent development in the history of mathematics. Before the work of Cantor and particularly the German mathematician, Richard Dedekind (1831–1916), during the last quarter of the 19th century, the question, "What is a real number?" was largely ignored.* Real numbers were used, of course, and elaborate theories were constructed with them, but the concept of a real number was vague. Fortunately, the intuitive idea of the real number system was substantial enough so that early mathematicians were seldom led to false results by the inexactness of the definition of numbers. The house of mathematics was built, so to speak, on the forms for its foundation. The forms were filled with concrete only after part of the house was completed.

The history of real numbers begins with the discovery, sometimes attributed to the Greek mathematician Pythagoras,† that there is no rational number whose square is 2. In current mathematical terminology, this fact is expressed by saying that $\sqrt{2}$ is *irrational*. Our interpretation of Pythagoras' discovery is that the rational number system must be enlarged if we wish to take square roots, cube roots, etc. However, for the Greeks, the theorem of Pythagoras was important because of its geometrical consequences. It implied to them, for example, that the ratio of the diagonal of a square to its side is not a rational number. This observation was a great blow to the idealistic number mystics of the Pythagorean cult.

The traditional and presumably the original proof that $\sqrt{2}$ is irrational runs as follows. If 2 is the square of a rational number, then we can write $2 = (a/m)^2$, where a and m are natural numbers with no common factor. Therefore, $a^2 = 2m^2$. Thus, a^2 is even. Since the square of an odd number is always odd, it follows that a must be even. That is $a = 2b$, where $b \in N$. Substituting, we obtain $4b^2 = a^2 = 2m^2$. Hence, $m^2 = 2b^2$.

---

* However, the theory of proportions developed by the Greek mathematician Eudoxus (408–355 B.C.) can be considered as a geometrical analogue of Dedekind's development of the real numbers.

† There is evidence that this discovery was not made by Pythagoras himself, but rather by one of his followers.

Therefore, m^2 is even. Consequently, m is even. Thus, the number a has the factor 2 in common with m. This contradicts the fact that a and m were selected to be relatively prime. Hence our assumption that 2 is the square of a rational number must be false.

By using the more sophisticated facts about the integers which were established in Chapter 5, we can prove a general theorem, from which Pythagoras' result is obtained as a special instance.

THEOREM 7–1.1. Let m be a natural number, and let a be an integer. If there is a rational number r such that

$$r^m = a,$$

then r is necessarily an integer.

This theorem does not state that there is, or is not, a solution of the equation $x^m = a$. Such results depend on m and a. For example, if $a = 4$ and $m = 2$, then $x^m = a$ has two rational solutions $x = 2$ and $x = -2$; on the other hand we have just seen that if $a = 2$ and $m = 2$, then $x^m = a$ has no solution which is a rational number. What Theorem 7–1.1 says is that in searching for a rational number r such that $r^m = a$, we can restrict our attention to integers.

To prove the theorem, suppose that r is a rational number such that $r^m = a$. Then r can be represented as a quotient b/n, where $b \in Z, n \in N$, and b is relatively prime to n. Consequently,

$$a \cdot n^m = r^m \cdot n^m = (r \cdot n)^m = [(b/n) \cdot n]^m = b^m.$$

If $n \neq 1$, then there is a prime p such that $p | n$. Consequently, $p | b^m$ and therefore, by (5–3.2), $p | b$. However, this is impossible, since n and b are relatively prime. Thus,

$$n = 1 \quad \text{and} \quad r = b \in Z.$$

Let us now see how Theorem 7–1.1 implies that $\sqrt{2}$ is irrational. Suppose that $\sqrt{2} = r \in Q$. Then $r^2 = 2$. Thus, by Theorem 7–1.1 (using the case $m = 2, a = 2$), it follows that r is an integer. However, this is impossible, since 2 is a prime. Therefore, 2 cannot be the square of a rational number.

The discovery of the irrationality of $\sqrt{2}$ did not lead Greek mathematicians to the introduction of real numbers, although it did inspire the development of Eudoxus' theory of incommensurable line segments (which is the geometrical analogue of Dedekind's theory of real numbers, created 2200 years later). The Greeks of Euclid's era carefully separated arithmetic from geometry, and as a result, concepts such as length and

area had only a geometrical meaning for them.   The use of numbers in
practical computations was spurned by the Greek ruling class as being
contrary to "Platonic idealism." Nevertheless, fractions were well known
and commonly used in ancient Greece.   In fact, there was one outstanding
exception to the purism of the Greek geometers.   That was Archimedes of
Syracuse (287–212 B.C.), who is considered to be the greatest of all mathematicians before Isaac Newton (1642–1727).   Archimedes used numbers
extensively in his studies of volumes and areas, and his idea of successive
approximation is close to the modern conception of real numbers.

The intuitive notion of a real number as a specific object appeared late
in the Renaissance.   To be sure, rational approximations of particular
numbers such as roots of integers and π were found and used by the
Babylonians even before the period when Greek mathematics flourished.
However, the idea of the system of *all* real numbers developed only after
the introduction around 1600 of the familiar "decimal point" notation for
decimal fractions:

$$1.04 \quad = 1 + 0 \cdot 10^{-1} + 4 \cdot 10^{-2},$$
$$311.001 \ = 3 \cdot 10^2 + 1 \cdot 10 + 1 + 0 \cdot 10^{-1} + 0 \cdot 10^{-2} + 1 \cdot 10^{-3},$$
$$-11.9999 = -(1 \cdot 10 + 1 + 9 \cdot 10^{-1} + 9 \cdot 10^{-2} + 9 \cdot 10^{-3} + 9 \cdot 10^{-4}).$$

DEFINITION 7–1.2.   A *decimal fraction* is a rational number r which is
either of the form

$$a_m 10^m + a_{m-1} 10^{m-1} + \cdots + a_1 10 + a_0$$
$$+ b_1 10^{-1} + b_2 10^{-2} + \cdots + b_n 10^{-n},$$

where the a's and b's are integers between 0 and 9 inclusive, or else r is
the negative of such a number.   If $r = a_m 10^m + a_{m-1} 10^{m-1} + \cdots$
$+ a_1 10 + a_0 + b_1 10^{-1} + b_2 10^{-2} + \cdots + b_n 10^{-n}$, then r is represented by the expression

$$a_m a_{m-1} \ldots a_1 a_0 . b_1 b_2 \ldots b_n.$$

The number of digits following the decimal point is called the *number of
decimal places* in the representation of the decimal fraction r.

Using Theorem 5–1.3, we can easily see that a rational number r is a
decimal fraction if and only if r can be written in the form $r = a/10^k$,
with $a \in Z$ and k some nonnegative integer.   Thus, not every rational
number is a decimal fraction.   However, every rational number can be
approximated by a decimal fraction.   In fact, one of our main goals after
defining the real numbers is to show that every real number can be approximated by a decimal fraction.

EXAMPLE 1. The rational number $\frac{1}{3}$ is not a decimal fraction. For $\frac{1}{3} = a/10^k$ implies $10^k = 2^k 5^k = 3a$, which is impossible by the fundamental theorem of arithmetic. However,

$$0.3 = \tfrac{3}{10} < \tfrac{1}{3} < \tfrac{4}{10} = 0.4,$$
$$0.33 = \tfrac{33}{100} < \tfrac{1}{3} < \tfrac{34}{100} = 0.34,$$
$$0.333 = \tfrac{333}{1000} < \tfrac{1}{3} < \tfrac{334}{1000} = 0.334,$$

etc. Thus, $\frac{1}{3}$ differs from the n place decimal fraction $0.33\ldots3$ by less than 10^{-n}.

EXAMPLE 2. It is possible to approximate $\sqrt{2}$ by trial and error. Note that $1^2 = 1 < 2$ and $2^2 = 4 > 2$. It therefore seems plausible that $\sqrt{2}$ lies between a pair of decimal fractions $1.b$ and $1.(b + 1)$, where $0 \le b < b + 1 \le 9$. By trial, we obtain

$$(1.1)^2 = 1.21, (1.2)^2 = 1.44, (1.3)^2 = 1.69, (1.4)^2 = 1.96, (1.5)^2 = 2.25.$$

Thus, $\sqrt{2}$ apparently lies between 1.4 and 1.5. If this procedure is repeated, additional decimal places are obtained:

$$(1.41)^2 = 1.9881, (1.42)^2 = 2.0664;$$
$$(1.411)^2 = 1.990921, (1.412)^2 = 1.993744, (1.413)^2 = 1.996569,$$
$$(1.414)^2 = 1.999396, (1.415)^2 = 2.002225;$$
$$(1.4141)^2 = 1.99967881, (1.4142)^2 = 1.99996064,$$
$$(1.4143)^2 = 2.00024549;$$
$$(1.41421)^2 = 1.9999899241, (1.41422)^2 = 2.0000181084.$$

Therefore, a perfectly straightforward search procedure yields a decimal fraction whose square is as close to 2 as desired. Our calculation shows that the square of 1.41421 differs from 2 by about 10^{-5}. By continuing the computation, we could improve this estimate as much as we wish.

The above examples suggest that infinite decimal sequences might be introduced to represent real numbers. Imagine an endless sequence of successive decimal fractions

$$a_m a_{m-1} \ldots a_1 a_0 . b_1,$$
$$a_m a_{m-1} \ldots a_1 a_0 . b_1 b_2,$$
$$a_m a_{m-1} \ldots a_1 a_0 . b_1 b_2 b_3,$$
$$\ldots$$

approximating a real number u. As in the above examples, it should be possible to obtain the n-place decimal approximation from the $(n - 1)$-place decimal approximation by adding a single decimal digit. Then, the result of all the approximations can be conveniently represented by an infinite sequence of decimal digits:

$$a_m a_{m-1} \ldots a_1 a_0 \,.\, b_1 b_2 b_3 \ldots b_n \ldots$$

From this infinite expression, the n-place decimal approximation is obtained by using only the first $(m + 1) + n$ symbols, that is, $a_m a_{m-1} \ldots a_1 a_0 \,.\, b_1 b_2 b_3 \ldots b_n$. The expression $a_m a_{m-1} \ldots a_1 a_0 \,.\, b_1 b_2 b_3 \ldots$ will be called the *infinite decimal sequence* representing u. For example, $\sqrt{2}$ is represented by the infinite decimal sequence

$$1.41421356\ldots$$

In practice it is not possible to specify the complete infinite decimal sequence representing a real number u, except for very special values of u. The decimal fractions are themselves represented by decimal sequences which end with an infinite string of zeros:

$$1 = 1.0000\ldots, \qquad 2.5 = 2.5000\ldots, \qquad -4.11 = -4.1100\ldots$$

We will prove later that rational numbers are characterized by the fact that their infinite decimal representations are ultimately periodic, that is, from some point on, the representations consist of the repetition of blocks of decimal digits. For example,

$$\tfrac{1}{3} \text{ is represented by } 0.333333\ldots,$$

$$\tfrac{1}{11} \text{ is represented by } 0.090909\ldots,$$

$$\tfrac{5}{12} \text{ is represented by } 0.416666\ldots.$$

If infinite decimal sequences are used to represent real numbers, there is a tendency to identify the numbers with the sequences which represent them. A similar temptation was encountered in our discussion of the rational numbers, where we were inclined to identify rational numbers with the quotients a/m. In fact, the definition of the rational numbers in Section 6–5 was motivated by the idea that rational numbers are represented by quotients a/m, with $a \in Z$, $m \in N$. Similarly, it is possible to define real numbers in terms of infinite decimal sequences, but this construction involves formidable technical difficulties. It will therefore be avoided. Instead, we will base the construction of R on the intuitive idea that there is a one-to-one correspondence between the set of all real numbers and the set of all points on a line. This geometrical motivation and the resulting construction of R, following the ideas of Dedekind, will be outlined in the next two sections. Infinite decimal sequences do, however, provide a useful way of representing real numbers, and this subject will be discussed in Section 7–9.

Problems

1. Indicate which of the following numbers are decimal fractions and give their decimal representation: $\frac{1}{8}$, $\frac{5}{24}$, $-\frac{6}{125}$, $\frac{25}{128}$.

2. Find the 2-, 3-, and 4-place decimal approximation of $\sqrt{5}$.

3. Find the infinite decimal sequence representing the numbers $\frac{1}{32}$, $\frac{2}{7}$, and $-\frac{1}{6}$.

4. Prove that a rational number r is a decimal fraction if and only if $r = a/10^k$ for some $a \in Z$ and nonnegative integer k.

5. Let $a = p_1^{e_1} p_2^{e_2} \ldots p_g^{e_g}$, where p_1, p_2, $\ldots$, p_g are distinct primes. Prove that the equation

$$x^m - a = 0$$

has a rational number solution $x = r$ if and only if m divides each of the exponents e_1, e_2, $\ldots$, and e_g.

6. Let n be a natural number. Suppose that u and v are rational numbers which are related by the equation

$$u = \frac{n}{2v} + \frac{v}{2}.$$

Show that

$$u^2 - n = \frac{(v^2 - n)^2}{4v^2}.$$

By repeated use of this observation, find a rational number u such that $u^2 - 5 < 10^{-7}$. Find a rational number u such that $u^2 - 10 < 10^{-8}$.

7. Show that if $t > 2$, then there is a rational number r such that $t > r^2 > 2$.

7–2 The coordinate line.

The motivation for Dedekind's construction of the real number system is geometrical. As we saw in Section 6–1, the use of numbers to measure distances led to the introduction of rational numbers. Rulers were constructed by subdividing a convenient unit of length into fractional parts. A number of these subdivided units could be laid out on a single "yard stick" or "tape measure." The mathematical idea behind all these measuring implements is the notion of a one-to-one correspondence between the rational numbers and certain points of a line. The early Greek geometers were the first to realize that not all the points of the line were "used up" in this correspondence, that is, there are points of the line which do not correspond to any rational number. From this they drew the conclusion that numbers are inadequate for describing geometrical notions such as length and area. The modern viewpoint is quite different. The fact that the rational numbers do not fill up the whole line is accepted as evidence that the rational number system should be enlarged. Moreover, the desire to have a one-to-one correspondence between the set of *all* numbers and the set of *all* points on a line is the principle which guides the construction of the real numbers.

If two points P_0 and P_1 are given on a line l, then there is a natural way to set up a one-to-one correspondence between the rational numbers and points of l so that 0 corresponds to P_0 and 1 corresponds to P_1. The construction of this correspondence parallels the steps of the construction of the rational number system given in Chapters 3, 4, and 6. Once the real numbers have been defined, this correspondence can be completed so that the real numbers are associated in a one-to-one way with all the points of l. The correspondence between numbers and points is called a *coordinate system* on l.*

In this section, the one-to-one correspondence between Q and points of a line will be described. We will then see in the next section how this correspondence leads to Dedekind's definition of the real number system. The geometrical ideas are introduced only to guide our intuition toward the appropriate definitions. Accordingly, no attempt will be made to give rigorous proofs of geometrical statements.

As is customary, assume that the distinguished points P_0 and P_1 on l are situated so that P_1 is on the right side of P_0 (see Fig. 7–1). The segment of l from P_0 to P_1 is called the *basic unit interval*. The length of this interval is the *unit of length* for the coordinate system on l. The points P_0 and P_1 are called the *origin* and *unit point*, respectively, of the coordinate system.

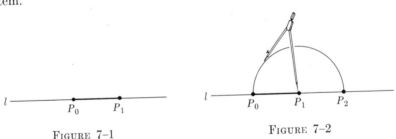

l ———————————•————————•————————
                  P_0 P_1

FIGURE 7–1

l ———————————•————————•————————•————
                  P_0 P_1 P_2

FIGURE 7–2

The first step in the construction of the coordinate line consists of associating the natural numbers with points of l. Let P_2 be the point to the right of P_1 whose distance from P_1 is the same as the distance from P_1 to P_0. Such a point can be constructed mechanically, using a pair of compasses, by drawing a semicircle centered at P_1, starting at the point P_0 (see Fig. 7–2). The other point of intersection of this semicircle with l is

---

* The term "coordinate system" may also refer to a one-to-one correspondence between the points of a plane and the set of all pairs of real numbers (see Section 8–3), or points in space and the set of all triples of real numbers. A line l together with a coordinate system on l is often called a *coordinate line*.

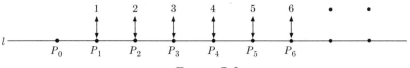

FIGURE 7–3

P_2. Let P_3 be the point to the right of P_2 whose distance from P_2 is also equal to the unit length. This can be constructed in the same way that P_2 was obtained, since the distance from P_2 to P_1 is also equal to the unit length. Continue this process, obtaining points P_4, P_5, P_6, ... so that the segments P_0P_1, P_1P_2, P_2P_3, P_3P_4, P_4P_5, ... are all congruent. (That is, they have the same length and the ordering of their endpoints is the same: P_1 is right of P_0, P_2 is right of P_1, P_3 is right of P_2, etc.). Now set up the correspondence

$$n \leftrightarrow P_n$$

between the natural numbers and the points constructed in this way (see Fig. 7–3). It is apparent that this correspondence is one-to-one. However, in order to prove this fact, it would be necessary to use some simple geometrical properties of straight lines (specifically, the fact that straight lines do not close back on themselves, as do the great circles on spheres, for example).

The next step in setting up a one-to-one correspondence between the rational numbers and points of l consists of defining a sequence P_{-1}, P_{-2}, P_{-3}, ... of points on l, moving from P_0 to the left in such a way that all of the segments $P_{-1}P_0$, $P_{-2}P_{-1}$, $P_{-3}P_{-2}$, ... are congruent to the basic unit interval P_0P_1. These points can be obtained using a pair of compasses in the same way that the points P_2, P_3, P_4, ... were constructed. Now define the correspondence

$$a \leftrightarrow P_a$$

between the integers and the set of points ... , P_{-3}, P_{-2}, P_{-1}, P_0, P_1, P_2, P_3, ... (see Fig. 7–4).

Let r be any rational number. Then r can be represented as a quotient of an integer by a natural number $r = a/m$. Thus, in order to obtain a correspondence between Q and points of l, it suffices to define points $P_{a,m}$ on l for each $a \in Z$ and $m \in N$, so that $P_{a,m} = P_{b,n}$ if and only if $a/m = b/n$.

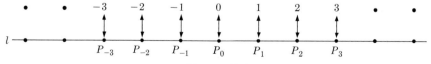

FIGURE 7–4

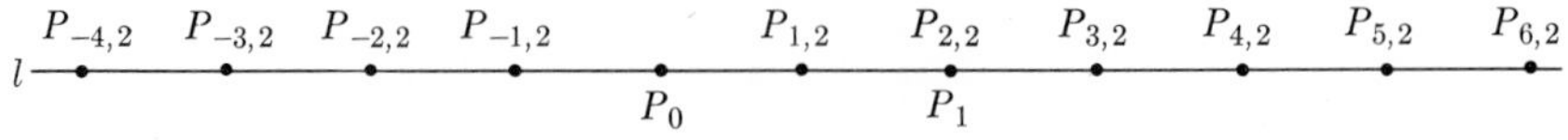

FIGURE 7-5

If this condition is satisfied, then the correspondence

$$\frac{a}{m} \leftrightarrow P_{a,m}$$

between Q and the points $P_{a,m}$ of l is well defined (since $a/m = b/n$ implies $P_{a,m} = P_{b,n}$) and one-to-one (since $a/m \neq b/n$ implies $P_{a,m} \neq P_{b,n}$).

To construct the points $P_{a,m}$, choose $P_{1,m}$ to be the first point to the right of P_0 in a subdivision of the basic unit interval into m equal parts. That is, $P_{1,m}$ is the point on the right-hand side of P_0 such that the distance from P_0 to P_1 is m times the distance from P_0 to $P_{1,m}$. For example, $P_{1,1} = P_1$, and $P_{1,2}$ is the point which bisects the segment $P_0 P_1$. To obtain the points $P_{a,m}$ for arbitrary $a \in Z$, we repeat the process used to obtain the points P_a associated with the integers, except that $P_0 P_{1,m}$ is used as the basic unit interval instead of $P_0 P_1$. That is, the points $P_{2,m}$, $P_{3,m}$, $P_{4,m}$, ... are constructed to the right of $P_{1,m}$ and $P_{-1,m}$, $P_{-2,m}$, $P_{-3,m}$, ... are constructed to the left of P_0, so that the intervals

$$\ldots, \quad P_{-3,m}P_{-2,m}, \quad P_{-2,m}P_{-1,m}, \quad P_{-1,m}P_0,$$

and

$$P_{1,m}P_{2,m}, \quad P_{2,m}P_{3,m}, \quad \ldots$$

are all congruent to the interval $P_0 P_{1,m}$. For example, if $m = 2$, the points shown in Fig. 7-5 are obtained.

It is clear from the definition of the points $P_{a,m}$ that for any natural number k, $P_{a,m} = P_{ka,km}$. Then if $a/m = b/n$, it follows that

$$P_{a,m} = P_{na,nm} = P_{mb,mn} = P_{b,n}.$$

If $a/m \neq b/n$, then either $na < mb$, or $mb < na$. In case $na < mb$, it is evident that $P_{a,m} = P_{na,nm}$ lies to the left of $P_{b,n} = P_{mb,nm}$. Similarly, if $mb < na$, then $P_{b,n}$ lies to the left of $P_{a,m}$. In either case $P_{a,m} \neq P_{b,n}$.

If r is any rational number, we can define P_r to be the point $P_{a,m}$, where $r = a/m$ is any representation of r as a quotient. Using this more convenient notation, we can express the correspondence between Q and the points of l in the form

$$r \leftrightarrow P_r.$$

Our discussion in the preceding paragraph shows that this correspondence has the following basic property.

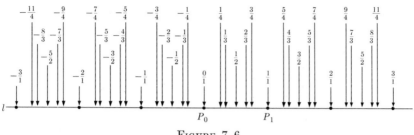

FIGURE 7–6

(7–2.1). The point P_r lies to the left of the point P_s if and only if $r < s$.

Since $P_{1,1} = P_1$, the unit interval which is used for the construction of the points $P_{a,1}$ is the same as the original basic unit interval P_0P_1. This means that the points $P_{a,1}$ are the same as the points P_a which were associated with the integers. Thus, the correspondence $a/1 \leftrightarrow P_{a/1}$ agrees with the previously defined association $a \leftrightarrow P_a$.

It is not possible to picture all of the points $P_{a/m}$ on a line segment, since as m gets large, these points become increasingly dense along every part of the line (see Fig. 7–6). In fact it is possible to prove the following important result.

(7–2.2). If S and T are two different points of l, then there is a point $P_{a/m}$ between S and T.

We will not give a proof of (7–2.2) since that would require a careful formulation of geometrical principles. However, it is worthwhile to give an informal argument in support of this statement. Suppose for definiteness that S lies to the left of T. Then the basic interval can be covered by a finite number of translates* of ST. That is, there are points T_1, T_2, T_3, ..., T_m on l such that T_m lies to the right of P_1 and the intervals P_0T_1, T_1T_2, T_2T_3, ..., $T_{m-1}T_m$ are all congruent to ST (see Fig. 7–7). Thus, we can suppose that m is the number of translates of ST needed to cover P_0P_1 in this way. Then if P_0P_1 is subdivided into m equal subintervals, each of these will be shorter than the intervals P_0T_1, T_1T_2, T_2T_3, ..., $T_{m-1}T_m$. In particular, $P_0P_{1/m}$ is properly contained in P_0T_1.

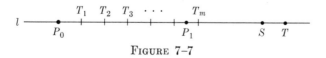

FIGURE 7–7

* This fundamental assumption about line segments is usually called *Archimedes' principle*.

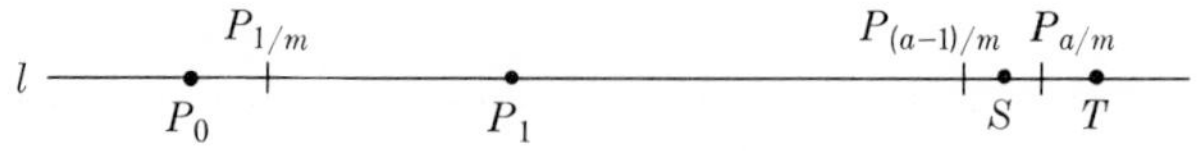

FIGURE 7–8

There is a unique integer a such that S lies in the interval $P_{(a-1)/m}P_{a/m}$ with $P_{a/m}$ to the right of S (see Fig. 7–8). Then $P_{a/m}$ lies on the left side of T, since otherwise the interval $P_{(a-1)/m}P_{a/m}$ would contain the interval ST. However, $P_{(a-1)/m}P_{a/m} \supseteq ST$ is impossible, since $P_{(a-1)/m}P_{a/m}$ is congruent to $P_0P_{1/m}$, ST is congruent to P_0T_1, and $P_0P_{1/m} \subset P_0T_1$. Therefore, the point $P_{a/m}$ lies strictly between S and T.

The density property (7–2.2) obscures the fact that the points P_r do not fill the whole line. The sets $\{P_{a/m}|a \in Z\}$ form a "mesh" on l which becomes arbitrarily fine as m increases. It is conceivable therefore that $\cup_{m \in N}\{P_{a/m}|a \in Z\}$ is the set of all points of l. The fact that the points P_r do not exhaust l is a consequence of Pythagoras' theorem that $\sqrt{2}$ is irrational. This discovery, which greatly influenced the development of Greek mathematics, was probably made by means of a geometrical example such as the following one.

―――――――――

EXAMPLE 1. Draw a line l through diagonally opposite corners of a square. Set up a coordinate system on l, using one corner of the square as the origin P_0, and choosing P_1 on the segment of l inside the square, so that the unit of length for the coordinate system is the same as the length of the sides of the square (that is, the distance from P_0 to P_1 is the same as the length of the side of the square). Let T be the point on l which is the corner of the square opposite to P_0 (see Fig. 7–9). Finally, let S be one of the two corners of the square which is not on l. Then P_0ST is a right triangle. Thus, by the Pythagorean triangle theorem

$$\overline{P_0T}^2 = \overline{P_0S}^2 + \overline{ST}^2 = 2 \cdot \overline{P_0P_1}^2,$$

where $\overline{P_0T}$, $\overline{P_0S}$, $\overline{ST}$, and $\overline{P_0P_1}$ represent the lengths* of the line segments P_0T, P_0S, ST, and P_0P_1. If $T = P_r$ for some rational number r, then the distance from P_0 to T is $|r|$ times the length of the basic unit interval P_0P_1. That

―――――――――

* The early Greek mathematicians always interpreted lengths and areas as different kinds of geometrical magnitudes (not numbers), so that the Pythagorean triangle theorem for them was a relation between the areas of three squares. However, they did assign a meaning to fractional multiples of lengths and areas, and they showed that if the length of the side of one square is r times the length of the side of another, then the area of the first square is r^2 times the area of the second. Thus, the proof given in this example would have made sense to the Greek geometers.

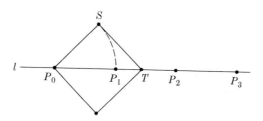

FIGURE 7–9

is, $\overline{P_0T} = |r| \cdot \overline{P_0P_1}$. Hence,

$$r^2 \cdot \overline{P_0P_1^2} = 2\overline{P_0P_1^2},$$

so that

$$r^2 = 2.$$

As we saw in Section 7–1, 2 cannot be the square of a rational number. Therefore, T must be different from all of the points P_r.

PROBLEMS

1. Using a ruler, draw a figure which extends the subdivision in Fig. 7–6 to include all points $a/5$ and $a/6$ between -3 and 3.

2. For which of the following values of k is it possible to construct a rectangle with sides of *integral* length whose diagonal has length $\sqrt{k}$:

$$k = 2, 3, 4, 5, 6, 7, 8, 9, 10?$$

3. Show how to subdivide a line segment into 7 equal subsegments, using only a ruler and a pair of compasses.

4. Show that the correspondence $r \leftrightarrow P_r$ satisfies (7–2.1).

5. Define the length of a line segment P_rP_s on the line l to be

$$\overline{P_rP_s} = |s - r|.$$

Describe the correspondence $r \leftrightarrow P_r$ in terms of this notion of distance.

7–3 Dedekind cuts. We turn now to the problem of constructing the real numbers so that they will correspond to *all* of the points on the line l. Our purpose in this section is to show how this requirement leads to the definition of real numbers. If T is a point on l, define

$$X_T = \{r | P_r \text{ lies to the right of } T\}. \tag{7–1}$$

That is, X_T is the set of rational numbers r corresponding to points P_r on

FIGURE 7–10

l which lie to the right of T (see Fig. 7–10). In the example shown in Fig. 7–10, $r \in X_T$ and $s \notin X_T$.

The properties (7–2.1) and (7–2.2) of the correspondence $r \leftrightarrow P_r$, together with the definition of the sets X_T, given in (7–1), lead to a number of important facts.

(7–3.1). Let T be any point on l. Then
   (a) $\Phi \subset X_T \subset Q$;
   (b) if r and s are rational numbers such that $r < s$ and $r \in X_T$, then
       $s \in X_T$;
   (c) X_T has no smallest element;
   (d) if $T = P_r$, then $X_T = \{s \in Q | r < s\}$;
   (e) if the point S on l lies to the left of T, then $X_S \supset X_T$;
   (f) the correspondence $T \leftrightarrow X_T$ is one-to-one.

We will prove (a), (b), and (c) and leave it for the reader to prove the remaining statements on the basis of (7–2.1) and (7–2.2). Let S and R be points on l such that S lies to the left of T and R lies to the right of T. By (7–2.2), there are rational numbers s and r such that P_s is between S and T and P_r is between T and R. Then P_s lies to the left of T and P_r lies to the right of T. By (7–1), $s \notin X_T$ and $r \in X_T$. Therefore X_T is a non-empty proper subset of Q, that is, $\Phi \subset X_T \subset Q$. To prove (b), we note that by (7–2.1) if $r < s$, then P_s lies to the right of P_r. Since $r \in X_T$, P_r lies to the right of T. Hence P_s lies to the right of T. Consequently, $s \in X_T$. The proof of (c) uses both (7–2.1) and (7–2.2). Suppose that $r \in X_T$, that is, P_r lies to the right of T. By (7–2.2) there is a rational number s such that the point P_s is between T and P_r. Therefore, P_s lies to the right of T, and to the left of P_r. Hence, $s \in X_T$ by (7–1), and $s < r$ by (7–2.1). This argument proves that for any element r of X_T, there is always a smaller element $s \in X_T$. Thus X_T cannot have a smallest element.

The fact stated in (7–3.1 f) that $T \leftrightarrow X_T$ is a one-to-one correspondence between the points of l and the sets X_T of rational numbers suggests that these sets might be the appropriate objects to call real numbers, since our stated objective is to define the real numbers so that they will correspond to all the points on l. However, the sets X_T are defined using rather vague geometrical ideas. The definition of real numbers should be based on the established properties of the rational number system. We would therefore like to find properties of the sets X_T which characterize these sets in an exact way. The properties (a), (b), and (c) of (7–3.1) satisfy this requirement.

DEFINITION 7–3.2. A *Dedekind cut** is a set X of rational numbers satisfying

(a) $\Phi \subset X \subset Q$;
(b) if $r < s$ and $r \in X$, then $s \in X$; and
(c) X has no smallest element.

It is now our contention that the sets of rational numbers thus defined can be identified with the sets X_T. By (7–3.1), every set X_T is a set of rational numbers X which satisfies the conditions of Definition 7–3.2. On the other hand, if X is a Dedekind cut, then there is a point T on the line l such that $X = X_T$. This is not a statement which we can prove, but rather it is a geometrical assumption about the set of points on a line. However, this assumption can be made plausible.

Let X be a Dedekind cut. Note that there is a point on l which lies to the left of every point P_r corresponding to a rational number r which belongs to X. Indeed, if this is not the case, then X contains every rational number, contrary to Definition 7–3.2(a). To see this, assume that there is no point of l which lies to the left of every point P_r with $r \in X$. This means that for every point S on l, there is some point P_r with $r \in X$ such that either $P_r = S$ or P_r lies to the left of S. Let s be an arbitrary element of Q, and choose S on l to be a point to the left of P_s. Then by assumption there is an $r \in X$ such that P_r lies to the left of P_s. By (7–2.1), $r < s$. Since $r \in X$, it follows from Definition 7–3.2(b) that $s \in X$. Thus, we have shown that X contains every rational number s, contradicting Definition 7–3.2(a), as predicted.

Now imagine that a movable point indicator is placed on l at a point which lies to the left of every point P_r with $r \in X$. Let the indicator be moved to the right, as far as it will go without passing through one of the points P_r corresponding to a rational number r which belongs to X. Since X is not empty by Definition 7–3.2(a), the indicator cannot be moved indefinitely. Therefore, it must stop at some point T, blocked by the condition that if it is moved any farther to the right, then it will pass through a point P_r with $r \in X$. We assert that $X = X_T$. In the first place, suppose that $s \in X$. We wish to show that $s \in X_T$, that is, the point P_s lies to the right of T. Since X has no smallest element by Definition

---

* The sets of rational numbers satisfying (a), (b), and (c) of Definition 7–3.2 are more properly called *upper Dedekind cuts*, but we will simply refer to them as "cuts." A *lower Dedekind cut* is defined to be a set X of rational numbers such that $\Phi \subset X \subset Q$, $r > s$ and $r \in X$ implies $s \in X$, and X has no largest element. The real numbers can be defined using lower Dedekind cuts, but it turns out that the definition of multiplication is less natural in terms of lower cuts.

7–3.2(c), there is an $r \in X$ such that $r < s$. Therefore, P_r lies to the left of P_s, by (7–2.1). Moreover, P_r cannot lie to the left of T, since otherwise the indicator would have passed through P_r in moving to the position T. Thus, either $P_r = T$ or P_r lies to the right of T. Since P_s lies to the right of P_r, it follows that in either case, P_s is to the right of T. Consequently, $X \subseteq X_T$. Now suppose that $s \in X_T$. Then P_s lies to the right of T. Since the indicator cannot be moved any closer to P_s than T without passing through some point P_r corresponding to a rational number r in X, there must be an $r \in X$ such that P_r lies to the left of P_s. Hence $r < s$ by (7–2.1). Therefore, by Definition 7–3.2(b), it follows that $s \in X$. This shows that $X_T \subseteq X$. Therefore, $X = X_T$.

Of course, this argument is not a proof in the mathematical sense. However, it does show, intuitively at least, that every Dedekind cut is of the form X_T for some point T on the line l. This means that $T \leftrightarrow X_T$ is a one-to-one correspondence between the set of all points on l and the set of all Dedekind cuts. It therefore seems reasonable to *formally define* the set of all real numbers to be the set of all Dedekind cuts. That is, by definition, real numbers *are* Dedekind cuts. Then we can say that there is a one-to-one correspondence between the set of all points on l and the set of all real numbers. The correspondence $T \leftrightarrow X_T$ is called the *coordinate system* on the line l (or the *coordinatization* of l) with the basic unit interval P_0P_1.

PROBLEMS

1. Which of the following sets are Dedekind cuts?
    (a) $\{r \in Q | r + 2 > 3\}$
    (b) $\{r \in Q | 1/r < -1\}$
    (c) $\{r \in Q | r^2 > 1\}$
    (d) $\{r \in Q | 1/r^3 \geq 0\}$
    (e) $\{r \in Q | 0 \leq (1 + r)^{-1} < 1\}$

2. Illustrate the proofs of (7–3.1a, b, c) by means of diagrams.

3. Prove (7–3.1d, e).

4. Can the definition of a Dedekind cut be extended to any ordered integral domain? If not, state why. If so, give a reformulation of the Definition 7–3.2.

7–4 Construction of the real numbers. The motivation given in the last two sections has prepared the way for the formal definition of the real numbers and their operations. For convenience, we repeat the definition given informally at the end of the last section.

DEFINITION 7–4.1. The *set R of all real numbers* is the set of all Dedekind cuts, that is, the totality of the sets X of rational numbers which satisfy conditions (a), (b), and (c) of Definition 7–3.2.

Thus the real numbers are defined strictly in terms of the set Q of rational numbers and the order relation $<$ in Q. The reader should be aware of the fact that our point of view is now changed. The real numbers *are* the Dedekind cuts. The operations in R must be defined and their properties derived solely on the basis of Definition 7–4.1 and known properties of the rational numbers.

Before considering the operations in R, it is necessary to establish some fundamental properties of Dedekind cuts.

(7–4.2). If X and Y are Dedekind cuts, then exactly one of the relations

$$X \subset Y, \qquad X = Y, \qquad \text{or} \qquad X \supset Y$$

is satisfied.

Proof. Suppose that neither $X \subset Y$ nor $X = Y$ is satisfied. Then there is an element $r \in X$ such that $r \notin Y$. If $s \in Y$, then $s \leq r$ is impossible, because otherwise $r \in Y$ by Definition 7–3.2(b). Therefore, $r < s$. Since $r \in X$, it follows from Definition 7–3.2(b) again that $s \in X$. Hence, we have shown that $s \in Y$ implies $s \in X$, that is, $Y \subseteq X$. By assumption $Y \neq X$. Therefore, $X \supset Y$. We have shown that if neither of the two relations $X \subset Y$, $X = Y$ is satisfied, then the third relation $X \supset Y$ must hold. This proves that at least one of the three relations is satisfied. It is obvious from the definition of set inclusion that at most one of the relations $X \subset Y$, $X = Y$, $X \supset Y$ can be satisfied.

The reader should remember that for an arbitrary pair of sets X and Y, none of the relations $X \subset Y$, $X = Y$, or $X \supset Y$ necessarily hold. Therefore (7–4.2) expresses an important special property of Dedekind cuts.

Corresponding to each rational number r there is a Dedekind cut given by the definition

$$X(r) = \{t \in Q | t > r\}. \tag{7–2}$$

The correspondence

$$r \leftrightarrow X(r)$$

is one-to-one, and it has the following properties.

(7–4.3). Let r and s be rational numbers.
  (a) $X(r) \supset X(s)$ if and only if $r < s$.
  (b) $X(r + s) = \{t + u | t \in X(r),\ u \in X(s)\}$.
  (c) If $r \geq 0$ and $s \geq 0$, then $X(r \cdot s) = \{t \cdot u | t \in X(r),\ u \in X(s)\}$.

Proof. The first of these statements follows easily from (7–2). We will prove (b) and leave the proof of (c) as an exercise. If $t \in X(r)$ and $u \in X(s)$, then $t > r$ and $u > s$, by (7–2). Therefore, $t + u > r + s$, that is, $t + u \in X(r + s)$. This shows that

$$\{t + u | t \in X(r), u \in X(s)\} \subseteq X(r + s).$$

Suppose that $v \in X(r + s)$. Then $v > r + s$, by (7–2). There is a rational number w satisfying $v > w > r + s$; for example, $w = \frac{1}{2}(r + s + v)$ has this property. Then $w - r > s$ and $(v - w) + r > r$. Thus, if $t = (v - w) + r$ and $u = w - r$, it follows that $t \in X(r)$, $u \in X(s)$, and $t + u = (v - w) + r + (w - r) = v$. Therefore,

$$v \in \{t + u | t \in X(r), u \in X(s)\}.$$

Since v was any rational number in $X(r + s)$, it follows that $X(r + s) \subseteq \{t + u | t \in X(r), u \in X(s)\}$. This proves (b).

It should be noted that (7–4.3c) is not true if either of the assumptions $r \geq 0$ and $s \geq 0$ is omitted. In fact, if $r < 0$, and s is any rational number, then $\{u \cdot v | u \in X(r), v \in X(s)\} = Q$ (see Problem 3 below).

The one-to-one correspondence $r \leftrightarrow X(r)$ which is established by (7–2) between the set Q of rational numbers and a set of Dedekind cuts serves to identify the rational numbers with a subset of R. Of course, Q itself is not a subset of R, and in order to be able to think of the rational number system as a part of the system of real numbers, it is necessary to "identify" each rational number r with the corresponding cut $X(r)$. A similar identification process was used when we enlarged the system of integers to the field of rational numbers (see Section 6–5). In effect, the rational numbers are redefined to be the set of all Dedekind cuts $X(r)$. It is important to show that the operations and ordering which will be defined in R agree for cuts of the form $X(r)$ with the usual operations and ordering in Q. Specifically, it will be necessary to prove

$$X(r) + X(s) = X(r + s),$$
$$-X(r) = X(-r),$$
$$X(r) \cdot X(s) = X(r \cdot s),$$

and

$$X(r) < X(s) \quad \text{if and only if} \quad r < s.$$

These facts will be established as each operation is defined in R.

It is convenient to discuss the ordering of R before defining the operations of addition, negation, and multiplication.

DEFINITION 7–4.4 *Order in R.* Let $X \in R$ and $Y \in R$. Define

$$X < Y \quad (\text{or } Y > X) \quad \text{if } X \supset Y.$$

In this case, X is said to be *less than* Y.

It may seem odd that the ordering of R is the reverse of the inclusion relation. This reversal is necessary, however, to make the ordering in R agree with the usual ordering in Q. In fact, by (7–4.3a), $X(r) \supset X(s)$ is equivalent to $r < s$. Hence, $X(r) < X(s)$ if and only if $r < s$ according to Definition 7–4.4.

THEOREM 7–4.5. The ordering of R has the properties:
(a) for any X and Y in R, exactly one of the relations $X < Y$, $X = Y$, or $Y < X$ is satisfied;
(b) if $X < Y$ and $Y < W$, then $X < W$.

The statement (a) is a reformulation of (7–4.2), using the Definition 7–4.4, and statement (b) is a consequence of the transitivity of inclusion.

DEFINITION 7–4.6. *Addition in R*. Let $X \in R$, $Y \in R$. Define

$$X + Y = \{r + s \,|\, r \in X, s \in Y\}.$$

Then $X + Y$ is called the *sum* of X and Y.

It is necessary to show that $X + Y$ is a Dedekind cut. Obviously, $\Phi \subset X + Y \subseteq Q$. Since $X \subset Q$ and $Y \subset Q$, there are rational numbers u and v such that $u < r$ for all $r \in X$ and $v < s$ for all $s \in Y$. Consequently, $u + v < r + s$ for all $r \in X$ and $s \in Y$. Therefore, $u + v \notin X + Y$. This proves that $X + Y \subset Q$. Next, suppose that r, s, and t are rational numbers and that $r + s < t$, where $r \in X$ and $s \in Y$. Then $r < t - s$. Thus, $t - s \in X$. Consequently, $t = (t - s) + s \in X + Y$. This shows that $X + Y$ satisfies Definition 7–3.2(b). Finally, to show that $X + Y$ has no smallest element, suppose that $t \in X + Y$. Then by definition, $t = r + s$ for some $r \in X$ and $s \in Y$. Since r is not the smallest element of X, there exists $r' \in X$ such that $r' < r$. Then $t = r + s > r' + s \in X + Y$. Hence, t is not the smallest element of $X + Y$, and since t was any number in $X + Y$, it follows that this set has no smallest element. Therefore, $X + Y$ satisfies all of the conditions required to be a Dedekind cut, so that $X + Y \in R$.

By Definition 7–4.6 and the equality (7–4.3b)

$$X(r) + X(s) = \{t + u \,|\, t \in X(r), u \in X(s)\} = X(r + s).$$

Therefore, addition of the elements of R which we have identified with rational numbers agrees with the usual addition in Q.

Defining negation in R is a bit tricky. The negative, $-X$, of a Dedekind cut $X \in R$ must be a cut such that the sum of X and $-X$ is the zero element of R. If the rational numbers [which we are identifying with the cuts of the form $X(r)$, $r \in Q$] are to be a subring of R, then the zero of R

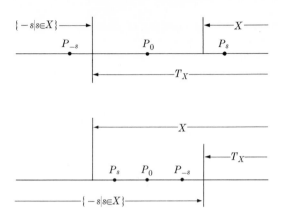

FIGURE 7–11

must be $X(0)$. By Definition 7–4.6, this means that

$$\{r + s | r \in X, s \in -X\} = X(0) = \{u \in Q | u > 0\}.$$

In particular, if $r \in X$, $s \in -X$, then $r + s > 0$, so that $s > -r$. Consequently, if $s \in -X$, then $s > -r$ for all $r \in X$; that is,

$$-X \subseteq \{s \in Q | s > -r \text{ for all } r \in X\}.$$

As a first guess, one might suppose that the set

$$T_X = \{s \in Q | s > -r \text{ for all } r \in X\}$$

is the cut $-X$ for which we are looking. Indeed, it is easy to see that T_X satisfies the first two conditions in Definition 7–3.2 of a Dedekind cut, namely, $\Phi \subset T_X \subset Q$, and if $s < t$ and $s \in T_X$, then $t \in T_X$ (see Fig. 7–11). What makes T_X most attractive as a candidate for the role of $-X$ is the fact (which we will not prove) that $\{r + s | r \in X, s \in T_X\} = X(0)$. That is, if T_X is a Dedekind cut, then according to Definition 7–4.6, $X + T_X = X(0)$. Unfortunately, the set T_X is not always a cut. In fact, if $X = X(r)$, where $r \in Q$, then

$$\begin{aligned}
T_X &= \{s \in Q | s > -t \text{ for all } t \in X(r)\} \\
&= \{s \in Q | s > -t \text{ for all } t \in Q \text{ such that } t > r\} \\
&= \{s \in Q | s > -t \text{ for all } t \in Q \text{ such that } -t < -r\} \\
&= \{s \in Q | s \geq -r\},
\end{aligned}$$

and the set T_X has a smallest element $-r$. Therefore, T_X is not a Dedekind cut, by Definition 7–3.2(c). It appears, however, that the negative of X

should be T_X if T_X has no least element, and it should be the set obtained from T_X by deleting the smallest element, in case T_X has a least element. A convenient way to formulate this definition is to say that $-X$ is the set of all elements in T_X which exceed some other element of T_X. This description of $-X$ is equivalent to the following one.

DEFINITION 7–4.7. *Negation in R.* Let $X \in R$. The *negative of* X is defined to be

$$-X = \{r \in Q | r > t \text{ for some } t \in Q \text{ such that } t > -s \text{ for all } s \in X\}.$$

We must prove that $-X$ is a Dedekind cut. Obviously, $-X \subseteq Q$. Moreover, if $r \in X$, then by Definition 7–4.7, $-r \notin -X$. Hence, $-X \subset Q$. Suppose that $t \notin X$. Then $t < s$ for all $s \in X$, by Definition 7–3.2(b). Consequently, $-t > -s$ for all $s \in X$. Thus, if $r > -t$, then $r \in -X$. Therefore, $\Phi \subset -X$. It is obvious from Definition 7–4.7 that if $r < s$ and $r \in -X$, then $s \in -X$. Finally, if $r \in -X$, then by Definition 7–4.7, $r > t$ for some t such that $t > -s$, for all $s \in X$. Let r' be a rational number satisfying $r > r' > t$ (see Problem 1). Then $r' \in -X$. Consequently, r is not the smallest element of $-X$. Since r was an arbitrary element of $-X$, it follows that $-X$ has no smallest element. Therefore, $-X$ is a Dedekind cut.

We note that negation in R agrees on cuts of the form $X(r)$ with negation in Q. In fact, by Definition 7–4.7,

$$-X(r) = \{u \in Q | u > t \text{ for some } t \in Q \text{ such that}$$
$$t > -s \text{ for all } s \in X(r)\}.$$

Since $X(r) = \{s \in Q | s > r\}$, we have

$$-X(r) = \{u \in Q | u > t \text{ for some } t \in Q \text{ such that}$$
$$t > -s \text{ for all } s > r\}.$$

If $t > -s$ for every rational number s which is greater than r, then $-t < s$ for all $s > r$. This implies that $-t \leq r$; that is, $t \geq -r$. Conversely, if $t \geq -r$, then $-t \leq r$, and therefore $-t < s$ for all $s > r$. We have shown that $t > -s$ for all $s > r$ if and only if $t \geq -r$. Consequently,

$$-X(r) = \{u \in Q | u > t \text{ for some } t \in Q \text{ such that } t \geq -r\}$$
$$= \{u \in Q | u > -r\} = X(-r).$$

Before we define multiplication in R, it is necessary to prove a simple fact about negation.

(7–4.8). If $X \in R$ and $X < X(0)$, then $X(0) < -X$.

Proof. By Definition 7–4.4, $X < X(0)$ implies

$$X \supset X(0) = \{r \in Q | r > 0\}.$$

Let s be an element of X which is not in $X(0)$. Then $s \leq 0$. Since X has no smallest element, there is a rational number $t \in X$ such that $t < s \leq 0$. Then $-t > 0$. Hence, $-t \in X(0)$. If $r \in -X$, then $r > -t$, so that $r \in X(0)$. This shows that $-X \subseteq X(0)$. Since $-t \in X(0)$ and $-t \notin -X$ (by Definition 7–4.7), it follows that $-X \subset X(0)$. Therefore $X(0) < -X$.

As one might expect, $X(0)$ is the zero element of R. Therefore, $X \in R$ is called *positive* if $X(0) < X$, *negative* if $X < X(0)$, and *nonnegative* if $X(0) < X$ or $X(0) = X$ (that is, $X(0) \leq X$). By (7–4.8), if X is negative, then $-X$ is positive.

DEFINITION 7–4.9. *Multiplication in R.* Let $X \in R$ and $Y \in R$. Define
    (a) $X \cdot Y = \{r \cdot s | r \in X, s \in Y\}$ if X and Y are nonnegative,
    (b) $X \cdot Y = -[(-X) \cdot Y]$ if X is negative and Y is nonnegative,
    (c) $X \cdot Y = -[X \cdot (-Y)]$ if X is nonnegative and Y is negative, and
    (d) $X \cdot Y = (-X) \cdot (-Y)$ if X and Y are negative.

To justify this definition,* three remarks are needed. First, if X and Y are nonnegative, then $\{r \cdot s | r \in X, s \in Y\}$ is a cut. The proof of this fact is similar to the argument which we gave to show that $\{r + s | r \in X, s \in Y\}$ is a Dedekind cut, and we leave it for the reader. [Note that since $X \subseteq X(0)$ and $Y \subseteq X(0)$, it follows that $\Phi \subset X \cdot Y \subseteq X(0) \subset Q$]. Second, if X is negative and Y is nonnegative, then $-X$ is positive, so that the expression $-[(-X) \cdot Y]$ makes sense because products of nonnegative cuts have been defined. A similar remark applies to the cases (c) and (d). Our final remark is that if r and s are rational numbers, then

$$X(r) \cdot X(s) = X(r \cdot s).$$

---

* It is unfortunate that to define the product of two Dedekind cuts, four cases must be considered separately. We can easily see, however, that if either X or Y is negative, then $\{r \cdot s | r \in X, s \in Y\} = Q$ (see Problem 3). Thus it would not do to use Definition 7–4.9(a) without some restriction on X and Y. This problem can be avoided by arranging the construction of R in a different order. Instead of proceeding from the natural numbers, to the integers, to the rational numbers, to the real numbers, as we have done in Chapters 3, 4, 6, and 7, the system R could have been obtained by the construction:

natural numbers → positive fractions → positive reals
→ positive and negative reals.

This route from N to R is somewhat more convenient, but less interesting, because it does not give us an opportunity to study the important rings Z and Q along the way.

If r and s are nonnegative rational numbers, this identity follows from (7–4.3c). Then using the identity $X(-r) = -X(r)$, together with Definition 7–4.9(b), (c), and (d), the desired result is easily obtained for all combinations of the signs of r and s. For example, if r is negative and s is nonnegative, then $X(r) \cdot X(s) = -[(-X(r)) \cdot X(s)] = -[X(-r) \cdot X(s)] = -[X((-r) \cdot s)] = X(-[(-r) \cdot s]) = X(r \cdot s)$.

Until now, the only examples of Dedekind cuts which we have seen are the sets $X(r)$ corresponding to rational numbers. In Section 7–10, it will be shown that the sets Q and R do not have the same cardinal number. Consequently, there must be a vast set of cuts which are not of the form $X(r)$ for any $r \in Q$. It seems worthwhile to give here a specific example of such a cut.

EXAMPLE 1. Let $X = \{r \in Q | r > 0 \text{ and } r^2 > 2\}$. Obviously, $\Phi \subset X \subset Q$, and if $r \in X$, $r < s$, then $s \in X$. To prove that X has no smallest element, suppose that $r \in X$. Let

$$s = \frac{r}{2} + \frac{1}{r}.$$

Then $r - s = r/2 - 1/r = (r^2 - 2)/2r > 0$. Hence, $r > s > 0$. Also, $s^2 - 2 = (r^2 - 2)^2/4r^2 > 0$, so that $s^2 > 2$. Therefore, $s \in X$. This proves that X is a Dedekind cut. Obviously X is nonnegative. Thus,

$$X^2 = \{r \cdot s | r \in X, s \in X\}.$$

If $r \in X$ and $s \in X$, then $(r \cdot s)^2 = r^2 \cdot s^2 > 2 \cdot 2 = 4$. Therefore, $r \cdot s > 2$. That is, $X^2 \subseteq X(2)$. On the other hand, if $t > 2$, it is possible to find positive rational number r such that $t > r^2 > 2$ (see, for example, Problem 7, Section 7–1). Hence, $r \in X$ and $t \in X^2$. This shows that $X^2 \supseteq X(2)$. Therefore, $X^2 = X(2)$. In other words, X is the real number $\sqrt{2}$. In particular, X cannot be of the form $X(t)$ for any rational number t, since otherwise $X(t)^2 = X(2)$ would imply $t^2 = 2$.

THEOREM 7–4.10. The system R of all real numbers, given by Definition 7–4.1, with the operations of addition, negation, multiplication, and order defined by Definitions 7–4.6, 7–4.7, 7–4.9, and 7–4.4, and with $X(0)$ and $X(1)$ as zero and identity element, is an ordered field.

The reader should refresh his memory by listing all the identities which have to be checked in the proof of this theorem. Some of these are trivial. For example,

$$X + Y = \{r + s | r \in X, s \in Y\} = \{s + r | s \in Y, r \in X\} = Y + X$$

establishes the commutative law of addition. The identities which involve multiplication (particularly the distributive law) are troublesome, because their proofs require the consideration of numerous cases. There are two rules whose proofs involve a new idea.

$X + (-X) = X(0)$.

If $X \in R$, $W \in R$, and $X \neq X(0)$, then there is a $Y \in R$ such that $X \cdot Y = W$.

The proofs of both these results use the following property of Dedekind cuts.

(7–4.11). If X is a Dedekind cut, and if r is a rational number greater than zero, then there is a rational number s such that $s \notin X$ and $s + r \in X$.

Proof. Since $X \subset Q$, there is some $s \in Q$ with $s \notin X$. Suppose that (7–4.11) is false. Then for any s not in X, it follows that $s + r \notin X$. Starting with such an s, we obtain $s + r \notin X$, $s + 2r = (s + r) + r \notin X$, $s + 3r = (s + 2r) + r \notin X$, etc. By induction, $s + nr \notin X$ for all natural numbers n. However, this is impossible. In fact, since $r > 0$, it is possible to choose n large enough so that $s + nr$ exceeds any rational number. In particular, choosing $t \in X$, we can find n so that $s + nr > t$. Then by Definition 7–3.2(b), $s + nr \in X$.

Using (7–4.11), we show that $X + (-X) = X(0)$. Let $r \in X$ and $s \in -X$. Then by Definition 7–4.7 there is a rational number t such that $s > t$, and $t > -u$ for all $u \in X$. In particular, $s > -r$, so that $r + s > 0$. Therefore, $X + (-X) = \{r + s | r \in X, s \in -X\} \subseteq X(0)$. On the other hand, suppose that $r \in X(0)$, that is, $r > 0$. By (7–4.11), it is possible to find $s \in Q$ such that $s \notin X$, and $s + (r/2) \in X$. Hence, $s < t$ for all $t \in X$. Consequently, $(-s) + r/2 > -s$ and $-s > -t$ for all $t \in X$. Therefore, $(-s) + r/2 \in -X$. It follows that

$$r = [s + (r/2)] + [(-s) + (r/2)] \in X + (-X).$$

Since r was an arbitrary element of $X(0)$, we have proved $X + (-X) \supseteq X(0)$. Therefore, $X + (-X) = X(0)$.

We conclude this Section by showing that if $X > X(0)$ and $W \geq X(0)$, then there is a Dedekind cut Y such that $X \cdot Y = W$. Define

$$Y = \{r/s | r \in W, 0 < s < t \text{ for all } t \in X\}.$$

There must be rational numbers s satisfying $0 < s < t$ for all $t \in X$, because X is a Dedekind cut which is *properly* contained in $X(0) = \{r \in Q | r > 0\}$. Hence, $\Phi \subset Y \subseteq X(0) \subset Q$. If $r \in W$ and $0 < s < t$

for all $t \in X$, and if $r/s < u$, then $r < su$. Hence, $su \in W$ and $u = su/s \in Y$. Finally, Y has no smallest element, because if $r/s \in Y$, with $r \in W$ and $0 < s < t$ for all $t \in X$, then there exists $r' \in W$ such that $r' < r$. Consequently $r'/s < r/s$ and $r'/s \in Y$. This proves that Y is a nonnegative Dedekind cut. By Definition 7–4.9,

$$X \cdot Y = \{u \cdot (r/s) | u \in X, r \in W, 0 < s < t \text{ for all } t \in X\}.$$

If $u \in X$ and $0 < s < t$ for all $t \in X$, then in particular $s < u$. More-over, since $r \in W$, and $W \geq X(0)$, it follows that $r > 0$. Therefore, $u \cdot (r/s) > r$. Hence, $X \cdot Y \subseteq W$. To reverse this inclusion, suppose that $r \in W$. Since W has no smallest element, there is an $r' \in W$ with $r' < r$. Then $(r - r')/r' > 0$. Select $s \in Q$ so that $0 < s < t$ for all $t \in X$. Then $s(r - r')/r' > 0$. Hence, by (7–4.11), there exists $s' \in Q$ such that $s' \notin X$ and $s' + [s(r - r')/r'] \in X$. We can suppose that $s' \geq s$, since otherwise s' could be replaced by s. Since $s' \notin X$, it follows that $0 < s' < t$ for all $t \in X$. Thus $r'/s' \in Y$ by the definition of Y. Therefore,

$$r = \{s' + [s'(r - r')/r']\} \cdot (r'/s')$$
$$\geq \{s' + [s(r - r')/r']\} \cdot (r'/s') \in X \cdot Y.$$

Consequently, $r \in X \cdot Y$. Since r was any element of W, we have proved that $X \cdot Y \supseteq W$. Therefore, $X \cdot Y = W$.

PROBLEMS

1. (a) Show that if u and v are rational numbers with $u < v$, then $w = \frac{1}{2}(u + v)$ is a rational number satisfying $u < w < v$.
   (b) Use part (a) to prove that $X(r)$ is a Dedekind cut for every rational number r.

2. Prove (7–4.3c).

3. Show that if $r < 0$ and s is any rational number, then

$$\{u \cdot v | u \in X(r), v \in X(s)\} = Q.$$

4. Suppose that $X > X(0)$. Define a cut Y such that $Y^2 = X$.

5. Show that $X < X(r)$ if and only if $r \in X$.

6. Prove that if X is a Dedekind cut, then the set $T_X = \{s \in Q | s > -r$ for all $r \in X\}$ satisfies Definition 7–3.2(a) and (b), and $\{r + s | r \in X, s \in T_X\} = X(0)$.

7. Draw a diagram to illustrate the proof that $X + (-X) \supseteq X(0)$.

8. Show from the definition of multiplication that $X \cdot X(0) = X(0)$ for all $X \in R$.

9. Show from the Definitions 7–4.4 and 7–4.7 that if $X < Y$, then

$$-Y < -X.$$

10. Prove the following laws in R.
   (a) $X + (Y + W) = (X + Y) + W$
   (b) $X + X(0) = X$
   (c) $X \cdot Y = Y \cdot X$
   (d) $X \cdot (Y \cdot W) = (X \cdot Y) \cdot W$
   (e) $X < Y$ implies $X + W < Y + W$
   (f) $X < Y$ and $W > X(0)$ implies $X \cdot W < Y \cdot W$

11. Show that $-(X + Y) = (-X) + (-Y)$.

12. Prove the distributive law $W \cdot (X + Y) = (W \cdot X) + (W \cdot Y)$ in the following cases.
   (a) X, Y and W are nonnegative
   (b) $W \geq X(0)$, $X < X(0)$, $X + Y \geq X(0)$
      [*Hint:* Consider $W \cdot (X + Y) + W \cdot (-X)$.]
   (c) $W \geq X(0)$, $X < X(0)$, $Y \geq X(0)$, $X + Y < X(0)$
   (d) $W \geq X(0)$, $X < X(0)$, $Y < X(0)$
   (e) $W < X(0)$, X, Y arbitrary

13. Prove directly that $X \cdot X(1) = X$ for all $X \in R$.

14. Show that if $X \neq X(0)$ and W is any element of R, then there exists Y such that $X \cdot Y = W$. It is necessary to consider the three cases: $X > X(0)$, $W < X(0)$; $X < X(0)$, $W \geq X(0)$; $X < X(0)$, $W < X(0)$. These can be reduced to the case $X > X(0)$, $W \geq X(0)$, which has already been considered.

7–5 The completeness of the real numbers. Theorem 7–4.10 shows that the system R of all real numbers is an ordered field. The same is true of the rational numbers, but we have seen that the field of real numbers is more versatile than the field Q. For example, such equations as $x^2 = 2$, $x^2 = 3$, $x^2 = 5$, etc., can be solved in R, but not in Q. Is it possible to find a property of R which distinguishes it from arbitrary ordered fields? In this section we will show that such a fundamental property exists.

DEFINITION 7–5.1. Let A be an ordered integral domain.* Let S be a subset of A.

   (a) An element $x \in A$ is called an *upper bound* of S in A if $x \geq y$ for all $y \in S$.
   (b) An element $x \in A$ is called a *lower bound* of S in A if $x \leq y$ for all $y \in S$.

---

* To state this definition, or Definition 7–5.2, it is not necessary that A be an integral domain. The only requirement is that A be a *partially ordered set*. That is, there is a relation $\leq$ defined on A which satisfies (i) $x \leq x$ for all $x \in A$; (ii) if $x \leq y$ and $y \leq x$, then $x = y$; (iii) if $x \leq y$ and $y \leq z$, then $x \leq z$.

EXAMPLE 1. Let $A = Q$. Let $S = \{r \in Q | r^2 < 2\}$. Then $t \in Q$ is an upper bound of S if $t > 0$ and $t^2 > 2$ (that is, considered as an element of R, $t > \sqrt{2}$). An element $u \in Q$ is a lower bound of S if $u < 0$ and $u^2 > 2$ (that is, $u < -\sqrt{2}$).

EXAMPLE 2. Let $A = Z$. Let $S = \{a \in Z | a^2 < 2\}$. Then $S = \{-1, 0, 1\}$. Consequently, the upper bounds of S in Z are all integers $b \geq 1$. The lower bounds of S are the integers $b \leq -1$.

EXAMPLE 3. If A is an ordered integral domain, and if S is a subset of A which has a greatest element x, then the upper bounds of S in A are all elements $y \in A$ such that $y \geq x$. Similarly if z is the least element of S, then the lower bounds of S are all of the elements $u \in A$ such that $u \leq z$.

EXAMPLE 4. Let $A = Q$, $S = Z$. Then S has no upper bound, and no lower bound in A.

———————

DEFINITION 7–5.2. Let A be an ordered integral domain. Suppose that S is a subset of A. An element $x \in A$ is called *the least upper bound* of S in A if x is the smallest element in the set of all upper bounds of S. An element $y \in A$ is called *the greatest lower bound* of S in A if y is the largest element in the set of all lower bounds of S.

It is sometimes convenient to have a more formal statement of this definition. Referring to Definition 4–6.3, we see that x is the least upper bound of S if and only if

   (a) $x \geq y$ for all $y \in S$,
   (b) if $z \geq y$ for all $y \in S$, then $z \geq x$.

Similarly, x is the greatest lower bound of S if and only if

   (a′) $x \leq y$ for all $y \in S$,
   (b′) if $z \leq y$ for all $y \in S$, then $z \leq x$.

Since the largest element in a set and the smallest element of a set are unique, if they exist at all, we are justified in speaking of *the* least upper bound and *the* greatest lower bound. Of course, the least upper bound and the greatest lower bound of a set may not exist at all.

The expressions l.u.b. S and g.l.b. S are frequently used as abbreviations for the least upper bound of S and the greatest lower bound of S, respectively. Often the Latin terms *"supremum"* and *"infimum"* are used instead of "least upper bound" and "greatest lower bound." In this case, the abbreviations sup S and inf S are used. Thus, l.u.b. S = sup S, and g.l.b. S = inf S.

———————

EXAMPLE 5. Let $A = Q$ and let $S = \{r \in Q | r^2 < 2\}$. Then S has no least upper bound and no greatest lower bound in Q, because the set

$$\{r \in Q | r > 0, r^2 > 2\}$$

of all upper bounds of S has no smallest element, and the set

$$\{r \in Q | r < 0, r^2 > 2\}$$

of all lower bounds of S has no largest element. (See the Example in Section 7–4.)

EXAMPLE 6. Let $A = R$ and let

$$S = \{X \in R | X^2 < 2\}.$$

Then l.u.b. $S = \sqrt{2}$ in R and g.l.b. $S = -\sqrt{2}$ in R. (See Example 1, Section 7–4.)

EXAMPLE 7. Let $A = R$ and let $T = \{X \in R | X^2 \leq 2\}$. Then l.u.b. $T = \sqrt{2}$ and g.l.b. $T = -\sqrt{2}$. Note that in this example, the least upper bound and the greatest lower bound of T actually belong to T, whereas in Example 6, this was not the case.

THEOREM 7–5.3. Let F be an ordered field. Let S and T be nonempty subsets of F such that g.l.b. S and g.l.b. T exist.

(a) If $U = \{x + y | x \in S, y \in T\}$, then g.l.b. $U =$ g.l.b. $S +$ g.l.b. T.

(b) If $V = \{x \cdot y | x \in S, y \in T\}$, and if all the elements of S and T are nonnegative, then g.l.b. $V = ($g.l.b. $S) \cdot ($g.l.b. $T)$.

(c) If $W = \{-x | x \in S\}$, then l.u.b. $W = -($g.l.b. $S)$.

Proof. We will prove (a) and (c), leaving (b) as a test for the reader. By definition of the greatest lower bound, it follows that g.l.b. $S \leq x$ for all $x \in S$ and g.l.b. $T \leq y$ for all $y \in T$. Hence, g.l.b. $S +$ g.l.b. $T \leq x + y$ for each $x \in S$ and $y \in T$. That is, g.l.b. $S +$ g.l.b. T is a lower bound of $\{x + y | x \in S, y \in T\} = U$. We wish to show that this sum is the greatest lower bound of U. That is, if $z \leq x + y$ for all $x \in S$ and $y \in T$, then $z \leq$ g.l.b. $S +$ g.l.b. T. Let x be an arbitrary element of S. Then $z \leq x + y$ for all $y \in T$, so that $z - x$ is a lower bound of T. Therefore, $z - x \leq$ g.l.b. T. Transposing, we obtain $z -$ g.l.b. $T \leq x$. Since x can be any element of S, it follows that $z -$ g.l.b. T is a lower bound of S. Thus, $z -$ g.l.b. $T \leq$ g.l.b. S. This gives the desired result: $z \leq$ g.l.b. $S +$ g.l.b. T. Therefore, (a) is proved.

To prove (c), note that by Definition 7–5.1, w is an upper bound of W if and only if $w \geq -x$ for all $x \in S$. The condition $w \geq -x$ is evidently equivalent to $-w \leq x$. Thus, w is an upper bound of W if and only if $-w$ is a lower bound of S. Since S has a greatest lower bound, the condition for $-w$ to be a lower bound of S is the same as $-w \leq$ g.l.b. S, or equivalently $w \geq -($g.l.b. $S)$. This sequence of equivalent statements shows that $-($g.l.b. $S)$ is an upper bound of W and every other upper bound of W is larger. Therefore, $-($g.l.b. $S)$ is the least upper bound of W.

A useful case of Theorem 7–5.3 occurs when the set T consists of a single element y. The laws (a) and (b) then become

(a') g.l.b. $\{x + y | x \in S\}$ = (g.l.b. S) + y,

(b') g.l.b. $\{x \cdot y | x \in S\}$ = (g.l.b. S) $\cdot y$, provided that y and all of the elements of S are nonnegative.

The reader should be able to formulate and prove an analogue of Theorem 7–5.3 for least upper bounds.

If A is any ordered integral domain and S is the empty set, then every element of A satisfies the condition for being an upper bound and a lower bound of S. This fact may seem strange, but a careful reading of Definition 7–5.1 shows that it is true. For instance, the condition $x \geq y$ for all $y \in \Phi$ is satisfied vacuously, because there is no y in Φ. It follows that the empty set has no least upper bound, and no greatest lower bound, since an ordered integral domain has no greatest element and no least element (see Problem 4 below). Also, if the set S has no upper bound, then it cannot have a least upper bound. If S has no lower bound, then it cannot have a greatest lower bound. There are two important examples of ordered integral domains in which every nonempty set which has an upper bound also has a least upper bound, and every nonempty set which has a lower bound also has a greatest lower bound. These are the rings Z and R.

DEFINITION 7–5.4. An ordered integral domain A is called *complete* if it satisfies:

(a) if S is a nonempty set in A which has an upper bound in A, then l.u.b. S exists;

(b) if S is a nonempty set in A which has a lower bound in A, then g.l.b. S exists.

We leave it as a problem for the reader to show that Z is complete.

THEOREM 7–5.5. R is a complete ordered field.

Proof. Let S be a nonempty set of Dedekind cuts which has a lower bound. That is, there exists a cut X such that $X \leq Y$ for all $Y \in S$. By definition of the ordering in R, this means that $Y \subseteq X$ for all $Y \in S$. Define

$$W = \cup(\{Y | Y \in S\}).$$

We will show that W is a Dedekind cut. Since S is not empty, there is some $Y \in S$. Therefore, $\Phi \subset Y \subseteq W$. Since every Y in S is contained in X, it follows that $W \subseteq X \subset Q$. Therefore, W satisfies condition (a) of the definition of a Dedekind cut. Suppose that $r \in W$ and $r < s$. Then there is some $Y \in S$ such that $r \in Y$. Since Y is a cut, $r \in Y$ and $r < s$ implies

$s \in Y$. Hence, $s \in Y \subseteq W$. Finally, W has no smallest element. For if $r \in W$, then $r \in Y$ for some $Y \in S$. Since Y has no smallest element, there is a rational number r' such that $r' < r$ and $r' \in Y \subseteq W$. That is, for every number in W, there is a smaller number in W. Consequently, W has no smallest element, as claimed. We have shown that W satisfies all the conditions of a Dedekind cut. Therefore, $W \in R$.

We next prove that W is the greatest lower bound of S. By definition of W, if $Y \in S$, then $Y \subseteq W$. Therefore, $W \leq Y$ for all $Y \in S$, so that W is a lower bound of S. Suppose that U is any lower bound of S. That is, $U \leq Y$ for all $Y \in S$. Thus, $Y \subseteq U$ for all $Y \in S$. Hence,

$$W = \cup(\{Y | Y \in S\}) \subseteq U.$$

Therefore, $U \leq W$. This shows that any lower bound of S in R is less than or equal to W, so that W is the greatest lower bound of S. Our proof up to this point shows that if S is a nonempty subset of R which has a lower bound, then g.l.b. S exists. To complete the proof, it is necessary to prove that if T is a nonempty subset of R which has an upper bound, then l.u.b. T exists. Let $S = \{-X | X \in T\}$. If U is an upper bound of T, then $-U$ is a lower bound of S. Hence, g.l.b. S exists. Noting that $T = \{-Y | Y \in S\}$, it follows from Theorem 7–5.3(c) that l.u.b. T exists and is equal to $-(\text{g.l.b. } S)$. This completes the proof of Theorem 7–5.5.

PROBLEMS

1. Which of the following sets have upper bounds in Q? Which ones have lower bounds in Q?

    (a) $\{|a - b| | a \in Z, b \in Z\}$
    (b) $\{r^n | n \in N\}$, where $r \in Q$, $0 < r < \frac{1}{2}$
    (c) $\{r^n | n \in N\}$, where $r \in Q$, $r > 1$
    (d) $\{-n | n \in N\}$
    (e) $\{a \cdot b/(a^2 + b^2) | a \in N, b \in N\}$

2. Determine the least upper bounds and greatest lower bounds in Q (whenever they exist) of the sets given in Problem 1.

3. Show that any nonempty finite subset of an ordered integral domain has a least upper bound and a greatest lower bound.

4. Show that if A is an ordered integral domain, and if $S = A$, then S has no upper bound in A and no lower bound in A.

5. Show that if S is a nonempty set in an ordered integral domain, then every upper bound of S is greater than or equal to every lower bound of S. Can the equality ever hold? If so, when? Show that for any set S such that g.l.b. S and l.u.b. S exist, the inequality g.l.b. $S \leq$ l.u.b. S is satisfied.

6. Give examples of nonempty subsets S of Q which have upper and lower bounds, satisfying (a) g.l.b. S exists, but l.u.b. S does not exist, (b) g.l.b. S does not exist, but l.u.b. S exists.

7. State the analogue of Theorem 7–5.3 for least upper bounds.

8. Use the well-ordering principle to show that Z is a complete ordered integral domain.

9. Let S be a subset of Z such that l.u.b. S exists. Prove that l.u.b. $S \in S$.

7–6 Properties of complete ordered fields. It is difficult to overestimate the importance of the completeness property of the real numbers. Almost all of the fundamental theorems of analysis make use of completeness. In fact, one naturally wonders if it would be possible to construct mathematical theories such as calculus, using an arbitrary complete ordered field rather than the particular field R. The answer is that this would be possible, but because of the following theorem the results of this theory would not be any more general than the usual theorems concerning the real numbers.

THEOREM 7–6.1. Let F be a complete ordered field. Then there is an isomorphism between F and R which preserves the ordering. That is, there is a one-to-one correspondence between F and R such that if x and y in F correspond respectively to X and Y in R, then

$$x + y \leftrightarrow X + Y, \qquad -x \leftrightarrow -X, \qquad x \cdot y \leftrightarrow X \cdot Y,$$

and

$$x < y \qquad \text{if and only if} \qquad X < Y.$$

Theorems 7–5.5 and 7–6.1 are the two most important results concerning the system of real numbers. Taken together, these theorems tell us that there is one, and, except for differences in the description of the elements and operations, only one complete, ordered field. Theorem 7–6.1 also shows that any property which can be proved for the real numbers is a consequence of the ordered field properties and completeness. The complicated description of R by means of Dedekind cuts can now be discarded.* It was needed only to prove the existence of a complete ordered field.

We will not prove Theorem 7–6.1 in spite of the importance of this result. Instead, the use of completeness will be illustrated by proving two important elementary theorems about R. To emphasize the fact that only

---

* However, there are a few results concerning R which are proved most easily by using the properties of Dedekind cuts. We will find such an example in Section 7–9.

the ordered field properties and completeness are used in the proofs, we will state these theorems for complete ordered fields. Then by Theorem 7–5.5, they are true for R in particular.

THEOREM 7–6.2. Let F be a complete ordered field.
   (a) Suppose that $x > 1$ in F. Then for any $y \in F$, there is a natural number n such that $x^n > y$.
   (b) Suppose that $0 \le x < 1$ in F. Then for any $y > 0$ in F, there is a natural number n such that $x^n < y$.

Proof. If statement (a) is false, then the set $S = \{x, x^2, x^3, \ldots\}$ has an upper bound y in F. Hence, by completeness there is a least upper bound w of S in F. Then $w \ge x^n$ for all $n \in N$. Since $x > 0$, it follows that $x^{-1} > 0$. Hence, $w \cdot x^{-1} \ge x^{n-1}$ for all $n \in N$. Thus, $w \cdot x^{-1}$ is also an upper bound of S. Since w is the least upper bound, this implies that $w \cdot x^{-1} \ge w$. Consequently, $x^{-1} \ge 1$ because $w > 0$. Thus, $x \le 1$. This inequality contradicts the original assumption that $x > 1$. To prove (b), we first dispose of a trivial case. If $x = 0$, then $y > 0 = x^1$, so that (b) holds with $n = 1$. If $x > 0$, then since $x < 1$, it follows that $1 < x^{-1}$. By (a), there is a natural number n such that $(x^{-1})^n > y^{-1}$. Consequently, $x^n < y$.

THEOREM 7–6.3.   Let F be a complete ordered field.   Let $z \in F$ be positive. Suppose that m is any natural number. Then there is one and only one positive $x \in F$ such that $x^m = z$.

Proof. This theorem is trivially true for $m = 1$, so that it can be assumed that $m > 1$. However, with minor changes of notation, the argument which follows is valid in the case $m = 1$, also. The proof is divided into three parts.
   (1) We will use the completeness of F to show that there is an element $x \in F$ satisfying the following conditions:
   (a) $x > 0$;
   (b) if $0 \le y < x$, then $y^m < z$;
   (c) if $x < w$, then $w^m \ge z$.
To obtain such an x, define

$$S = \{y \in F | y \ge 0, y^m < z\}.$$

Then S contains some positive element of F. For example, if

$$y = \min \{1, z/2\}, \qquad \text{then} \qquad 0 < y \le 1 \qquad \text{and} \qquad y < z,$$

so that

$$y^m = y \cdot y^{m-1} \le y \cdot 1^{m-1} = y < z.$$

Hence, $y \in S$. Moreover, S has an upper bound. In fact, if $w \geq \max \{1, z\}$, then $w \geq 1$ and $w \geq z$, so that

$$w^m = w \cdot w^{m-1} \geq w \cdot 1^{m-1} = w \geq z.$$

Thus, $w \geq y$ for all $y \in S$. For if this is not the case, then $w < y$ for some $y \in S$. It would then follow that $w^m < y^m < z$, which is contrary to $w^m \geq z$. Therefore, in particular, $\max \{1, z\}$ is an upper bound of S. By the completeness of F, the set S has a least upper bound in F. Let

$$x = \text{l.u.b. } S.$$

We will show that x satisfies (a), (b), and (c). Since $x \geq y$ for all $y \in S$ and some $y \in S$ satisfies $y > 0$, it follows that $x > 0$. To prove (b), suppose that $0 \leq y < x$. Then y is not an upper bound of S, since x is the *least* upper bound of S. Therefore, $y < y_1$ for some $y_1 \in S$. Consequently by the definition of S, $y^m < y_1^m < z$. To prove (c), suppose that $x < w$. Then $w \notin S$, because x is an upper bound of S. Therefore, w^m is not less than z, that is, $w^m \geq z$.

   (2) We now show that if x satisfies (a), (b), and (c), then both of the inequalities $x^m > z$ and $x^m < z$ lead to contradictions. Therefore, $x^m = z$. Suppose first that $x^m > z$. Let

$$y = \max \{0, x - (x^m - z) \cdot (m \cdot x^{m-1})^{-1}\}.$$

Then
   (d) $0 \leq y < x$,
   (e) $(x - y) \cdot (m \cdot x^{m-1}) \leq x^m - z$.

Therefore,

$$
\begin{aligned}
x^m - y^m &= (x - y)(x^{m-1} + x^{m-2} \cdot y + \cdots + x \cdot y^{m-2} + y^{m-1}) \\
&\leq (x - y) \cdot (x^{m-1} + x^{m-2} \cdot x + \cdots + x \cdot x^{m-2} + x^{m-1}) \\
&= (x - y) \cdot (mx^{m-1}) \leq x^m - z.
\end{aligned}
$$

Consequently, $z \leq y^m$. However, by (d) and (b), $y^m < z$. Thus, $x^m > z$ leads to a contradiction. Next, assume that $x^m < z$. Define

$$w = \min \{2x, x + (z - x^m) \cdot (2^m \cdot x^{m-1})^{-1}\}.$$

Then
   (f) $x < w \leq 2x$,
   (g) $(w - x) \cdot (2^m x^{m-1}) \leq z - x^m$.

Therefore, using the identity

$$2^{m-1} + 2^{m-2} + \cdots + 2 + 1 = \frac{2^m - 1}{2 - 1}$$

(see Problem 6, Section 2–1), we obtain

$$w^m - x^m = (w - x)(w^{m-1} + w^{m-2} \cdot x + \cdots + w \cdot x^{m-2} + x^{m-1})$$
$$\leq (w - x)[(2x)^{m-1} + (2x)^{m-2} \cdot x + \cdots$$
$$+ (2x) \cdot x^{m-2} + x^{m-1}]$$
$$= (w - x) \cdot x^{m-1} \cdot (2^{m-1} + 2^{m-2} + \cdots + 2 + 1)$$
$$= (w - x) \cdot x^{m-1} \cdot \left(\frac{2^m - 1}{2 - 1}\right)$$
$$< (w - x) \cdot (2^m \cdot x^{m-1}) \leq z - x^m.$$

Hence, $w^m < z$. However, by (f) and (c), $z \leq w^m$. Therefore, the assumption $x^m < z$ also leads to a contradiction. The only remaining possibility is $x^m = z$.

(3) We complete the proof of Theorem 7–6.3 by showing that there is only one positive $x \in F$ such that $x^m = z$. Suppose that x and y are in F, $0 < x$, $0 < y$, $x^m = z$, and $y^m = z$. Then $x^m = y^m$, so that

$$0 = x^m - y^m = (x - y)(x^{m-1} + x^{m-2}y + \cdots + xy^{m-2} + y^{m-1}).$$

Since $0 < x$ and $0 < y$, it follows that

$$w = x^{m-1} + x^{m-2}y + \cdots + xy^{m-2} + y^{m-1} > 0.$$

We have $0 = (x - y)w$ and $w \neq 0$. Therefore, $x - y = 0$, that is, $x = y$. This completes the proof.

This proof is a typical sample of the reasoning methods which are used in analysis. To a beginning student, such proofs look very mysterious and complicated. Often the problem is that the details obscure the simple idea on which the argument is based. In order to understand such a proof, it is necessary to strip away the details and find the underlying idea. The above proof provides a good example. As the quantity y increases, starting at zero, the value y^m also increases continuously, that is, it does not jump. Since y^m will ultimately exceed z, there must be some first value x of y for which $x^m \geq z$. This value is obtained in (1) by taking the least upper bound of $\{y \in F | y \geq 0, y^m < z\}$. Then the fact that the increase of y^m is continuous implies that y^m cannot have "jumped over" z at x. Therefore, $x^m = z$. This is what was established in part (2) of the proof.

The unique positive $x \in F$ satisfying $x^m = z$ is called the *mth root of z in F*. This quantity is usually denoted by

$$\sqrt[m]{z} \qquad \text{or} \qquad z^{1/m}.$$

(If $m = 2$, the expression $\sqrt[2]{z}$ is customarily abbreviated to $\sqrt{z}$.) It is convenient to define $\sqrt[m]{0} = 0$. If $z < 0$, then the expression $\sqrt[m]{z}$ is not defined.* By Theorems 7–5.5 and 7–6.3, we have proved that every positive real number has a unique positive mth root for all natural numbers m.

PROBLEMS

1. Let e be the identity element of a complete ordered field F. Show that if $y \in F$, then there exists a natural number n such that $y < ne$.

2. Let F be a complete ordered field. Let m be an odd natural number. Let $z \in F$ (either positive or negative). Prove that there is one and only one $x \in F$ such that $x^m = z$.

3. Let F be a complete ordered field. Suppose that $x \geq 0$ in F. Define for $a \in Z$, $m \in N$,

$$x^{a/m} = (x^{1/m})^a.$$

Show that if $a/m = b/n$, then $x^{a/m} = x^{b/n}$. Thus, x^r is well defined for every rational number r. Prove the following rules of exponents.

(a) $x^r \cdot x^s = x^{r+s}$ for $x \geq 0$ in F, $r \in Q$, and $s \in Q$.
(b) $(x^r)^s = x^{(r \cdot s)}$ for $x \geq 0$ in F, $r \in Q$, and $s \in Q$.
(c) $(x \cdot y)^r = x^r \cdot y^r$ for $x \geq 0$ and $y \geq 0$ in F, and $r \in Q$.

4. Write the proof of Theorem 7–6.3 in the particular case $m = 2$.

The following problems lead to a proof of Theorem 7–6.1. They should be done in order. In all of these problems, e denotes the identity element of a complete ordered field F.

5. Suppose that $y \in F$, $z \in F$ are such that $z - y > e$. Show by the well-ordering principle (using the result of Problem 1) that there is an integer a such that $y < ae < z$.

6. Suppose that $y \in F$, $z \in F$ are such that $y < z$. Show that there is an integer a and a natural number m such that

$$y < \frac{ae}{me} < z.$$

[*Hint:* Choose m so that $me > (z - y)^{-1}$, and apply Problem 5 to $(me) \cdot y$ and $(me) \cdot z$.]

7. Show that for $a \in Z$, $b \in Z$, $m \in N$, and $n \in N$,

$$\frac{ae}{me} = \frac{be}{ne}$$

if and only if $a/m = b/n$ in Q.

---

* For odd values of m, it would make sense to let $\sqrt[m]{z} = -(\sqrt[m]{|z|})$. However, for m even and $z < 0$, the expression $\sqrt[m]{z}$ is meaningless in an ordered field, because of Theorem 4–5.5.

8. For $x \in F$, define $X(x) = \{a/m \in Q | a \in Z,\ m \in N,\ x < (ae)/(me)\}$. Show that $X(x)$ is a Dedekind cut.

9. With the notation of Problem 8, prove that if $x < y$ in F, then

$$X(x) \supset X(y).$$

10. Show that if X is a Dedekind cut, then there exists $x \in F$ such that $X = X(x)$, where $X(x)$ is defined as in Problem 8. [*Hint:* Let x be the greatest lower bound in F of the set $\{(ae)/(me) | a \in Z,\ m \in N,\ a/m \in X\}$.]

11. With the notation of Problem 8, prove that

$$X(x + y) = X(x) + X(y)$$

12. (a) Show that $X(0) = \{a/m \in Q | a \in Z,\ m \in N, 0 < (ae)/(me) \text{ in } F\}$ is the zero of R.

    (b) Use this fact, together with the properties of addition in R, to show that $X(-x) = -X(x)$.

13. (a) Prove that $X(0) \cdot X(x) = X(0 \cdot x)$ for all $x \in F$.

    (b) Prove that $X(x) \cdot X(y) = X(x \cdot y)$ for $x > 0$ and $y > 0$ in F.

    (c) Prove that $X(x) \cdot X(y) = X(x \cdot y)$ for all x and y in F.

14. Show that $x \to X(x)$ is an isomorphism between F and R which preserves order (see Theorem 7–6.1).

*7–7 Infinite sequences. In order to bring our discussion of the real number system back to its starting point, we must show that the real numbers (considered as Dedekind cuts) can be represented by means of the infinite decimal sequences discussed in Section 7–1. This will be done in Section 7–9. The theoretical foundation of decimal representations will be laid in this section and the following one.

Since the real numbers often occur as elements of sets, it is confusing to use capital letter set symbols to denote these objects. We will therefore change our notation, beginning in this section, and denote real numbers by small Latin letters u, v, w, etc. The ring of rational numbers will always be considered to be a subring of R, and this convention leads to the inclusions

$$N \subset Z \subset Q \subset R.$$

It is clear from the discussion of Theorem 7–6.1 that we can ignore the way in which the real numbers are constructed without losing any essential information about them. The vital fact to remember is that R is a complete ordered field.

DEFINITION 7–7.1. Let u_1, u_2, u_3, $\ldots$ be an infinite sequence of real numbers. This sequence is said to *converge* to a real number v if, for any real numbers w_1 and w_2 satisfying $w_1 < v < w_2$, there is a natural number k (depending on how close w_1 and w_2 are to v) such that if $n \geq k$, then

$$w_1 < u_n < w_2,$$

that is,

$$w_1 < u_k < w_2, \qquad w_1 < u_{k+1} < w_2, \qquad w_1 < u_{k+2} < w_2,$$

and so forth.

This definition is so important in mathematics that it deserves some discussion. The meaning which we wish to convey by saying that u_1, u_2, u_3, ... converges to v is that the numbers u_n get close to v as we move to the right along the sequence. It is natural to ask, how close to v? The answer is "arbitrarily close to v" by going out "sufficiently far." The expressions in quotation marks are vague, but they can be made exact. The phrase "the u's are arbitrarily close to v" must be replaced by an expression such as "the u's lie in an arbitrarily small interval around v," and the phrase "sufficiently far out along the sequence" should be changed to "from some point on in the sequence." Combining these replacements gives a better informal definition of convergence of a sequence to v: no matter how small an interval is prescribed around v, all the numbers of the sequence from a certain point on lie in this interval. The reader can now see that Definition 7–7.1 is only a formal restatement (using mathematical symbolism) of this informal definition.

It appears offhand that for any sequence u_1, u_2, u_3, ... there might be three possibilities:

(a) u_1, u_2, u_3, ... does not converge to any real number;

(b) u_1, u_2, u_3, ... converges to exactly one real number;

(c) u_1, u_2, u_3, ... converges to two or more real numbers.

We will show that this last possibility is inconsistent with the definition of convergence.

THEOREM 7–7.2. It is impossible for an infinite sequence to converge to two different real numbers.

Proof. Suppose that the sequence u_1, u_2, u_3, ..., converged to numbers v_1 and v_2 with $v_1 < v_2$. Let w_1, w_2, and w_3 be any numbers satisfying $w_1 < v_1 < w_2 < v_2 < w_3$. Then by Definition 7–7.1, there are natural numbers k_1 and k_2 such that if $n \geq k_1$, then $w_1 < u_n < w_2$, and if $m \geq k_2$, then $w_2 < u_m < w_3$. However, if n is larger than both k_1 and k_2, these conditions imply $u_n < w_2 < u_n$, which is impossible. Thus, the sequence u_1, u_2, u_3, ... cannot converge to two different numbers.

Because of this theorem, we are justified in saying that v is *the limit* of the sequence $u_1, u_2, u_3, \ldots$ if this sequence converges to v. In this case it is customary to write

$$v = \lim_{n \to \infty} u_n.$$

EXAMPLE 1. Let $u_1, u_2, u_3, \ldots$ be the sequence $1, 2, 3, \ldots$. Then this sequence does not converge to any real number v, since for any v, there is some m such that $v + 1 < m < m + 1 < \cdots$. In particular, it is not possible to find a natural number k such that $v - 1 < u_k < v + 1$ for all $n \geq k$. This example shows that the possibility (a) listed above can occur.

EXAMPLE 2. Let $u_1, u_2, u_3, \ldots$ be the sequence $1, 0, 1, 0, 1, 0, \ldots$. Then this sequence does not converge to any real number v. In fact, no matter what the number v might be, it is impossible to have $v - \frac{1}{2} < 0 < v + \frac{1}{2}$ and $v - \frac{1}{2} < 1 < v + \frac{1}{2}$, which is what would be required if we took $w_1 = v - \frac{1}{2}$ and $w_2 = v + \frac{1}{2}$ in Definition 7-7.1.

EXAMPLE 3. Let $u_1, u_2, u_3, \ldots$ be the sequence $1, \frac{1}{2}, \frac{1}{3}, \frac{1}{4}, \frac{1}{5}, \ldots$. Then $\lim_{n \to \infty} u_n = 0$. For suppose that $w_1 < 0 < w_2$. Choose k to be the smallest natural number which is greater than $(w_2)^{-1}$. If $n \geq k$, then $n > (w_2)^{-1}$. Therefore, $w_1 < 0 < u_n = 1/n < w_2$. This example shows that the possibility (b) listed above can also occur.

EXAMPLE 4. Let $u_1, u_2, u_3, \ldots$ be the infinite sequence of real numbers $u, u, u, \ldots$, all of which are the same. Then it is evident, and even easy to prove, that $\lim_{n \to \infty} u_n = u$.

EXAMPLE 5. Let $u_1, u_2, u_3, \ldots$ be the infinite sequence $t, t^2, t^3, \ldots$, where t is some real number. Suppose that $|t| < 1$. Then $|t| > |t|^2 > |t|^3 > \cdots$. It is a familiar fact that $|t|^n$ "gets close to zero" as n gets large. On a more rigorous level, it follows from Theorem 7-6.2(b) that if $w > 0$, then there is a natural number k such that $w > |t|^k$. Therefore, $w > |t|^n$, or equivalently $-w < t^n < w$, for all $n \geq k$. If $w_1 < 0 < w_2$, let $w = \min \{-w_1, w_2\}$. Then

$$w_1 \leq -w < t^n < w \leq w_2,$$

for all $n \geq k$. Thus, $t, t^2, t^3, \ldots$ converges to 0 when $|t| < 1$. If $|t| > 1$, then for any v there is a natural number n such that $|t|^n > |v|$, by Theorem 7-6.2(a). It follows easily that the sequence $t, t^2, t^3, \ldots$ does not converge if $|t| > 1$. If $|t| = 1$, then either $t = 1$ and the sequence is $1, 1, 1, \ldots$, or $t = -1$ and the sequence is $-1, 1, -1, \ldots$. In the first case the sequence converges to 1, and in the second case it does not converge.

EXAMPLE 6. Let $u_1, u_2, u_3, \ldots$ be the sequence $0, \frac{1}{2}, -\frac{1}{3}, 0, \frac{1}{5}, -\frac{1}{6}, 0, \ldots$. That is, $u_n = 0$ if $n \equiv 1 \pmod 3$, $u_n = 1/n$ if $n \equiv 2 \pmod 3$, and $u_n = -1/n$ if $n \equiv 0 \pmod 3$. Then $\lim_{n \to \infty} u_n = 0$. We leave the proof of this fact as a problem for the reader.

EXAMPLE 7. Let $u_1, u_2, u_3, \ldots$ be the sequence 0.3, 0.33, 0.333, 0.3333, $\ldots$. Then $\lim_{n \to \infty} u_n = \frac{1}{3}$.

There are some useful properties of the limits of sequences which will be needed in the succeeding sections.

THEOREM 7–7.3. Let $u_1, u_2, u_3, \ldots$ and $v_1, v_2, v_3, \ldots$ be infinite sequences of real numbers which have limits. Let w be any real number. Then

  (a) $\lim_{n \to \infty}(u_n + v_n) = \lim_{n \to \infty} u_n + \lim_{n \to \infty} v_n$, and
  (b) $\lim_{n \to \infty}(w \cdot u_n) = w \cdot \lim_{n \to \infty} u_n$.

The meaning of (a) is that the sequence $u_1 + v_1, u_2 + v_2, u_3 + v_3, \ldots$ has a limit which is the sum of the limits of the sequences $u_1, u_2, u_3, \ldots$ and $v_1, v_2, v_3, \ldots$. Equality (b) means that the sequence $wu_1, wu_2, wu_3, \ldots$ has a limit which is w times the limit of the sequence $u_1, u_2, u_3, \ldots$. Suppose that $\lim_{n \to \infty} u_n = u$, and that $\lim_{n \to \infty} v_n = v$. To prove (a), we must show that if $w_1 < u + v < w_2$, then there is a natural number k such that for $n \geq k$, $w_1 < u_n + v_n < w_2$. From the inequality $w_1 < u + v < w_2$, it follows that $w_1 - u < v < w_2 - u$. Choose w_1' and w_2' so that $w_1 - u < w_1' < v < w_2' < w_2 - u$. Then $w_1 - w_1' < u < w_2 - w_2'$. This, together with the inequality $w_1' < v < w_2'$, allows us to use the hypotheses $\lim_{n \to \infty} u_n = u$ and $\lim_{n \to \infty} v_n = v$. Indeed, by Definition 7–7.1, there must be natural numbers k_1 and k_2 such that if $n \geq k_1$, then $w_1 - w_1' < u_n < w_2 - w_2'$, and if $n \geq k_2$, then $w_1' < v_n < w_2'$. Let $k = \max \{k_1, k_2\}$. Then if $n \geq k$, it follows that $n \geq k_1$ and $n \geq k_2$. Therefore, $n \geq k$ implies $w_1 - w_1' < u_n < w_2 - w_2'$ and $w_1' < v_n < w_2'$. Adding these inequalities gives $w_1 < u_n + v_n < w_2$ for all $n \geq k$. This proves (a). The proof of (b) must be separated into three cases: $w = 0$, $w > 0$, and $w < 0$. If $w = 0$, then the statement to be proved is that the limit of the sequence $0, 0, 0, \ldots$ is 0. This is clear. Suppose that $w > 0$. Let $\lim_{n \to \infty} u_n = u$, as before. We wish to show that $\lim_{n \to \infty} w \cdot u_n = w \cdot u$. That is, if $w_1 < w \cdot u < w_2$, then there is a natural number k such that $w_1 < w \cdot u_n < w_2$ for all $n \geq k$. The inequality $w_1 < w \cdot u < w_2$ and the fact that $w > 0$ yields $w^{-1} \cdot w_1 < u < w^{-1} \cdot w_2$. Since $\lim_{n \to \infty} u_n = u$, there is a k such that $w^{-1} \cdot w_1 < u_n < w^{-1} \cdot w_2$ for all $n \geq k$. Consequently, $w_1 < w \cdot u_n < w_2$ for all $n \geq k$. The proof for $w < 0$ differs from the proof in the case $w > 0$ only in that the inequality $w_1 < w \cdot u < w_2$ is equivalent to $w^{-1} \cdot w_2 < u < w^{-1} \cdot w_1$, rather than $w^{-1} \cdot w_1 < u < w^{-1} \cdot w_2$.

As a particular case of Theorem 7–7.3(b), we obtain (for $w = -1$)

$$\lim_{n \to \infty}(- u_n) = -(\lim_{n \to \infty} u_n).$$

Using this observation and Theorem 7–7.3(a), we have

$$\lim_{n\to\infty}(u_n - v_n) = (\lim_{n\to\infty}u_n) - (\lim_{n\to\infty}v_n).$$

Finally, it should be mentioned that

$$\lim_{n\to\infty}(u_n \cdot v_n) = (\lim_{n\to\infty}u_n) \cdot (\lim_{n\to\infty}v_n).$$

This formula is more general than Theorem 7–7.3(b), but we will not prove it. (See Problem 9, however.)

There are two problems associated with every sequence. Does the sequence converge to some number? If so, to what real number does it converge? It appears from Definition 7–7.1 that in order to give a "yes" answer to the first of these questions, it would be necessary to have the answer to the second. It turns out that this is not always the case. Many methods have been devised which, for particular types of sequences, yield a criterion for convergence. One of the simplest is the following.

THEOREM 7–7.4. Let u_1, u_2, u_3, ... be an increasing sequence of real numbers, that is, $u_1 \leq u_2 \leq u_3 \leq \cdots$. Then this sequence converges if and only if it has an upper bound (in other words, there is a real number w such that $u_n \leq w$ for all n).

Proof. First suppose that u_1, u_2, u_3, ... converges to v. Choose any real numbers w_1 and w_2 satisfying $w_1 < v < w_2$. Then by Definition 7–7.1, there is a natural number k such that if $n \geq k$, then $w_1 < u_n < w_2$. In particular, $u_1 \leq u_2 \leq \cdots \leq u_k \leq u_{k+1} \leq \cdots \leq u_n < w_2$ for all $n > k$. That is, w_2 is an upper bound of $\{u_n | n \in N\}$. Conversely, assume that $\{u_n | n \in N\}$ has an upper bound. Then by the completeness of R, this set also has a least upper bound v. We will prove that $\lim_{n\to\infty}u_n = v$. Suppose that $w_1 < v < w_2$. Then $u_n \leq v < w_2$, for all n, since v is an upper bound of $\{u_n | n \in N\}$. Moreover, because v is the *least* upper bound of $\{u_n | n \in N\}$, and $w_1 < v$, it follows that w_1 cannot be an upper bound of the set of u_n's. Hence, there is some natural number k such that $w_1 < u_k$. Then

$$w_1 < u_k \leq u_{k+1} \leq u_{k+2} \leq \cdots,$$

so that $w_1 < u_n < w_2$ for all $n \geq k$. Hence, by Definition 7–7.1, $\lim_{n\to\infty} u_n = v$.

It is possible to prove a theorem similar to Theorem 7–7.4 for decreasing sequences of real numbers. A decreasing sequence converges if and only if it has a lower bound. These results do not give any information about sequences which are neither increasing nor decreasing. Such sequences can be bounded but not converge, as Example 2 shows.

PROBLEMS

1. Which of the following sequences converge?
   (a) $1, 2, 4, 8, \ldots, 2^{n-1}, \ldots$
   (b) $-1, -\frac{1}{2}, -\frac{1}{3}, -\frac{1}{4}, \ldots, -1/n, \ldots$
   (c) $1, -\frac{1}{2}, \frac{1}{3}, -\frac{1}{4}, \ldots, (-1)^{n-1}/n, \ldots$
   (d) $1, -\frac{1}{2}, 1, -\frac{1}{3}, 1, -\frac{1}{4}, \ldots$
   (e) $1, 1-\frac{1}{2}, 1+\frac{1}{3}, 1-\frac{1}{4}, 1+\frac{1}{5}, 1-\frac{1}{6}, 1+\frac{1}{7}, \ldots$

2. Show that if u is any real number, then the sequence $u, u, u, \ldots$ converges to u.

3. Prove the statement made in Example 6.

4. Show that if $u_1, u_2, u_3, \ldots$ is any infinite sequence of real numbers, and if $v_1, v_2, v_3, \ldots$ is the sequence obtained from $u_1, u_2, u_3, \ldots$ by omitting the first m terms, then $v_1, v_2, v_3, \ldots$ converges to w if $u_1, u_2, u_3, \ldots$ converges to w, and it does not converge if $u_1, u_2, u_3, \ldots$ does not converge.

5. Show that if $u_1, u_2, u_3, \ldots$ converges to v, then $|u_1|, |u_2|, |u_3|, \ldots$ converges to $|v|$.

6. Let $u_1, u_2, u_3, \ldots$ be an infinite sequence of real numbers. Suppose that for each real number v, there is some n such that $|u_n| > |v|$. Prove that the sequence does not converge.

7. Use Theorem 7–7.3(b) (with $w = -1$) to prove the analogue of Theorem 7–7.4 for decreasing sequences.

8. Show that any convergent sequence, considered as a set, has an upper bound and a lower bound.

9. Prove that $\lim_{n\to\infty} (u_n \cdot v_n) = (\lim_{n\to\infty} u_n) \cdot (\lim_{n\to\infty} v_n)$ in the following cases.
   (a) $\lim_{n\to\infty} u_n = 0$
   (b) $\lim_{n\to\infty} u_n > 0$

*7–8 Infinite series. A particularly important class of sequences is obtained from the formal expressions called *infinite series*. To motivate the concept of an infinite series, let us return to the decimal fractions which were discussed in Section 7–1. The usual notation

$$a_n a_{n-1} \ldots a_0 . b_1 b_2 \ldots b_m$$

is an abbreviation for the expression

$$a_n \cdot 10^n + a_{n-1} \cdot 10^{n-1} + \cdots + a_0 + b_1 \cdot 10^{-1} + b_2 \cdot 10^{-2} + \cdots$$
$$+ b_m \cdot 10^{-m}.$$

For example,

$$12.1617 = 1 \cdot 10 + 2 + 1 \cdot 10^{-1} + 6 \cdot 10^{-2} + 1 \cdot 10^{-3} + 7 \cdot 10^{-4},$$

and

$$333.3333 = 3 \cdot 10^2 + 3 \cdot 10 + 3 + 3 \cdot 10^{-1} + 3 \cdot 10^{-2} + 3 \cdot 10^{-3}$$
$$+ 3 \cdot 10^{-4}.$$

This observation tempts us to use a similar interpretation for infinite decimal sequences. We would like to write

$$a_m a_{m-1} \ldots a_0 . b_1 b_2 \ldots b_n \ldots$$
$$= a_m \cdot 10^m + a_{m-1} \cdot 10^{m-1} + \cdots + a_0$$
$$+ b_1 \cdot 10^{-1} + b_2 \cdot 10^{-2} + \cdots + b_n \cdot 10^{-n} + \cdots.$$

However, the sum of infinitely many numbers is not defined. By using the definition of convergence of sequences, it is sometimes possible to assign a meaning to infinite sums. In particular, this definition covers all of the sums which are associated with infinite decimal sequences.

DEFINITION 7–8.1. An *infinite series* is an expression

$$v_1 + v_2 + v_3 + \cdots + v_n + \cdots, \qquad \text{or} \qquad \sum_{k=1}^{\infty} v_k$$

where $v_1, v_2, v_3, \ldots$ is a given sequence of numbers. The elements of this sequence are called the *terms* of the series.

DEFINITION 7–8.2. Let $\sum_{k=1}^{\infty} v_k$ be an infinite series. The number

$$u_n = \sum_{k=1}^{n} v_k$$

is called the nth *partial sum* of this series. The series is said to *converge to* u, or to have the *sum* u, or simply to be *convergent*, if the sequence $u_1, u_2, u_3, \ldots$ converges to u. In this case, we write

$$\sum_{k=1}^{\infty} v_k = u.$$

If the sequence $u_1, u_2, u_3, \ldots$ does not converge, then the series is called *divergent*.

A convenient way to abbreviate the definition of the sum of an infinite series is by the formula

$$\sum_{k=1}^{\infty} v_k = \lim_{n \to \infty} \left(\sum_{k=1}^{n} v_k \right)$$

EXAMPLE 1. Let $v_1 = 1, v_2 = 1, v_3 = 1, \ldots$. Then the nth partial sum of $\sum_{k=1}^{\infty} v_k$ is $1 + 1 + \cdots + 1 = n$. Since the sequence $1, 2, 3, \ldots$ of partial sums is not convergent (Example 1, Section 7–7), it follows from Definition 7–8.2 that this series is divergent.

EXAMPLE 2. Let $v_1 = 1, v_2 = -1, v_3 = 1, \ldots, v_k = (-1)^{k+1}, \ldots$. Then $v_1 = 1, v_1 + v_2 = 1 - 1 = 0, v_1 + v_2 + v_3 = 1 - 1 + 1 = 1, v_1 + v_2 + v_3 + v_4 = 1 - 1 + 1 - 1 = 0, \ldots$. That is, the sequence of partial sums of the series $\sum_{k=1}^{\infty} v_k$ is $1, 0, 1, 0, \ldots$. Since this sequence does not converge (Example 2, Section 7–7), it follows that $\sum_{k=1}^{\infty} (-1)^{k+1}$ is divergent.

EXAMPLE 3. Let $v_1 = 1/1 \cdot 2, v_2 = 1/2 \cdot 3, v_3 = 1/3 \cdot 4, \ldots$. Then

$$\sum_{k=1}^{\infty} v_k = \sum_{k=1}^{\infty} \frac{1}{k \cdot (k+1)}.$$

It is easy to evaluate the nth partial sum of this particular series:

$$u_n = \sum_{k=1}^{n} \frac{1}{k \cdot (k+1)} = \frac{1}{1 \cdot 2} + \frac{1}{2 \cdot 3} + \frac{1}{3 \cdot 4} + \cdots + \frac{1}{n \cdot (n+1)}$$

$$= \left(\frac{1}{1} - \frac{1}{2}\right) + \left(\frac{1}{2} - \frac{1}{3}\right) + \left(\frac{1}{3} - \frac{1}{4}\right) + \cdots + \left(\frac{1}{n} - \frac{1}{(n+1)}\right)$$

$$= \frac{1}{1} - \frac{1}{(n+1)} = 1 - \frac{1}{(n+1)}.$$

By Example 3, Section 7–7 and Theorem 7–7.3,

$$\lim_{n \to \infty} u_n = 1 - \lim_{n \to \infty} 1/(n+1) = 1 - 0 = 1.$$

Thus, the series $\sum_{k=1}^{\infty} 1/k \cdot (k+1)$ converges to 1.

EXAMPLE 4. Let $v_1 = 1, v_2 = t, v_3 = t^2, \ldots, v_k = t^{k-1}, \ldots$. That is, $\sum_{k=1}^{\infty} v_k = \sum_{k=1}^{\infty} t^{k-1}$. It is easy to prove by induction* [see Problem 6(a), Section 2–1] that the nth partial sum of this series is

$$1 + t + t^2 + \cdots + t^{n-1} = \frac{1 - t^n}{1 - t},$$

provided that $t \neq 1$. It follows from Theorem 7–7.3 and Example 5, Section 7–7, that

$$\lim_{n \to \infty} \frac{1 - t^n}{1 - t} = \frac{1}{1 - t}$$

---

* Another proof is obtained from the identity

$$(1 - t)(1 + t + t^2 + \cdots + t^{n-1}) = 1 + t + t^2 + \cdots + t^{n-1}$$
$$- (t + t^2 + \cdots + t^{n-1} + t^n)$$
$$= 1 - t^n.$$

if $|t| < 1$, and this limit does not exist if $|t| > 1$. Hence, by Definition 7–8.2, the series $\sum_{k=1}^{\infty} t^{k-1}$ converges to $1/(1 - t)$ if $|t| < 1$, and it diverges if $|t| > 1$. If $|t| = 1$, then $t = 1$ or $t = -1$. In these cases, the series $\sum_{k=1}^{\infty} t^{k-1}$ is the same as the ones discussed in Examples 1 and 2, both of which diverge. This example, and Example 5, Section 7–7, upon which it is based, should be studied carefully. Both results have important applications in the theory of infinite sequences and series.

Many of the results concerning infinite sequences lead to theorems about infinite series. A typical example is the following.

THEOREM 7–8.3. Let $\sum_{k=1}^{\infty} v_k$ and $\sum_{k=1}^{\infty} w_k$ be infinite series which converge. Let w be any real number. Then

(a) $\displaystyle\sum_{k=1}^{\infty} (v_k + w_k) = \left(\sum_{k=1}^{\infty} v_k\right) + \left(\sum_{k=1}^{\infty} w_k\right),$

(b) $\displaystyle\sum_{k=1}^{\infty} (w \cdot v_k) = w \cdot \left(\sum_{k=1}^{\infty} v_k\right).$

That is, under the assumptions that $\sum_{k=1}^{\infty} v_k$ and $\sum_{k=1}^{\infty} w_k$ converge, the series

$$\sum_{k=1}^{\infty} (v_k + w_k) \qquad \text{and} \qquad \sum_{k=1}^{\infty} (w \cdot v_k)$$

converge to the corresponding expressions on the right-hand side of (a) and (b). To prove (a), note that by the generalized commutative law (4–3.1)

$$\sum_{k=1}^{n} (v_k + w_k) = \left(\sum_{k=1}^{n} v_k\right) + \left(\sum_{k=1}^{n} w_k\right).$$

Thus by Definition 7–8.2 and Theorem 7–7.3,

$$\sum_{k=1}^{\infty} (v_k + w_k) = \lim_{n\to\infty} \left(\sum_{k=1}^{n} (v_k + w_k)\right)$$

$$= \lim_{n\to\infty} \left[\left(\sum_{k=1}^{n} v_k\right) + \left(\sum_{k=1}^{n} w_k\right)\right]$$

$$= \lim_{n\to\infty} \left(\sum_{k=1}^{n} v_k\right) + \lim_{n\to\infty} \left(\sum_{k=1}^{n} w_k\right)$$

$$= \sum_{k=1}^{\infty} v_k + \sum_{k=1}^{\infty} w_k.$$

The proof of (b) is similar. By the generalized distributive law (4–7),

$$\sum_{k=1}^{n} w \cdot v_k = w \cdot \left(\sum_{k=1}^{n} v_k \right).$$

Thus,

$$\sum_{k=1}^{\infty} w \cdot v_k = \lim_{n \to \infty} \left(\sum_{k=1}^{n} w \cdot v_k \right) = \lim_{n \to \infty} \left[w \cdot \left(\sum_{k=1}^{n} v_k \right) \right]$$

$$= w \cdot \left[\lim_{n \to \infty} \left(\sum_{k=1}^{n} v_k \right) \right] = w \cdot \sum_{k=1}^{\infty} v_k.$$

The generalized commutative and distributive laws used in the proof of Theorem 7–8.3 are concerned only with finite sums. This theorem is in a sense a generalization of these laws to infinite series. If $\sum_{k=1}^{\infty} v_k$ and $\sum_{k=1}^{\infty} w_k$ both diverge, one might expect that $\sum_{k=1}^{\infty} (v_k + w_k)$ also diverges. However, the series

$$\sum_{k=1}^{\infty} \left(1 + \frac{1}{k(k+1)} \right) \qquad \text{and} \qquad \sum_{k=1}^{\infty} (-1)$$

both diverge, while

$$\sum_{k=1}^{\infty} \left[\left(1 + \frac{1}{k(k+1)} \right) + (-1) \right] = \sum_{k=1}^{\infty} \frac{1}{k(k+1)}$$

converges.

The infinite series discussed in Examples 3 and 4, above, are unusual, because the sum of these series can be determined. Generally, it is very difficult to find the sum of a series. Often we need only to know whether or not a given series converges. For this problem, numerous tests have been devised. Most of these tests apply only to series with nonnegative terms. They are based on the following consequence of Theorem 7–7.4.

THEOREM 7–8.4. Let $\sum_{k=1}^{\infty} v_k$ be an infinite series such that $v_k \geq 0$ for all k. Then this series is convergent if and only if the set of its partial sums has an upper bound, that is, there is a real number w such that $\sum_{k=1}^{n} v_k = u_n \leq w$ for all n.

Proof. By Definition 7–8.2, the series $\sum_{k=1}^{\infty} v_k$ is convergent if and only if its sequence of partial sums $u_1, u_2, u_3, \ldots$ is convergent. Since $v_k \geq 0$ for all k, it follows that $u_1 \leq u_1 + v_2 = u_2 \leq u_2 + v_3 = u_3 \leq \cdots$. Hence, the partial sums of $\sum_{k=1}^{\infty} v_k$ form an increasing sequence. By

Theorem 7–7.4, such a sequence converges if and only if it is bounded. This proves the theorem.

As it stands, Theorem 7–8.4 is not a very useful criterion for deciding whether or not a series converges. However, there are numerous tricks for determining whether the partial sums of particular infinite series are bounded or not. Such tests are studied at length in calculus courses. We will implicitly use one well-known test (the "comparison test") to prove a result which makes it possible to assign a real number to every infinite decimal sequence.

THEOREM 7–8.5. The infinite series

$$a_m \cdot 10^m + a_{m-1} \cdot 10^{m-1} + \cdots + a_0 + b_1 \cdot 10^{-1} + b_2 \cdot 10^{-2} + \cdots$$
$$+ b_n \cdot 10^{-n} + \cdots,$$

where $a_m, a_{m-1}, \ldots, a_0, b_1, b_2, \ldots, b_n, \ldots$ are integers between 0 and 9 (inclusive), converges to a real number.

Proof. The $(m + 1 + n)$th partial sum of this series is

$$a_m \cdot 10^m + a_{m-1} \cdot 10^{m-1} + \cdots + a_0 + b_1 \cdot 10^{-1} + b_2 \cdot 10^{-2} + \cdots$$
$$+ b_n \cdot 10^{-n}.$$

Since each a_i and b_j is ≤ 9, this partial sum is at most equal to

$$9 \cdot 10^m + 9 \cdot 10^{m-1} + \cdots + 9 + 9 \cdot 10^{-1} + 9 \cdot 10^{-2} + \cdots + 9 \cdot 10^{-n}$$
$$= (10 - 1) \cdot 10^m + (10 - 1) \cdot 10^{m-1} + \cdots + (10 - 1)$$
$$+ (10 - 1) \cdot 10^{-1} + (10 - 1) \cdot 10^{-2} + \cdots$$
$$+ (10 - 1) \cdot 10^{-n}$$
$$= 10^{m+1} + 10^m + \cdots + 10 + 1 + 10^{-1} + \cdots + 10^{-(n-1)}$$
$$- 10^m - \cdots - 10 - 1 - 10^{-1} - \cdots - 10^{-(n-1)} - 10^{-n}$$
$$= 10^{m+1} - 10^{-n} < 10^{m+1}.$$

Thus, 10^{m+1} is an upper bound of the set of all partial sums of

$$a_m \cdot 10^m + a_{m-1} \cdot 10^{m-1} + \cdots + a_0 + b_1 \cdot 10^{-1} + b_2 \cdot 10^{-2} + \cdots$$
$$+ b_n \cdot 10^{-n} + \cdots,$$

so that by Theorem 7–8.4, this series converges to a real number.

By Theorem 7–8.5, we see that an infinite decimal sequence can be considered as an abbreviation for a convergent infinite series:

$$a_m a_{m-1} \ldots a_0 . b_1 b_2 \ldots b_n \ldots \leftrightarrow a_m \cdot 10^m + a_{m-1} \cdot 10^{m-1} + \cdots$$
$$+ a_0 + b_1 \cdot 10^{-1} + b_2 \cdot 10^{-2} + \cdots + b_n \cdot 10^{-n} + \cdots.$$

Thus, associated with every infinite decimal sequence is a real number (the sum of the corresponding series). This definition of the real number associated with an infinite decimal sequence agrees with the intuitive idea of the decimal representation of real numbers which we discussed in Section 7–1. Indeed, the decimal representation of a real number u was described there as a sequence of progressively more accurate approximations of u by decimal fractions. This sequence of decimal fractions is exactly the sequence of partial sums of the series associated with the infinite decimal sequence representing u, so that if the intuitive idea of "progressively more accurate approximations of u" agrees with the exact notion of convergence, then the series associated with the infinite decimal representation of u must converge to u. In the next section we will completely justify this viewpoint.

PROBLEMS

1. In Example 4, it was stated that

$$\lim_{n \to \infty} \frac{1 - t^n}{1 - t}$$

does not exist if $|t| > 1$. Prove this in detail, using Theorem 7–7.3.

2. What is the numerical value of the 10th term of the series $\sum_{k=1}^{\infty} u_k$ if

(a) $u_k = \dfrac{k + 2}{2k - 1}$, (b) $u_k = \dfrac{2^k}{k!}$, (c) $u_k = k \cdot 10^{-k}$.

3. Prove that if $\sum_{k=1}^{\infty} u_k$ is an infinite series such that $0 = u_{n+1} = u_{n+2} = u_{n+3} = \cdots$, that is, all terms after the nth one are zero, then $\sum_{k=1}^{\infty} u_k$ converges to $\sum_{k=1}^{n} u_k$.

4. Show that if an infinite series $\sum_{k=1}^{\infty} u_k$ converges, then $\lim_{k \to \infty} u_k = 0$.

5. Prove that the converse of the theorem of Problem 4 is false by showing that (a) $\lim_{k \to \infty} 1/(\sqrt{k + 1} + \sqrt{k}) = 0$, and (b) the series

$$\sum_{k=1}^{\infty} \frac{1}{\sqrt{k + 1} + \sqrt{k}}$$

diverges. [*Hint:* First show that $1/(\sqrt{k + 1} + \sqrt{k}) = \sqrt{k + 1} - \sqrt{k}$.]

6. Prove the *comparison test:*

If $\sum_{k=1}^{\infty} u_k$ is an infinite series with $u_k \geq 0$ for all k, such that (a) $u_k \leq v_k$ for $k = 1, 2, \ldots$, and (b) $\sum_{k=1}^{\infty} v_k$ converges, then $\sum_{k=1}^{\infty} u_k$ converges.

7. Use the comparison test to show that the following infinite series are convergent.

(a) $\displaystyle\sum_{k=1}^{\infty} \frac{1}{2^{k+1}}$ (b) $\displaystyle\sum_{k=1}^{\infty} \frac{2^{k-1}}{5^k}$ (c) $\displaystyle\sum_{k=1}^{\infty} \frac{1}{k!}$

*7–9 Decimal representation. At the end of the last section, it was shown that every infinite decimal sequence can be considered as the representation of a real number, namely,

$$a_m a_{m-1} \ldots a_0 \cdot b_1 b_2 \ldots b_n \ldots = a_m \cdot 10^m + a_{m-1} \cdot 10^{m-1} + \cdots$$
$$+ a_0 + b_1 \cdot 10^{-1} + b_2 \cdot 10^{-2} + \cdots + b_n \cdot 10^{-n} + \cdots.$$

This observation provokes the two main questions which will be answered in this section. Can every real number be represented in this way by a decimal sequence? Can certain real numbers be represented by more than one decimal sequence, and if so, which ones, and in how many ways?

Throughout this section, both finite and infinite decimal sequences will be considered as abbreviations of their corresponding decimal sums; that is

$$a_m a_{m-1} \ldots a_0 \cdot b_1 b_2 \ldots b_n = a_m \cdot 10^m + a_{m-1} \cdot 10^{m-1} + \cdots$$
$$+ a_0 + b_1 \cdot 10^{-1} + b_2 \cdot 10^{-2} + \cdots + b_n \cdot 10^{-n},$$

$$a_m a_{m-1} \ldots a_0 \cdot b_1 b_2 \ldots b_n \ldots = a_m \cdot 10^m + a_{m-1} \cdot 10^{m-1} + \cdots$$
$$+ a_0 + b_1 \cdot 10^{-1} + b_2 \cdot 10^{-2} + \cdots + b_n \cdot 10^{-n} + \cdots.$$

A decimal fraction which has n decimal places (see Definition 7–1.2) is called an *n-place decimal fraction* or an *n-place decimal sequence*. These are the decimal sequences with n digits following the decimal point, that is, $a_m a_{m-1} \ldots a_0 \cdot b_1 b_2 \ldots b_n$. A nonnegative rational number r is an n-place decimal fraction if and only if $10^n \cdot r$ is an integer (see Problem 4, Section 7–1).

It is convenient to summarize some familiar properties of decimal sequences which will be used in this section.

THEOREM 7–9.1. (a) If r is an n-place decimal fraction, then $r + 10^{-n}$ is an n-place decimal fraction.

(b) If r and s are n-place decimal fractions, and $r < s$, then

$$r + 10^{-n} \le s.$$

(c) If $a_m a_{m-1} \ldots a_0 \cdot b_1 b_2 \ldots b_n = c_m c_{m-1} \ldots c_0 \cdot d_1 d_2 \ldots d_n$, then $a_m = c_m$, $a_{m-1} = c_{m-1}$, ..., $a_0 = c_0$, $b_1 = d_1$, $b_2 = d_2$, ..., $b_n = d_n$.

(d) $a_m a_{m-1} \ldots a_0 \cdot b_1 b_2 \ldots b_n$
$\le a_m a_{m-1} \ldots a_0 \cdot b_1 b_2 \ldots b_n b_{n+1} \ldots b_{n+k}$
$< (a_m a_{m-1} \ldots a_0 \cdot b_1 b_2 \ldots b_n) + 10^{-n}.$

Proof. By the remark preceding this theorem, if r is an n-place decimal fraction, then $10^n r$ is an integer. Therefore, $10^n r + 1 = 10^n (r + 10^{-n})$ is also an integer. Consequently $r + 10^{-n}$ is an n-place decimal fraction. This proves (a). The proof of (b) is based on the same idea. Since $r < s$, $10^n r$ is an integer less than $10^n s$. Thus, $10^n r + 1 \le 10^n s$. Hence, $r + 10^{-n} \le s$. To prove (c), note that if $a_m a_{m-1} \ldots a_0 . b_1 b_2 \ldots b_n = c_m c_{m-1} \ldots c_0 . d_1 d_2 \ldots d_n$ is multiplied by 10^n, then we obtain

$$a_m a_{m-1} \ldots a_0 b_1 b_2 \ldots b_n = c_m c_{m-1} \ldots c_0 d_1 d_2 \ldots d_n.$$

Thus, by the uniqueness of the decimal representation of a natural number (Theorem 5–1.3), $a_m = c_m$, $a_{m-1} = c_{m-1}, \ldots,$ $a_0 = c_0$, $b_1 = d_1$, $b_2 = d_2, \ldots, b_n = d_n$. Finally, the proof of (d) is a simple calculation:

$$
\begin{aligned}
a_m a_{m-1} \ldots a_0 . b_1 b_2 \ldots b_n &= a_m \cdot 10^m + a_{m-1} \cdot 10^{m-1} + \cdots + a_0 \\
&\quad + b_1 \cdot 10^{-1} + b_2 \cdot 10^{-2} + \cdots + b_n \cdot 10^{-n} \\
&\le a_m \cdot 10^m + a_{m-1} \cdot 10^{m-1} + \cdots + a_0 + b_1 \cdot 10^{-1} + b_2 \cdot 10^{-2} + \cdots \\
&\quad + b_n \cdot 10^{-n} + b_{n+1} \cdot 10^{-(n+1)} + \cdots + b_{n+k} \cdot 10^{-(n+k)} \\
&= a_m a_{m-1} \ldots a_0 . b_1 b_2 \ldots b_n b_{n+1} \ldots b_{n+k} \\
&\le (a_m \cdot 10^m + a_{m-1} \cdot 10^{m-1} + \cdots + a_0 + b_1 \cdot 10^{-1} + b_2 \cdot 10^{-2} + \cdots + b_n \cdot 10^{-n}) \\
&\quad + (9 \cdot 10^{-(n+1)} + \cdots + 9 \cdot 10^{-(n+k)}) \\
&= (a_m \cdot 10^m + a_{m-1} \cdot 10^{m-1} + \cdots + a_0 + b_1 \cdot 10^{-1} + b_2 \cdot 10^{-2} + \cdots + b_n \cdot 10^{-n}) \\
&\quad + (10^{-n} - 10^{-(n+k)}) \\
&< (a_m \cdot 10^m + a_{m-1} \cdot 10^{m-1} + \cdots + a_0 + b_1 \cdot 10^{-1} + b_2 \cdot 10^{-2} + \cdots + b_n \cdot 10^{-n}) + 10^{-n} \\
&= (a_m a_{m-1} \ldots a_0 . b_1 b_2 \ldots b_n) + 10^{-n}.
\end{aligned}
$$

THEOREM 7–9.2. For infinite decimal sequences:

(a) $10^n \cdot (a_m a_{m-1} \ldots a_0 . b_1 b_2 \ldots b_n b_{n+1} b_{n+2} \ldots)$
$$= a_m a_{m-1} \ldots a_0 b_1 b_2 \ldots b_n . b_{n+1} b_{n+2} \ldots .$$

(b) If
$$0 \le c_i \le a_i \le 9 \quad \text{for} \quad i = m, m-1, \ldots, 0,$$
$$0 \le d_j \le b_j \le 9 \quad \text{for} \quad j = 1, 2, 3, \ldots,$$
$$e_i = a_i - c_i, \quad f_j = b_j - d_j,$$

then

$$(a_m a_{m-1} \ldots a_0 . b_1 b_2 \ldots b_n \ldots) - (c_m c_{m-1} \ldots c_0 . d_1 d_2 \ldots d_n \ldots)$$
$$= e_m e_{m-1} \ldots e_0 . f_1 f_2 \ldots f_n \ldots .$$

(c) $a_m a_{m-1} \ldots a_0 . b_1 b_2 \ldots b_n 000 \ldots = a_m a_{m-1} \ldots a_0 . b_1 b_2 \ldots b_n.$

(d) $a_m a_{m-1} \ldots a_0 . b_1 b_2 \ldots b_n \le a_m a_{m-1} \ldots a_0 . b_1 b_2 \ldots b_n b_{n+1} \ldots$
$\le (a_m a_{m-1} \ldots a_0 . b_1 b_2 \ldots b_n) + 10^{-n}.$

The identities (a), (b), and (c) are easily proved, using the interpretation of decimal sequences as sums, together with Theorem 7–8.3. The proof of Theorem 7–9.2(d) is based on the corresponding result for finite decimal sequences Theorem 7–9.1(d), and the definition of an infinite decimal sequence as the sum of an infinite series. Suppose that

$$a_m a_{m-1} \ldots a_0 . b_1 b_2 \ldots b_n b_{n+1} \ldots = u$$

and

$$a_m a_{m-1} \ldots a_0 . b_1 b_2 \ldots b_n = r.$$

We have to prove that $r \le u \le r + 10^{-n}$. Suppose that $u < r$. Then by Theorem 7–9.1(d),

$$u < r \le a_m a_{m-1} \ldots a_0 . b_1 b_2 \ldots b_n b_{n+1} \ldots b_{n+k} \qquad \text{for all } k \in N.$$

However, this is impossible, since by the definition of u, we have

$$u = \lim_{k \to \infty} (a_m a_{m-1} \ldots a_0 . b_1 b_2 \ldots b_n b_{n+1} \ldots b_{n+k}),$$

and in particular, if $u < r$, there is a $k \in N$ such that

$$a_m a_{m-1} \ldots a_0 . b_1 b_2 \ldots b_n b_{n+1} \ldots b_{n+k} < r.$$

Consequently, $r \le u$. In the same way, we see that $u \le r + 10^{-n}$. Note that the second strict inequality of Theorem 7–9.1(d) has been weakened to $\le$ in Theorem 7–9.2(d). In Theorem 7–9.4 it will be shown that this weakening is essential.

In the proof of the fundamental theorem of decimal representation of real numbers we will use an important property of the real number system which has not yet been discussed.

(7–9.3). Let x and y be real numbers such that $x < y$. Then there is a rational number r such that $x < r \le y$.

This result has been proved for complete ordered fields in Problems 5 and 6 of Section 7–6. However, a simpler proof can be given for the real number system if we go back to the construction of real numbers by Dedekind cuts. By Definition 7–4.4, the inequality $x < y$ means that x, considered as a set of rational numbers, properly contains y. Hence, there is a rational number r such that r belongs to x, but not to y. Then the Dedekind cut corresponding to r contains y and is contained properly in x. (See Problem 3, Section 7–4.) Thus, if we identify r with the cut to which it corresponds and use Definition 7–4.4 again, we obtain $x < r \le y$.

THEOREM 7–9.4. *Fundamental theorem of decimal representation.* Let u be a positive real number. Then u is represented by some infinite decimal sequence

$$a_m a_{m-1} \ldots a_0 . b_1 b_2 \ldots b_n \ldots .$$

That is, u is the limit of the infinite series corresponding to this decimal sequence.

Proof. The proof of this theorem consists of several steps. First we show that for any n, there is a unique n-place decimal fraction r_n such that

$$r_n \leq u < r_n + 10^{-n}.$$

The rational number r_n is called the *n-place decimal approximation of u*. The next step of the proof is to show that there is an infinite decimal sequence

$$a_m a_{m-1} \ldots a_0 . b_1 b_2 \ldots b_n \ldots$$

such that for each natural number n, the n-place decimal approximation r of u is exactly $a_m a_{m-1} \ldots a_0 . b_1 b_2 \ldots b_n$. The proof is completed by showing that the infinite series

$$a_m \cdot 10^m + a_{m-1} \cdot 10^{m-1} + \cdots + a_0 + b_1 \cdot 10^{-1} + b_2 \cdot 10^{-2} + \cdots$$
$$+ b^n \cdot 10^{-n} + \cdots$$

corresponding to $a_m a_{m-1} \ldots a_0 . b_1 b_2 \ldots b_n \ldots$ converges to u.

(1) By (7–9.3), there is a rational number r such that

$$u - 10^{-n} < r \leq u.$$

Let $10^n r = a/m$, where $a \in Z$ and $m \in N$. By the division algorithm, we can write $a = m \cdot b + d$, where b and d are integers, and $0 \leq d < m$. Then $10^n r = b + (d/m)$. In particular,

$$b \leq 10^n r < b + 1.$$

There are two possible cases: either $b > 10^n u - 1$, or $b \leq 10^n u - 1$. Suppose first that $b > 10^n u - 1$. Define $r_n = 10^{-n} \cdot b$. Then

$$u - 10^{-n} = 10^{-n}(10^n u - 1) < 10^{-n} b = r_n \leq r \leq u.$$

Consequently, $r_n \leq u < r_n + 10^{-n}$. Moreover, r_n is an n-place decimal fraction, since $10^n \cdot r_n = b$ is an integer, and $b + 1 > 10^n u \geq 0$, so that $b \geq 0$. In the second case, where $b \leq 10^n u - 1$, define $r_n = 10^{-n}(b + 1)$. Then $u - 10^{-n} < r < r_n \leq u$, so that $r_n \leq u < r_n + 10^{-n}$. As in the first case, r_n is an n-place decimal fraction, since $10^n r_n = b + 1 \in Z$, and $-1 < 10^n u - 1 < 10^n r < b + 1$ implies $b + 1 \geq 0$.

It is easy to see that there is at most one n-place decimal fraction r_n such that $r_n \leq u < r_n + 10^{-n}$. Indeed, suppose that s_n is an n-place decimal fraction such that $s_n \leq u < s_n + 10^{-n}$. If $r_n < s_n$, then

$r_n + 10^{-n} \leq s_n$, by Theorem 7-9.1(b). However, this yields the contradiction $s_n \leq u < r_n + 10^{-n} \leq s_n$. For a similar reason, the inequality $s_n < r_n$ is impossible. Therefore, $r_n = s_n$. This completes the proof of the first step.

(2) Suppose that $r_n = a_m a_{m-1} \ldots a_0 . b_1 b_2 \ldots b_n$ is the n-place decimal approximation of u, and that $r_{n+1} = c_m c_{m-1} \ldots c_0 . d_1 d_2 \ldots d_n d_{n+1}$ is the $(n + 1)$-place decimal approximation of u. (We may assume that the number of digits to the left of the decimal point is the same for r_n and r_{n+1} by adjoining zeros, if necessary.) Let $s_n = c_m c_{m-1} \ldots c_0 . d_1 d_2 \ldots d_n$ be the n-place decimal fraction obtained from r_{n+1} by deleting the last digit. Since $r_{n+1} = s_n + d_{n+1} \cdot 10^{-(n+1)}$ and $0 \leq d_{n+1} \leq 9$, it follows that $s_n \leq r_{n+1} \leq s_n + 9 \cdot 10^{-(n+1)}$. Moreover, $r_{n+1} \leq u < r_{n+1} + 10^{-(n+1)}$, because r_{n+1} is the $(n + 1)$-place decimal approximation of u. Hence,

$$s_n \leq r_{n+1} \leq u < r_{n+1} + 10^{-(n+1)} \leq s_n + 9 \cdot 10^{-(n+1)} + 10^{-(n+1)}$$
$$= s_n + 10^{-n}.$$

Therefore, s_n is the n-place decimal approximation of u. By the uniqueness of such n-place approximations, which was proved in (1), it follows that $s_n = r_n$. Hence by Theorem 7-9.1(c),

$$c_m = a_m, c_{m-1} = a_{m-1}, \ldots, c_0 = a_0, d_1 = b_1, d_2 = b_2, \ldots, d_n = b_n.$$

We have proved that $r_{n+1} = a_m a_{m-1} \ldots a_0 . b_1 b_2 \ldots b_n d_{n+1}$, that is, the $(n + 1)$-place decimal approximation of u is obtained from the n-place approximation by adding a single decimal digit. Thus, the sequence $r_1, r_2, r_3, \ldots$ of decimal approximations of u gives rise to the infinite decimal sequence $a_m a_{m-1} \ldots a_0 . b_1 b_2 \ldots b_n \ldots$ such that for each n,

$$r_n = a_m a_{m-1} \ldots a_0 . b_1 b_2 \ldots b_n.$$

This completes the second step of the proof.

(3) The $(m + 1 + n)$th partial sum of the infinite series

$$a_m \cdot 10^m + a_{m-1} \cdot 10^{m-1} + \cdots + a_0 + b_1 \cdot 10^{-1} + b_2 \cdot 10^{-2} + \cdots$$
$$+ b_n \cdot 10^{-n} + \cdots$$

is

$$a_m \cdot 10^m + a_{m-1} \cdot 10^{m-1} + \cdots + a_0 + b_1 \cdot 10^{-1} + b_2 \cdot 10^{-2} + \cdots$$
$$+ b_n \cdot 10^{-n} = a_m a_{m-1} \ldots a_0 . b_1 b_2 \ldots b_n = r_n.$$

Therefore, to complete the proof, we have only to show that if $w_1 < u < w_2$, then there is a natural number k such that $w_1 < r_n < w_2$ for all

$n \geq k$. By Definitions 7–8.1 and 7–8.2, this will imply that the infinite series corresponding to the infinite decimal sequence

$$a_m a_{m-1} \ldots a_0 . b_1 b_2 \ldots b_n \ldots$$

converges to u. By Theorem 7–6.2(b), there is a natural number k such that $10^{-k} = (10^{-1})^k < u - w_1$. Then $w_1 < u - 10^{-k}$. Therefore, if $n \geq k$,

$$w_1 < u - 10^{-k} \leq u - 10^{-n} < r_n \leq u < w_2.$$

This completes the proof of Theorem 7–9.4.

We now consider the second question which was mentioned at the beginning of this section: which real numbers can be represented by two or more infinite decimal sequences? It is easy to show that there are numbers which have different representations.

EXAMPLE 1.   We will show that $0.999\ldots = 1 = 1.000\ldots$. By Theorem 7–9.2(a), $10 \cdot (0.999\ldots) = 9.999\ldots = 9 + (0.999\ldots)$. Hence, $9 \cdot (0.999\ldots) = 10 \cdot (0.999\ldots) - (0.999\ldots) = 9$. Dividing by 9 gives the desired conclusion.

This example can easily be generalized.

THEOREM 7–9.5. Let $a_m, a_{m-1}, \ldots, a_0, b_1, b_2, \ldots, b_n$ be any decimal digits. Then

$$a_m a_{m-1} \ldots a_0 . b_1 b_2 \ldots b_n 999 \ldots = a_m a_{m-1} \ldots a_0 . b_1 b_2 \ldots b_n + 10^{-n}.$$

Proof. By Theorem 7–9.2 and Example 1,

$$10^n \cdot (a_m a_{m-1} \ldots a_0 . b_1 b_2 \ldots b_n 999 \ldots)$$
$$= a_m a_{m-1} \ldots a_0 b_1 b_2 \ldots b_n . 999 \ldots$$
$$= (a_m a_{m-1} \ldots a_0 b_1 b_2 \ldots b_n) + (0.999 \ldots)$$
$$= (a_m a_{m-1} \ldots a_0 b_1 b_2 \ldots b_n) + 1$$
$$= 10^n [(a_m a_{m-1} \ldots a_0 . b_1 b_2 \ldots b_n) + 10^{-n}].$$

Dividing by 10^n gives the theorem.

This theorem shows that every n-place decimal fraction can be represented by two different infinite decimal sequences, one of which has all zeros after the nth digit to the right of the decimal point, and the other one having all nines after the nth digit to the right of the decimal point. We will prove that this is the only case in which a real number has more than one decimal representation.

THEOREM 7–9.6. Suppose that the real number u is represented by two different decimal sequences,

$$a_m a_{m-1} \ldots a_0 . b_1 b_2 \ldots b_n b_{n+1} \ldots = u$$
$$= c_m c_{m-1} \ldots c_0 . d_1 d_2 \ldots d_n d_{n+1} \ldots ,$$

where for some n,

$$a_m a_{m-1} \ldots a_0 . b_1 b_2 \ldots b_n < c_m c_{m-1} \ldots c_0 . d_1 d_2 \ldots d_n.$$

Then

$$b_{n+1} = 9, \quad b_{n+2} = 9, \quad b_{n+3} = 9, \quad \ldots ,$$

and

$$d_{n+1} = 0, \quad d_{n+2} = 0, \quad d_{n+3} = 0, \quad \ldots .$$

Proof. For $k \geq 1$, let

$$r_k = a_m a_{m-1} \ldots a_0 . b_1 b_2 \ldots b_k, \quad s_k = c_m c_{m-1} \ldots c_0 . d_1 d_2 \ldots d_k.$$

By Theorem 7–9.2(d),

$$r_k \leq u \leq r_k + 10^{-k}, \quad s_k \leq u \leq s_k + 10^{-k}.$$

If $r_k < s_k$, then by Theorem 7–9.1(b),

$$r_k + 10^{-k} \leq s_k \leq u \leq r_k + 10^{-k}.$$

Hence, $r_k < s_k$ implies

$$u = s_k = r_k + 10^{-k}.$$

By Theorem 7–9.1(d), if $r_k < s_k$ it also follows that

$$r_{k+1} < r_k + 10^{-k} = s_k \leq s_{k+1},$$

so that $r_k < s_k$ also yields $r_{k+1} < s_{k+1}$. Since by assumption $r_n < s_n$, an induction argument proves that for all $k \geq n$,

$$r_k < s_k, \quad \text{and} \quad u = s_k = r_k + 10^{-k}.$$

Thus, if $k \geq n$,

$$c_m c_{m-1} \ldots c_0 . d_1 d_2 \ldots d_n d_{n+1} \ldots d_k = s_k = u = s_n$$
$$= c_m c_{m-1} \ldots c_0 . d_1 d_2 \ldots d_n 0 \ldots 0.$$

By the uniqueness theorem for finite decimal sequences [Theorem 7–9.1(c)],

$$d_{n+1} = 0, \quad d_{n+2} = 0, \quad \ldots, \quad d_k = 0.$$

Moreover,

$$r_k = s_k - 10^{-k}.$$

Performing this decimal subtraction in the usual way gives

$$
\begin{array}{llllll}
c_m c_{m-1} & \cdots & c_0 . d_1 d_2 & \cdots & d_n 00 & \cdots & 00 & (=s_k) \\
- & & 0.00 & \cdots & 000 & \cdots & 01 & (=10^{-k}) \\
\hline
e_m e_{m-1} & \cdots & e_0 . f_1 f_2 & \cdots & f_n 99 & \cdots & 99 & (=r_k).
\end{array}
$$

Consequently, by Theorem 7–9.1(c) again, $a_m = e_m$, $a_{m-1} = e_{m-1}$, $\ldots$, $a_0 = e_0$, $b_1 = f_1$, $b_2 = f_2$, $\ldots b_n = f_n$, $b_{n+1} = 9$, $b_{n+2} = 9$, $\ldots$, $b_k = 9$. (Note that if $d_n > 0$, then $b_n = d_n - 1$, $b_{n-1} = d_{n-1}$, $\ldots$, $b_1 = d_1$, $a_0 = c_0$, $\ldots$, $a_{m-1} = c_{m-1}$, $a_m = c_m$.) Since k can be any natural number greater than or equal to n, this completes the proof of Theorem 7–9.6.

We can summarize the results of Theorems 7–9.4, 7–9.5, and 7–9.6 as follows:

THEOREM 7–9.7. If u is a positive real number which is not a decimal fraction, then u can be represented in exactly one way as an infinite decimal sequence. If u is a decimal fraction, then u can be represented in exactly two ways as an infinite decimal fraction. One of these representations ends with a sequence of nines and the other ends with a sequence of zeros.

PROBLEMS

1. Give all possible infinite decimal representations of the following numbers.
   (a) 1.01   (b) $\frac{1}{4}$ (c) $\frac{1}{3}$ (d) $\frac{4}{25}$

2. Carry out the proof of Theorem 7–9.5 for the particular case of the number 0.4999... .

3. In which of the following proofs is the completeness property of R used either directly or indirectly: the proof of Theorem 7–8.5; the proof of Theorem 7–9.4; the proof of Theorem 7–9.5; the proof of Theorem 7–9.6.

4. Prove Theorem 7–9.2(a), (b), and (c).

5. Prove the following refinement of (7–9.3): let x and y be real numbers such that $x < y$; then there is a rational number r such that $x < r < y$.

6. An infinite binary sequence is an expression

$$a_m a_{m-1} \ldots a_0 . b_1 b_2 \ldots b_n \ldots ,$$

where a_m, a_{m-1}, ..., a_0, b_1, b_2, ..., b_n, ... are binary digits 0 or 1. Such a binary sequence represents the number

$$a_m \cdot 2^m + a_{m-1} \cdot 2^{m-1} + \cdots + a_0 + b_1 \cdot 2^{-1} + \cdots + b_n \cdot 2^{-n} + \cdots .$$

    (a) State the analogue for infinite binary sequences of each of Theorems 7–8.5, 7–9.4, 7–9.5 and 7–9.6.

    (b) Find the binary sequence representing $\frac{1}{10}$.

7. If x is any real number, define the *greatest integer function* $[x]$ as follows:

$$[x] = \max \{n \in N | n \leq x\}.$$

If x has the decimal representation $a_m a_{m-1} \ldots a_0 . b_1 b_2 \ldots b_n \ldots$, what is $[x]$?

*7–10 Applications of decimal representations. The possibility of representing real numbers by infinite decimal sequences is of considerable practical importance. However, the theorems on decimal representation also have theoretical applications of some importance. One of these will be presented in this section. This application leads naturally to a discussion of the decimal representation of rational numbers.

    Cantor's theorem. One of the most interesting applications of the decimal representation theorem for real numbers is Cantor's proof that the set of all real numbers is not denumerable. That is, there is no one-to-one correspondence between the set R of all real numbers and the set N of natural numbers. The proof is by contradiction: we assume that such a correspondence exists and show that this assumption leads to a contradiction. Suppose that

$$n \leftrightarrow u_n$$

is a one-to-one correspondence between R and N. Let

$$M = \{n \in N | n \leftrightarrow u_n, \text{ where } 0 \leq u_n < 1\}.$$

Let the elements of M be labeled $n_1, n_2, n_3, \ldots$, with $n_1 < n_2 < n_3 < \ldots$. Note that M must be infinite, since the set of all real numbers between 0 and 1 is infinite. Therefore, we obtain the one-to-one correspondence

$$k \leftrightarrow n_k \leftrightarrow u_{n_k}$$

between N and the set of all real numbers u such that $0 \leq u < 1$. Expressing each u_{n_k} as an infinite decimal sequence, we obtain the table

$$
\begin{array}{llllll}
1 \leftrightarrow u_{n_1} & = 0 . b_{1,1} & b_{1,2} & \ldots & b_{1,n} & b_{1,n+1} & \ldots \\
2 \leftrightarrow u_{n_2} & = 0 . b_{2,1} & b_{2,2} & \ldots & b_{2,n} & b_{2,n+1} & \ldots \\
\quad\vdots \\
k \leftrightarrow u_{n_k} & = 0 . b_{k,1} & b_{k,2} & \ldots & b_{k,k} & b_{k,k+1} & \ldots \\
k + 1 \leftrightarrow u_{n_{k+1}} & = 0 . b_{k+1,1} & b_{k+1,2} & \ldots & b_{k+1,k} & b_{k+1,k+1} & \ldots \\
\quad\vdots
\end{array}
$$

The contradiction which we are seeking is obtained by constructing a decimal sequence $0 . c_1 c_2 \ldots c_k c_{k+1} \ldots$ corresponding to a number v, different from 1, which cannot occur in the list

$$u_{n_1}, \quad u_{n_2}, \quad \ldots, \quad u_{n_k}, \quad u_{n_{k+1}}, \quad \ldots$$

(contradicting the assumption that this list contains all real numbers u satisfying $0 \leq u < 1$). To obtain v, let c_1 be any decimal digit which is different from $b_{1,1}$, 0, and 9; let c_2 be any decimal digit which is different from $b_{2,2}$, 0, and 9; . . . ; let c_k be any decimal digit which is different from $b_{k,k}$, 0, and 9; and so forth. Note that there are at least six possible choices for each of the numbers c_1, c_2, c_3, ... Define

$$v = 0 . c_1 c_2 c_3 \ldots .$$

Then v is a positive real number, less than 1, which does not end with a sequence of zeros or nines. Hence, the decimal representation of v is unique, by Theorem 7–9.7. Moreover, for every k, $v \neq u_{n_k}$. In fact, by the way that v was constructed, the decimal representation of v is different from the decimal representation of u_{n_k}. Since v has only one decimal representation, this implies that $v \neq u_{n_k}$. This completes the proof.

THEOREM 7–10.1. *Cantor's theorem.* The set of all real numbers is not denumerable.

Cantor's theorem shows conclusively that it is not possible in any way to set up a one-to-one correspondence between the points of a line and the rational numbers. The example given in Section 7–2 showed that the natural coordinate correspondence between Q and the points of a line l does not exhaust all points of l. The fact that it is not possible to establish *any* correspondence between Q and the points of l is a much stronger result. To prove that no such correspondence is possible, observe that by the discussion of Section 7–3, there is a one-to-one correspondence between the real numbers and the points of l. Therefore, the existence of a one-to-one correspondence between the points of l and Q would lead to a one-to-one correspondence between R and Q. However, since Q is denumerable (Problem 5, Section 1–2), this contradicts Cantor's theorem.

Perhaps even more important than the result of Cantor's theorem is the method used for its proof. The crucial step in this proof is the observation that if an infinite list of sequences is given, arranged in the form of a rectangular array,

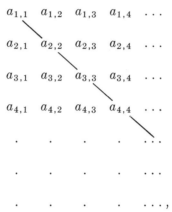

then any sequence $c_1, c_2, c_3, c_4, \ldots$ which differs at each entry from the "diagonal" sequence $a_{1,1}, a_{2,2}, a_{3,3}, a_{4,4}, \ldots$ must differ from every one of the sequences $a_{i,1}, a_{i,2}, a_{i,3}, a_{i,4}, \ldots$, which are the rows of the rectangular array. This type of argument is usually called the *diagonal method*. It occurs in the proofs of some of the most important theorems of modern mathematics.

The representation of rational numbers. In Section 7–2 the term "irrational" was introduced to describe those real numbers which do not belong to Q. Cantor's theorem shows in a striking way that the irrational numbers are much more abundant than the rational numbers. It is natural to ask if there is some way to recognize the decimal representation of a rational number. We will now prove that the infinite decimal sequences which represent positive rational numbers are exactly the ones which are ultimately periodic.

DEFINITION 7–10.2. A decimal sequence is called *ultimately periodic* if it is of the form

$$a_m a_{m-1} \ldots a_0 . b_1 b_2 \ldots b_n b_{n+1} \ldots b_{n+k} b_{n+1} \ldots b_{n+k} b_{n+1} \ldots b_{n+k} \ldots .$$

That is, from a certain point on, the decimal sequence consists of repetitions of a finite sequence of decimal digits.

It is convenient to abbreviate ultimately periodic decimal sequences by writing

$$a_m a_{m-1} \ldots a_0 . b_1 b_2 \ldots b_n \overline{b_{n+1} \ldots b_{n+k}}$$

instead of

$$a_m a_{m-1} \ldots a_0 . b_1 b_2 \ldots b_n b_{n+1} \ldots b_{n+k} b_{n+1} \ldots b_{n+k} b_{n+1} \ldots b_{n+k} \ldots .$$

The line over the block of digits indicates that this finite sequence is repeated indefinitely in the decimal sequence.

EXAMPLE 1. The expression $33.\overline{3}$ stands for $33.3333\ldots = 100/3$. This number could just as well be abbreviated $33.3\overline{3}$, or even $33.3\overline{33}$, etc.

EXAMPLE 2. The expression $121.4\overline{27}$ stands for $121.4272727\ldots$. This could also be written $121.42\overline{72}$, or $121.42\overline{727}$. The possibility of expressing the number u represented by $121.4\overline{27}$ as $121.42\overline{727}$ leads to a method of determining u as a rational fraction. In fact

$$10^3 \cdot u = 10^3 \cdot (121.42\overline{727}) = 121427.\overline{27} = 121427 + 0.\overline{27},$$

and

$$10 \cdot u = 10 \cdot (121.4\overline{27}) = 1214.\overline{27} = 1214 + 0.\overline{27}.$$

Subtracting these equations, the terms $0.\overline{27}$ on the right-hand sides cancel each other, leaving

$$990 \cdot u = 120213, \quad \text{or} \quad u = 120213/990 = 13357/110.$$

The argument used in Example 2 can easily be generalized to show that every ultimately periodic decimal sequence represents a rational number.

THEOREM 7–10.3. Let $u = a_m a_{m-1} \ldots a_0 . b_1 b_2 \ldots b_n \overline{b_{n+1} \ldots b_{n+k}}$. Then u is the rational number

$$\frac{(a_m a_{m-1} \ldots a_0 b_1 b_2 \ldots b_n b_{n+1} \ldots b_{n+k}) - (a_m a_{m-1} \ldots a_0 b_1 b_2 \ldots b_n)}{10^{n+k} - 10^n}.$$

In fact,

$(10^{n+k} - 10^n) \cdot u$

$= [(a_m a_{m-1} \ldots a_0 b_1 b_2 \ldots b_n b_{n+1} \ldots b_{n+k}) + 0 . \overline{b_{n+1} \ldots b_{n+k}}]$

$\quad - [(a_m a_{m-1} \ldots a_0 b_1 b_2 \ldots b_n) + 0 . \overline{b_{n+1} \ldots b_{n+k}}]$

$= [(a_m a_{m-1} \ldots a_0 b_1 b_2 \ldots b_n b_{n+1} \ldots b_{n+k}) - (a_m a_{m-1} \ldots a_0 b_1 b_2 \ldots b_n)]$

$\quad + 0.000\ldots,$

by Theorem 7–9.2(b). Dividing gives the desired result.

A theorem such as this always suggests a converse. In this case we are led to ask if every decimal representation of a nonnegative rational number is ultimately periodic. There is evidence to support this conjecture. For example, by Theorem 7–9.7 the two decimal representations of any decimal fraction are ultimately periodic since they end in a sequence of zeros or nines. Consider also the following example.

EXAMPLE 3. It is possible to obtain the decimal expansion of rational numbers by long division. For instance,

$$
\begin{array}{r}
0.571428 \\
7\overline{)4.000000} \\
3\,5 \\
\hline
50 \\
49 \\
\hline
10 \\
7 \\
\hline
30 \\
28 \\
\hline
20 \\
14 \\
\hline
60 \\
56 \\
\hline
4
\end{array}
$$

Since the remainder 4 is the same as the number which we began dividing, it is clear that continuation of the process will give the block 571428 repeatedly. Therefore, it seems certain that

$$4/7 = 0.\overline{571428}.$$

(The only reason for not trusting this conclusion is that we have not shown that the continued use of long division does really lead to the decimal representation of a fraction. However, the validity of the result can be checked directly from Theorem 7–10.3.)

THEOREM 7–10.4. Every decimal representation of a positive rational number is ultimately periodic.

The idea underlying the proof of this theorem is the same as the principle operating in Example 3. The process of dividing the numerator of the fraction by the denominator must somewhere yield two remainders which are equal. When the same remainder occurs a second time, the decimal begins to repeat. This idea is somewhat disguised in the following proof.

Let u be the positive rational number c/d where c and d are natural numbers. If u is a decimal fraction, then its two decimal representations are ultimately periodic, by Theorem 7–9.7. Therefore suppose that u is not a decimal fraction, so that its decimal representation

$$u = a_m a_{m-1} \ldots a_0 . b_1 b_2 \ldots b_n \ldots$$

is unique. Using the division algorithm, we can write

$$c = q_0 \cdot d + r_0,$$
$$10 \cdot c = q_1 \cdot d + r_1,$$
$$10^2 \cdot c = q_2 \cdot d + r_2,$$
$$\vdots$$

where $q_0, q_1, q_2, \ldots, r_0, r_1, r_2, \ldots$ are nonnegative integers, and $0 \leq r_i < d$ for $i = 0, 1, 2, \ldots$. There are at most d different values which r_i can take (actually, at most $d - 1$, since the assumption that u is not a decimal fraction implies that $r_i \neq 0$). Therefore, in the list of numbers

$$r_0, r_1, r_2, \ldots, r_d$$

there must be two which are equal. Suppose that

$$r_n = r_{n+k} = r, \qquad n \geq 0, \qquad k > 0.$$

Then

$$q_n + (r/d) = 10^n \cdot (c/d) = 10^n \cdot u$$
$$= a_m a_{m-1} \ldots a_0 b_1 b_2 \ldots b_n . b_{n+1} b_{n+2} \ldots b_{n+k} b_{n+k+1} \ldots,$$
$$q_{n+k} + (r/d) = 10^{n+k} \cdot (c/d) = 10^{n+k} \cdot u$$
$$= a_m a_{m-1} \ldots a_0 b_1 b_2 \ldots b_n b_{n+1} \ldots b_{n+k} . b_{n+k+1} \ldots b_{n+2k} b_{n+2k+1} \ldots.$$

Note that r/d, $q_n + r/d$, and $q_{n+k} + r/d$ are not decimal fractions, since otherwise c/d would be a decimal fraction. This fact is needed so that we can use the uniqueness of the decimal representations which was proved in Theorem 7–9.6. Because q_n and q_{n+k} are integers and $0 \leq r/d < 1$, it follows that

$$0 . b_{n+1} \ldots b_{n+k} b_{n+k+1} \ldots b_{n+2k} b_{n+2k+1} \ldots$$
$$= r/d = 0 . b_{n+k+1} \ldots b_{n+2k} b_{n+2k+1} \ldots b_{n+3k} \ldots.$$

Therefore,

$$b_{n+k+1} = b_{n+1}, \ldots, \quad b_{n+2k} = b_{n+k}, \quad b_{n+2k+1} = b_{n+k+1} = b_{n+1}, \ldots,$$
$$b_{n+3k} = b_{n+2k} = b_{n+k}, \ldots.$$

Consequently,

$$u = a_m a_{m-1} \ldots a_0 . b_1 b_2 \ldots b_n \overline{b_{n+1} \ldots b_{n+k}},$$

that is, the decimal representation of u is ultimately periodic.

PROBLEMS

1. Find the rational numbers which are represented by the following ultimately periodic decimal sequences.
   (a) $21.\overline{01}$
   (b) $4.\overline{0010012}$
   (c) $0.00\overline{111}$.

2. Find the decimal sequences which represent the following rational numbers.
   (a) 2/7,   (b) 201/999   (c) 18/17

3. Let u be the real number 0.1010010001000010... whose decimal representation consists of a sequence of ones separated by blocks of zeros, with the length of each block equal to the number of ones which precede it. Show that u is irrational.

4. Show that the number

$$\sum_{k=1}^{\infty} 10^{-(k!)}$$

is irrational.

5. Let A be a set containing at least two elements. Use the diagonal method to prove that the set S of all sequences a_1, a_2, a_3, ... of elements of A is not denumerable. Use this result to show that the set of all subsets of the set N is not denumerable. [*Hint:* Let $A = \{0, 1\}$ and establish a one-to-one correspondence between the set $P(N)$ of all subsets of N and the set S of all sequences a_1, a_2, a_3, ... of zeros and ones. For instance, let

$$M \leftrightarrow a_1, a_2, a_3, \ldots ,$$

where for each i, $a_i = 0$ if $i \notin M$ and $a_i = 1$ if $i \in M$.]

6. Let

$$\langle a_m a_{m-1} \ldots a_0 . b_1 b_2 \ldots b_n \ldots , c_m c_{m-1} \ldots c_0 . d_1 d_2 \ldots d_n \ldots \rangle$$
$$\leftrightarrow a_m c_m a_{m-1} c_{m-1} \ldots a_0 c_0 . b_1 d_1 b_2 d_2 \ldots b_n d_n \ldots .$$

[For example, $\langle 121.2121..., 003.3333... \rangle \leftrightarrow 102013.23132313....$]
   (a) Show that this definition establishes a one-to-one correspondence between the set of all pairs $\langle u, v \rangle$ of real numbers and a subset T of R, provided the following convention is accepted: each real number is represented by an infinite decimal sequence (which may begin with a finite number of zeros), possibly ending with a sequence of all zeros, but not with a sequence of nines.
   (b) Show that T is not all of R.

7. Use Theorem 7–10.4 and the proof of Theorem 7–10.3 to show that any natural number k which is not divisible by 2 or 5 will divide some number of the sequence

$$9, 99, 999, 9999, \ldots.$$

8. Show that if m is a natural number which is relatively prime to 10, then the decimal expansion of $1/m$ is of the form

$$0.\overline{b_1 b_2 \ldots b_d},$$

where d is the order of 10 modulo m (see Definition 5–8.8).

CHAPTER 8

THE COMPLEX NUMBERS

8–1 The construction of the complex numbers. One of the properties of the system of real numbers which was derived in the preceding chapter concerned the solution of the equation $x^m = u$, where m is a natural number and u is a real number. If m is odd, then $x^m = u$ has exactly one real solution, and if m is even and u is positive, there are exactly two solutions which are real numbers. However, if m is even and u is negative, then the equation $x^m = u$ has no real solution (see Theorem 7–6.3, and Problem 7, Section 4–5). In particular, the equation $x^2 = -1$ has no solution in the field of real numbers. The desirability of solving such equations poses a problem which should now be familiar to the reader: invent a new number system which contains R and which includes numbers which satisfy the equations under consideration. More precisely, we wish to construct a number system C which satisfies the following conditions:

(i) C is a field containing R as a subring, and

(ii) C contains a number* i which satisfies $i^2 = -1$. $\qquad$ (8–1)

It is also reasonable to require that C be minimal among the systems satisfying these conditions. That is, there should be no proper subring of C which also satisfies (8–1). For otherwise, we could attain our objectives more economically with the subring than with C.

The construction which gives the desired field turns out to be remarkably easy. The result is the complex number system, which not only contains a solution of $x^2 = -1$, but also solutions of the most general algebraic equations.

Complex numbers were introduced in about 1560 by the Italian mathematician Rafael Bombelli (1530–1572?). Bombelli was a teacher at the University of Bologna, an important center of mathematics during the Renaissance. Until about 1800, complex numbers were viewed as mysterious objects, devoid of any real meaning.† At the end of the eighteenth century, several mathematicians independently gave logically correct definitions and useful geometrical interpretations of these numbers.

---

* The use of the symbol i to represent $\sqrt{-1}$ in C is standard mathematical notation. This element is usually called the *imaginary unit*.

† A vestige of the early mysticism surrounding complex numbers is the common use of the term "imaginary" to distinguish them from "real" numbers.

In order to see how the complex numbers and their operations should be defined, we suppose that there is a field F which satisfies the conditions (8–1). Then F contains R and the number i, and therefore it will contain all expressions of the form $u + i \cdot v$, where u and v are real numbers. Also, since the usual rules of arithmetic are available in a field, it is easy to derive expressions for the sum, negative, and product of such numbers:

$$
\begin{aligned}
(x + i \cdot y) + (u + i \cdot v) &= (x + u) + i \cdot (y + v) \\
-(x + i \cdot y) &= (-x) + i \cdot (-y), \\
(x + i \cdot y) \cdot (u + i \cdot v) &= xu + i \cdot (yu + xv) + i^2 yv \\
&= (xu - yv) + i \cdot (yu + xv).
\end{aligned}
\tag{8–2}
$$

These identities show that the collection of all the elements which can be written in the form $u + i \cdot v$ is a subring of F. Moreover, it is not hard to show that this subring also satisfies the conditions (8–1). In particular, if F is a field C with all of the desired properties, then the assumption that C is minimal implies that C coincides with the subring of all elements of the form $u + i \cdot v$. Therefore, it must be possible to write every element of C in the form $u + i \cdot v$, where u and v are real numbers.

It is apparent that $u + i \cdot v$ is determined by the two real numbers u and v. Moreover, if $x + i \cdot y = u + i \cdot v$, then $x = u$ and $y = v$. Indeed, if $y \neq v$, then $i = (x - u)/(v - y)$. However, $i^2 = -1$, and since $(x - u)/(v - y)$ is a real number, it follows that $[(x - u)/(v - y)]^2 \geq 0$, which is a contradiction. Therefore, $y = v$, and consequently $x = u$.

We can summarize this discussion by saying that if a number system C with the desired properties exists at all, then there is a one-to-one correspondence,

$$\langle u, v \rangle \leftrightarrow u + i \cdot v,$$

between the set $R \times R$ of all ordered pairs of real numbers and C. This observation suggests that a way to construct the complex numbers is to define suitable operations on the set $R \times R$. The identities of (8–2) show how the operations of addition, negation, and multiplication must be defined for the ordered pairs.

There is another important fact which is a consequence of the above discussion. Any two rings which satisfy all of the requirements desired for C are isomorphic. That is, if C exists at all, then C is unique.

DEFINITION 8–1.1.   The *set C of all complex numbers* consists of all ordered pairs $\langle u, v \rangle$ of real numbers. If $\langle x, y \rangle \in C$ and $\langle u, v \rangle \in C$, then

(a) $\langle x, y \rangle + \langle u, v \rangle = \langle x + u, y + v \rangle$;

(b) $-\langle x, y \rangle = \langle -x, -y \rangle$; and

(c) $\langle x, y \rangle \cdot \langle u, v \rangle = \langle x \cdot u - y \cdot v, y \cdot u + x \cdot v \rangle$.

The ordered pairs of real numbers are definite objects which can be interpreted as complex numbers without any logical contradiction. However, the set of all ordered pairs of real numbers often occurs in mathematics with other interpretations. The intended meaning of $\langle u, v \rangle$ should be specified whenever such pairs are used. In the case of complex numbers, this will usually be unnecessary, because once we show that the system C defined above satisfies the requirements listed in (8–1), it will be possible to return to the convenient notation $u + i \cdot v$.

The reader should be aware of the double use of the signs $+$, $-$, and $\cdot$ in Definition 8–1.1. On the left-hand sides of the identities (a), (b), and (c), they represent the operations which are being defined for ordered pairs, while on the right-hand sides of these equalities, they indicate the known operations in the field R of real numbers.

There is no problem about the operations in Definition 8–1.1 being well defined, as there was in the case of the rational numbers and the real numbers. Definition 8–1.1 involves no arbitrary choice, such as was made in defining the operations on the equivalence classes which are the elements of Q. Also, the expressions on the right-hand sides of (a), (b), and (c) obviously belong to the set C of all ordered pairs of real numbers, so that the problem of closure, which was troublesome in defining addition, negation, and multiplication of real numbers, does not arise.

It must now be shown that the complex numbers as defined above satisfy the description given in (8–1). This result is the content of the two following theorems.

THEOREM 8–1.2. The set C of all complex numbers with the operations defined in Definition 8–1.1 is a field with $\langle 0, 0 \rangle$ as the zero element and $\langle 1, 0 \rangle$ as the identity element. The complex number $\langle 0, 1 \rangle$ is a solution of the equation

$$x^2 = -\langle 1, 0 \rangle.$$

Proof. The proof that C is a commutative ring with $\langle 0, 0 \rangle$ as the zero element and $\langle 1, 0 \rangle$ as the identity element consists of checking the identities of Definition 4–2.1 in a straightforward way. For example, we will prove the associative law of multiplication:

$$\langle u_1, v_1 \rangle \cdot (\langle u_2, v_2 \rangle \cdot \langle u_3, v_3 \rangle) = \langle u_1, v_1 \rangle \cdot \langle u_2 u_3 - v_2 v_3, v_2 u_3 + u_2 v_3 \rangle$$
$$= \langle u_1(u_2 u_3 - v_2 v_3) - v_1(v_2 u_3 + u_2 v_3),$$
$$v_1(u_2 u_3 - v_2 v_3) + u_1(v_2 u_3 + u_2 v_3) \rangle$$
$$= \langle u_1 u_2 u_3 - (u_1 v_2 v_3 + v_1 u_2 v_3 + v_1 v_2 u_3),$$
$$(v_1 u_2 u_3 + u_1 v_2 u_3 + u_1 u_2 v_3) - v_1 v_2 v_3 \rangle,$$

$$(\langle u_1, v_1 \rangle \cdot \langle u_2, v_2 \rangle) \cdot \langle u_3, v_3 \rangle = \langle u_1 u_2 - v_1 v_2, v_1 u_2 + u_1 v_2 \rangle \cdot \langle u_3, v_3 \rangle$$
$$= \langle (u_1 u_2 - v_1 v_2) u_3 - (v_1 u_2 + u_1 v_2) v_3,$$
$$(v_1 u_2 + u_1 v_2) u_3 + (u_1 u_2 - v_1 v_2) v_3 \rangle$$
$$= \langle u_1 u_2 u_3 - (u_1 v_2 v_3 + v_1 u_2 v_3 + v_1 v_2 u_3),$$
$$(v_1 u_2 u_3 + u_1 v_2 u_3 + u_1 u_2 v_3) - v_1 v_2 v_3 \rangle.$$

Hence, $\langle u_1, v_1 \rangle \cdot (\langle u_2, v_2 \rangle \cdot \langle u_3, v_3 \rangle) = (\langle u_1, v_1 \rangle \cdot \langle u_2, v_2 \rangle) \cdot \langle u_3, v_3 \rangle$.

To prove that C is a field, it is necessary to show that if $\langle u, v \rangle \neq \langle 0, 0 \rangle$ in C and $\langle w, z \rangle \in C$, then there exists $\langle x, y \rangle \in C$ such that

$$\langle u, v \rangle \cdot \langle x, y \rangle = \langle w, z \rangle. \tag{8–3}$$

If both sides of this equality are multiplied on the left by $\langle u, -v \rangle$, then by the associative law just proved, we obtain

$$\langle u^2 + v^2, 0 \rangle \cdot \langle x, y \rangle = \langle u, -v \rangle \cdot \langle w, z \rangle = \langle uw + vz, (-v)w + uz \rangle.$$

The real number $u^2 + v^2$ is not zero, since otherwise

$$0 = u^2 + v^2 \geq u^2 \geq 0, \qquad 0 = u^2 + v^2 \geq v^2 \geq 0,$$

so that $u = v = 0$. This contradicts the assumption that $\langle u, v \rangle \neq \langle 0, 0 \rangle$. Thus, $(u^2 + v^2)^{-1}$ exists in R, and

$$\langle x, y \rangle = \langle 1, 0 \rangle \cdot \langle x, y \rangle = (\langle (u^2 + v^2)^{-1}, 0 \rangle \cdot \langle u^2 + v^2, 0 \rangle) \cdot \langle x, y \rangle$$
$$= \langle (u^2 + v^2)^{-1}, 0 \rangle \cdot \langle u, -v \rangle \cdot \langle w, z \rangle$$
$$= \langle (u^2 + v^2)^{-1} \cdot (uw + vz), (u^2 + v^2)^{-1} \cdot (uz - vw) \rangle.$$

As frequently happens in elementary algebra, the steps which lead to the solution of (8–3) can be reversed to prove that the expression obtained for $\langle x, y \rangle$ really is a solution:

$$\langle u, v \rangle \cdot \langle (u^2 + v^2)^{-1} \cdot (uw + vz), (u^2 + v^2)^{-1} \cdot (uz - vw) \rangle$$
$$= \langle u, v \rangle \cdot \langle u, -v \rangle \cdot \langle (u^2 + v^2)^{-1}, 0 \rangle \cdot \langle w, z \rangle$$
$$= \langle u^2 + v^2, 0 \rangle \cdot \langle (u^2 + v^2)^{-1}, 0 \rangle \cdot \langle w, z \rangle = \langle 1, 0 \rangle \cdot \langle w, z \rangle$$
$$= \langle w, z \rangle.$$

By Definition 8–1.1(c) and (b), $\langle 0, 1 \rangle^2 = \langle -1, 0 \rangle = -\langle 1, 0 \rangle$. This observation completes the proof of Theorem 8–1.2.

The definition of a complex number as an ordered pair $\langle u, v \rangle$ of real numbers was suggested by the correspondence $\langle u, v \rangle \leftrightarrow u + i \cdot v$, where u and v are real and $i^2 = -1$. In particular, a real number $u = u + i \cdot 0$ should correspond to the pair $\langle u, 0 \rangle$.

THEOREM 8–1.3.   The correspondence $u \leftrightarrow \langle u, 0 \rangle$ is an isomorphism between R and the subring $R' = \{\langle u, 0 \rangle | u \in R\}$ of C. Each element of C can be expressed in the form $\langle u, 0 \rangle + \langle 0, 1 \rangle \cdot \langle v, 0 \rangle$.

This theorem, whose proof we leave for the reader, is the justification for identifying each real number u with the corresponding element $\langle u, 0 \rangle$ of R'. If this identification is made, then R becomes a subring of C. Thus, C satisfies condition (i) of (8–1). In particular, we have now attained the following chain of inclusions relating the classical number systems of mathematics:

$$N \subset Z \subset Q \subset R \subset C.$$

For simplicity, each element of R in C will be denoted by a single symbol such as 0, 1, $\frac{1}{3}$, 2, u, and v, rather than by the corresponding pair $\langle 0, 0 \rangle$, $\langle 1, 0 \rangle$, $\langle \frac{1}{3}, 0 \rangle$, $\langle 2, 0 \rangle$, $\langle u, 0 \rangle$, and $\langle v, 0 \rangle$. Note that with this notation, 0 and 1 represent the zero and identity of C, as they should. Moreover, by Theorem 8–1.2, $\langle 0, 1 \rangle^2 = -1$, which leads to an exact definition of the symbol i as an abbreviation for $\langle 0, 1 \rangle$. Therefore,

$$i^2 = -1,$$

and C satisfies condition (ii) of (8–1).

By virtue of the notation just introduced, the expression $u + i \cdot v$ takes on a definite meaning as a complex number. In fact,

$$u + i \cdot v = \langle u, 0 \rangle + \langle 0, 1 \rangle \cdot \langle v, 0 \rangle = \langle u, v \rangle.$$

We see from this equality that every complex number can be represented uniquely in the form $u + i \cdot v$, with u and v real numbers. From this fact it follows easily that no proper subring of C satisfies (8–1); that is, C is minimal.

PROBLEMS

1. Express the following complex numbers in the form $u + iv$.
   (a) $\langle -1, 1 \rangle$ (b) $\langle 0, 1 \rangle + \langle 2, -1 \rangle$ (c) $\langle 2, 1 \rangle \cdot \langle 1, 2 \rangle$ (d) $\langle 3, 2 \rangle / \langle 1, 1 \rangle$
   (e) $\langle u, v \rangle^{-1}$, where $\langle u, v \rangle \neq \langle 0, 0 \rangle$

2. Complete the proof of Theorem 8–1.2.

3. Prove Theorem 8–1.3.

4. Determine the value of the sum $\sum_{k=0}^{n} i^k$ for all values of n.

5. Show that the following sets are subrings of C.
   (a) $\{\langle r, s \rangle | r \in Q, s \in Q\}$
   (b) $\{\langle a, b \rangle | a \in Z, b \in Z\}$

Is either of these subrings a field? Is either of them isomorphic to N, Z, Q, or R?

8-2 Complex conjugates and the absolute value in C. It is not possible to define an ordering of the complex numbers such that they will form an ordered field. For if C could be made into an ordered field, then $i^2 = -1$ would have to be both positive and negative, by Theorem 4–5.5. However, the field C has some important special properties which are not present in every field, or even in ordered fields. In this section the consequences of some of these properties will be examined.

Throughout this section and the remainder of the book, we will represent complex numbers either by single letters, such as z and w, or else by the notation $x + iy$ and $u + iv$, where x, y, u, and v denote real numbers. The discussion at the end of Section 8–1 justifies this convention.

Since $x + iy = u + iv$ implies that $x = u$ and $y = v$, we see that the real numbers x and y appearing in the representation $z = x + iy$ are uniquely determined by the complex number z. The real number x is called the *real part* of z, and y is called the *imaginary part* of z. It is convenient to write $x = \Re(z)$ and $y = \mathcal{I}(z)$ in this case. That is,

$$\Re(x + iy) = x, \qquad \mathcal{I}(x + iy) = y. \qquad (8\text{–}4)$$

It is obvious from the definition of addition and negation in C that

$$\begin{aligned} \Re(z + w) &= \Re(z) + \Re(w), &&\text{and} && \Re(-z) = -\Re(z), \\ \mathcal{I}(z + w) &= \mathcal{I}(z) + \mathcal{I}(w), &&\text{and} && \mathcal{I}(-z) = -\mathcal{I}(z). \end{aligned} \qquad (8\text{–}5)$$

DEFINITION 8–2.1. Let $z = x + iy$ be a complex number. The *complex conjugate* of z is the number

$$\bar{z} = x + i(-y).$$

We will often simplify the phrase "complex conjugate of z" to "conjugate of z," although the latter expression has a broader meaning in other phases of algebra. Also, it is customary to write $x - iy$ instead of $x + i(-y)$.

EXAMPLE 1. $\overline{1 + i2} = 1 - i2$; $\bar{i} = -i$; $\bar{2} = 2$.

THEOREM 8–2.2. Let z and w be complex numbers. Then
(a) $\overline{z + w} = \bar{z} + \bar{w}$;
(b) $\overline{(-z)} = -\bar{z}$;
(c) $\overline{z \cdot w} = \bar{z} \cdot \bar{w}$;
(d) if $w \neq 0$, then $\overline{z/w} = \bar{z}/\bar{w}$;
(e) if $w = \bar{z}$, then $\bar{w} = z$, that is, $\bar{\bar{z}} = z$;
(f) $z + \bar{z} = 2\Re(z)$, $z - \bar{z} = 2i\mathcal{I}(z)$.

We will omit the proof of (a), (b), (e), and (f). The proof of (c) is obtained by direct computation. Let $z = x + iy$, $w = u + iv$. Then $\bar{z} = x + i(-y)$, and $\bar{w} = u + i(-v)$. Hence,

$$\overline{z \cdot w} = \overline{[(xu - yv) + i(yu + xv)]} = (xu - yv) + i[-(yu + xv)],$$

and

$$\bar{z} \cdot \bar{w} = [xu - (-y)(-v)] + i[(-y)u + x(-v)]$$
$$= (xu - yv) + i[-(yu + xv)] = \overline{z \cdot w}.$$

To prove (d), note that by what we have just shown

$$\overline{(z/w)} \cdot \bar{w} = \overline{(z/w) \cdot w} = \bar{z}.$$

Hence, $\overline{z/w} = \bar{z}/\bar{w}$.

If $z = x + iy$, then

$$z \cdot \bar{z} = (x + iy)[x + i(-y)]$$
$$= [x^2 - y(-y)] + i[yx + x(-y)] = x^2 + y^2.$$

Therefore $z \cdot \bar{z}$ is a nonnegative real number, and it has a square root in R.

DEFINITION 8–2.3. Let $z = x + iy$ be a complex number. The *absolute value* or *modulus* of z is the nonnegative real number

$$|z| = \sqrt{x^2 + y^2}.$$

EXAMPLE 2. $|1 + i2| = \sqrt{5}$; $|i| = 1$; $|2| = 2$; $|-3| = 3$.

If z is a real number, say $z = x + i \cdot 0$, then $|z| = \sqrt{x^2}$. If $x \geq 0$, then $\sqrt{x^2} = x$. If $x < 0$, then $\sqrt{x^2} = -x$. Therefore, the definition of the absolute value of z given above is consistent with Definition 4–6.6 for the absolute value of elements of an ordered integral domain (in particular, the absolute value in R).

THEOREM 8–2.4. Let z and w be complex numbers. Then
  (a) $|z| \geq 0$; if $|z| = 0$, then $z = 0$;
  (b) $z \cdot \bar{z} = |z|^2$;
  (c) $|\bar{z}| = |z|$;
  (d) $|-z| = |z|$;
  (e) $|z \cdot w| = |z| \cdot |w|$;
  (f) if $w \neq 0$, then $|z/w| = |z|/|w|$;
  (g) $|\Re(z)| \leq |z|$, $|\Im(z)| \leq |z|$;
  (h) $|z + w| \leq |z| + |w|$.

Proof. Let $z = x + iy$. By Definition 8–2.3, $|z| \geq 0$. If $|z| = 0$, then $0 = x^2 + y^2 \geq x^2 \geq 0$; hence, $x = 0$; similarly, $y = 0$. To prove (b), observe that

$$z \cdot \bar{z} = (x + iy) \cdot [x + i(-y)] = x^2 + y^2 = |z|^2.$$

The equality (c) is obtained from (b) and Theorem 8–2.2(e) by taking the square root of both sides of the identity $|\bar{z}|^2 = \bar{z} \cdot \bar{\bar{z}} = \bar{z} \cdot z = z \cdot \bar{z} = |z|^2$. Using Definition 8–2.3,

$$|-z| = |(-x) + i(-y)| = \sqrt{(-x)^2 + (-y)^2} = \sqrt{x^2 + y^2} = |z|.$$

The identity (e) is obtained from (b) and Theorem 8–2.2(c) by taking the square root of both sides of the equality

$$|z \cdot w|^2 = (z \cdot w) \cdot (\overline{z \cdot w}) = (z \cdot w) \cdot (\bar{z} \cdot \bar{w}) = (z \cdot \bar{z}) \cdot (w \cdot \bar{w})$$
$$= |z|^2 \cdot |w|^2 = (|z| \cdot |w|)^2.$$

Using this result, we have $|z/w| \cdot |w| = |(z/w) \cdot w| = |z|$. If $w \neq 0$, then $|w| \neq 0$ by (a), so that this identity can be divided by $|w|$ to obtain (f). If $z = x + iy$, then by definition,

$$|\mathcal{R}(z)| = |x| = \sqrt{x^2} \leq \sqrt{x^2 + y^2} = |z|.$$

The second statement of (g) is proved in a similar way. Finally, to obtain the *triangle inequality* (h), note that by Theorem 8–2.2,

$$|z + w|^2 = (z + w) \cdot (\overline{z + w}) = (z + w) \cdot (\bar{z} + \bar{w})$$
$$= z \cdot \bar{z} + z \cdot \bar{w} + \bar{z} \cdot w + w \cdot \bar{w}$$
$$= |z|^2 + (z \cdot \bar{w} + \overline{z \cdot \bar{w}}) + |w|^2 = |z|^2 + 2\mathcal{R}(z \cdot \bar{w}) + |w|^2$$
$$\leq |z|^2 + 2|\mathcal{R}(z \cdot \bar{w})| + |w|^2 \leq |z|^2 + 2|z \cdot \bar{w}| + |w|^2$$
$$= |z|^2 + 2|z| \cdot |\bar{w}| + |w|^2 = |z|^2 + 2|z| \cdot |w| + |w|^2$$
$$= (|z| + |w|)^2.$$

Taking the square root of the first and last term of this inequality yields (h).

The theorem we have just proved contains the most important elementary properties of the absolute value. The reader should become thoroughly familiar with these facts.

The result of Theorem 8–2.4(b) can be used to calculate quotients in C. The general idea, which was used implicitly in the proof of Theorem 8–1.2, is that

$$\frac{z}{w} = \frac{z}{w} \cdot \frac{\bar{w}}{\bar{w}} = \frac{z \cdot \bar{w}}{|w|^2}.$$

EXAMPLE 3. $\dfrac{3+i}{5+i2} = \dfrac{(3+i)\cdot(5-i2)}{(5+i2)\cdot(5-i2)} = \dfrac{17-i}{29} = \dfrac{17}{29} + i\left(\dfrac{-1}{29}\right).$

We will use the results of Theorems 8–2.2 and 8–2.4 and the fact that every nonnegative real number has a square root to prove that every complex number w has a square root z in C. In fact, an explicit expression for z in terms of w can be obtained.

Let $w \in C$. First assume that there is a complex number z which satisfies

$$z^2 = w.$$

We will solve this equation for z in terms of w. By Theorem 8–2.4, $z^2 = w$ implies

$$|w| = |z^2| = |z|^2 = z \cdot \bar{z}.$$

Therefore,

$$|w| + w = z \cdot \bar{z} + z^2 = z \cdot (\bar{z} + z) = 2z \cdot \Re(z). \qquad (8\text{–}6)$$

Moreover, by Theorem 8–2.2,

$$[2\Re(z)]^2 = (z + \bar{z})^2 = z^2 + 2z \cdot \bar{z} + \bar{z}^2 = w + 2|w| + \bar{w}$$
$$= 2|w| + (w + \bar{w}) = 2|w| + 2\Re(w) = 2[|w| + \Re(w)].$$

Thus, $2[|w| + \Re(w)]$ is a nonnegative real number. Taking square roots, we obtain:

$$2\Re(z) = \pm\sqrt{[2\Re(z)]^2} = \pm\sqrt{2[|w| + \Re(w)]}. \qquad (8\text{–}7)$$

There are now two cases to consider. If $|w| + \Re(w) \neq 0$, then by (8–7), $2\Re(z) \neq 0$. Then (8–6) can be written in the form

$$z = \frac{|w| + w}{2\Re(z)}.$$

Using (8–7) again, we find that z has the two possible values,

$$z = \pm \frac{|w| + w}{\sqrt{2[|w| + \Re(w)]}}. \qquad (8\text{–}8)$$

If $|w| + \Re(w) = 0$, then

$$\Re(w)^2 = (-|w|)^2 = |w|^2 = \Re(w)^2 + \Im(w)^2.$$

Hence $\Im(w) = 0$, and $w = \Re(w) = -|w|$. That is, $w = -u$, where u is a nonnegative real number. By (8–7), $\Re(z) = 0$. Hence, $z = i\Im(z)$, and

$$-[\Im(z)^2] = z^2 = w = -|w|.$$

Therefore, $\mathcal{I}(z) = \pm\sqrt{|w|}$. Consequently, in this case z has the two possible values,

$$z = \pm i\sqrt{|w|}. \tag{8–9}$$

Our discussion shows that if there is a complex number z satisfying $z^2 = w$, then z must have the form (8–8) if $|w| + \mathfrak{R}(w) \neq 0$, and z is given by (8–9) if $|w| + \mathfrak{R}(w) = 0$. It remains to show conversely that if z is given by (8–8) in case $|w| + \mathfrak{R}(w) \neq 0$, and by (8–9) when $|w| + \mathfrak{R}(w) = 0$, then $z^2 = w$. This is done by an easy computation. Suppose first that $|w| + \mathfrak{R}(w) \neq 0$. Then

$$\left[\pm \frac{|w| + w}{\sqrt{2[|w| + \mathfrak{R}(w)]}}\right]^2 = \frac{|w|^2 + 2w \cdot |w| + w^2}{2[|w| + \mathfrak{R}(w)]} = \frac{w \cdot \overline{w} + 2w \cdot |w| + w^2}{2[|w| + \mathfrak{R}(w)]}$$

$$= \frac{w[2|w| + (w + \overline{w})]}{2[|w| + \mathfrak{R}(w)]} = \frac{w[2|w| + 2\mathfrak{R}(w)]}{2|w| + 2\mathfrak{R}(w)} = w.$$

If $|w| + \mathfrak{R}(w) = 0$, then $(\pm i\sqrt{|w|})^2 = -|w| = w$.

THEOREM 8–2.5. If w is any nonzero complex number, then there are exactly two complex numbers z such that $z^2 = w$. If $|w| + \mathfrak{R}(w) \neq 0$, then these numbers are given by

$$z = \frac{|w| + w}{\sqrt{2[|w| + \mathfrak{R}(w)]}} \quad \text{and} \quad z = -\frac{|w| + w}{\sqrt{2[|w| + \mathfrak{R}(w)]}}.$$

If $|w| + \mathfrak{R}(w) = 0$, the solutions of $z^2 = w$ are

$$z = i\sqrt{|w|} \quad \text{and} \quad z = -i\sqrt{|w|}.$$

For any complex number w, it is convenient to let the symbol $\sqrt{w}$ stand for

$$\frac{|w| + w}{\sqrt{2[|w| + \mathfrak{R}(w)]}}$$

if $|w| + \mathfrak{R}(w) \neq 0$, and for $i\sqrt{|w|}$ if $|w| + \mathfrak{R}(w) = 0$. Then we can say that the two square roots of w are $\sqrt{w}$ and $-\sqrt{w}$.

EXAMPLE 4. Let $w = 3 + i4$. Then $|w| = 5$, $\mathfrak{R}(w) = 3$, and $2[|w| + \mathfrak{R}(w)] = 16$. Hence

$$\sqrt{w} = \frac{|w| + w}{\sqrt{2[|w| + \mathfrak{R}(w)]}} = \frac{1}{4}[5 + (3 + i4)] = 2 + i.$$

In the case of square roots of complex numbers, just as for square roots of real numbers, we must be careful not to assume that $\sqrt{w^2}$ is always equal to w. It is in fact easy to see that

$$
\begin{aligned}
\sqrt{w^2} &= w \text{ if } \Re(w) > 0, \qquad \sqrt{w^2} = -w \text{ if } \Re(w) < 0, \\
\sqrt{w^2} &= w \text{ if } \Re(w) = 0, \qquad \text{and } \mathscr{I}(w) > 0, \qquad\qquad (8\text{--}10)\\
\sqrt{w^2} &= -w \text{ if } \Re(w) = 0, \qquad \text{and } \mathscr{I}(w) < 0.
\end{aligned}
$$

In any case, $\sqrt{w^2} = \pm w$. More generally, we obtain the following result.

(8–2.6). Let z and w be complex numbers. Then
    (a) $\sqrt{z \cdot w} = \pm(\sqrt{z} \cdot \sqrt{w})$;
    (b) if $w \neq 0$, then $\sqrt{z/w} = \pm(\sqrt{z}/\sqrt{w})$.

We leave the proof of these identities for the reader.

The theorem that every complex number has a square root in C can be used to show that any quadratic equation

$$
ax^2 + bx + c = 0, \qquad\qquad (8\text{--}11)
$$

where a, b, and c are complex numbers and $a \neq 0$, has a solution x in C. Suppose that x is a complex number which satisfies (8–11). Rewrite (8–11) in the form

$$
a\left(x^2 + \frac{b}{a}x + \frac{b^2}{4a^2}\right) - \frac{b^2}{4a} + c = 0.
$$

That is, the term $b^2/4a$ is added and subtracted on the left-hand side of (8–11), so that the expression in parentheses becomes a perfect square. This is the familiar method of *completing the square*. It leads to the equality

$$
\left(x + \frac{b}{2a}\right)^2 = \frac{b^2 - 4ac}{4a^2}.
$$

By (8–10),

$$
x + \frac{b}{2a} = \pm\frac{\sqrt{b^2 - 4ac}}{2a}.
$$

Therefore,

$$
x = \frac{-b + \sqrt{b^2 - 4ac}}{2a}, \qquad \text{or} \qquad x = \frac{-b - \sqrt{b^2 - 4ac}}{2a}. \qquad (8\text{--}12)
$$

Conversely, it can be checked by direct substitution that the two numbers given in (8–12) are solutions of (8–11). That is, the following result holds.

THEOREM 8–2.7. Let a, b, and c be complex numbers and $a \neq 0$. Then the solutions of the equation

$$ax^2 + bx + c = 0$$

are given by the formula

$$x = \frac{-b \pm \sqrt{b^2 - 4ac}}{2a}.$$

EXAMPLE 5. Find the solutions of the equation

$$(1 + i)x^2 + (1 + i2)x - 2 = 0.$$

Apply the formula of Theorem 8–2.7 with $a = 1 + i$, $b = 1 + i2$, and $c = -2$:

$$b^2 - 4ac = (1 + i2)^2 - 4(1 + i)(-2)$$
$$= (-3 + i4) + (8 + i8) = 5 + i(12),$$

$$|b^2 - 4ac| = \sqrt{5^2 + 12^2} = \sqrt{169} = 13,$$

$$\Re(b^2 - 4ac) = 5,$$

$$\sqrt{2(|b^2 - 4ac| + \Re(b^2 - 4ac))} = \sqrt{36} = 6,$$

$$\sqrt{b^2 - 4ac} = (1/6)(13 + (5 + i(12))) = 3 + i2,$$

$$x = \frac{-(1 + i2) + (3 + i2)}{2(1 + i)} = \frac{2}{2(1 + i)} = \frac{1}{2}(1 - i),$$

$$x = \frac{-(1 + i2) - (3 + i2)}{2(1 + i)} = \frac{-4(1 + i)}{2(1 + i)} = -2.$$

PROBLEMS

1. Simplify the following quotients.

   (a) $\dfrac{i}{2 + i}$ (b) $\dfrac{2 - i}{1 + i}$ (c) $\dfrac{7}{i}$ (d) $\dfrac{1 + i}{1 - i}$

2. Find the square roots:

   (a) $\sqrt{7 + i(24)}$ (b) $\sqrt{i}$ (c) $\sqrt{24 - i7}$ (d) $\sqrt{1 + i}$ (e) $\sqrt{\sqrt{i}}$

3. Find the solutions of the following equations.

   (a) $x^2 + 2ix + 1 = 0$ (b) $(3 + i)x^2 + 10x - (9 + i3) = 0$
   (c) $-5x^2 + \sqrt{2}\,x - 1 = 0$

4. Prove Theorem 8–2.2(a), (b), (e), and (f).

5. Show that if z and w are complex numbers, then the following are true.
   (a) $|z - w| \leq |z| + |w|$
   (b) $|z - w| \geq |z| - |w|$
   (c) $|z + w|^2 + |z - w|^2 = 2(|z|^2 + |w|^2)$

6. Show that for any complex number w, $\Re(\sqrt{w}) \geq 0$.

7. Prove (8–10).

8. Prove (8–2.6).

9. Show that if $\Re(w) > 0$ and $\Re(z) > 0$, then $\sqrt{z \cdot w} = \sqrt{z} \cdot \sqrt{w}$.

10. Show that the numbers given by (8–12) are solutions of (8–11).

11. Prove that if $w = u + iv$, and $v \neq 0$, then

$$ w = \frac{1}{\sqrt{2}} \left(\sqrt{\sqrt{u^2 + v^2} + u} + i \frac{v}{|v|} \sqrt{\sqrt{u^2 + v^2} - u} \right). $$

12. Let $w = a + ib$, where a and b are integers. Prove that $|w|$ is an integer if and only if $w = t \cdot z^2$ or $w = it \cdot z^2$, where $z = r + is$ with r, s, and t integers. [*Hint:* See Theorem 5–5.4.]

13. Solve for z in terms of w in the equation $z^4 = w$.

8–3 The geometrical representation of complex numbers. We mentioned in Section 8–1 that ordered pairs $\langle u, v \rangle$ of real numbers have several interpretations in mathematics. One of the most familiar applications of these pairs occurs in analytic geometry. In fact, analytic geometry is based on the "coordinatization" of the plane, that is, a one-to-one correspondence between the set of all points P of the plane, and the set of all pairs $\langle x, y \rangle$ of real numbers. This correspondence provides an important way of representing complex numbers by points in the plane.

For the reader who is not familiar with analytic geometry, we will discuss briefly the process of defining coordinate systems in a plane. The construction begins with the choice of any two perpendicular lines. It is convenient to take one of these to be horizontal. This line is called the *x-axis*, and is denoted by X. The other line must then be vertical. It is called the *y-axis*, and is denoted by Y. Let O be the point of intersection of X and Y. The point O is called the *origin* of the coordinate system in the plane. Let I be a point on X which lies to the right of O. Using OI as the basic unit interval, define a coordinate system on X by the construction described in Section 7–3. Let J be a point on Y, above O, such that the distance $\overline{OJ}$ is equal to the distance $\overline{OI}$. That is, the segments OI and OJ are congruent. Establish a coordinate system on Y using OJ as the basic unit interval.

Let P be any point in the plane. Construct the line l through P and parallel to X (hence perpendicular to Y). Also draw the line m passing

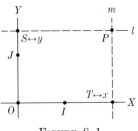

FIGURE 8–1

through P and parallel to Y (hence perpendicular to X). Then l meets Y at some point S, and m meets X at some point T. Let x be the real number corresponding to T in the coordinate system on X. Let y be the real number corresponding to S in the coordinate system on Y. We associate with P the number pair $\langle x, y \rangle$ (see Fig. 8–1):

$$P \leftrightarrow \langle x, y \rangle.$$

Different points evidently correspond in this way to different number pairs, and every pair of real numbers is associated with some point. In fact, the point corresponding to $\langle x, y \rangle$ can be found as the intersection of the vertical line through the point associated with x on X and the horizontal line through the point corresponding to y on Y. Thus, $P \leftrightarrow \langle x, y \rangle$ is a one-to-one correspondence between the set of all points of the plane and the set of all pairs of real numbers. A plane, together with a correspondence between points and number pairs defined in this way, is called a *coordinate plane.*

The numbers x and y in the pair $\langle x, y \rangle$ corresponding to the point P are called the *cartesian* coordinates* of P. Sometimes, to be more specific, x is called the *X-coordinate* or *abscissa* of P, and y is called the *Y-coordinate* or *ordinate* of P.

The points on the x-axis are exactly the points whose coordinates are of the form $\langle x, 0 \rangle$. The points on the y-axis have coordinates $\langle 0, y \rangle$. In particular, $0 \leftrightarrow \langle 0, 0 \rangle$, $I \leftrightarrow \langle 1, 0 \rangle$, and $J \leftrightarrow \langle 0, 1 \rangle$.

(8–3.1). Let S and T be points with cartesian coordinates $\langle x_S, y_S \rangle$ and $\langle x_T, y_T \rangle$, respectively. Then the distance $\overline{ST}$ between S and T is

$$\sqrt{(x_S - x_T)^2 + (y_S - y_T)^2}.$$

---

* The term "cartesian" is used in honor of the French mathematician and philosopher Rene Descartes (1596–1650), who was the founder of analytic geometry.

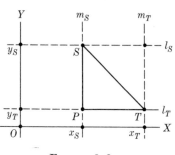

FIGURE 8–2

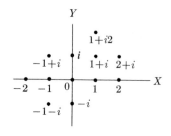

FIGURE 8–3

Proof. The proof of this statement is based on the Pythagorean triangle theorem. Let l_S and l_T be horizontal lines through S and T, respectively, and let m_S and m_T be vertical lines through these same points. Let P be the point of intersection of the perpendicular lines m_S and l_T. Then PST is a right triangle with ST as its hypotenuse. Figure 8–2 illustrates a typical situation. If ST is horizontal or vertical, the triangle PST is degenerate, and this case requires special treatment. The lines m_S and m_T intersect the x-axis at points corresponding to the real numbers x_S and x_T, and these two points, together with T and P, determine a rectangle. Thus, the distance between P and T is the same as the distance between the points on the x-axis corresponding to x_S and x_T:

$$\overline{TP} = |x_S - x_T|.$$

Similarly,

$$\overline{PS} = |y_S - y_T|.$$

Hence,

$$\overline{ST}^2 = \overline{TP}^2 + \overline{PS}^2 = |x_S - x_T|^2 + |y_S - y_T|^2$$
$$= (x_S - x_T)^2 + (y_S - y_T)^2.$$

Taking the square root completes the proof.

We now turn to the representation of complex numbers as points in a coordinate plane. This representation is obtained simply by using the definition of complex numbers as pairs of real numbers, and associating each complex number $x + iy = \langle x, y \rangle$ with the point in the coordinate plane whose coordinates are x and y. It is then possible to use the complex numbers as labels for the corresponding points in the plane (see Fig. 8–3), just as the real numbers are used to represent the points on a line. The term *complex plane* is often used to describe a coordinate plane whose points are labeled by complex numbers.

If complex numbers are interpreted in this way, then the operations with them have interesting geometrical meanings. For example, if $z = x + iy$, then $\Re(z) = x$ is the abscissa of z and $\Im(z) = y$ is the ordinate of z. Thus, in particular, the real numbers represent points on the x-axis. The absolute value $|z| = \sqrt{x^2 + y^2}$ is the distance from the origin O to z. More generally, if z and w are complex numbers, then $|z - w|$ is the distance between the point z and the point w. To see this, let $z = x + iy$ and $w = u + iv$. Then $|z - w| = |(x - u) + i(y - v)| = \sqrt{(x - u)^2 + (y - v)^2}$, which, by (8–3.1), is the distance between the point with coordinates $\langle x, y \rangle$ and the point with coordinates $\langle u, v \rangle$.

Often it is possible to give concise descriptions of sets of points in the plane, using complex numbers.

EXAMPLE 1. $\{z | \Im(z) > 0\}$ is the set of all points in the upper half plane; in other words, the set of all points which lie above the x-axis.

EXAMPLE 2. $\{z | \, |z| < 1\}$ is the set of all points which have distance less than one from the origin O, that is, the set of points which lie inside a circle of radius one with center at O.

EXAMPLE 3. $\{z | \, |z - i| = 1\}$ is the set of all points on the circle with center at i, and radius equal to one.

EXAMPLE 4. $\{z | \Im(z) = m\Re(z)\}$, where m is a real number, is the set of all points on a line l through the origin, with slope equal to m (see Fig. 8–4).

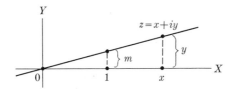

FIGURE 8–4

The addition of complex numbers has an interesting geometrical meaning. Let z and w be complex numbers representing points in the complex plane. Let O be the origin in the plane. If z, w, and O lie on a line l which is not the y-axis, then by Example 4, $\Im(z) = m\Re(z)$ and $\Im(w) = m\Re(w)$ for some real number m. Consequently, $\Im(z + w) = \Im(z) + \Im(w) = m[\Re(z) + \Re(w)] = m\Re(z + w)$. Therefore, $z + w$ corresponds to a point on l. [If z and w lie on the y-axis, then $\Re(z) = \Re(w) = 0$ implies $\Re(z + w) = 0$, and $z + w$ is on the y-axis.] If the origin O does not separate z from w on l, then $z + w$ is at a distance $|z| + |w|$ from O on the same side as z and w. If O is between z and w, then $z + w$ is at a distance $||z| - |w||$ from O, on the same side as z if $|z| > |w|$, and on the same side as w if $|w| > |z|$ (see Fig. 8–5). If z, w, and O do not lie on the same line, then the point corresponding to $z + w$ can be determined by the *parallelogram rule*.

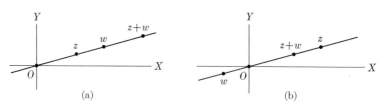

FIGURE 8–5

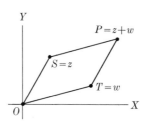

FIGURE 8–6

(8–3.2). *Parallelogram rule.* Let z and w be complex numbers representing points S and T, such that O, S, and T do not lie on a line. If P is the point corresponding to $z + w$, then $OSPT$ is a parallelogram (see Fig. 8–6).

It should be remarked in connection with (8–3.2) that $OSPT$ is the order in which the vertices are encountered in moving around the sides of the parallelogram. That is, ST and OP are diagonals, not sides of the figure.

The proof of (8–3.2) is an exercise in elementary geometry, which we will leave for the interested reader.

PROBLEMS

1. Draw coordinate axes in a plane, and plot the points with the following coordinates: $\langle 2, 1 \rangle$, $\langle -1, 2 \rangle$, $\langle -1, -1 \rangle$, $\langle -\frac{3}{2}, \frac{1}{2} \rangle$.

2. Find the distance between the following pairs of points in the complex plane. (a) 4, $i9$ (b) i, $2 - i$ (c) $-1 + i$, $1 - i$ (d) $9 + i(15)$, $4 - i9$

3. Describe the following sets in geometrical terms.
   (a) $\{z | -1 \le \mathcal{I}(z) \le 1\}$
   (b) $\{z | \mathcal{I}(iz) = 1\}$
   (c) $\{z | |z - 1| > 1\}$
   (d) $\{z | |z^2| = 4\}$
   (e) $\{z | |z^2 - 2z + 1| > 0\}$
   (f) $\{z | \mathcal{R}(z) = \pm 1, \mathcal{I}(z) = \pm 1\}$
   (g) $\{z | \mathcal{I}(z) = 2\mathcal{R}(z), \mathcal{I}(z) \ge 0\}$

4. Show that $\{z\mid |z - w| = \sqrt{2}\,|z|\}$ is the circle with center at $-w$, with radius $\sqrt{2}\,|w|$. [*Hint:* Use the identity obtained in Problem 5(c), Section 8–2: $|z + w|^2 + |z - w|^2 = 2(|z|^2 + |w|^2)$.]

5. What is the geometrical interpretation of the law $|z + w| \le |z| + |w|$? Use this interpretation to decide when the equality $|z + w| = |z| + |w|$ holds.

6. What is the geometrical meaning of the identity given in Problem 5(c), Section 8–2?

7. Describe the method of finding the point corresponding to $z + w$, if you are given the points corresponding to z and w.

8. What is the geometrical interpretation of $\bar{z}$, $-z$, and $z - w$ (in terms of the points represented by z and w)?

9. Show that if $z \ne 0$, where z is a complex number, and if t is any real number, then the points O, z, and tz are all in a line. Show that O, z, and w lie on a line if and only if either $z = 0$, or w is a real multiple of z.

10. Prove (8–3.2).

8–4 Polar representation. To interpret multiplication, we introduce a new way of representing complex numbers. This representation is based on the polar coordinate system* used in analytic geometry, and for this reason it is called the *polar representation* of complex numbers.

Let O be the origin of a cartesian coordinate system in the plane. As in the last section, the points of the plane will be labeled by complex numbers. Let $z = x + iy$ be a nonzero complex number. The line segment from O to the point z has length $|z| = \sqrt{x^2 + y^2}$. Let θ denote the angle† which this line segment makes with the right half of the x-axis (see Fig. 8–7). As is customary, we will measure angles counterclockwise between 0 and 360 degrees. The components x and y of z can be expressed in terms of $|z|$ and θ by the equations

$$x = |z| \cos \theta, \qquad y = |z| \sin \theta.$$

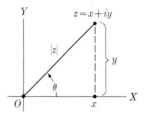

FIGURE 8–7

---

* The definition of polar coordinates makes use of the geometrical concept of "angle" and the trigonometric functions "sine" and "cosine." In order to obtain results such as Theorem 8–4.3, below, without resorting to the use of "geometrically evident" facts, we would have to define angles, sines, and cosines more carefully, and work hard to show that these notions have the properties which are obvious to our geometrical intuition. However, no attempt will be made to carry out such a program here.

† The symbol θ is the small Greek letter theta. Angles in mathematics are often represented by lower case Greek letters, such as θ, ϕ (phi), and χ (chi).

Hence, we can write

$$z = |z| \, (\cos \theta + i \sin \theta). \qquad (8\text{–}13)$$

This expression is called the polar representation of z.

The angle θ is called the *argument*, or *amplitude*, of the complex number z. This angle will be denoted by

$$\text{Arg } z.$$

It should be remembered that the argument of the complex number 0 is not defined. Since we are measuring angles in degrees* between 0 and 360, the argument of every nonzero complex number satisfies

$$0 \leq \text{Arg } z < 360.$$

It is evident that if z is a positive real number, then $\text{Arg } z = 0$, and if z is a negative real number, then $\text{Arg } z = 180$. Although the argument of a complex number z is always between 0 and 360, it should be noted that if $z = |z| \, (\cos \theta + i \sin \theta)$, where $\theta = \text{Arg } z$, then we also have

$$z = |z| \, [\cos (\theta + n \cdot 360) + i \sin (\theta + n \cdot 360)]$$

for $n = 0, \pm 1, \pm 2, \ldots$. Thus, for example,

$$z = 3 \, (\cos 410 + i \sin 410)$$

is a complex number with $\text{Arg } z \neq 410$. In fact, $\text{Arg } z = 410 - 360 = 50$.

Let z and w be two nonzero complex numbers, with $\text{Arg } z = \theta$, and $\text{Arg } w = \phi$. Then

$$z = |z| \, (\cos \theta + i \sin \theta), \qquad w = |w| \, (\cos \phi + i \sin \phi).$$

Hence,

$$z \cdot w = |z| \cdot |w| \, [(\cos \theta \cos \phi - \sin \theta \sin \phi) + i \, (\sin \theta \cos \phi + \cos \theta \sin \phi)].$$

This expression can be simplified by using the sum formulas of trigonometry:

$$\cos (\theta + \phi) = \cos \theta \cos \phi - \sin \theta \sin \phi,$$
$$\sin (\theta + \phi) = \sin \theta \cos \phi + \cos \theta \sin \phi.$$

We obtain

$$z \cdot w = |z| \cdot |w| \, [\cos (\theta + \phi) + i \sin (\theta + \phi)]. \qquad (8\text{–}14)$$

---

* In most higher mathematics, angles are measured in *radians* rather than degrees. However, for the applications in this book, radians have no advantage over degrees. In computational work, it is more convenient to use degrees rather than radians, since most trigonometric tables list angles in degrees.

Comparing this formula with the equation which expresses the trigonometric representation of $z \cdot w$, we obtain the rule for determining the argument of the product of two numbers.

THEOREM 8–4.1. Let z and w be nonzero complex numbers. Then

$$\text{Arg } z \cdot w = \text{Arg } z + \text{Arg } w,$$

if $\text{Arg } z + \text{Arg } w < 360$, and

$$\text{Arg } z \cdot w = \text{Arg } z + \text{Arg } w - 360,$$

if $\text{Arg } z + \text{Arg } w \geq 360$.

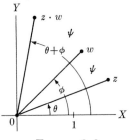

FIGURE 8–8

This theorem provides the desired geometrical interpretation of multiplication in C. The point $z \cdot w$ is the point on the half line which makes an angle of $(\text{Arg } z + \text{Arg } w)$ with the positive real axis, and which is at a distance $|z| \cdot |w|$ from O (see Fig. 8–8).

A particularly important case of (8–14) occurs when $w = z$. This formula then becomes $z^2 = |z|^2 (\cos 2\theta + i \sin 2\theta)$. We can easily generalize this result by induction:

$$z^n = |z|^n (\cos n\theta + i \sin n\theta), \qquad \text{where } \theta = \text{Arg } z. \qquad (8\text{–}15)$$

In particular, if $|z| = 1$, this identity gives *Demoivre's theorem*.

THEOREM 8–4.2. $(\cos \theta + i \sin \theta)^n = \cos n\theta + i \sin n\theta$.

The theorem of Demoivre has numerous applications. One which students often appreciate is its use as a device for deriving trigonometric formulas for multiple angles.

EXAMPLE 1. We use Theorem 8–4.2 to determine $\cos 4\theta$ and $\sin 4\theta$. Taking $n = 4$ in this formula, and using the binomial theorem, we obtain:

$$\begin{aligned}
\cos 4\theta + i \sin 4\theta &= (\cos \theta + i \sin \theta)^4 \\
&= \cos^4 \theta + 4 \cos^3 \theta\, (i \sin \theta) + 6 \cos^2 \theta\, (i \sin \theta)^2 \\
&\quad + 4 \cos \theta\, (i \sin \theta)^3 + (i \sin \theta)^4 \\
&= (\cos^4 \theta - 6 \cos^2 \theta \sin^2 \theta + \sin^4 \theta) \\
&\quad + i\, (4 \cos^3 \theta \sin \theta - 4 \cos \theta \sin^3 \theta).
\end{aligned}$$

Thus,

$$\cos 4\theta = \cos^4 \theta - 6 \cos^2 \theta \sin^2 \theta + \sin^4 \theta,$$
$$\sin 4\theta = 4 \cos^3 \theta \sin \theta - 4 \cos \theta \sin^3 \theta.$$

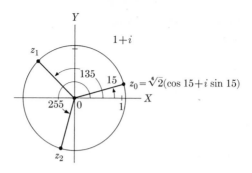

FIGURE 8–9

A more significant application of this theorem occurs in the proof of the following result.

THEOREM 8–4.3. Let w be any nonzero complex number. Let n be a natural number. Then there are exactly n distinct complex numbers z satisfying $z^n = w$. If $w = |w| (\cos \theta + i \sin \theta)$, with $\theta = $ Arg w, then these numbers are given by $z = z_0, z = z_1, \ldots, z = z_{n-1}$, where

$$z_j = \sqrt[n]{|w|} \left[\cos \left(\frac{\theta + j\,360}{n} \right) + i \sin \left(\frac{\theta + j\,360}{n} \right) \right]. \qquad (8\text{–}16)$$

This theorem is illustrated in Fig. 8–9, with $w = 1 + i$ and $n = 3$. The polar representation of $1 + i$ is

$$1 + i = \sqrt{2}\,(\cos 45 + i \sin 45).$$

In order to prove Theorem 8–4.3, first note that by Theorem 8–4.2,

$$\left\{ \sqrt[n]{|w|} \left[\cos \left(\frac{\theta + j\,360}{n} \right) + i \sin \left(\frac{\theta + j\,360}{n} \right) \right] \right\}^n$$

$$= |w| \left[\cos \left(\theta + j\,360 \right) + i \sin \left(\theta + j\,360 \right) \right]$$

$$= |w| \left(\cos \theta + i \sin \theta \right) = w.$$

Thus, for any nonnegative integer j, the formula (8–16) gives a solution of the equation $z^n = w$. What we must show is that for $j = 0, 1, \ldots, n - 1$, the numbers given by (8–16) are all different, and that for any z such that $z^n = w$, there is some $j = 0, 1, \ldots, n - 1$, such that $z = z_j$. First observe that if $0 \le j < n$, then

$$0 \le \frac{\theta + j\,360}{n} < 360.$$

Therefore,

$$\text{Arg } z_j = \frac{\theta + j\,360}{n}.$$

(Note however that

$$\text{Arg } z_j \neq \frac{\theta + j\,360}{n}$$

if $j \geq n$. For example, $\text{Arg } z_n = \theta/n$.) Suppose that

$$0 \leq j_1 < j_2 < n.$$

Then by what has just been observed,

$$\text{Arg } z_{j_1} = \frac{\theta + j_1\,360}{n} \neq \frac{\theta + j_2\,360}{n} = \text{Arg } z_{j_2}.$$

Therefore, $z_{j_1} \neq z_{j_2}$. This proves that the numbers $z_0, z_1, \ldots, z_{n-1}$ are all different. Assume next that z is a complex number which satisfies $z^n = w$. We want to prove that z is one of the numbers $z_0, z_1, \ldots, z_{n-1}$, that is, $|z| = \sqrt[n]{|w|}$ and

$$\text{Arg } z = \frac{\theta + j\,360}{n}$$

for some $j = 0, 1, \ldots, n - 1$. It follows from Theorem 8–2.4(e) (using mathematical induction) that $z^n = w$ implies $|z|^n = |w|$. Therefore, $|z| = \sqrt[n]{|w|}$. Let $z = |z|\,(\cos \phi + i \sin \phi)$ be the polar representation of z, with $\phi = \text{Arg } z$. Then by Theorem 8–4.2,

$$|z|^n\,(\cos n\phi + i \sin n\phi) = z^n = w = |w|\,(\cos \theta + i \sin \theta).$$

Therefore, since $|z|^n = |w|$, this equality implies $\cos n\phi = \cos \theta$, and $\sin n\phi = \sin \theta$. Using the fact that two angles which have the same sine and cosine differ by an integral multiple of 360, we obtain $n\phi - \theta = j\,360$, where $j \in Z$. Therefore,

$$\phi = \frac{\theta + j\,360}{n}.$$

Since $0 \leq \phi = \text{Arg } z < 360$, $0 \leq \theta = \text{Arg } w < 360$, and $j = (n\phi - \theta)/360$, it follows that

$$j \geq \frac{0 - \theta}{360} > \frac{-360}{360} = -1, \quad \text{and} \quad j < \frac{n\,360 - \theta}{360} \leq \frac{n\,360}{360} = n.$$

However, j is an integer, so that these strict inequalities imply

$$0 \leq j \leq n - 1.$$

PROBLEMS

1. Find the arguments of the following complex numbers. (a) 5 (b) $-i$ (c) $-1 + i$ (d) $1 + i3$ (e) $3 - i4$

2. Use Demoivre's theorem to obtain expressions for $\cos 5\theta$ and $\sin 5\theta$ in terms of $\cos \theta$ and $\sin \theta$.

3. Give the inductive proof of (8–15) in detail.

4. Show that Demoivre's theorem is valid for negative exponents; that is

$$(\cos \theta + i \sin \theta)^{-n} = \cos (-n\theta) + i \sin (-n\theta)$$

for all $n \in N$.

5. Use Theorems 8–4.3 and 8–2.5 to obtain expressions for $\cos (\theta/2)$ and $\sin (\theta/2)$ in terms of $\cos \theta$ and $\sin \theta$.

6. Using a table of sines and cosines, find all the solutions z of the following equations (giving the real and imaginary parts with four decimal accuracy).

    (a) $z^3 = 1 + i$
    (b) $z^5 = 1$
    (c) $z^4 = i$
    (d) $z^6 = -1$
    (e) $z^3 = -2 - i2$

7. Let n be a natural number. Define

$$\zeta = \cos \frac{360}{n} + i \sin \frac{360}{n}.$$

    (a) Show that $z = 1, z = \zeta, z = \zeta^2, \ldots, z = \zeta^{n-1}$ are all of the different solutions of the equation $z^n = 1$.
    (b) Prove that if $z = u$ is one solution of $z^n = w$, then all the other solutions are of the form $u \cdot \zeta^j$, where $j = 1, 2, \ldots, n - 1$.

8. Let ζ be defined as in Problem 7. Show that for $k \in N$

$$1 + \zeta^k + \zeta^{2k} + \cdots + \zeta^{(n-1)k} = 0 \quad \text{if } n \text{ does not divide } k,$$
$$1 + \zeta^k + \zeta^{2k} + \cdots + \zeta^{(n-1)k} = n \quad \text{if } n \text{ divides } k.$$

CHAPTER 9

THE THEORY OF ALGEBRAIC EQUATIONS

9–1 Algebraic equations. The problem of solving algebraic equations has interested the mathematicians and engineers of all ages, as far in the past as the civilizations of Babylon and Egypt. There is evidence that the Egyptians solved certain complicated quadratic equations as early as 2000 B.C. The first steps toward the development of a *theory* of equations were taken by Diophantus of Alexandria in about the third century A.D. Important advances in the subject were made by Hindu and Arabian scholars from about 800 to 1100 A.D. The modern era of algebra (and indeed of all mathematics) came with the Renaissance in the sixteenth century. The Italian mathematicians Scipio Ferro (1465–1526), Niccolo Fontana, nicknamed Tartaglia (1500–1557), Girolamo Cardan (1501–1576), Bombelli, and the French mathematicians Vieta and Descartes, among others, lifted the theory of algebraic equations to about the level which is presently taught to high-school algebra students in the United States. The development of algebra after Descartes followed more sophisticated and abstract lines. Our purpose in this chapter is to examine critically the familiar results of algebra, and to lead the reader a short way into the realm of the modern theory of equations.

Elementary algebra courses are concerned largely with linear equations, such as

$$x + 1 = 2, \qquad \tfrac{1}{2}x + 5 = 3, \qquad 3x - \tfrac{1}{3} = 0,$$

and quadratic equations, such as

$$x^2 + 2x + 1 = 0, \qquad 3x^2 - x = 2, \qquad 2x^2 - 2x + 1 = 0.$$

The solution of equations of higher degree is also considered, but usually only in the cases where the polynomials involved can be factored; for example,

$$0 = x^3 - 3x^2 + 3x - 2 = (x - 2)(x^2 - x + 1).$$

These examples are all special cases of the general nth degree equation

$$a_0 + a_1 x + a_2 x^2 + \cdots + a_n x^n = 0.$$

In this expression x is the "unknown" and the a_i are real or complex

309

numbers. The problem is to find values of x which, if they are substituted into the "polynomial"

$$a_0 + a_1 x + a_2 x^2 + \cdots + a_n x^n,$$

make this quantity zero. For first- and second-degree equations, convenient formulas exist which give the solutions explicitly. The solution of the linear equation

$$a_0 + a_1 x = 0, \qquad (a_1 \neq 0)$$

is given by the formula

$$x = -\frac{a_0}{a_1}.$$

The quadratic equation

$$a_0 + a_1 x + a_2 x^2 = 0, \qquad (a_2 \neq 0)$$

has two solutions (which may be the same):

$$x = (1/2a_2)(-a_1 + \sqrt{a_1^2 - 4a_0 a_2}),$$

and

$$x = (1/2a_2)(-a_1 - \sqrt{a_1^2 - 4a_0 a_2}).$$

There is no reason to suppose that for equations of degree higher than two it will always be possible to find solutions among the complex numbers. We saw that in order to solve equations such as $x^2 - 2 = 0$ and $x^2 - 5 = 0$ it was necessary to extend the rational number system to the real number field; to solve $x^2 + 1 = 0$ it was necessary to go beyond the reals to the complex numbers. Is there any reason then to suppose that it is possible to solve such equations as

$$x^3 + 3x + 1 = 0, \qquad \text{and} \qquad x^5 + (1 + i)x^3 + 2x^2 - ix - 1 = 0$$

within the complex number field? Moreover, even if the general nth degree equation has solutions in the complex field C, can we expect to obtain explicit expressions for these solutions such as we have for the solutions of linear and quadratic equations? These two questions will be discussed more completely in Sections 9–8 and 9–9.

In the theory of numbers, the study of algebraic congruences is almost as important as the study of algebraic equations. The problem of solving linear congruences,

$$ax + b \equiv 0 \pmod{m},$$

was discussed in Section 5–7. Congruences of higher degree, such as

$$x^4 + 3x^2 + 5x + 1 \equiv 0 \pmod{8} \qquad \text{and} \qquad 4x^{213} + x + 37 \equiv 0 \pmod{89},$$

are more difficult to solve. Of course, integral solutions x of any congruence can be found by trial and error if they exist. However, this method is practical only for congruences of small modulus.

———————

EXAMPLE 1. Let us solve

$$x^4 + 3x^2 + 5x + 1 \equiv 0 \; (\text{mod } 8).$$

We wish to determine the set

$$\{x \in Z \,|\, x^4 + 3x^2 + 5x + 1 \equiv 0 \; (\text{mod } 8)\}.$$

First observe that $x \equiv y \; (\text{mod } 8)$ implies that $x^4 + 3x^2 + 5x + 1 \equiv y^4 + 3y^2 + 5y + 1 \; (\text{mod } 8)$. Therefore, if x is a solution of $x^4 + 3x^2 + 5x + 1 \equiv 0 \; (\text{mod } 8)$, then so is y, and vice versa. This means that to solve the congruence $x^4 + 3x^2 + 5x + 1 \equiv 0 \; (\text{mod } 8)$, it is only necessary to find the numbers in the set

$$\{0, 1, 2, \ldots, 7\}$$

which are solutions. Every solution is congruent to a solution which is in this set, and conversely, every number which is congruent to a solution x satisfying $0 \leq x < 8$ is itself a solution. Before starting the work of substituting each of these numbers into the given congruence, let us note that the theorems of Chapter 5 can be used to simplify our work. If x is even, then

$$x^4 + 3x^2 + 5x + 1 \equiv 1 \; (\text{mod } 2).$$

Therefore, by Theorem 5–6.4(b), no even value of x can be a solution of $x^4 + 3x^2 + 5x + 1 \equiv 0 \; (\text{mod } 8)$. By Euler's Theorem, 5–8.6,

$$x^4 = x^{\varphi(8)} \equiv 1 \; (\text{mod } 8),$$

provided that x is relatively prime to 8. Thus, for odd values of x,

$$x^4 + 3x^2 + 5x + 1 \equiv 3x^2 + 5x + 2 \; (\text{mod } 8).$$

Now let us check the values $x = 1, 3, 5,$ and 7:

$$x^4 + 3x^2 + 5x + 1 \equiv 3 \cdot 1^2 + 5 \cdot 1 + 2 \equiv 2 \; (\text{mod } 8) \qquad \text{for } x = 1,$$

$$x^4 + 3x^2 + 5x + 1 \equiv 3 \cdot 3^2 + 5 \cdot 3 + 2 \equiv 4 \; (\text{mod } 8) \qquad \text{for } x = 3,$$

$$x^4 + 3x^2 + 5x + 1 \equiv 3 \cdot 5^2 + 5 \cdot 5 + 2 \equiv 6 \; (\text{mod } 8) \qquad \text{for } x = 5,$$

$$x^4 + 3x^2 + 5x + 1 \equiv 3 \cdot 7^2 + 5 \cdot 7 + 2 \equiv 0 \; (\text{mod } 8) \qquad \text{for } x = 7.$$

Therefore, the required set of solutions is

$$\{\ldots, -9, -1, 7, 15, 23, \ldots\}.$$

The problem of solving congruences with a prime modulus p is equivalent to finding the solution of equations

$$a_0 + a_1 x + \cdots + a_n x^n = 0,$$

where $a_0, a_1, \ldots,$ and a_n are elements of the field Z_p which was discussed in Example 1, Section 6–3. This fact is important because it enables us to apply the theory of algebraic equations to obtain theorems about congruences. Such an application will be given in Section 9–7.

Problems

1. Find the real values of x which are solutions of the following equations.

(a) $x^2 - 4x - 2 = 0$
(b) $3x^3 - 1 = 0$
(c) $x^2 + x + 1 = 0$
(d) $x^4 - 2x^2 + 1 = 0$
(e) $x^{75} - 1 = 0$

2. Find the real and complex values of x which are solutions of the following equations.

(a) $x^4 + 1 = 0$
(b) $x^3 + x^2 + x + 1 = 0$
(c) $x^{10} + 5x^5 + 4 = 0$
(d) $x^{2n} + 2x^n - 1 = 0$
(e) $x^6 - 3x^4 + 3x^2 - 1 = 0$

3. Let a, b, and c be real numbers, with $c \neq 0$. Show that the equation

$$ax^2 + bx + c = 0$$

(a) has two (different) real solutions if $b^2 > 4ac$,
(b) has one real solution if $b^2 = 4ac$, and
(c) has two complex conjugate solutions if $b^2 < 4ac$.

4. Find all integers x which are solutions of the following congruences.

(a) $x^2 - 2x + 1 \equiv 0 \pmod{2}$
(b) $x^{46} + 7x^{32} + 8x^{17} + 5x^{16} + 2x^9 + 4x^3 + 3x + 1 \equiv 0 \pmod{3}$
(c) $x^6 - 1 \equiv 0 \pmod{7}$
(d) $x^{10} + 63x^4 + x \equiv 0 \pmod{9}$
(e) $2x^{25} + 57x + 1 \equiv 0 \pmod{30}$

9–2 Polynomials. The theory of equations is based on the algebra of polynomials. From elementary algebra, the reader is familiar with the procedures for adding, subtracting, multiplying, and factoring polynomials. All of the operational rules which were given in Section 4–2 as the postulates for a ring are used in manipulating polynomials. In order to justify the use of these rules, it is necessary to examine the concept of a polynomial more critically than is customary in elementary algebra courses. This is particularly imperative for our purposes, because we want to develop the theory so that it can be applied to equations in the fields Z_p, as well as the fields of complex and real numbers.

Our plan in this section is to first review the intuitive definitions concerning polynomials and their operations. Then we will examine these notions more critically, and see how they can be put on a sound basis. The reader who is not interested in the formal development of polynomials may omit the last part of this section.

Let D be an integral domain. A *polynomial in x with coefficients in D,* is (tentatively) defined to be a formal expression

$$a_0x^0 + a_1x^1 + a_2x^2 + \cdots + a_nx^n, \tag{9-1}$$

where $a_0, a_1, a_2, \ldots$, and a_n are elements in D. For the present the symbols $x^0, x^1, \ldots, x^n$ and the plus signs in (9–1) are to be thought of as nothing more than punctuation marks which separate $a_0, a_1, \ldots$, and a_n. The notation $a_0x^0 + a_1x^1 + \cdots + a_nx^n$ is adopted because this expression will ultimately be interpreted as a sum of products.

For $0 \le i \le n$, the expressions a_ix^i are called *terms* of the polynomial. The elements $a_0, a_1, a_2, \ldots, a_n$ of D are called the *coefficients* of $x^0, x^1, x^2, \ldots$, and x^n, respectively, in this polynomial.

DEFINITION 9–2.1. Two polynomials in x with coefficients in D are *equal* if they have exactly the same terms, except for terms with zero coefficients. That is,

$$a_0x^0 + a_1x^1 + a_2x^2 + \cdots + a_nx^n$$
$$= b_0x^0 + b_1x^1 + b_2x^2 + \cdots + b_mx^m$$

if $a_0 = b_0$, $a_1 = b_1$, $a_2 = b_2$, $\ldots$, and $a_j = 0$ for $m < j \le n$ if $m < n$, or $b_j = 0$ for $n < j \le m$ if $n < m$.

For example,

$$2x^0 + \tfrac{1}{2}x^1 + 3x^2 + 0x^3 + 0x^4 = 2x^0 + \tfrac{1}{2}x^1 + 3x^2.$$

In writing a polynomial, it is customary (a) to omit terms with coefficient 0, (b) to write a_0 instead of a_0x^0, (c) to write x instead of x^1, (d) to write x^j instead of $1x^j$ for $j > 0$, and (e) to write $-a_jx^j$ instead of $+ (-a_j)x^j$.

For instance, instead of

$$1x^0 + 2x^1 + 0x^2 + 1x^3 + (-5)x^4 + 0x^5$$

we would write
$$1 + 2x + x^3 - 5x^4.$$

We will later see that these conventions are entirely justified. It is also a common practice to use expressions such as $a(x)$, $b(x)$, $c(x)$, $f(x)$, $g(x)$, and $p(x)$ to represent polynomials.

It follows from Definition 9–2.1 that any two polynomials can be written with the same number of terms. For example, suppose that $a_0x^0 + a_2x^2 + \cdots + a_mx^m$ and $b_0x^0 + b_1x^1 + \cdots + b_nx^n$ are polynomials with $m < n$. Then we can write

$$a_0x^0 + a_1x^1 + \cdots + a_mx^m$$
$$= a_0x^0 + a_1x^1 + \cdots + a_mx^m + 0x^{m+1} + \cdots + 0x^n.$$

This observation shows that the following definition of addition of two polynomials is completely general.

DEFINITION 9–2.2. *Addition of polynomials.* Let

$$a(x) = a_0x^0 + a_1x^1 + a_2x^2 + \cdots + a_nx^n,$$
and
$$b(x) = b_0x^0 + b_1x^1 + b_2x^2 + \cdots + b_nx^n$$

be polynomials in x with coefficients in D. The *sum* of $a(x)$ and $b(x)$ is the polynomial

$$a(x) + b(x) = (a_0 + b_0)x^0 + (a_1 + b_1)x^1 + (a_2 + b_2)x^2 + \cdots$$
$$+ (a_n + b_n)x^n.$$

As an example, let $a(x) = 2 + x - x^2$ and $b(x) = 3 + x^2 + 2x^3$. Then $a(x) + b(x) = 5 + x + 2x^3$. Indeed, we can consider $2 + x - x^2$ as an abbreviation for $2x^0 + 1x^1 + (-1)x^2 + 0x^3$, and $3 + x^2 + 2x^3$ as an abbreviation of $3x^0 + 0x^1 + 1x^2 + 2x^3$; therefore, by Definition 9–2.2,

$$a(x) + b(x) = (2 + 3)x^0 + (1 + 0)x^1 + [(-1) + 1]x^2 + (0 + 2)x^3$$
$$= 5x^0 + 1x^1 + 0x^2 + 2x^3 = 5 + x + 2x^3.$$

In elementary algebra courses, the process of multiplying two polynomials is usually carried out in several steps. First, all combinations of two terms, one from each polynomial, are multiplied. Then the rule of exponents is applied to the powers of x, and finally the coefficients of equal powers of x are collected. The whole procedure can be carried out, using the familiar arrangement for multiplication:

$$
\begin{array}{l}
1 + 2x - x^2 + x^3 \\
1 - 2x + x^2 \\
\hline
1 + 2x - x^2 + x^3 \\
 - 2x - 4x^2 + 2x^3 - 2x^4 \\
 x^2 + 2x^3 - x^4 + x^5 \\
\hline
1 - 4x^2 + 5x^3 - 3x^4 + x^5
\end{array}
$$

It is not convenient to use this description of the process of multiplying polynomials as the definition of multiplication, but the end product of the method can be described in general terms and provides a satisfactory definition.

DEFINITION 9–2.3. *Multiplication of polynomials.* Let

$$a(x) = a_0 x^0 + a_1 x^1 + a_2 x^2 + \cdots + a_m x^m,$$

and

$$b(x) = b_0 x^0 + b_1 x^1 + b_2 x^2 + \cdots + b_n x^n$$

be polynomials in x with coefficients in D. The *product* of $a(x)$ and $b(x)$ is the polynomial

$$
\begin{aligned}
a(x) \cdot b(x) = {} & (a_0 b_0) x^0 + (a_0 b_1 + a_1 b_0) x^1 \\
& + (a_0 b_2 + a_1 b_1 + a_2 b_0) x^2 + \cdots \\
& + (a_m b_n) x^{m+n}.
\end{aligned}
$$

The coefficient of x^i in the product $a(x) \cdot b(x)$ is the element

$$a_0 b_i + a_1 b_{i-1} + \cdots + a_{i-1} b_1 + a_i b_0 = \sum_{j=0}^{i} a_j b_{i-j},$$

where $a_j = 0$ if $j > m$, and $b_k = 0$ if $k > n$.

DEFINITION 9–2.4. *Negation of polynomials.* Let

$$a(x) = a_0 x^0 + a_1 x^1 + a_2 x^2 + \cdots + a_n x^n$$

be a polynomial in x with coefficients in D. The *negative* of $a(x)$ is the polynomial

$$-a(x) = (-a_0) x^0 + (-a_1) x^1 + (-a_2) x^2 + \cdots + (-a_n) x^n.$$

In this definition, the coefficients $-a_0, -a_1, -a_2, \ldots, -a_n$ are the negatives of the elements $a_0, a_1, a_2, \ldots, a_n$ in the integral domain D.

THEOREM 9–2.5. Let $D[x]$ be the set of all polynomials in x with coefficients in an integral domain D. Define equality, addition, multiplication, and negation in $D[x]$ by Definitions 9–2.1, 9–2.2, 9–2.3, and 9–2.4, respectively. Then $D[x]$ is an integral domain.

Proof. In order to prove that $D[x]$ is a commutative ring with $0x^0$ as its zero and $1x^0$ as its identity, it is necessary to verify such identities as the associative, commutative, and distributive laws. This is a rather tedious job which we will leave to the reader. It should be remarked that the proofs of these laws use the fact that addition, multiplication, and negation in D satisfy the postulates for a commutative ring. For example, if $a(x) = a_0 x^0 + a_1 x^1 + \cdots + a_m x^m$ and $b(x) = b_0 x^0 + b_1 x^1 + \cdots + b_n x^n$ are in $D[x]$, then by Definition 9–2.3, the coefficient of x^i in the product $a(x) \cdot b(x)$ is

$$a_0 b_i + a_1 b_{i-1} + \cdots + a_{i-1} b_1 + a_i b_0.$$

Again using Definition 9–2.3, the coefficient of x^i in the product $b(x) \cdot a(x)$ is

$$b_0 a_i + b_1 a_{i-1} + \cdots + b_{i-1} a_1 + b_i a_0.$$

Since D is a commutative ring, it follows that these two expressions are equal for every i. Therefore, by Definition 9–2.1, $a(x) \cdot b(x) = b(x) \cdot a(x)$. That is, multiplication is commutative in $D[x]$. In order to prove that $D[x]$ is an integral domain, it suffices by Theorem 4–4.5 to show that if $a(x)$ and $b(x)$ are nonzero polynomials, then $a(x)b(x)$ is not the zero polynomial $0x^0$. Since $a(x)$ and $b(x)$ are not zero, it is possible to write

$$a(x) = a_0 x^0 + a_1 x^1 + \cdots + a_m x^m,$$
$$b(x) = b_0 x^0 + b_1 x^1 + \cdots + b_n x^n,$$

where $a_m \neq 0$ and $b_n \neq 0$ in D. By Definition 9–2.3, the coefficient of x^{m+n} in $a(x)b(x)$ is $a_m b_n$. Since D is an integral domain, $a_m b_n \neq 0$, by Theorem 4–4.5. Therefore, $a(x) \cdot b(x) \neq 0x^0$. This proves the theorem.

It is time to justify the notation $a_0 x^0 + a_1 x^1 + a_2 x^2 + \cdots + a_n x^n$ for polynomials. It is clear from Definitions 9–2.2 and 9–2.3 that

$$\begin{aligned} a_0 x^0 + a_1 x^1 + \cdots + a_n x^n = \; &(a_0 x^0) + (a_1 x^0) \cdot (0x^0 + 1x^1) \\ &+ (a_2 x^0) \cdot (0x^0 + 1x^1)^2 + \cdots \\ &+ (a_n x^0) \cdot (0x^0 + 1x^1)^n, \end{aligned}$$

where the right-hand side of this equality is no longer a formal expression, but is an actual sum of products of polynomials. This observation suggests that we should use the symbol x to denote the polynomial $0x^0 + 1x^1$, and each element $a \in D$ should be identified with the polynomial ax^0. This last identification can be easily justified. Indeed, by Definitions 9–2.2, 9–2.3, and 9–2.4,

$$ax^0 + bx^0 = (a + b)x^0, \qquad ax^0 \cdot bx^0 = (ab)x^0, \qquad -(ax^0) = (-a)x^0,$$

so that the correspondence $a \leftrightarrow ax^0$ is an isomorphism. Making these identifications, it follows that $a(x) = a_0 + a_1x + a_2x^2 + \cdots + a_nx^n$ is actually a sum of the products

$$\overset{i \text{ factors}}{\overbrace{a_i \cdot x \cdot x \cdot \cdots \cdot x}}$$

in the integral domain $D[x]$. A number of useful consequences follow from this observation. For example, we can rearrange the terms in a polynomial in any way which might be convenient. In particular, the polynomial $a_0 + a_1x + \cdots + a_{n-1}x^{n-1} + a_nx^n$ can be written in "descending powers" of x, that is, in the form $a_nx^n + a_{n-1}x^{n-1} + \cdots + a_1x + a_0$.

It is customary to denote the integral domain of all polynomials in x with coefficients in D, as we have done in Theorem 9–2.5, by $D[x]$. The identification of x with $0x^0 + 1x^1$ and of each $a \in D$ with ax^0 will always be made. The polynomial x is often called an *indeterminate*, and $D[x]$ is referred to as the *domain of polynomials* in the indeterminate x with coefficients in D. The elements of D, when regarded as elements of $D[x]$, are called *constant polynomials*. The term a_0 in $a(x) = a_0 + a_1x + a_2x^2 + \cdots + a_nx^n$ is called the *constant term* of $a(x)$. The zero and identity of D are also the zero and identity of $D[x]$.

Let us now examine our definition of polynomials more critically. There are two weak points in the construction of $D[x]$ which we have given. First, the idea of a "formal expression" is vague. Second, Definition 9–2.1, for "equality" of polynomials, needs to be clarified. It is possible to give a definition of polynomials and their operations which avoids both of these problems. However, some discussion is needed to see that this definition is reasonable.

The definition of equality given above implies that a polynomial can be expressed using any number of terms with zero coefficients. For instance,

$$1x^0 + 1x^1 = 1x^0 + 1x^1 + 0x^2 = 1x^0 + 1x^1 + 0x^2 + 0x^3 = \cdots.$$

In fact, there is no harm in thinking of a polynomial as an infinite "sum,"

$$\sum_{n=0}^{\infty} a_nx^n,$$

in which the coefficients are zero from some point on. This viewpoint has the advantage that there is no ambiguity about the number of terms in a polynomial. Two polynomials $\sum_{n=0}^{\infty} a_n x^n$ and $\sum_{n=0}^{\infty} b_n x^n$ are equal when $a_n = b_n$ for every n.

The problem of giving an exact meaning to the formal expressions

$$a_0 x^0 + a_1 x^1 + a_2 x^2 + \cdots + a_n x^n, \qquad \text{or} \qquad \sum_{n=0}^{\infty} a_n x^n$$

can be avoided. It is evident that a polynomial is completely determined by the sequence $(a_0, a_1, a_2, \ldots, a_n)$ of its coefficients. Thus, if we want concrete mathematical objects for our polynomials, we can take them to be the sequences of elements in D which up to now have been thought of as the coefficients of the "powers" of x. For the reasons explained above, it is advantageous to let all of these sequences be infinite, but of course zero from some point on. These remarks motivate the following construction of an integral domain whose elements are definite objects, and which has the same algebraic properties as the ring of all polynomials in x with coefficients in D.

Let A be the set of all infinite sequences

$$(a_0, a_1, a_2, a_3, \ldots)$$

of elements from the integral domain D, such that $a_k = 0$ for all except finitely many values of k. That is, the sequences which belong to A are those which are of the form

$$(a_0, a_1, a_2, \ldots, a_n, 0, 0, \ldots).$$

Two such sequences are equal if they contain exactly the same elements of D in the same order. The operations of addition, multiplication, and negation in A are defined by the rules

$$(a_0, a_1, a_2, a_3, \ldots) + (b_0, b_1, b_2, b_3, \ldots)$$
$$= (a_0 + b_0, a_1 + b_1, a_2 + b_2, a_3 + b_3, \ldots),$$

$$(a_0, a_1, a_2, a_3, \ldots) \cdot (b_0, b_1, b_2, b_3, \ldots)$$
$$= (a_0 b_0, \quad a_0 b_1 + a_1 b_0, \quad a_0 b_2 + a_1 b_1 + a_2 b_0, \qquad (9\text{-}2)$$
$$a_0 b_3 + a_1 b_2 + a_2 b_1 + a_3 b_0, \ldots),$$

and

$$-(a_0, a_1, a_2, a_3, \ldots)$$
$$= (-a_0, -a_1, -a_2, -a_3, \ldots).$$

The sums $a_i + b_i$, the sums of products $a_0 b_i + a_1 b_{i-1} + \cdots + a_{i-1} b_1 + a_i b_0$, and the negatives $-a_i$ are formed in the integral domain D. It is easy to see that the set A is closed under the three operations of (9–2), that is, if the sequences $(a_0, a_1, a_2, a_3, \ldots)$ and $(b_0, b_1, b_2, b_3, \ldots)$ have only a finite number of nonzero elements, then the same is true of the sum, product, and negatives of these sequences. For example, if $a_j = 0$ for all $j > m$ and $b_k = 0$ for all $k > n$, then for $l > m + n$,·

$$a_0 b_l + a_1 b_{l-1} + \cdots + a_{l-1} b_1 + a_l b_0 = 0,$$

since if $j + k = l > m + n$, then either $j > m$, or $k > n$. Consequently, all terms are zero after the $m + n + 1$st in the sequence

$$(a_0 b_0, a_0 b_1 + a_1 b_0, a_0 b_2 + a_1 b_1 + a_2 b_0, a_0 b_3 + a_1 b_2 + a_2 b_1 + a_3 b_0, \ldots),$$

which is the product of $(a_0, a_1, a_2, a_3, \ldots)$ and $(b_0, b_1, b_2, b_3, \ldots)$. A few straightforward calculations show that A is an integral domain whose zero is $(0, 0, 0, 0, \ldots)$, and whose identity is $(1, 0, 0, 0, \ldots)$. Moreover, the correspondence

$$a \leftrightarrow (a, 0, 0, 0, \ldots)$$

is an isomorphism between D and the subring of A consisting of all sequences of the form $(a, 0, 0, 0, \ldots)$. As usual, we identify D with this subring, and write a instead of $(a, 0, 0, 0, \ldots)$. It follows from (9–2) that the element

$$x = (0, 1, 0, 0, \ldots)$$

satisfies

$$x^2 = (0, 0, 1, 0, \ldots),$$
$$x^3 = (0, 0, 0, 1, \ldots),$$
$$\vdots$$

and

$$ax = (a, 0, 0, 0, \ldots) \cdot (0, 1, 0, 0, \ldots) = (0, a, 0, 0, \ldots),$$
$$ax^2 = (a, 0, 0, 0, \ldots) \cdot (0, 0, 1, 0, \ldots) = (0, 0, a, 0, \ldots),$$
$$ax^3 = (a, 0, 0, 0, \ldots) \cdot (0, 0, 0, 1, \ldots) = (0, 0, 0, a, \ldots),$$

etc. Consequently,

$$(a_0, a_1, a_2, \ldots, a_{n-1}, a_n, 0, 0, \ldots) = a_0 + a_1 x + a_2 x^2 + \cdots$$
$$+ a_{n-1} x^{n-1} + a_n x^n.$$

In other words, the elements of A can be expressed in the same way as the polynomials which we have been thinking of as "formal expressions." It is easy to see that the correspondence between polynomials and the elements of A is a ring isomorphism between $D[x]$ and A.

PROBLEMS

1. Use Definition 9–2.2 to find the sums of the following pairs of polynomials with coefficients in Z.

    (a) $0x^0 + 7x^1 + (-3)x^2 + 1x^3$, $5x^0 + 6x^1 + (-3)x^2$

    (b) $1 + 7x^4 - x^7$, $x^3 + 5x^5$

    (c) $1x^0 + 0x^1 + 0x^2 + \cdots + 0x^{24} + 1x^{25}$,
        $1x^0 + 0x^1 + 0x^2 + \cdots + 0x^{24} + 1x^{25}$.

2. Use Definition 9–2.3 to find the products of the pairs of polynomials listed in Problem 1.

3. Write in full the expression for the product

$$(a_0x^0 + a_1x^1 + a_2x^2 + a_3x^3 + a_4x^4) \cdot (b_0x^0 + b_1x^1 + b_2x^2 + b_3x^3).$$

Show that this is the expression which is obtained by multiplying all combinations of terms from each factor and collecting the coefficients of equal powers of x.

4. Prove that addition is commutative and associative in $D[x]$. Show that $a(x) + 0 \cdot x^0 = a(x)$ for $a(x) \in D[x]$. Prove that $a(x) + [-a(x)] = 0x^0$ for $a(x) \in D[x]$.

5. Prove that multiplication is distributive with respect to addition in $D[x]$. Show that $1x^0$ is the identity of $D[x]$.

6. Prove the following properties of multiplication in $D[x]$.

    (a) $(a_0x^0 + a_1x^1 + a_2x^2 + \cdots + a_nx^n) \cdot (cx^i)$
$$= a_0cx^i + a_1cx^{i+1} + a_2cx^{i+2} + \cdots + a_ncx^{i+n}.$$

    (b) $ax^i \cdot [b(x) \cdot (cx^i)] = [(ax^i) \cdot b(x)] \cdot (cx^i)$ for $b(x) \in D[x]$ and $a \in D$, $c \in D$.

    (c) Use the distributive law and (b) to prove that
$$a(x) \cdot [b(x) \cdot (cx^i)] = [a(x) \cdot b(x)] \cdot (cx^i) \text{ for } a(x), b(x) \in D[x] \text{ and } c \in D.$$

    (d) Use the distributive law and (c) to prove that multiplication is associative in $D[x]$.

7. Show by direct computation that the multiplication defined in (9–2) is associative.

8. Prove in detail that the ring A of all sequences $(a_0, a_1, a_2, a_3, \ldots)$ of elements in D with $a_n = 0$ for all but a finite number of n, and with the operations defined by (9–2), is isomorphic to $D[x]$.

9–3 The division algorithm for polynomials. In this and the following two sections, we will investigate the arithmetic of polynomial rings. It will be seen that the theory of the rings $F[x]$ of all polynomials in x with coefficients in a *field* F is remarkably similar to the theory of the ring Z of all integers. The reader is advised to compare the results in Sections 9–3, 9–4, and 9–5 with the theorems about the integers which were proved in Sections 5–1, 5–2, and 5–3.

DEFINITION 9–3.1. Let $a(x) = a_0 + a_1 x + a_2 x^2 + \cdots + a_n x^n$ be a polynomial with coefficients in an integral domain D. Suppose that $a(x)$ is not the zero polynomial. The *degree* of $a(x)$ is the largest $m \geq 0$ such that $a_m \neq 0$. The coefficient a_m is called the *leading coefficient* of $a(x)$.

The degree of any nonzero polynomial is a nonnegative integer. For example,

$$\text{the degree of } 2 + 3x - 4x^3 \text{ is three;}$$
$$\text{the degree of } 3 + 0x \quad\quad \text{is zero;}$$
$$\text{the degree of } 3 + (-1)x \quad \text{is one.}$$

The polynomials of degree zero are exactly the nonzero constant polynomials; the polynomials of degree one are the polynomials of the form $a + bx$ with $b \neq 0$, etc. No degree is assigned to the zero polynomial.

It is convenient to denote the degree of a nonzero polynomial $a(x)$ by

$$\text{Deg } [a(x)].$$

For instance,

$$\text{Deg } [2 + 3x - 4x^3 + 0x^4] = 3,$$
$$\text{Deg } [x^{10}] = 10,$$
$$\text{Deg } [\tfrac{1}{3}] = 0,$$
$$\text{Deg } [25x^2] = 2.$$

It is obvious from (9–1) that if $\text{Deg } [a(x)] = n$, then it is possible to write

$$a(x) = a_n x^n + a_{n-1} x^{n-1} + \cdots + a_0,$$

where $a_n \neq 0$. Of course, the converse statement is also true:

if $a(x) = a_n x^n + a_{n-1} x^{n-1} + \cdots + a_0$, with $a_n \neq 0$, then $\text{Deg } [a(x)] = n$.

These two observations are often useful.

THEOREM 9–3.2. Let $a(x)$ and $b(x)$ be nonzero polynomials in $D[x]$, where D is any integral domain. Then
  (a) $\text{Deg } [a(x) \cdot b(x)] = \text{Deg } [a(x)] + \text{Deg } [b(x)]$;
  (b) if $a(x) + b(x) \neq 0$, then $\text{Deg } [a(x) + b(x)]$
$$\leq \max \{\text{Deg } [a(x)], \text{Deg } [b(x)]\};$$
  (c) if $\text{Deg } [a(x)] \neq \text{Deg } [b(x)]$, then $\text{Deg } [a(x) + b(x)]$
$$= \max \{\text{Deg } [a(x)], \text{Deg } [b(x)]\}.$$

Proof. Let $a(x) = a_n x^n + a_{n-1} x^{n-1} + \cdots + a_0$ and $b(x) = b_m x^m + b_{m-1} x^{m-1} + \cdots + b_0$, where $a_n \neq 0$ and $b_m \neq 0$. Therefore,

$$\text{Deg } [a(x)] = n \quad\quad \text{and} \quad\quad \text{Deg } [b(x)] = m.$$

Then

$$a(x) \cdot b(x) = a_n b_m x^{n+m} + (a_{n-1} b_m + a_n b_{m-1}) x^{n+m-1} + \cdots + a_0 b_0.$$

Since D is an integral domain, $a_n b_m \neq 0$. Therefore, $\text{Deg} [a(x) \cdot b(x)] = m + n = \text{Deg} [a(x)] + \text{Deg} [b(x)]$. To prove (b) and (c), suppose first that $n > m$. Then

$$b(x) = 0x^n + \cdots + b_m x^m + b_{m-1} x^{m-1} + \cdots + b_0.$$

Therefore,

$$a(x) + b(x) = a_n x^n + \cdots + (a_m + b_m) x^m$$
$$+ (a_{m-1} + b_{m-1}) x^{m-1} + \cdots + (a_0 + b_0).$$

Thus, $\text{Deg} [a(x) + b(x)] = n = \max \{\text{Deg} [a(x)], \text{Deg} [b(x)]\}$.   By a similar argument, if $n < m$, then

$$\text{Deg} [a(x) + b(x)] = m = \max \{\text{Deg} [a(x)], \text{Deg} [b(x)]\}.$$

This proves (c), and also (b) except in the case that $n = m$. When $n = m$,

$$a(x) + b(x) = (a_n + b_n) x^n + (a_{n-1} + b_{n-1}) x^{n-1} + \cdots + (a_0 + b_0).$$

If $a(x) + b(x) \neq 0$, then $a_k + b_k \neq 0$ for some k not exceeding n. The degree of $a(x) + b(x)$ is the largest such k. Clearly,

$$\text{Deg} [a(x) + b(x)] \leq n = \max \{\text{Deg} [a(x)], \text{Deg} [b(x)]\}.$$

Except for certain special results concerning $Z[x]$, we will restrict our discussion to the integral domains $F[x]$, where F is a field. Since every field is an integral domain, the definitions and results which have already been given in Sections 9–2 and 9–3 apply to $F[x]$. The fields which particularly concern us are C, R, Q, and Z_p.

The degree of a polynomial is used in the study of the arithmetic of polynomials in much the same way as the absolute value is used in the study of Z. The principal of mathematical induction is applied to the study of Z by means of the absolute value of an integer. Similarly, it is through the degree of a polynomial that induction can be used in $F[x]$. The division algorithm for polynomials is our first example of a theorem about polynomials which is proved by induction on degrees.

THEOREM 9–3.3.   *The division algorithm in $F[x]$.* Let $a(x)$ and $b(x)$ be polynomials in $F[x]$, where F is a field. Suppose that $b(x) \neq 0$. Then there exist unique polynomials $q(x)$ and $r(x)$ in $F[x]$ such that

$$a(x) = q(x) \cdot b(x) + r(x),$$

and either $r(x) = 0$, or else $\text{Deg} [r(x)] < \text{Deg} [b(x)]$.

This fundamental result is a statement of the process of long division for polynomials. The reader is probably familiar with the mechanics of this process, without having thought about its formal statement and proof.

EXAMPLE 1. Let $a(x) = x^3 + 2x + 3$ and $b(x) = 2x^2 - 3x + 1$. We will think of these polynomials as elements of $Q[x]$, even though they have integral coefficients. To find the polynomials $q(x)$ and $r(x)$ whose existence is guaranteed by Theorem 9–3.3, the familiar long division process will be used:

$$
\begin{array}{r}
\frac{1}{2}x + \frac{3}{4} \\
2x^2 - 3x + 1\overline{\smash{\big)}\, x^3 \qquad\;\; + 2x\;\; + 3} \\
\underline{x^3 - \tfrac{3}{2}x^2 + \tfrac{1}{2}x} \\
\tfrac{3}{2}x^2 + \tfrac{3}{2}x \\
\underline{\tfrac{3}{2}x^2 - \tfrac{9}{4}x + \tfrac{3}{4}} \\
\tfrac{15}{4}x + \tfrac{9}{4}
\end{array}
$$

Therefore,

$$x^3 + 2x + 3 = (\tfrac{1}{2}x + \tfrac{3}{4}) \cdot (2x^2 - 3x + 1) + (\tfrac{15}{4}x + \tfrac{9}{4}).$$

The validity of this identity can be checked by direct computation.

The proof of the division algorithm is based on an induction in the form of the well-ordering principle. It is convenient to prove a result which plays the role of the induction step in the proof of Theorem 9–3.3.

(9–3.4). Suppose that $b(x)$ and $c(x)$ are nonzero polynomials in $F[x]$, such that Deg $[b(x)] \leq$ Deg $[c(x)]$. Then there is a polynomial $f(x)$ such that either $c(x) = f(x) \cdot b(x)$, or else

$$\text{Deg } [c(x) - f(x) \cdot b(x)] < \text{Deg } [c(x)].$$

Proof. Let $b(x) = b_n x^n + b_{n-1}x^{n-1} + \cdots + b_0$, and $c(x) = c_m x^m + c_{m-1}x^{m-1} + \cdots + c_0$, where $b_n \neq 0$, $c_m \neq 0$, and $n \leq m$. Define $f(x) = (c_m \cdot b_n^{-1})x^{m-n}$. Then

$c(x) - f(x) \cdot b(x)$

$$= [c_m - (c_m \cdot b_n^{-1}) \cdot b_n]x^m + [c_{m-1} - (c_m \cdot b_n^{-1}) \cdot b_{n-1}]x^{m-1} + \cdots$$

$$+ [c_{m-n} - (c_m \cdot b_n^{-1}) \cdot b_0]x^{m-n} + c_{m-n-1}x^{m-n-1} + \cdots + c_0.$$

$$= 0x^m + [c_{m-1} - (c_m \cdot b_n^{-1}) \cdot b_{n-1}]x^{m-1} + \cdots.$$

Thus, if $c(x) - f(x) \cdot b(x) \neq 0$, then the degree of this polynomial is less than m, the degree of $c(x)$. This is exactly what had to be shown for the proof of (9–3.4).

We will now prove Theorem 9–3.3. We first prove the existence of polynomials $q(x)$ and $r(x)$ with the required properties. If there is a polynomial $q(x)$ such that $a(x) = q(x) \cdot b(x)$, then $r(x)$ can be taken to be 0. Therefore, suppose that $a(x) \neq g(x) \cdot b(x)$ for all $g(x) \in F[x]$. Then Deg $[a(x) - g(x) \cdot b(x)]$ is defined for all polynomials $g(x) \in F[x]$. Consequently,

$$\{\text{Deg } [a(x) - g(x) \cdot b(x)] | g(x) \in F[x]\}$$

is a nonempty set of nonnegative integers. By the well-ordering principle, this set contains a smallest integer k. That is, there is a polynomial $q(x) \in F[x]$ such that

$$\text{Deg } [a(x) - q(x) \cdot b(x)] = k \leq \text{Deg } [a(x) - g(x) \cdot b(x)]$$

for all $g(x) \in F[x]$. If $k \geq \text{Deg } [b(x)]$, then by (9–3.4), there exists $f(x) \in F[x]$ such that either

$$a(x) - q(x) \cdot b(x) = f(x) \cdot b(x),$$

or else

$$\text{Deg } [a(x) - q(x) \cdot b(x) - f(x) \cdot b(x)] < \text{Deg } [a(x) - q(x) \cdot b(x)].$$

In the first case, $a(x) = [q(x) + f(x)] \cdot b(x)$, which is contrary to the assumption that $a(x) \neq g(x) \cdot b(x)$ for all $g(x) \in F[x]$. In the second case, Deg $[a(x) - [q(x) + f(x)] \cdot b(x)] < k$, which contradicts $k \leq$ Deg $[a(x) - g(x) \cdot b(x)]$ for all $g(x) \in F[x]$. The only alternative to these contradictions is that k is less than the degree of $b(x)$. Thus, if we call $r(x) = a(x) - q(x) \cdot b(x)$, it follows that $a(x) = q(x) \cdot b(x) + r(x)$, and Deg $[r(x)] <$ Deg $[b(x)]$. It remains to show that the polynomials $q(x)$ and $r(x)$ satisfying the conditions of Theorem 9–3.3 are unique. Suppose that

$$a(x) = q_1(x) \cdot b(x) + r_1(x) \qquad \text{and} \qquad a(x) = q_2(x) \cdot b(x) + r_2(x),$$

where $r_1(x)$ and $r_2(x)$ are either zero, or else they have degree less than Deg $[b(x)]$. By subtracting these expressions, we obtain

$$[q_1(x) - q_2(x)] \cdot b(x) = r_2(x) - r_1(x).$$

Assume that $r_2(x) - r_1(x) \neq 0$. Then $q_1(x) - q_2(x) \neq 0$. Thus, by Theorem 9–3.2,

$$\text{Deg } [q_1(x) - q_2(x)] + \text{Deg } [b(x)] = \text{Deg } [r_2(x) - r_1(x)] < \text{Deg } [b(x)].$$

This is impossible, because Deg $[q_1(x) - q_2(x)] \geq 0$. Therefore, $r_2(x) - r_1(x) = 0$, and since $[q_1(x) - q_2(x)] \cdot b(x) = r_2(x) - r_1(x) = 0$ and

$b(x) \neq 0$, we also have $q_1(x) - q_2(x) = 0$. This completes the proof of the uniqueness of $q(x)$ and $r(x)$.

The polynomials $q(x)$ and $r(x)$ in the expression

$$a(x) = q(x) \cdot b(x) + r(x)$$

given by the division algorithm are called, respectively, the *quotient* and *remainder* on dividing $a(x)$ by $b(x)$.

The division algorithm for polynomials can be generalized in a way which is analogous to the way that Theorem 5–1.3 generalizes the division algorithm for integers. We limit ourselves to stating a special case of this generalization.

THEOREM 9–3.5. Let $c \in F$, where F is a field. Then every nonzero polynomial $f(x)$ can be uniquely represented in the form

$$f(x) = a_n(x - c)^n + a_{n-1}(x - c)^{n-1} + \cdots + a_0,$$

where $n = \mathrm{Deg}\,[f(x)]$ and $a_n, a_{n-1}, \ldots, a_0$ are elements of F.

This theorem can be proved from Theorem 9–3.3 by induction on $\mathrm{Deg}\,[f(x)]$ in the same way that Theorem 5–1.3 is obtained from Theorem 5–1.1. We omit the proof.

PROBLEMS

1. Use the division algorithm to find the quotient and remainder on dividing $a(x)$ by $b(x)$ for the following pairs of polynomials.
  (a) $a(x) = 2x^3 - 3x^2 + x - 1$ and $b(x) = x^2 + 2$ are in $Q[x]$
  (b) $a(x) = x^2 + 2$ and $b(x) = 2x^3 - 3x^2 + x - 1$ are in $Q[x]$
  (c) $a(x) = x^7 + \frac{1}{2}x$ and $b(x) = x - 1$ are in $Q[x]$
  (d) $a(x) = x^2 + \sqrt{2}x - 1$ and $b(x) = x - (\sqrt{6} - \sqrt{2})/2$ are in $R[x]$
  (e) $a(x) = x^3 + ix^2 + x + i$ and $b(x) = x^2 + i$ are in $C[x]$
  (f) $a(x) = 3x^4 + 8x^2 + 2$ and $b(x) = 12x^2 + x + 3$ are in $Z_{13}[x]$

2. Let $f(x) = ax^2 + bx + c$, where a, b, and c are elements of the field F. Let $d \in F$. Let a_2, a_1, and a_0 be the coefficients of the powers of $x - d$ in the representation

$$f(x) = a_2(x - d)^2 + a_1(x - d) + a_0.$$

Find expressions which give a_2, a_1, and a_0 in terms of a, b, c, and d. Show directly that Theorem 9–3.5 is true in this case.

3. Let $f(x) = x^9 - 1$. Express $f(x)$ as a sum of powers of $x - 1$.

4. State a general analogue of Theorem 5–1.3 for $F[x]$, where F is a field.

5. Prove Theorem 9–3.5.

6. Show that Theorem 9–3.3 can be generalized as follows: let $a(x)$ and $b(x)$ be polynomials in $D[x]$, where D is an integral domain. Suppose that $b(x) \neq 0$, and the leading coefficient (see Definition 9–3.1) of $b(x)$ is 1. Then there exist unique polynomials $q(x)$ and $r(x)$ in $D[x]$ such that

$$a(x) = q(x) \cdot b(x) + r(x),$$

and either $r(x) = 0$, or else $\text{Deg}\,[r(x)] < \text{Deg}\,[b(x)]$.

9–4 Greatest common divisor in $F[x]$. The divisibility of elements in an integral domain was discussed briefly in Section 4–4. The concepts and notation introduced in that section apply to the ring $F[x]$ of polynomials with coefficients in a field F. For convenience let us recall that according to Definition 4–4.6, a polynomial $b(x)$ divides $a(x)$ in $F[x]$ if there is a polynomial $c(x) \in F[x]$ such that $a(x) = b(x) \cdot c(x)$. It is also customary to say in this case that $b(x)$ *is a factor* of $a(x)$. Thus, $b(x)$ divides $a(x)$ in $F[x]$ if and only if the remainder on dividing $a(x)$ by $b(x)$ is the zero polynomial. The statement that $b(x)$ divides $a(x)$ is abbreviated by writing

$$b(x)|a(x).$$

The relation $b(x)|a(x)$ in $F[x]$ has certain useful properties which depend on the particular nature of the integral domain $F[x]$.

(9–4.1). (a) If $b(x)|a(x)$ in $F[x]$, then $d \cdot b(x)|a(x)$ and $b(x)|f(x) \cdot a(x)$, where d is any nonzero element of F, and $f(x)$ is any polynomial of $F[x]$.
  (b) A nonzero constant polynomial divides every polynomial in $F[x]$.
  (c) If $b(x)|a(x)$ and $a(x) \neq 0$, then the degree of $b(x)$ is less than or equal to the degree of $a(x)$.
  (d) If $b(x)|a(x)$ and $a(x)$ and $b(x)$ have the same degree, then each polynomial is a nonzero constant multiple of the other.
  (e) If $c(x)|a(x)$, $c(x)|b(x)$, then $c(x)|[f(x)a(x) + g(x)b(x)]$ for every $f(x)$ and $g(x)$ in $F[x]$.

Proof. To prove (a), we note that $a(x) = b(x) \cdot c(x)$ for some $c(x) \in F[x]$. Then $a(x) = [d \cdot b(x)] \cdot [d^{-1} \cdot c(x)]$ and $f(x) \cdot a(x) = b(x) \cdot [f(x) \cdot c(x)]$. Therefore, $d \cdot b(x)|a(x)$ and $b(x)|f(x) \cdot a(x)$. Statement (b) follows from (a) and the fact that the identity element $1 \in F[x]$ divides every polynomial in $F[x]$ [see Theorem 4–4.7(f)]. The properties (c) and (d) follow from Theorem 9–3.2(a). If $b(x)|a(x)$, then by definition, there is a polynomial $c(x)$ such that $a(x) = b(x) \cdot c(x)$. Since $a(x) \neq 0$, it follows that $b(x) \neq 0$ and $c(x) \neq 0$. Therefore, by Theorem 9–3.2(a),

$$\text{Deg}\,[a(x)] = \text{Deg}\,[b(x)] + \text{Deg}\,[c(x)].$$

Since the degrees are nonnegative integers, it follows that Deg $[b(x)] \leq$ Deg $[a(x)]$. Moreover, if Deg $[b(x)] =$ Deg $[a(x)]$, then Deg $[c(x)] = 0$, so that $c(x)$ is a nonzero constant. This proves (c) and (d). Finally, the property (e) is no more than a restatement of Theorem 4–4.7(e).

EXAMPLE 1. In $Q[x]$, $(\frac{1}{2} + 2x + \frac{1}{3}x^2)|(\frac{1}{2} + 2x + \frac{5}{6}x^2 + 2x^3 + \frac{1}{3}x^4)$, since

$$\tfrac{1}{2} + 2x + \tfrac{5}{6}x^2 + 2x^3 + \tfrac{1}{3}x^4 = (\tfrac{1}{2} + 2x + \tfrac{1}{3}x^2)(1 + x^2).$$

We also have

$$\tfrac{1}{2} + 2x + \tfrac{5}{6}x^2 + 2x^3 + \tfrac{1}{3}x^4 = [3 \cdot (\tfrac{1}{2} + 2x + \tfrac{1}{3}x^2)] \cdot [\tfrac{1}{3} \cdot (1 + x^2)]$$
$$= (\tfrac{3}{2} + 6x + x^2)(\tfrac{1}{3} + \tfrac{1}{3}x^2),$$

and

$$6(\tfrac{1}{2} + 2x + \tfrac{5}{6}x^2 + 2x^3 + \tfrac{1}{3}x^4) = 3 + 12x + 5x^2 + 12x^3 + 2x^4$$
$$= (\tfrac{1}{2} + 2x + \tfrac{1}{3}x^2) \cdot [6(1 + x^2)]$$
$$= (\tfrac{1}{2} + 2x + \tfrac{1}{3}x^2) \cdot (6 + 6x^2).$$

Definition 5–2.1 of the greatest common divisor of two integers was based on the ordering of the integers. Such a definition does not make sense in rings such as $F[x]$ which are not ordered. However, the conditions (5–1) and (5–2) for the greatest common divisor make sense in any integral domain, and as we observed in Section 5–2, these conditions can be used to define the greatest common divisor of two elements (not both zero) in any integral domain. For convenience, let us restate this definition for the integral domain $F[x]$.

DEFINITION 9–4.2. Let $a(x)$ and $b(x)$ be polynomials in $F[x]$ which are not both zero. Then $d(x) \in F[x]$ is a *greatest common divisor* (g.c.d.) of $a(x)$ and $b(x)$, in $F[x]$ if
   (a) $d(x)|a(x)$ and $d(x)|b(x)$;
   (b) if $c(x) \in F[x]$ satisfies $c(x)|a(x)$ and $c(x)|b(x)$, then $c(x)|d(x)$.

It follows from (9–4.1a, b) that if $d(x)$ is a greatest common divisor of $a(x)$ and $b(x)$, then so is $c \cdot d(x)$, where c is any nonzero element of F. Thus, a g.c.d. of $a(x)$ and $b(x)$ is not unique. Moreover, it is by no means obvious that two polynomials $a(x)$ and $b(x)$ necessarily have any greatest common divisor.

DEFINITION 9–4.3. A nonzero polynomial $f(x)$ is called *monic* if the leading coefficient of $f(x)$ is 1. That is, $f(x)$ has the form

$$x^n + a_{n-1}x^{n-1} + \cdots + a_0.$$

If $g(x) = b_n x^n + b_{n-1}x^{n-1} + \cdots + b_0$ is a nonzero polynomial in $F[x]$, with $b_n \neq 0$, then

$$f(x) = b_n^{-1}g(x) = x^n + (b_n^{-1}b_{n-1})x^{n-1} + \cdots + (b_n^{-1}b_0)$$

is a monic polynomial. Thus, for any nonzero polynomial $g(x)$, there is a unique monic polynomial $f(x)$ which is a multiple of $g(x)$ by a nonzero element of F. It is customary to call $f(x)$ the *monic polynomial associated with $g(x)$* [or simply the *monic associate* of $g(x)$].

THEOREM 9–4.4. Let $a(x)$ and $b(x)$ be polynomials in $F[x]$ which are not both zero. Then there exists a unique monic polynomial $d(x) \in F[x]$ which is a greatest common divisor of $a(x)$ and $b(x)$. Moreover,

$$d(x) = g(x)a(x) + h(x)b(x)$$

for some $g(x)$ and $h(x)$ in $F[x]$.

Proof. Suppose that $a(x) = 0$. Then $b(x) \neq 0$, and it is easy to see that the monic polynomial associated with $b(x)$ is a greatest common divisor of $a(x)$ and $b(x)$. Similarly, if $b(x) = 0$, then the monic associate of $a(x)$ is a g.c.d. of $a(x)$ and $b(x)$. In both of these cases, this monic g.c.d. can be expressed in the form $g(x)a(x) + h(x)b(x)$, in fact, with $g(x)$ and $h(x)$ constant polynomials. Assume therefore that $a(x) \neq 0$ and $b(x) \neq 0$. We will prove the statement of the theorem (except the uniqueness) by course of values induction on

$$\min \{\text{Deg}\,[a(x)], \text{Deg}\,[b(x)]\}.$$

If $\min \{\text{Deg}\,[a(x)], \text{Deg}\,[b(x)]\} = 0$, then either $a(x)$ or $b(x)$ is a nonzero constant polynomial, and the only common divisors of $a(x)$ and $b(x)$ are the nonzero constant polynomials. Hence, 1 is a monic g.c.d. of $a(x)$ and $b(x)$ in this case. Moreover, if $a(x) = a \in F$, then $1 = a^{-1} \cdot a + 0 \cdot b(x)$, and if $b(x) = b \in F$, then $1 = 0 \cdot a(x) + b^{-1} \cdot b$. Assume inductively that if $s(x)$ and $t(x)$ are polynomials such that $\min \{\text{Deg}\,[s(x)], \text{Deg}\,[t(x)]\} < n$, then $s(x)$ and $t(x)$ have a monic g.c.d. $d(x)$, which can be expressed in the form $d(x) = e(x) \cdot s(x) + f(x) \cdot t(x)$ for some $e(x)$ and $f(x)$ in $F[x]$. Suppose that $n = \text{Deg}\,[b(x)] \leq \text{Deg}\,[a(x)]$. The proof is similar if $n = \text{Deg}\,[a(x)] \leq \text{Deg}\,[b(x)]$. By the division algorithm,

$$a(x) = q(x) \cdot b(x) + r(x),$$

where either $r(x) = 0$, or else $r(x) \neq 0$ and Deg $[r(x)] <$ Deg $[b(x)]$. If $r(x) = 0$, then $b(x)|a(x)$, and it follows easily from Definition 9–4.2 that the monic polynomial associated with $b(x)$ is a greatest common divisor of $a(x)$ and $b(x)$. The monic associate of $b(x)$ has the form $g(x) \cdot a(x) + h(x) \cdot b(x)$, where $g(x) = 0$ and $h(x)$ is a nonzero constant polynomial.

Consider the case in which $r(x) \neq 0$. Then

$$\text{min } \{\text{Deg } [r(x)], \text{ Deg } [b(x)]\} = \text{Deg } [r(x)] < \text{Deg } [b(x)]$$
$$= \text{min } \{\text{Deg } [a(x)], \text{ Deg } [b(x)]\} = n.$$

Thus, by the induction hypothesis, $r(x)$ and $b(x)$ have a monic greatest common divisor $d(x)$, which can be written in the form

$$d(x) = e(x)r(x) + f(x)b(x).$$

Since $d(x)|b(x)$ and $d(x)|r(x)$, it follows that $d(x)|[q(x)b(x) + r(x)]$, by (9–4.1e). That is, $d(x)|a(x)$. Suppose that $c(x) \in F[x]$ is such that $c(x)|a(x)$ and $c(x)|b(x)$. Then $c(x)$ divides $a(x) - q(x) \cdot b(x) = r(x)$. Therefore, since $d(x)$ is a g.c.d. of $b(x)$ and $r(x)$, Definition 9–4.2(b) requires that $c(x)|d(x)$. We have shown that $d(x)$ satisfies both of the conditions of Definition 9–4.2 for a g.c.d. of $a(x)$ and $b(x)$. Therefore, $d(x)$ is a g.c.d. of $a(x)$ and $b(x)$. Moreover,

$$d(x) = e(x) \cdot r(x) + f(x) \cdot b(x) = e(x)\big(a(x) - q(x) \cdot b(x)\big) + f(x) \cdot b(x)$$
$$= g(x) \cdot a(x) + h(x) \cdot b(x),$$

where $g(x) = e(x)$ and $h(x) = f(x) - e(x) \cdot q(x)$.

To prove that $d(x)$ is the unique monic g.c.d. of $a(x)$ and $b(x)$, assume that $d_1(x)$ is also a monic polynomial which satisfies Definition 9–4.2. Since $d(x)$ satisfies part (a) and $d_1(x)$ satisfies part (b), it follows that $d(x)|d_1(x)$. Similarly, since $d_1(x)$ satisfies (a) and $d(x)$ satisfies (b), it follows that $d_1(x)|d(x)$. Therefore, Deg $[d_1(x)] =$ Deg $[d(x)]$, by (9–4.1c). By (9–4.1d), $d_1(x)$ is a constant multiple of $d(x)$, say $d_1(x) = k\, d(x)$, where $k \neq 0$ is in F. Since both $d_1(x)$ and $d(x)$ have leading coefficient 1, it follows that $k = 1$. Hence, $d_1(x) = d(x)$. This completes the proof of the theorem.

The result of Theorem 9–4.4 allows us to speak of *the* monic g.c.d. of two polynomials $a(x)$ and $b(x)$ in $F[x]$ which are not both zero. It is convenient to denote this unique monic g.c.d. by the expression

$$(a(x), b(x)).$$

This is similar to the notation introduced in Definition 5–2.1 for the g.c.d. of two integers.

It is possible to prove Theorem 9–4.4 by a method which resembles the proof of the analogous Theorem 5–2.2 (see Problem 5). However, the proof which we have given provides a practical method of finding the g.c.d. of two polynomials $a(x)$ and $b(x)$. If $b(x) = 0$, then $(a(x), b(x))$ is the monic associate of $a(x)$. If $a(x) \neq 0$, $b(x) \neq 0$, and Deg $b(x) \leq$ Deg $a(x)$, then $(a(x), b(x)) = (b(x), r(x))$, where $r(x)$ is the remainder obtained from the division of $a(x)$ by $b(x)$. Consequently, by repeated application of the division algorithm, it is possible to find the g.c.d. of $a(x)$ and $b(x)$.

EXAMPLE 2.   Let $a(x) = x^5 + 3x^4 + 5x^3 + 4x^2 + 4x + 1$ and $b(x) = x^5 + 2x^4 + 3x^3 + 2x^2 + 2x$. Then by repeated use of the division algorithm:

$x^5 + 3x^4 + 5x^3 + 4x^2 + 4x + 1$
$\quad = 1 \cdot (x^5 + 2x^4 + 3x^3 + 2x^2 + 2x) + (x^4 + 2x^3 + 2x^2 + 2x + 1),$
$x^5 + 2x^4 + 3x^3 + 2x^2 + 2x = x \cdot (x^4 + 2x^3 + 2x^2 + 2x + 1) + (x^3 + x),$
$x^4 + 2x^3 + 2x^2 + 2x + 1 = (x + 2)(x^3 + x) + (x^2 + 1)$
$x^3 + x = x(x^2 + 1) + 0.$

Therefore,

$(x^5 + 3x^4 + 5x^3 + 4x^2 + 4x + 1, x^5 + 2x^4 + 3x^3 + 2x^2 + 2x)$
$\quad = (x^5 + 2x^4 + 3x^3 + 2x^2 + 2x, x^4 + 2x^3 + 2x^2 + 2x + 1)$
$\quad = (x^4 + 2x^3 + 2x^2 + 2x + 1, x^3 + x)$
$\quad = (x^3 + x, x^2 + 1)$
$\quad = (x^2 + 1, 0) = x^2 + 1.$

The method of obtaining the g.c.d. of two polynomials as in Example 2 by repeated use of the division algorithm is called the *Euclidean algorithm,* because it is similar to the process of obtaining the g.c.d. of two integers which has been passed down to us in the works of Euclid. In general terms, the process consists of forming the successive equations

$$a(x) \quad = q_1(x)b(x) + r_1(x),$$
$$b(x) \quad = q_2(x)r_1(x) + r_2(x),$$
$$r_1(x) \quad = q_3(x)r_2(x) + r_3(x),$$
$$\vdots$$
$$r_{n-2}(x) = q_n(x)r_{n-1}(x) + r_n(x),$$
$$r_{n-1}(x) = q_{n-1}(x)r_n(x) + 0,$$

$r_2(x), \ldots, r_n(x)$ are not zero, Deg $[b(x)] >$ Deg $[r_1(x)] > \cdots >$ Deg $[r_n(x)]$. It follows from the proof of Theo- the monic polynomial associated with $r_n(x)$ is the monic g.c.d. of $a(x)$ and $b(x)$. Indeed,

$$\big(a(x), b(x)\big) = \big(b(x), r_1(x)\big) = \big(r_1(x), r_2(x)\big) = \cdots$$
$$= \big(r_{n-1}(x), r_n(x)\big) = \big(r_n(x), 0\big),$$

and $\big(r_n(x), 0\big)$ is the monic polynomial associated with $r_n(x)$.

Two polynomials $a(x)$ and $b(x)$ in $F[x]$ are *relatively prime* if the monic g.c.d. of $a(x)$ and $b(x)$ is 1. The proof of the following result is identical with the proof of Theorem 5–2.6.

THEOREM 9–4.5. *If $a(x)$ and $b(x)$ are relatively prime polynomials in $F[x]$, and if $a(x)|b(x) \cdot c(x)$, where $c(x) \in F[x]$, then $a(x)|c(x)$.*

PROBLEMS

1. Find the monic g.c.d. of the following pairs of polynomials.
   (a) $x^4 - x^3 + 3x^2 - 2x + 2,\ x^3 + x^2 + 2x + 2$
   (b) $x^4 - 3x^3 + 4x^2 - 12x,\ x^3 - 4x^2 + 4x - 3$
   (c) $x^6 - x^5 + 2x^4 - 3x^3 + x^2 - 2x + 2,\ x^5 - x^3 - x^2 + 1$
   (d) $x^2 - 2,\ x^2 - (\sqrt{2} + \sqrt{3})x + \sqrt{6}$

2. Prove that $a(x)$ and $b(x)$ are relatively prime if and only if there exist polynomials $f(x)$ and $g(x)$ in $F[x]$ such that $f(x)a(x) + g(x)b(x) = 1$.

3. Let $a(x)$ and $b(x)$ be polynomials in $D[x]$, where D is an integral domain. The polynomial $a(x)$ is called an *associate* of $b(x)$ if $a(x)|b(x)$ and $b(x)|a(x)$. If $a(x)$ is an associate of $b(x)$, we write $a(x) \sim b(x)$.
   (a) Prove that $\sim$ is an equivalence relation on $D[x]$.
   (b) Let $D = Z$. Prove that $a(x) \sim b(x)$ if and only if $b(x) = a(x)$ or $b(x) = -a(x)$.
   (c) Let $D = F$, a field. Prove that $a(x) \sim b(x)$ if and only if $b(x) = k \cdot a(x)$, where k is a nonzero element of F.
   (d) Suppose that $d_1(x)$ and $d_2(x)$ are greatest common divisors of $a(x)$ and $b(x)$. Prove that $d_1(x) \sim d_2(x)$. (The definition of a greatest common divisor of two polynomials in $D[x]$, where D is an integral domain, is obtained from Definition 9–4.2 by replacing the field F by D).

4. Find an example which shows that the polynomials $f(x)$ and $g(x)$ in the expression $d(x) = f(x)a(x) + g(x)b(x)$ for the monic g.c.d. of $a(x)$ and $b(x)$ in Theorem 9–4.4 are not unique.

5. Let $a(x)$ and $b(x)$ be polynomials in $F[x]$ which are not both zero. Let

$$S = \{f(x)a(x) + g(x)b(x)|f(x) \in F[x],\ g(x) \in F[x]\}.$$

   (a) Show that S contains at least one nonzero, monic polynomial.
   (b) Without using Theorem 9–4.4, prove that the monic polynomial of smallest degree in S is a g.c.d. of $a(x)$ and $b(x)$.

6. Show that the only greatest common divisors of 2 and x in $Z[x]$ are 1 and -1. [See Problem 3(d) for the definition of greatest common divisor in $Z[x]$.] Prove that it is impossible to find $f(x) \in Z[x]$ and $g(x) \in Z[x]$ satisfying $1 = f(x) \cdot 2 + g(x) \cdot x$. This shows that Theorem 9–4.4 is false in $D[x]$, where D is an integral domain.

7. Let $a(x)$ and $b(x)$ be polynomials, not both zero, with coefficients in the rational field Q. Prove that the monic g.c.d. of $a(x)$ and $b(x)$ in $R[x]$ has rational coefficients. Is the same conclusion true if $R[x]$ is replaced by $C[x]$? [*Hint:* Prove that the monic g.c.d. of $a(x)$ and $b(x)$ in $Q[x]$ is also a g.c.d. of $a(x)$ and $b(x)$ in $R[x]$, then use the uniqueness statement in Theorem 9–4.4.]

8. Let $a(x)$, $b(x)$, and $c(x)$ be polynomials in $F[x]$, with $a(x) \neq 0$, $b(x) \neq 0$, and $a(x)$ monic. Prove that $(a(x) \cdot b(x), a(x) \cdot c(x)) = a(x) \cdot (b(x), c(x))$.

9. Let $\{a_1(x), a_2(x), \ldots, a_n(x)\}$ $(n \geq 2)$ be a set of polynomials in $F[x]$ with $a_1(x) \neq 0$. A *greatest common divisor* of $\{a_1(x), a_2(x), \ldots, a_n(x)\}$ in $F[x]$ is a polynomial $d(x) \in F[x]$ such that (i) $d(x)|a_i(x)$ for $i = 1, 2, \ldots, n$, and (ii) if $c(x)|a_i(x)$ for $i = 1, 2, \ldots, n$, then $c(x)|d(x)$.

 (a) Prove that $(\ldots ((a_1(x), a_2(x)), a_3(x)), \ldots, a_n(x))$ is a g.c.d. of $\{a_1(x), a_2(x), \ldots, a_n(x)\}$ in $F[x]$.

 (b) State and prove a theorem similar to Theorem 9–4.4 for sets of $n \geq 2$ polynomials.

10. Find the monic g.c.d. of the following sets of polynomials.

 (a) $x^4 - x^3 + 3x^2 - 2x + 2$, $x^3 + x^2 + 2x + 2$, $x + \sqrt{2}\,i$

 (b) $x^4 - 1$, $x^3 + x^2 + x + 1$, $x^2 - 1$

 (c) $x^5 + 13x^4 + 63x^3 + 148x^2 + 208x + 192$,
  $4x^4 + 52x^3 + 189x^2 + 296x + 208$, $20x^3 + 156x^2 + 378x + 296$

11. A *least common multiple* (l.c.m.) of two nonzero polynomials $a(x)$ and $b(x)$ in $F[x]$ is a polynomial $m(x) \in F[x]$ which satisfies

 (i) $a(x)|m(x)$ and $b(x)|m(x)$, and

 (ii) if $l(x)$ is any polynomial in $F[x]$ such that $a(x)|l(x)$ and $b(x)|l(x)$, then $m(x)|l(x)$.

  Prove that if $a(x)$ and $b(x)$ are nonzero polynomials in $F[x]$, then $a(x) \cdot b(x)/(a(x), b(x))$ is a l.c.m. of $a(x)$ and $b(x)$.

12. Find a least common multiple for the following pairs of polynomials.

 (a) $x^5 + 3x^4 + 5x^3 + 4x^2 + 4x + 1$, $x^5 + 2x^4 + 3x^3 + 2x^2 + 2x$

 (b) $x^4 - x^3 + 3x^2 - 2x + 2$, $x^3 + x^2 + 2x + 2$

 (c) $x^3 - 2x + 1$, $x^2 + 1$

nique factorization theorem for polynomials. The fundamental
ithmetic, which was proved in Section 5–3, states that every
er can be written uniquely as a product of prime numbers.
this section is to prove a similar theorem about the arith-
gral domain $F[x]$, where F is a field.

Our first task is to define the analogue in $F[x]$ of a prime number.

DEFINITION 9–5.1. Let $p(x)$ be a polynomial of positive degree in $F[x]$. Then $p(x)$ is *irreducible in $F[x]$* if $p(x)$ is not divisible by any polynomial in $F[x]$ except constant polynomials and constant multiples of $p(x)$. Otherwise, $p(x)$ is called *reducible in $F[x]$*.

This definition requires some discussion. By (9–4.1a, b), any polynomial $a(x)$ in $F[x]$ is divisible by every nonzero constant polynomial and by every nonzero constant multiple of $a(x)$. Thus, the irreducible polynomials in $F[x]$ are exactly those which have no divisors other than these "trivial" ones. This parallels closely the definition of a prime number (Definition 5–3.1).

Suppose that $a(x)$ is a polynomial of positive degree which is reducible in $F[x]$. Then by Definition 9–5.1, $a(x) = f(x) \cdot g(x)$, where $f(x)$ is not a constant and $f(x)$ is not a constant multiple of $a(x)$. It follows that $\text{Deg}\,[f(x)] < \text{Deg}\,[a(x)]$. For if $\text{Deg}\,[f(x)] = \text{Deg}\,[a(x)]$, then by Theorem 9–3.2(a), $\text{Deg}\,[g(x)] = 0$. Therefore, $g(x)$ is a nonzero constant which implies that $f(x)$ is a constant multiple of $a(x)$. This contradiction proves that $\text{Deg}\,[f(x)] < \text{Deg}\,[a(x)]$. Therefore, a reducible polynomial $a(x)$ in $F[x]$ has a factor $f(x)$ such that $0 < \text{Deg}\,[f(x)] < \text{Deg}\,[a(x)]$. Conversely, it is easy to show that if $a(x) \in F[x]$ has a factor $f(x) \in F[x]$ which satisfies $0 < \text{Deg}\,[f(x)] < \text{Deg}\,[a(x)]$, then $a(x)$ is reducible in $F[x]$.

Since Definition 9–5.1 applies only to polynomials of positive degree, the constant polynomials are neither reducible nor irreducible. These polynomials play a special role in $F[x]$ similar to that of the integers 1 and -1 in the arithmetic of Z.

It is very important to observe that irreducibility is defined relative to a particular field F. That is, a polynomial which is irreducible in $F[x]$ may be reducible in $K[x]$ for some field K containing F.

EXAMPLE 1. The polynomial $x^2 - 3$ is irreducible in $Q[x]$. Suppose that $x^2 - 3$ is reducible. Then

$$x^2 - 3 = (ax + b)(cx + d) = acx^2 + (ad + bc)x + bd,$$

where a, b, c, and d are rational numbers. This implies that $ac = 1$, $ad + bc = 0$, and $bd = -3$. Thus, $c = 1/a$, $d = -3/b$, and substituting in $ad + bc = 0$, we obtain

$$0 = \frac{-3a}{b} + \frac{b}{a} = \frac{-3a^2 + b^2}{ab}.$$

Therefore, $-3a^2 + b^2 = 0$ and $(b/a)^2 = 3$. However, $\sqrt{3}$ is not a rational number. Thus, $x^2 - 3$ is irreducible in $Q[x]$. On the other hand, $x^2 - 3 = (x - \sqrt{3})(x + \sqrt{3})$, so that $x^2 - 3$ is reducible in $R[x]$.

EXAMPLE 2. Any polynomial of degree one, $ax + b$, $a \neq 0$, with coefficients in a field F, is irreducible in $F[x]$. In fact $ax + b = f(x) \cdot g(x)$ with $0 <$ Deg $[f(x)] < 1$ is obviously impossible. Moreover, if K is any field containing F as a subring, then $ax + b$ is also irreducible in $K[x]$.

The principal result of this section is that every polynomial of positive degree in $F[x]$ can be expressed as a product of an element in F and one or more monic irreducible polynomials in $F[x]$. Moreover, this factorization is unique, except possibly for the order of the factors. This is the unique factorization theorem in $F[x]$, which is the analogue of the fundamental theorem of arithmetic.

The following preliminary results are needed for the proof of this important theorem.

(9–5.2). If $p(x)$ is irreducible in $F[x]$ and $f(x) \in F[x]$, then either $p(x)|f(x)$ in $F[x]$, or $p(x)$ and $f(x)$ are relatively prime.

Proof. Let $d(x) = (p(x), f(x))$. Then $d(x)|p(x)$, by Definition 9–4.2. Since $p(x)$ is irreducible, it follows that either $d(x)$ is a constant or $d(x)$ is a nonzero constant multiple of $p(x)$. If $d(x)$ is a constant, then $d(x) = 1$ (because $d(x)$ is monic), so that $p(x)$ and $f(x)$ are relatively prime. If $d(x)$ is a nonzero constant multiple of $p(x)$, then $p(x) = k \cdot d(x)$ for some nonzero $k \in F$. Since $d(x)|f(x)$, it follows that $p(x)|f(x)$, by (9–4.1a).

(9–5.3). If $p(x)$ is irreducible in $F[x]$, and $p(x)$ divides the product $a_1(x) \cdot a_2(x) \cdot \cdots \cdot a_n(x)$ of polynomials in $F[x]$, then $p(x)$ divides at least one of the polynomials $a_i(x)$.

The proof is the same as the proof of (5–3.2).

THEOREM 9–5.4. *Unique factorization theorem in $F[x]$.* Every polynomial $a(x) \in F[x]$ of positive degree can be written as a product of a nonzero element of F and monic irreducible polynomials in $F[x]$. Except for the order of the factors, the expression of $a(x)$ in this form is unique.

Proof. ᵗʰ parts of this theorem are proved by course of values induc- Deg $[a(x)]$. The proof that $a(x)$ can be factored into a product lement of F and monic irreducible polynomials in $F[x]$ is corresponding part of the fundamental theorem of arith- that Deg $[a(x)] = 1$. Then $a(x) = bx + c$, where $b \in F$, 0. By Example 2, $x + (b^{-1} \cdot c)$ is a monic irreducible polynomial in $F[x]$, and

$$a(x) = b \cdot [x + (b^{-1} \cdot c)].$$

Suppose that $a(x)$ has degree $n > 1$, and assume that every polynomial of degree m, with $1 \leq m < n$, can be expressed in the form

$$cp_1(x)p_2(x) \ldots p_k(x),$$

where $c \neq 0$ is in F and the $p_i(x)$ are monic irreducible polynomials in $F[x]$. If

$$a(x) = a_n x^n + a_{n-1}x^{n-1} + \cdots + a_0 \qquad (a_n \neq 0)$$

is irreducible, then

$$a(x) = a_n[x^n + (a_n^{-1}a_{n-1})x^{n-1} + \cdots + (a_n^{-1}a_0)]$$

is the desired expression for $a(x)$, since $x^n + (a_n^{-1}a_{n-1})x^{n-1} + \cdots + (a_n^{-1}a_0)$ is monic and irreducible, by (9–4.1). If $a(x)$ is not irreducible, then $a(x) = b(x) \cdot c(x)$, where $b(x)$ and $c(x)$ are polynomials in $F[x]$ satisfying $1 \leq \text{Deg}[b(x)] < \text{Deg}[a(x)]$ and $1 \leq \text{Deg}[c(x)] < \text{Deg}[a(x)]$. Therefore, by the induction hypothesis

$$b(x) = c_1 \cdot p_1(x) \cdot p_2(x) \cdot \cdots \cdot p_r(x)$$

and

$$c(x) = c_2 \cdot q_1(x) \cdot q_2(x) \cdot \cdots \cdot q_s(x),$$

where c_1 and c_2 are nonzero elements of F, and the $p_i(x)$ and $q_j(x)$ are monic irreducible polynomials. Thus,

$$\begin{aligned} a(x) &= b(x) \cdot c(x) \\ &= (c_1 \cdot c_2) \cdot p_1(x) \cdot p_2(x) \cdot \cdots \cdot p_r(x) \cdot q_1(x) \cdot q_2(x) \cdot \cdots \cdot q_s(x), \end{aligned}$$

which is the required form.

To prove that the factorization of a polynomial $a(x)$ is unique, we can use induction either on the degree of $a(x)$, or on the number of monic irreducible polynomials which occur in some decomposition of $a(x)$ into a product of irreducible polynomials. This last method corresponds to the proof of the uniqueness given in Theorem 5–3.3. However, for the proof of Theorem 9–5.4, it is slightly easier to induce on the degree of $a(x)$. Suppose first that $a(x)$ has degree one and that

$$a(x) = a_1(x + b_1) = a_2(x + b_2).$$

Then $a_1 = a_2 \neq 0$, and $a_1 b_1 = a_2 b_2$. Multiplying the last equation by $a_1^{-1} = a_2^{-1}$, we obtain $b_1 = b_2$. Therefore, any two factorizations of

$a(x)$ are identical. Now, suppose that $a(x)$ has degree $n > 1$, and assume that the unique factorization theorem is true for all polynomials of degree less than n. Let

$$a(x) = c_1 p_1(x) p_2(x) \ldots p_r(x) = c_2 q_1(x) q_2(x) \ldots q_s(x),$$

be any two factorizations of $a(x)$ into products of an element of F and one or more monic irreducible polynomials. Since the $p_i(x)$ and $q_j(x)$ are monic polynomials, the leading coefficient of $a(x)$ is both c_1 and c_2. That is, $c_1 = c_2$. Thus,

$$p_1(x) p_2(x) \ldots p_r(x) = q_1(x) q_2(x) \ldots q_s(x),$$

so that $p_1(x)$ divides $q_1(x) q_2(x) \ldots q_s(x)$. Since $p_1(x)$ is irreducible, it follows from (9–5.3) that $p_1(x)$ divides one of the polynomials $q_j(x)$. However, $q_j(x)$ is irreducible, and $p_1(x)$ is not a constant, so that $p_1(x)$ must be a constant multiple of $q_j(x)$. Since $p_1(x)$ and $q_j(x)$ are both monic polynomials, it follows that $p_1(x) = q_j(x)$. If $r = 1$, then $a(x)$ is irreducible, so that $s = j = 1$. In this case, the factorizations $a(x) = c_1 p_1(x) = c_2 q_1(x)$ are identical. Otherwise, $p_1(x)$ can be cancelled from the above expression to obtain

$$p_2(x) \ldots p_r(x) = q_1(x) q_2(x) \ldots q_{j-1}(x) q_{j+1}(x) \ldots q_s(x).$$

Since $n = \mathrm{Deg}\,[p_1(x)] + \mathrm{Deg}\,[p_2(x) \ldots p_r(x)]$ and $\mathrm{Deg}\,[p_1(x)] \geq 1$, it follows that

$$\mathrm{Deg}\,[p_2(x) \ldots p_r(x)] < n.$$

By the induction hypothesis, the polynomials $p_2(x), \ldots, p_r(x)$ are just the polynomials $q_1(x), q_2(x), \ldots, q_{j-1}(x), q_{j+1}(x), \ldots, q_s(x)$ in some order. Therefore, the two factorizations of $a(x)$ are the same, except possibly for the order of the factors.

The process of expressing a polynomial as a product of an element of F and a product of monic polynomials which are irreducible in $F[x]$ is the familiar "complete factorization" which is studied in elementary algebra. It would be convenient to have a systematic method which would give a complete factorization of any polynomial $a(x)$ in any integral domain $F[x]$. Simply to have a way of deciding whether or not a given polynomial in $F[x]$ is irreducible in $F[x]$ would be helpful. Unfortunately, such methods exist only for particular fields F. For example, if the field F is a finite field of the form Z_p (where p is a prime), then there are only finitely many polynomials of a given degree. By examining all products of two polynomials of degree less than $a(x)$, it is possible to decide whether or not $a(x)$ is irreducible.

EXAMPLE 3. By a method which is similar to the "sieve of Eratosthenes" (see Section 5–4), the monic irreducible polynomials of any degree in the rings $Z_p[x]$ can be determined. Actually, the method is practical only for small p, and for polynomials of low degree. We will consider the case $p = 3$. The following list includes every monic polynomial in $Z_3[x]$ of degree less than or equal to two:

$$x$$
$$x + 1$$
$$x + 2$$
$$x^2 \qquad\qquad = x \cdot x$$
$$x^2 \qquad + 1$$
$$x^2 \qquad + 2 = (x + 1) \cdot (x + 2)$$
$$x^2 + x \qquad = x \cdot (x + 1)$$
$$x^2 + x \ + 1 = (x + 2) \cdot (x + 2)$$
$$x^2 + x \ + 2$$
$$x^2 + 2x \qquad = x \cdot (x + 2)$$
$$x^2 + 2x + 1 = (x + 1) \cdot (x + 1)$$
$$x^2 + 2x + 2$$

It follows that the monic, irreducible polynomials of degree one and two in $Z_3[x]$ are

$$x, \quad x + 1, \quad x + 2, \quad x^2 + 1, \quad x^2 + x + 2, \quad \text{and} \quad x^2 + 2x + 2.$$

PROBLEMS

1. Determine which of the following polynomials are irreducible in $Q[x]$. (a) $x^3 - 2$ (b) $x^3 + 2x^2 + 2x + 1$ (c) $x^4 + 1$ (d) $x^4 - x^2 - 1$ (e) $x^2 - 2x + 4$ (f) $x^6 + 2x^3 + 1$

2. Which of the polynomials listed in Problem 1 are irreducible in $R[x]$?

3. Let $f(x) = ax^2 + bx + c$ be a polynomial with rational coefficients, where $a \neq 0$. (a) Prove that $f(x)$ is irreducible in $Q[x]$ if and only if $b^2 - 4ac$ is not the square of a rational number. (b) Prove that $f(x)$ is irreducible in $R[x]$ if and only if $b^2 - 4ac < 0$. (c) Prove that $f(x)$ is reducible in $C[x]$ for all values of a, b, and c.

4. Express the polynomials listed in Problem 1 as a product of monic irreducible polynomials in $Q[x]$, $R[x]$, and $C[x]$.

5. Use the method of Example 3 to find all irreducible monic polynomials of the third degree in $Z_3[x]$.

6. Find the complete factorization of all polynomials of degree four in $Z_2[x]$.

7. Prove that if $p(x)$ is irreducible in $F[x]$, and $c \neq 0$ in F, then $cp(x)$ is irreducible in $F[x]$.

8. Let $a(x) = cp_1(x)^{n_1}p_2(x)^{n_2} \ldots p_r(x)^{n_r}$ be a polynomial in $F[x]$, where the $p_i(x)$ are monic polynomials which are irreducible in $F[x]$, $p_i(x) \neq p_j(x)$ for $i \neq j$, and the exponents n_i are natural numbers. Prove that $b(x) \in F[x]$ divides $a(x)$ if and only if $b(x) = dp_1(x)^{m_1}p_2(x)^{m_2} \ldots p_r(x)^{m_r}$, where $0 \leq m_i \leq n_i$ for $i = 1, 2, \ldots, r$.

9. Any two nonzero polynomials $a(x)$ and $b(x)$ in $F[x]$ can be expressed in the forms

$$a(x) = cp_1(x)^{n_1}p_2(x)^{n_2} \ldots p_r(x)^{n_r},$$
$$b(x) = dp_1(x)^{m_1}p_2(x)^{m_2} \ldots p_r(x)^{m_r},$$

where the $p_i(x)$ are monic irreducible polynomials, $p_i(x) \neq p_j(x)$ if $i \neq j$, and the exponents n_i and m_i are nonnegative integers.

(a) Prove that the monic g.c.d. of $a(x)$ and $b(x)$ is

$$d(x) = p_1(x)^{t_1}p_2(x)^{t_2} \ldots p_r(x)^{t_r},$$

where $t_i = \min \{m_i, n_i\}$ for $i = 1, 2, \ldots, r$.

(b) Prove that a least common multiple of $a(x)$ and $b(x)$ is

$$m(x) = p_1(x)^{s_1}p_2(x)^{s_2} \ldots p_r(x)^{s_r},$$

where $s_i = \max \{m_i, n_i\}$ for $i = 1, 2, \ldots, r$ (see Problem 11, Section 9–4).

9–6 Derivatives. Up to now, our discussion of the rings of polynomials with coefficients in a field has run parallel to the development of the fundamental theorem of arithmetic. In this section we introduce an idea which has no analogue in the arithmetic of integers. This is the concept of the derivative of a polynomial. This concept is one of the basic notions of calculus. The derivative of a polynomial plays an important role in the theory of equations, and for its application in this subject, it can be defined in a purely algebraic way.

DEFINITION 9–6.1. If

$$a(x) = a_nx^n + a_{n-1}x^{n-1} + \cdots + a_2x^2 + a_1x + a_0$$

is a nonconstant polynomial in $F[x]$, then the polynomial

$$(n \cdot a_n)x^{n-1} + ((n - 1) \cdot a_{n-1})x^{n-2} + \cdots + (2 \cdot a_2)x + 1 \cdot a_1$$

is called the *derivative* of $a(x)$. The derivative of a constant polynomial is zero. It is customary to denote the derivative of $a(x)$ by $a'(x)$, the derivative of $b(x)$ by $b'(x)$, etc.

The expressions $n \cdot a_n$, $(n - 1) \cdot a_{n-1}$, $\ldots$, $2 \cdot a_2$, and $1 \cdot a_1$ for the coefficients of $a'(x)$ denote the elements of F which are obtained by repeated addition. That is,

$$\overbrace{n \cdot a_n = a_n + a_n + \cdots + a_n,}^{n \text{ summands}}$$

$$\overbrace{(n-1) \cdot a_{n-1} = a_{n-1} + \cdots + a_{n-1},}^{n-1 \text{ summands}}$$

$$\vdots$$

$$2 \cdot a_2 = a_2 + a_2,$$

$$1 \cdot a_1 = a_1.$$

Note that if the characteristic of the field F is a prime p with $p \leq n$, then $p \cdot a_p = 0$ in F. Also, if $2p \leq n$, then $(2p) \cdot a_{2p} = 0$, etc.

EXAMPLE 1. If $a(x) = x^4 + \sqrt{2}\, x^3 - x + \sqrt{3} \in R[x]$, then the derivative of $a(x)$ is

$$a'(x) = 4x^3 + 3\sqrt{2}\, x^2 - 1.$$

If $a(x) = x^5 + 2x^3 + 3x + 1 \in Z_5[x]$, that is, the coefficients belong to the field of integers modulo 5, then

$$a'(x) = 5 \cdot x^4 + 3 \cdot 2x^2 + 1 \cdot 3 = x^2 + 3.$$

If $a'(x)$ is the derivative of $a(x)$, then the derivative of $a'(x)$ is called the *second derivative* of $a(x)$, and is denoted by $a''(x)$. For any natural number n, the result of taking n successive derivatives of a polynomial $a(x)$ is called the *nth derivative* of $a(x)$. The nth derivative of $a(x)$ can be denoted by

$$a'' \cdots '(x),$$

with n primes. However, this notation is unusual if $n > 3$. For large n it is customary to write $a^{(n)}(x)$ for the nth derivative of $a(x)$, and we will follow this practice if $n > 2$.

THEOREM 9–6.2. Let $b(x)$ and $c(x)$ be polynomials in $F[x]$.
  (a) If $a(x) = b(x) + c(x)$, then $a'(x) = b'(x) + c'(x)$.
  (b) If $a(x) = b(x) \cdot c(x)$, then $a'(x) = b(x) \cdot c'(x) + b'(x) \cdot c(x)$.
  (c) If $a(x) = b(x)^n$, where $n \geq 1$, then $a'(x) = n \cdot b(x)^{n-1} \cdot b'(x)$.

Proof. First consider (a). Let

$$b(x) = b_n x^n + b_{n-1} x^{n-1} + \cdots + b_1 x + b_0,$$

$$c(x) = c_n x^n + c_{n-1} x^{n-1} + \cdots + c_1 x + c_0.$$

(As we observed in Section 9–2, there is no loss of generality in assuming that $b(x)$ and $c(x)$ are written with the same number of terms.) Then

$$a(x) = (b_n + c_n)x^n + (b_{n-1} + c_{n-1})x^{n-1} + \cdots$$
$$+ (b_1 + c_1)x + (b_0 + c_0).$$

Hence, by Definition 9–6.1,

$$a'(x) = n \cdot (b_n + c_n)x^{n-1} + (n-1) \cdot (b_{n-1} + c_{n-1})x^{n-2} + \cdots$$
$$+ 1 \cdot (b_1 + c_1)$$
$$= [(n \cdot b_n)x^{n-1} + ((n-1) \cdot b_{n-1})x^{n-2} + \cdots + 1 \cdot b_1]$$
$$+ [(n \cdot c_n)x^{n-1} + ((n-1) \cdot c_{n-1})x^{n-2} + \cdots + 1 \cdot c_1]$$
$$= b'(x) + c'(x).$$

This proves (a).

We prove (b) first in the case that $b(x) = ex^m$ and $c(x) = fx^n$ where e, $f \in F$, $m \geq 0$ and $n \geq 0$. Then $a(x) = b(x) \cdot c(x) = (ef)x^{m+n}$. By definition,

$$a'(x) = [(m + n) \cdot ef]x^{m+n-1},$$

and

$$b'(x) \cdot c(x) + b(x) \cdot c'(x) = [(m \cdot e)x^{m-1}] \cdot (fx^n) + (ex^m) \cdot [(n \cdot f)x^{n-1}]$$
$$= [(m + n) \cdot ef]x^{m+n-1},$$

so that $a'(x) = b'(x) \cdot c(x) + b(x) \cdot c'(x)$. Next observe that if the identity (b) is correct for $a_1(x) = b_1(x) \cdot c(x)$ and $a_2(x) = b_2(x) \cdot c(x)$, then it is true for $a(x) = b(x) \cdot c(x)$, where $b(x) = b_1(x) + b_2(x)$. Indeed, $a(x) = [b_1(x) + b_2(x)] \cdot c(x) = b_1(x) \cdot c(x) + b_2(x) \cdot c(x) = a_1(x) + a_2(x)$, so that

$$a'(x) = a_1'(x) + a_2'(x) = [b_1'(x) \cdot c(x) + b_1(x) \cdot c'(x)]$$
$$+ [b_2'(x) \cdot c(x) + b_2(x) \cdot c'(x)]$$
$$= [b_1'(x) + b_2'(x)] \cdot c(x) + [b_1(x) + b_2(x)] \cdot c'(x)$$
$$= b'(x) \cdot c(x) + b(x) \cdot c'(x).$$

Similarly, if the identity (b) holds for $b(x) \cdot c_1(x)$ and $b(x) \cdot c_2(x)$, then it holds for $b(x) \cdot [c_1(x) + c_2(x)]$. The proof of the identity (b) can now be completed by induction. It is convenient to use two steps. First we prove by induction on m that (b) is valid when

$$b(x) = e_0x^0 + e_1x^1 + \cdots + e_mx^m,$$
$$c(x) = fx^n.$$

The general case

$$b(x) = e_0 x^0 + e_1 x^1 + \cdots + e_m x^m, \qquad c(x) = f_0 x^0 + f_1 x^1 + \cdots + f_n x^n$$

is then obtained by induction on n. The reader can renew his skill in the use of mathematical induction by filling in the details of this argument.

In order to prove (c), we use induction on n. If $n = 1$, the statement is that if $a(x) = b(x)$, then $a'(x) = 1 \cdot b(x)^0 \cdot b'(x)$. Since $b(x)^0$ is 1 (the usual convention for the exponent zero), this identity is correct. Assume that $n > 1$, and that the derivative of $b(x)^{n-1}$ is $(n - 1) \cdot b(x)^{n-2} \cdot b'(x)$. Write $b(x)^{n-1} = c(x)$. Then if $a(x) = b(x)^n = b(x) \cdot c(x)$, it follows from (b) and the induction hypothesis that

$$
\begin{aligned}
a'(x) &= b(x) \cdot c'(x) + b'(x) \cdot c(x) \\
&= b(x) \cdot (n - 1) \cdot b(x)^{n-2} \cdot b'(x) + b'(x) \cdot b(x)^{n-1} \\
&= (n - 1) \cdot b(x)^{n-1} \cdot b'(x) + b(x)^{n-1} \cdot b'(x) \\
&= n \cdot b(x)^{n-1} \cdot b'(x).
\end{aligned}
$$

Therefore, the induction is complete, and Theorem 9–6.2 is completely proved.

The reader should examine the proof of (b) very carefully, since the method is common in mathematical arguments. Our proof consists of three steps. First, it is shown that the identity is true for the simplest polynomials, that is, the monomials. Next we prove that the set of polynomials satisfying the identity is closed under addition. Finally, since every polynomial is a sum of monomials, it follows that the identity is true for all polynomials. This last step is of course a form of mathematical induction. It is possible to prove (b) by straightforward calculation, but the notation becomes unwieldy.

EXAMPLE 2. Let $a(x) = (x - c)^n$. Then
$$a'(x) = n \cdot (x - c)^{n-1},$$
$$a''(x) = n \cdot (n - 1) \cdot (x - c)^{n-2},$$
$$\vdots$$
$$a^{(n-1)}(x) = n \cdot (n - 1) \cdot \cdots \cdot 2 \cdot (x - c),$$
$$a^{(n)}(x) = n! \cdot 1.$$

The derivative is useful for studying the multiple factors of a polynomial. For this application, we need the following formula, which is a combination of Theorem 9–6.2(b) and (c).

THEOREM 9–6.3. Let $a(x) = cp_1(x)^{n_1} \ldots p_k(x)^{n_k}$, $k \geq 1$, where $c \in F$, $p_1(x), \ldots, p_k(x)$ are polynomials in $F[x]$ which are not constant, and $n_1, \ldots, n_k$ are natural numbers. Then

$$a'(x) = \sum_{j=1}^{k} \frac{a(x)}{p_j(x)} \cdot n_j \cdot p'_j(x).$$

This result is easily obtained from Theorem 9–6.2 by induction on k. We leave the details for the reader to supply.

THEOREM 9–6.4. Let $a(x) = cp_1(x)^{n_1} \ldots p_k(x)^{n_k}$, $k \geq 1$, where
(a) $c \in F$,
(b) $p_1(x), \ldots, p_k(x)$ are distinct monic, irreducible polynomials in $F[x]$,
(c) $n_1 \geq 1, \ldots, n_k \geq 1$, and
(d) F has characteristic zero.
Then the monic greatest common divisor of $a(x)$ and $a'(x)$ is

$$p_1(x)^{n_1-1} \ldots p_k(x)^{n_k-1}.$$

Proof. It is immediate that $p_1(x)^{n_1-1} \ldots p_k(x)^{n_k-1}$ divides $a(x) = cp_1(x)^{n_1} \ldots p_k(x)^{n_k}$. We next observe that $p_1(x)^{n_1-1} \ldots p_k(x)^{n_k-1}$ divides $a(x)/p_j(x)$ for $j = 1, \ldots, k$. Therefore,

$$p_1(x)^{n_1-1} \ldots p_k(x)^{n_k-1}$$

divides

$$a'(x) = \sum_{j=1}^{k} \frac{a(x)}{p_j(x)} \cdot n_j \cdot p'_j(x),$$

where we have used the formula for $a'(x)$ given by Theorem 9–6.3. Thus $p_1(x)^{n_1-1} \ldots p_k(x)^{n_k-1}$ is a common divisor of $a(x)$ and $a'(x)$. To complete the proof, we must show that every common divisor of $a(x)$ and $a'(x)$ divides $p_1(x)^{n_1-1} \ldots p_k(x)^{n_k-1}$. Let $f(x)$ be a common divisor of $a(x)$ and $a'(x)$. Then since $f(x)|a(x)$, it follows that

$$f(x) = dp_1(x)^{m_1} \ldots p_k(x)^{m_k},$$

where $m_1 \leq n_1, \ldots, m_k \leq n_k$. It is now sufficient to show that $m_1 \neq n_1$, $\ldots, m_k \neq n_k$, for in this case $m_1 \leq n_1 - 1, \ldots, m_k \leq n_k - 1$, so that $f(x)$ divides $p_1(x)^{n_1-1} \ldots p_k(x)^{n_k-1}$. Assume that $m_1 = n_1$. Then $f(x)|a'(x)$ implies that $p_1(x)^{n_1}|a'(x)$. Moreover,

$$p_1(x)^{n_1} \Big| \sum_{j=2}^{k} \frac{a(x)}{p_j(x)} \cdot n_j p'_j(x).$$

Therefore, $p_1(x)^{n_1}$ divides

$$a'(x) - \sum_{j=2}^{k} \frac{a(x)}{p_j(x)} \cdot n_j p_j'(x) = \frac{a(x)}{p_1(x)} \cdot n_1 p_1'(x)$$

$$= c p_1(x)^{n_1-1} p_2(x)^{n_2} \cdots p_k(x)^{n_k} \cdot n_1 p_1'(x).$$

Hence, by the unique factorization theorem, and the fact that $p_1(x), \ldots,$ $p_k(x)$ are distinct monic irreducible polynomials, it follows that $p_1(x)|n_1 p_1'(x)$. We now observe that $n_1 p_1'(x) \neq 0$. In fact, the leading coefficient of $n_1 p_1'(x)$ is $n_1 \cdot \text{Deg}\,[p_1(x)]$ times the identity element of F, which is not zero because of assumption (d). Therefore, $\text{Deg}\,[n_1 p_1'(x)] = \text{Deg}\,[p_1(x)] - 1$. By (9–4.1c), this contradicts $p_1(x)|n_1 p_1'(x)$. This contradiction was obtained by assuming that $m_1 = n_1$. Therefore, $m_1 \neq n_1$, and similarly $m_2 \neq n_2, \ldots, m_k \neq n_k$. As we remarked above, these inequalities imply the theorem.

A special case of Theorem 9–6.4 is worth emphasizing.

THEOREM 9–6.5. If $p(x)$ is an irreducible polynomial in $F[x]$, where F is a field of characteristic zero, then

$$\bigl(p(x), p'(x)\bigr) = 1.$$

Theorem 9–6.4 is useful for factoring certain polynomials, because the derivative, $a'(x)$, and the greatest common divisor, $\bigl(a(x), a'(x)\bigr)$, can both be effectively calculated in $F[x]$.

———————

EXAMPLE 3. We wish to factor

$$a(x) = x^9 + 4x^8 - 16x^6 - 16x^5 + 2x^4 + 13x^3 + 30x^2 + 28x + 8$$

completely in $Q[x]$. The derivative of $a(x)$ is

$$a'(x) = 9x^8 + 32x^7 - 96x^5 - 80x^4 + 8x^3 + 39x^2 + 60x + 28.$$

Denote $d(x) = \bigl(a(x), a'(x)\bigr)$. The Euclidean algorithm yields

$$d(x) = x^4 + 3x^3 - x^2 - 8x - 4.$$

Then $d'(x) = 4x^3 + 9x^2 - 2x - 8$, and

$$\bigl(d(x), d'(x)\bigr) = x + 2.$$

By Theorem 9–6.4, we know that $(x + 2)^2|d(x)$.
Carrying out the division,

$$d(x) = (x + 2)^2(x^2 - x - 1).$$

The polynomial $x^2 - x - 1$ is irreducible in $Q[x]$ (see Problem 3, Section 9–5). Again by Theorem 9–6.4, $(x + 2)^3(x^2 - x - 1)^2$ divides $a(x)$. Dividing, we obtain

$$a(x) = (x + 2)^3(x^2 - x - 1)^2(x^2 + 1).$$

This is the complete factorization of $a(x)$ in $Q[x]$.

Problems

1. Find the derivatives of the following polynomials.

(a) $5x^5 + \frac{1}{2}x^4 + \frac{2}{3}x^2 - x + 6$, in $Q[x]$

(b) $x^4 + \sqrt{2}\,x^2 + 1$, in $R[x]$

(c) $x^5 - ix^3 + (2 + 3i)x^2 + \sqrt{3}\,x + i$, in $C[x]$

(d) $x^n - 1$, in $Q[x]$

(e) $x^n - 1$, in $Z_p[x]$

(f) $x^{p+1} + 1$, in $Z_p[x]$

2. Find the successive derivatives $a''(x)$, $a^{(3)}(x)$, $a^{(4)}(x)$, ... for the polynomials given in Problem 1. In each case, find the smallest natural number m such that $a^{(m)}(x) = 0$.

3. Prove that for any nonzero polynomial $a(x) \in F[x]$ there is a natural number $m \le \mathrm{Deg}\,[a(x)]$ such that $a^{(n)}(x) = 0$ for all $n > m$. Prove that if the characteristic of F is zero, then $m = \mathrm{Deg}\,[a(x)]$. What can m be if the characteristic of F is a prime p?

4. Complete the details of the proof of Theorem 9–6.2(b).

5. Prove Theorem 9–6.3.

6. Use the method of Example 3 to factor the following polynomials completely in the indicated $F[x]$.

(a) $x^5 + 4x^4 + 7x^3 + 8x^2 + 3x + 2$, in $Q[x]$

(b) $x^6 + 6x^5 + 11x^4 + 12x^3 + 19x^2 + 6x + 9$, in $Q[x]$

(c) $x^3 + ix^2 + x + i$, in $C[x]$

(d) $x^4 - 15x^2 - 28x - 12$, in $R[x]$

(e) $x^3 + (2\sqrt{2} + \sqrt{3})x^2 + (2 + 2\sqrt{6})x + 2\sqrt{3}$, in $R[x]$

(f) $x^4 + x^3 + x + 1$, in $Q[x]$

7. Use Theorem 9–6.5 to show that the following polynomials are not irreducible in $Q[x]$.

(a) $x^4 + 2x^3 + 3x^2 + 2x + 1$

(b) $4x^3 + 16x^2 + 21x + 9$

(c) $x^6 + x^4 - x^2 - 1$

8. Show that Theorem 9–6.4 is correct if the assumption that the characteristic of F is zero is replaced by the condition that the characteristic of F is a prime which is larger than $\mathrm{Deg}\,[a(x)]$. Give an example which shows that Theorem 9–6.4 may fail if the assumption (d) is omitted entirely.

9. A nonzero polynomial $a(x)$ in $F[x]$ is said to have a *multiple factor* if there exists a polynomial $b(x) \in F[x]$, of positive degree, such that $b(x)^2 | a(x)$. Prove that if F is a field of characteristic zero, then a polynomial $a(x) \in F[x]$ has a multiple factor if and only if $a(x)$ and $a'(x)$ are not relatively prime.

10. Use the result of Problem 9 to prove that the following polynomials have no multiple factors in $Q[x]$.

(a) $x^4 + x^3 + x^2 + x + 1$
(b) $x^3 + 2x - 1$
(c) $x^n - 1$
(d) $x^5 + 3x^2 + 2x - 4$

11. Let $x^3 + ax + b$ be a polynomial with rational coefficients. Find the condition on a and b in order that the given polynomial have a multiple factor.

9–7 The roots of a polynomial. We now return to our study of the solutions of algebraic equations. The work of the last five sections makes it possible to discuss this subject more critically than we did in Section 9–1.

DEFINITION 9–7.1. Let D be an integral domain, and let A be a commutative ring which contains D as a subring. If

$$a(x) = a_0 + a_1 x + \cdots + a_n x^n \in D[x]$$

and $u \in A$, then the element $a_0 + a_1 u + \cdots + a_n u^n \in A$ is called the *value of $a(x)$ for $x = u$*, and is denoted by $a(u)$. The element $a(u)$ is said to be obtained by *substituting u for x in $a(x)$*.

Since the representation $a(x) = a_0 + a_1 x + \cdots + a_n x^n$ is unique (by Definition 9–2.1), it follows that $a(u)$ is uniquely defined by Definition 9–7.1.

_____

EXAMPLE 1. The polynomial $a(x) = x^3 + 2x + 1$ has coefficients in Z. Suppose that $A = Z[x]$. Then if $u = x - 1$, $a(u) = a(x - 1) = (x - 1)^3 + 2(x - 1) + 1 = x^3 - 3x^2 + 5x - 2$. If $A = Q$ and $u = \frac{1}{2}$, then $a(u) = a(\frac{1}{2}) = (\frac{1}{2})^3 + 2(\frac{1}{2}) + 1 = \frac{17}{8}$.

_____

The substitution process has some elementary properties which are useful.

(9–7.2). Let D be an integral domain which is a subring of a commutative ring A. Let $f(x)$, $a(x)$, and $b(x)$ be in $D[x]$. Suppose that $u \in A$.

(a) If $f(x) = a(x) + b(x)$, then $f(u) = a(u) + b(u)$.
(b) If $f(x) = a(x) \cdot b(x)$, then $f(u) = a(u) \cdot b(u)$.
(c) If $f(x)$ is a constant d in F, then $f(u) = d$.
(d) If $f(x) = a(b(x))$, that is, $f(x)$ is the polynomial obtained by substituting $b(x)$ for x in $a(x)$, then $f(u) = a(b(u))$.

Let us prove (b). Suppose that $a(x) = \sum_{i=0}^{m} a_i x^i$ and $b(x) = \sum_{j=0}^{n} b_j x^j$. Then

$$f(x) = \sum_{k=0}^{m+n} \left(\sum_{i+j=k} a_i b_j \right) x^k.$$

Therefore,

$$a(u) \cdot b(u) = \left(\sum_{i=0}^{m} a_i u^i \right) \cdot \left(\sum_{j=0}^{n} b_j u^j \right) = \sum_{j=0}^{n} \left(\sum_{i=0}^{m} a_i u^i \right) b_j u^j$$

$$= \sum_{j=0}^{n} \sum_{i=0}^{m} a_i b_j u^{i+j} = \sum_{k=0}^{m+n} \left(\sum_{i+j=k} a_i b_j u^k \right)$$

$$= \sum_{k=0}^{m+n} \left(\sum_{i+j=k} a_i b_j \right) u^k = f(u).$$

The property (d) is obtained from (a), (b), and (c) by induction on the degree of $a(x)$.

DEFINITION 9–7.3. Let D be an integral domain, and let A be a commutative ring containing D as a subring. Let $a(x) \in D[x]$. An element c in A is called a *root* of $a(x)$ [or a *zero* of $a(x)$] in A if $a(c) = 0$.

The problem of finding the roots of the polynomial $a(x)$ in A is exactly the same as the problem of solving the equation $a(x) = 0$ in A.

We now restrict our attention to polynomials with coefficients in a field F. The results of Sections 9–3, 9–4, 9–5, and 9–6 (for example, the division algorithm, the properties of greatest common divisors, and the unique factorization theorem) can be used to obtain important information about the roots in F of polynomials in $F[x]$. Since many of the theorems proved in these sections do not apply to polynomials with coefficients in an integral domain, this restriction is essential.

THEOREM 9–7.4. *Remainder theorem.* Let F be a field. If $a(x) \in F[x]$ and $c \in F$, then $a(c)$ is the remainder obtained on dividing $a(x)$ by $x - c$. That is, there is a unique polynomial $q(x) \in F[x]$ such that

$$a(x) = q(x) \cdot (x - c) + a(c).$$

Proof. By the division algorithm,

$$a(x) = q(x) \cdot (x - c) + r(x),$$

where either $r(x) = 0$, or the degree of $r(x)$ is less than the degree of $x - c$. Since $\mathrm{Deg}\,[x - c] = 1$, it follows in either case that $r(x)$ is a constant $d \in F$. By (9–7.2), we obtain

$$a(c) = q(c) \cdot (c - c) + r(c) = 0 + d = d.$$

THEOREM 9–7.5. *Factor theorem.* An element c in the field F is a root of the polynomial $a(x) \in F[x]$ if and only if $x - c$ is a factor of $a(x)$ in $F[x]$.

Proof. By Theorem 9–7.4, the remainder obtained on dividing $a(x)$ by $x - c$ is $a(c)$. Therefore, $x - c$ divides $a(x)$ in $F[x]$ if and only if $a(c) = 0$.

The factor theorem is often useful when one is trying to factor a polynomial.

EXAMPLE 2. By inspection, the polynomial $x^3 + x^2 + x + 1$ has -1 as a root. Thus, by Theorem 9–7.5, $x - (-1) = x + 1$ is a factor of $x^3 + x^2 + x + 1$. Dividing, we find

$$x^3 + x^2 + x + 1 = (x^2 + 1)(x + 1).$$

The polynomial $x^2 + 1$ is irreducible in $Q[x]$ and $R[x]$, because otherwise it would have a real root, by Theorem 9–7.5. Thus, $(x^2 + 1)(x + 1)$ is the complete factorization of $x^3 + x^2 + x + 1$ in $Q[x]$ and $R[x]$. However, in $C[x]$, $x^2 + 1 = (x + i)(x - i)$. Thus,

$$x^3 + x^2 + x + 1 = (x + i)(x - i)(x + 1)$$

is a complete factorization in $C[x]$.

Using the factor theorem and the unique factorization theorem, we can now prove one of the most useful general theorems about the roots of polynomials.

THEOREM 9–7.6. Let F be a field, and let $a(x) \in F[x]$ be a nonzero polynomial of degree n. Then $a(x)$ has at most n distinct roots in F. If $c_1, c_2, \ldots, c_k$ are all of the different roots of $a(x)$ in F, then

$$a(x) = (x - c_1)^{m_1} \cdot (x - c_2)^{m_2} \cdot \cdots \cdot (x - c_k)^{m_k} \cdot b(x),$$

where $m_1, m_2, \ldots,$ and m_k are natural numbers, and $b(x)$ is a nonzero polynomial in $F[x]$ which has no roots in F.

Proof. If $c \in F$ is a root of $a(x)$, then $x - c$ is a monic irreducible factor of $a(x)$ in $F[x]$, by Theorem 9–7.5. By the unique factorization theorem and Theorem 9–3.2(a), $a(x)$ has at most n different monic irreducible factors in $F[x]$. Therefore, $a(x)$ has at most n distinct roots in F. Let these be $c_1, c_2, \ldots, c_k$. Then $x - c_1, x - c_2, \ldots, x - c_k$ must occur among the irreducible factors in the complete factorization of $a(x)$ in $F[x]$. Thus we can write

$$a(x) = (x - c_1)^{m_1} \cdot (x - c_2)^{m_2} \cdot \cdots \cdot (x - c_k)^{m_k} \cdot b(x),$$

where $m_1 \geq 1, m_2 \geq 1, \ldots, m_k \geq 1$, and $b(x)$ is a product of irreducible polynomials which are different from $x - c_1, x - c_2, \ldots,$ and $x - c_k$. If $b(x)$ had a root c in F, then $a(c) = 0$, so that c would be one of $c_1, c_2, \ldots,$ or c_k. By the factor theorem, this would imply that $x - c_j | b(x)$ for some j. This would contradict the fact that $b(x)$ is the product of all the irreducible factors of $a(x)$ which are different from $x - c_1, x - c_2, \ldots,$ and $x - c_k$. Therefore, $b(x)$ has no root in F.

A particularly useful case of Theorem 9–7.6 is the following.

THEOREM 9–7.7. If a monic polynomial $a(x) \in F[x]$ of degree n has n distinct roots $c_1, c_2, \ldots, c_n$ in F, then

$$a(x) = (x - c_1) \cdot (x - c_2) \cdot \cdots \cdot (x - c_n)$$

in $F[x]$.

Proof. By Theorem 9–7.6, it is possible to write

$$a(x) = (x - c_1)^{m_1} \cdot (x - c_2)^{m_2} \cdots \cdot (x - c_n)^{m_n} \cdot b(x),$$

where $m_1, m_2, \ldots, m_n$ are greater than zero. Taking the degrees on both sides, we obtain from Theorem 9–3.2(a),

$$\begin{aligned} n &= \text{Deg}\,[a(x)] \\ &= \text{Deg}\,[(x - c_1)^{m_1}] + \text{Deg}\,[(x - c_2)^{m_2}] + \cdots \\ &\qquad\qquad + \text{Deg}\,[(x - c_n)^{m_n}] + \text{Deg}\,[b(x)] \\ &= m_1 + m_2 + \cdots + m_n + \text{Deg}\,[b(x)]. \end{aligned}$$

Since $m_1, m_2, \ldots, m_n$ are natural numbers, this equality implies that $m_1 = m_2 = \cdots = m_n = 1$, and $\text{Deg}\,[b(x)] = 0$. Hence, $b(x)$ is a nonzero constant, and since $a(x)$ is monic this constant must be 1. Thus,

$$a(x) = (x - c_1) \cdot (x - c_2) \cdot \cdots \cdot (x - c_n).$$

A root $c \in F$ of the polynomial $a(x) \in F[x]$ is said to have *multiplicity* m, or to be an *m-fold* root of $a(x)$ if $(x - c)^m$ divides $a(x)$, but $(x - c)^{m+1}$ does not divide $a(x)$ in $F[x]$. Thus, c is a root of multiplicity m of $a(x)$ if

$$a(x) = (x - c)^m \cdot b(x),$$

where $b(x) \in F[x]$ is a polynomial such that $b(c) \neq 0$. Roots of multiplicity one are usually called *simple* roots. Roots of multiplicity two or more are called *multiple* roots. If the field F has characteristic zero, then it follows from Theorem 9–6.4 that a root of multiplicity $m > 1$ of $a(x)$ is a root of multiplicity $m - 1$ of $a'(x)$, and a simple root of $a(x)$ is not a root of $a'(x)$.

EXAMPLE 3. Let us find the roots in C of $x^7 + 2x^6 + 3x^5 + 2x^4 + x^3$, along with the multiplicities of each root. We have

$$
\begin{aligned}
x^7 + 2x^6 + 3x^5 + 2x^4 + x^3 &= x^3(x^4 + 2x^3 + 3x^2 + 2x + 1) \\
&= x^3[x^4 + 2x^2(x+1) + x^2 + 2x + 1] \\
&= x^3[x^4 + 2x^2(x+1) + (x+1)^2] \\
&= x^3[x^2 + (x+1)]^2 = x^3(x^2 + x + 1)^2
\end{aligned}
$$

The roots of $x^2 + x + 1$ can be obtained using Theorem 8–2.7. They are

$$
-\tfrac{1}{2} + i(\sqrt{3}/2) \qquad \text{and} \qquad -\tfrac{1}{2} - i(\sqrt{3}/2).
$$

Therefore,

$$
\begin{aligned}
x^7 + 2x^6 + 3x^5 &+ 2x^4 + x^3 \\
&= x^3 \cdot (x - [-\tfrac{1}{2} + i(\sqrt{3}/2)])^2 \cdot (x - [-\tfrac{1}{2} - i(\sqrt{3}/2)])^2,
\end{aligned}
$$

and the desired roots are 0, $-\tfrac{1}{2} + i(\sqrt{3}/2)$, and $-\tfrac{1}{2} - i(\sqrt{3}/2)$, with multiplicities 3, 2, and 2, respectively.

Theorem 9–7.6 has a useful application in the theory of numbers.

THEOREM 9–7.8. Let p be a prime number. Suppose that

$$
a(x) = a_0 + a_1 x + \cdots + a_n x^n
$$

is a polynomial with integral coefficients, such that $a_n \not\equiv 0 \pmod{p}$. Then there are at most n integers d which are incongruent modulo p, and satisfy

$$
a(d) \equiv 0 \pmod{p}.
$$

If $a(x) = a_0 + a_1 x + \cdots + a_n x^n$ and $b(x) = b_0 + b_1 x + \cdots + b_n x^n$ are polynomials with integral coefficients, it is customary to write $a(x) \equiv b(x) \pmod{p}$ if

$$
a_0 \equiv b_0 \pmod{p}, \qquad a_1 \equiv b_1 \pmod{p}, \qquad \ldots,
$$

and

$$
a_n \equiv b_n \pmod{p}.
$$

It is clear from Theorem 5–6.3, which gives the properties of congruence, that

$$a(x) \equiv b(x) \ (\mathrm{mod}\ p)$$

implies $a(d) \equiv b(d) \ (\mathrm{mod}\ p)$ for any integer d, and

$$d \equiv e \ (\mathrm{mod}\ p)$$

implies $a(d) \equiv a(e) \ (\mathrm{mod}\ p)$ for any $a(x) \in Z[x]$. Because of these two observations, the study of the congruence modulo p of polynomials in $Z[x]$ is equivalent to the study of polynomials with coefficients in the field Z_p. Theorem 9–7.8 is simply a reinterpretation of Theorem 9–7.6 from this new viewpoint. So that the reader can get a better understanding of the method of translating theorems about the field Z_p into statements about congruences modulo p, we will give the proof of Theorem 9–7.8 in full detail.

Suppose that $d_1, d_2, \ldots, d_k$ are integers such that

$$d_i \not\equiv d_j \ (\mathrm{mod}\ p) \qquad \text{for } i \neq j,$$

and

$$a(d_i) \equiv 0 \ (\mathrm{mod}\ p) \qquad \text{for all } i.$$

We must show that $k \leq n$. Let $b_0, b_1, \ldots, b_n$ be the remainders obtained on dividing $a_0, a_1, \ldots, a_n$, respectively, by p. Let $e_1, e_2, \ldots, e_k$ be the remainders on dividing $d_1, d_2, \ldots, d_k$ by p. That is,

$$a_j \equiv b_j \ (\mathrm{mod}\ p), \qquad 0 \leq b_i < p,$$

and

$$d_i \equiv e_i \ (\mathrm{mod}\ p), \qquad 0 \leq e_i < p.$$

for $0 \leq j \leq n$ and $1 \leq i \leq k$. Let

$$b(x) = b_0 + b_1 x + \cdots + b_n x^n.$$

Then $a(x) \equiv b(x) \ (\mathrm{mod}\ p)$, and

$$b(e_i) \equiv 0 \ (\mathrm{mod}\ p).$$

The integers $b_0, b_1, \ldots, b_n$, and $e_1, e_2, \ldots, e_k$ can be regarded as elements of the field Z_p. Thus, $b(x)$ can be considered as a polynomial with coefficients in $Z_p[x]$. Since $a_n \not\equiv 0 \ (\mathrm{mod}\ p)$, the leading coefficient b_n of $b(x)$ is not zero. Therefore, Deg $[b(x)] = n$. Note that the addition and multiplication operations of Z_p are different from the operations in Z, so that the result of substituting e_i into $b(x)$ when e_i is thought of as an element of Z_p, and $b(x)$ is considered as belonging to $Z_p[x]$ will be different from the result obtained when e_i is taken as an integer, and $b(x)$ as a polynomial with integral coefficients. In Z_p we have

$$b(e_i) = b_0 \oplus (b_1 \odot e_i) \oplus (b_2 \odot e_i \odot e_i) \oplus \cdots$$
$$\oplus (b_n \odot e_i \odot e_i \odot \cdots \odot e_i),$$

whereas in Z, $b(e_i) = b_0 + b_1 e_i + b_2 e_i^2 + \cdots + b_n e_i^n$. However, by Theorem 6–3.4,

$$b_0 \oplus (b_1 \odot e_i) \oplus (b_2 \odot e_i \odot e_i) \oplus \cdots \oplus (b_n \odot e_i \odot e_i \odot \cdots \odot e_i)$$
$$\equiv b_0 + b_1 e_i + b_2 e_i^2 + \cdots + b_n e_i^n \equiv 0 \pmod{p}.$$

Thus, in Z_p, $b(e_i) = 0$. That is, e_i is a root of $b(x)$ in Z_p. Since

$$d_i \not\equiv d_j \pmod{p} \qquad \text{for} \qquad i \neq j,$$

it follows that $e_1, e_2, \ldots, e_k$ are distinct elements of Z_p. Therefore,

$$k \leq \operatorname{Deg} [b(x)] = n,$$

by Theorem 9–7.6.

EXAMPLE 4. We illustrate the proof of Theorem 9–7.8 by an example. Let $a(x) = x^3 - x^2 + x + 9$. Then

$$a(x) \equiv b(x) = x^3 + 4x^2 + x + 4 \pmod 5.$$

Considered as a polynomial with integral coefficients,

$$b(0) = 4, \qquad b(1) = 10, \qquad b(2) = 30, \qquad b(3) = 70, \qquad b(4) = 136.$$

However, if $b(x)$ is thought of as an element of $Z_5[x]$,

$$b(0) = 4, \qquad b(1) = 0, \qquad b(2) = 0, \qquad b(3) = 0, \qquad b(4) = 1.$$

Thus, $b(x)$ has roots 1, 2, and 3 in Z_5. Since Z_5 is a field and $\operatorname{Deg} [b(x)] = 3$, the polynomial $b(x)$ cannot have more than three roots. Returning to the original polynomial $a(x)$, we see that

$$a(1) \equiv 0 \pmod 5, \qquad a(2) \equiv 0 \pmod 5, \qquad a(3) \equiv 0 \pmod 5,$$

and if d is any integer such that $a(d) \equiv 0 \pmod 5$, then either $d \equiv 1 \pmod 5$, $d \equiv 2 \pmod 5$, or else $d \equiv 3 \pmod 5$.

Although at first glance it seems somewhat trivial, Theorem 9–7.8 is a powerful tool in number theory. To support this statement, we digress from our study of the theory of equations and use Theorem 9–7.8 to prove the fact, mentioned in Section 5–8, that if p is a prime, then there are $\varphi(\varphi(p)) = \varphi(p - 1)$ primitive roots modulo p among the numbers $1, 2, \ldots,$ $p - 1$. The reader who is not familiar with the material in Sections 1–6 and 5–8 can pass on to the next section.

Recall that if a is an integer prime to p, then the order of a modulo p is the smallest natural number d such that $a^d \equiv 1 \pmod{p}$. By Theorem 5–8.9, the order d of a modulo p is a divisor of $p - 1$, and a is called a primitive root modulo p if its order is $p - 1$. The desired result is a special case of the following theorem.

THEOREM 9–7.9. Let p be a prime. Suppose that $d|p - 1$. Then among the numbers $1, 2, \ldots, p - 1$, there are exactly $\varphi(d)$ integers which have order d modulo p.

The proof is carried out in three stages. Only the first step uses Theorem 9–7.8.

(1) Among the integers of the set $S = \{1, 2, \ldots, p - 1\}$ there are exactly d which satisfy $x^d - 1 \equiv 0 \pmod{p}$.

Proof. Since $d|p - 1$, we have

$$x^{p-1} - 1 = (x^d - 1)c(x),$$

where $c(x) = 1 + x^d + x^{2d} + \cdots + x^{k \cdot d}$, with $k = [(p - 1)/d] - 1$. By Fermat's theorem,

$$x^{p-1} - 1 \equiv 0 \pmod{p}$$

has $p - 1$ solutions in S. By Theorem 9–7.8,

$$c(x) \equiv 0 \pmod{p}$$

can have at most $kd = p - 1 - d$ solutions in S. Therefore,

$$x^d - 1 \equiv 0 \pmod{p}$$

must have at least d solutions in S. On the other hand, by Theorem 9–7.8, there can be at most d solutions of $x^d - 1 \equiv 0 \pmod{p}$ in the set S.

(2) To obtain Theorem 9–7.9 from the result (1), we will use induction on d. To carry out this induction, an important identity is needed:

$$\sum_{e|d} \varphi(e) = d,$$

that is, the sum of $\varphi(e)$ over all natural numbers e which divide d (including 1 and d) is exactly equal to d.

Proof. Let $T = \{1, 2, \ldots, d\}$. For each divisor e of d, define $T_e = \{k \in T | (d, k) = e\}$. Then each number $k \in T$ belongs to exactly one of the sets T_e, with $e|d$, that is, T is the union of the pairwise disjoint collection $\{T_e | e \text{ divides } d\}$. Hence, by Theorem 1–6.4,

$$d = |T| = \sum_{e|d} |T_e|.$$

In order to determine $|T_e|$, the number of elements in T_e, note that k belongs to T_e if and only if $(d, k) = e$, and that $(d, k) = e$ is equivalent to $e|k$ and $(d/e, k/e) = 1$. Hence, there is a one-to-one correspondence between T_e and the set $\{m \in Z | 1 \leq m \leq d/e, (d/e, m) = 1\}$, given by

$$m \leftrightarrow e \cdot m.$$

Therefore, $|T_e| = |\{m \in Z | 1 \leq m \leq d/e, (d/e, m) = 1\}| = \varphi(d/e)$, by the definition of the totient, Definition 5–8.5. Consequently,

$$d = \sum_{e|d} \varphi(d/e).$$

As e ranges over the divisors of d, so does d/e, in reverse order. Hence,

$$\sum_{e|d} \varphi(e) = \sum_{e|d} \varphi(d/e) = d.$$

(3) We can now prove Theorem 9–7.9. There is exactly one natural number a in the set $S = \{1, 2, \ldots, p - 1\}$ which has order 1 modulo p, namely, $a = 1$. Hence, the theorem is true for $d = 1$. We can therefore make the induction hypothesis that if $e|p - 1$ and $e < d$, then there are exactly $\varphi(e)$ integers in S which have order e modulo p. For each divisor e of d, define

$$S_e = \{a \in S | a \text{ has order } e \text{ modulo } p\}.$$

It is obvious that the collection $\{S_e | e \text{ divides } d\}$ is pairwise disjoint. By Theorem 5–8.9,

$$\cup(\{S_e | e \text{ divides } d\}) = \{a \in S | a^d - 1 \equiv 0 \ (\mathrm{mod}\ p)\}.$$

Hence, by (1),

$$d = \sum_{e|d} |S_e| = |S_d| + \sum_{e|d, e<d} |S_e|.$$

By the induction hypothesis, $|S_e| = \varphi(e)$ if $e|d$ and $e < d$. Therefore, using (2), we have

$$|S_d| + \sum_{e|d, e<d} \varphi(e) = d = \sum_{e|d} \varphi(e) = \varphi(d) + \sum_{e|d, e<d} \varphi(e).$$

Consequently,

$$|S_d| = \varphi(d).$$

This completes the induction, and proves the theorem.

PROBLEMS

1. Without actual division, find the remainder when (a) $x^3 + 2x - 4$ is divided by $x - 1$; (b) $x^{25} + 14x^{17} + 24$ is divided by $x + 1$; (c) $x^5 + 12x^4 + 13x^2 + x + 27$ is divided by $x + 3$.

2. Completely factor the following polynomials in $C[x]$.

   (a) $x^2 + ix + 2$
   (b) $x^8 - 1$
   (c) $x^4 + x^2 + 1$
   (d) $x^4 - 2x^3 - 5x^2 - 2x + 24$
   (e) $x^3 - 2$
   (f) $x^3 - 5x^2 - 9x + 12$

3. Let $a(x) = x^n - 1$. Find $a(u)$ when u has the following values.

   (a) $u = -1$
   (b) $u = i$
   (c) $u = x + 1$
   (d) $u = x^n - 1$

4. Find all monic fifth-degree polynomials $f(x)$ in $C[x]$ such that (a) $f(x)$ has i as a root of multiplicity four; (b) $f(x)$ has 0, 1, 2, and 3 as simple roots; (c) $f(x)$ has 1 and i as roots of multiplicity two; (d) $f(x)$ has i and $-i$ as simple roots and -1 as a root of multiplicity two.

5. Show that the sum of the multiplicities of the roots of a polynomial $a(x) \in F[x]$ is less than or equal to the degree of $a(x)$.

6. Show that if $a(x)$ and $b(x)$ are polynomials of degree less than n in $F[x]$, and if $a(d_i) = b(d_i)$ for $i = 1, 2, \ldots, n$, where $d_1, d_2, \ldots, d_n$ are distinct elements of F, then $a(x) = b(x)$ in $F[x]$.

7. Let $a(x) = x^p - x + 1 \in Z_p[x]$. Prove that $a(d) = 1$ for all $d \in Z_p$.

8. Prove *Taylor's theorem*: If $f(x)$ is a polynomial of degree n in $F[x]$, where F has characteristic zero, and if c is any element of F, then

$$f(x) = f(c) + [f'(c)/1!](x - c) + [f''(c)/2!](x - c)^2 + \cdots$$
$$+ [f^{(n)}(c)/n!](x - c)^n.$$

[*Hint:* Use Theorem 9–3.5 and Example 2, Section 9–6.]

9. State which of postulates of ring theory are used in the proof of (9–7.2b). Prove (9–7.2c).

10. Prove that the derivative of $a(b(x))$ is $a'(b(x)) \cdot b'(x)$.

11. Show that if $f(x) = ax^2 + bx + c \in F[x]$, $a \neq 0$, then either (a) $f(x)$ has two distinct roots in F, (b) $f(x)$ has one root of multiplicity two in F, or (c) $f(x)$ is irreducible in $F[x]$.

12. Show that in $Z_p[x]$ there are exactly $\frac{1}{2}p(p-1)$ polynomials of the form $x^2 + ax + b$ which are irreducible. [*Hint:* Show that there are $\frac{1}{2}p(p+1)$ polynomials of this form which are reducible.]

13. Let $a(x)$ be a monic polynomial of degree n in $Z[x]$. Suppose that p is a prime. Assume that $d_1, d_2, \ldots, d_n$ are integers such that $d_i \not\equiv d_j \pmod p$ if $i \neq j$, and $a(d_i) \equiv 0 \pmod p$ for all i. Prove that

$$a(x) \equiv (x - d_1)(x - d_2) \ldots (x - d_n) \pmod p.$$

14. Use Problem 13 and Fermat's theorem to show that if p is a prime, then

$$x^{p-1} - 1 \equiv (x - 1)(x - 2) \ldots [x - (p - 1)] \pmod p.$$

From this identity, deduce Wilson's theorem:

$$(p - 1)! \equiv -1 \pmod p.$$

9–8 The fundamental theorem of algebra. We come now to what is probably the most important result in the theory of equations.

THEOREM 9–8.1. *The fundamental theorem of algebra.* If $f(x) \in C[x]$ is a nonzero polynomial with $\mathrm{Deg}\,[f(x)] \geq 1$, then $f(x)$ has at least one root in C.

This theorem was surmised as early as the sixteenth century. Several incorrect proofs of it were published before a satisfactory proof was found by Gauss in 1797. Gauss ultimately gave five different proofs of the fundamental theorem of algebra, each of which introduced new ideas and methods which have greatly influenced the development of mathematics. Of course, many other proofs of this theorem have been discovered since Gauss's time. Unfortunately, all of the known paths from elementary mathematical principles to Theorem 9–8.1 are quite long. We will not try to give a proof in this section. The reader who is interested in seeing a complete and correct proof can study Appendix 3 of this book, after he has read the remainder of this chapter. It is possible for us to give a geometrical argument which shows that the fundamental theorem of algebra is plausible.

Let $f(x) = a_n x^n + a_{n-1} x^{n-1} + \cdots + a_0 \in C[x]$, where $a_n \neq 0$ and $n \geq 1$. Since every root of

$$a_n^{-1} f(x) = x^n + (a_n^{-1} a_{n-1}) x^{n-1} + \cdots + (a_n^{-1} a_0)$$

is also a root of $f(x)$, we can assume that $a_n = 1$. If $a_0 = 0$, then $x = 0$ is a

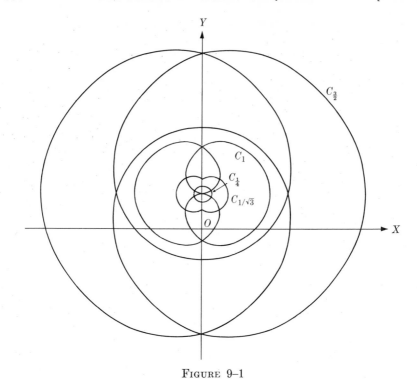

FIGURE 9–1

root of $f(x)$. Therefore, assume that $a_0 \neq 0$, that is,

$$f(x) = x^n + a_{n-1}x^{n-1} + \cdots + a_0, \qquad a_0 \neq 0.$$

If a complex number z is substituted for x in $f(x)$, then we obtain a complex number $f(z)$. We interpret the numbers z and $f(z)$ as points in the complex plane. As z ranges over a circle of radius r with center at the origin O of the complex plane, the corresponding point $f(z)$ describes a closed curve C_r. Figure 9–1 shows the curves $C_{1/4}$, $C_{1/\sqrt{3}}$, C_1, and $C_{3/2}$ for the polynomial $f(x) = x^3 + x + i$. If $r = 0$, then C_r is not a curve, but instead it is the point a_0, and for small positive values of r, C_r lies very close to this point. In particular, for sufficiently small values of r, C_r does not enclose the origin of the complex plane, because $a_0 \neq 0$. If r is very large, the curve C_r is approximated by the curve C'_r corresponding to the polynomial x^n, since for values of z which have large absolute value, the term z^n in $f(z)$ dominates the sum $a_{n-1}z^{n-1} + \cdots + a_1z + a_0$ of the remaining terms. If $z = r(\cos\theta + i\sin\theta)$, then $z^n = r^n(\cos n\theta + i\sin n\theta)$ (see Section 8–4). Thus, C'_r is a circle of radius r^n which is traversed n times as z circles the origin once. From this observation, it follows that for large r, C_r is a curve which encircles the origin of the complex plane n times and lies relatively close to the circle with center O and radius r^n. As r increases from small to large values, C_r is deformed from a curve which does not enclose the origin into one which encircles the origin n times. The reader should try to visualize this deformation process in Fig. 9–1. It is geometrically evident that at some stage of this deformation process, the corresponding curve must pass through O. That is, there exists an $r > 0$ such that C_r passes through O. By definition of C_r, this means that for some complex number z with $|z| = r$, the value of $f(x)$ for $x = z$ is 0. Thus, z is the desired root of $f(x)$.

It is possible to make this intuitive argument into a valid proof of the fundamental theorem of algebra by giving exact definitions of the geometrical concept of a curve, of the deformation of one curve into another, and of the idea of a curve enclosing a point. In addition, it is necessary to establish some properties of these notions which seem obvious, but turn out to be very difficult to prove. To carry out this program would require a fairly deep penetration into the field of geometry which mathematicians call *topology*. Since our main interest in this book is algebra, we will not pursue this topic.

We now examine some of the consequences of the fundamental theorem of algebra.

THEOREM 9–8.2. The irreducible polynomials in $C[x]$ are exactly the polynomials of degree one. Hence, every polynomial $a(x) \in C[x]$ of positive degree can be written in the form

$$a(x) = b \cdot (x - c_1) \cdot (x - c_2) \cdot \dots \cdot (x - c_n),$$

where b is a nonzero complex number, $c_1, c_2, \dots, c_n$ are all of the roots of $a(x)$ in C (possibly with repetitions), and $n = \text{Deg}\,[a(x)]$. This factorization of $a(x)$ is unique up to the order of the factors.

Proof. Suppose that $p(x)$ is an irreducible polynomial in $C[x]$. By Definition 9–5.1, $p(x) \neq 0$ and $\text{Deg}\,[p(x)] > 0$. Therefore, by the fundamental theorem, $p(x)$ has a root $c \in C$. By the factor theorem, $x - c$ divides $p(x)$ in $C[x]$. Thus, $x - c = b \cdot p(x)$ for some $b \neq 0$ in C (by Definition 9–5.1), so that $p(x) = b^{-1} \cdot (x - c)$ has degree one. Since polynomials of degree one are always irreducible (see Example 2, Section 9–5), this proves the first statement of Theorem 9–8.2. The second statement is a consequence of the unique factorization theorem, taking into account what we have just shown.

The reader should bear in mind that since $Z \subset Q \subset R \subset C$, polynomials with coefficients in Z, Q, or R are polynomials in $C[x]$, and therefore they have roots in C. This observation leads to the characterization of the irreducible polynomials in $R[x]$. First we need an important property of the complex roots of real polynomials.

THEOREM 9–8.3. Let $f(x) \in R[x] \subseteq C[x]$. If $c = a + ib$ is a complex number which is a root of $f(x)$, then the complex conjugate $\bar{c} = a - ib$ of c is also a root of $f(x)$.

Of course, it may happen that c itself is real, in which case $\bar{c} = c$. In this case, the theorem is trivial. To prove this theorem, let

$$f(x) = a_0 + a_1 x + \cdots + a_n x^n,$$

where $a_0, a_1, \ldots, a_n$ are real numbers. Then

$$a_0 + a_1 c + \cdots + a_n c^n = f(c) = 0.$$

Taking the complex conjugate of the left-hand side of this equation, we obtain from Theorem 8–2.2

$$\bar{a}_0 + \bar{a}_1 \bar{c} + \cdots + \bar{a}_n \bar{c}^n = 0.$$

Since $a_0, a_1, \ldots, a_n$ are real, it follows that $\bar{a}_0 = a_0, \bar{a}_1 = a_1, \ldots$, and $\bar{a}_n = a_n$. Therefore,

$$f(\bar{c}) = a_0 + a_1 \bar{c} + \cdots + a_n \bar{c}^n = \bar{a}_0 + \bar{a}_1 \bar{c} + \cdots + \bar{a}_n \bar{c}^n = 0.$$

Thus, $\bar{c}$ is a root of $f(x)$.

THEOREM 9–8.4. The irreducible polynomials in $R[x]$ are exactly the polynomials of degree one and the polynomials

$$ax^2 + bx + c,$$

with a, b, and c real, and $b^2 - 4ac < 0$. Hence, every polynomial $a(x) \in R[x]$ of positive degree can be written in the form

$$a(x) = b \cdot (x - c_1) \cdot (x - c_2) \cdot \cdots \cdot (x - c_r) \cdot d_1(x) \cdot d_2(x) \cdot \cdots \cdot d_s(x),$$

where b is a nonzero real number, $c_1, c_2, \ldots, c_r$ are all of the roots of $a(x)$ in R (possibly with repetitions), and $d_1(x), d_2(x), \ldots, d_s(x)$ are quadratic polynomials in $R[x]$ which have no real roots.

Proof. Suppose that $p(x)$ is an irreducible polynomial in $R[x]$. Then $p(x) \neq 0$ and $\text{Deg}\,[p(x)] > 0$. By Theorem 9–8.1, there is a complex number z such that $p(z) = 0$. If z is real, then $x - z$ divides $p(x)$ in $R[x]$, so that $p(x)$ has degree one, as in the proof of Theorem 9–8.2. Therefore, suppose that z is not real. By Theorem 9–8.3, $\bar{z}$ is a root of $p(x)$, and $\bar{z} \neq z$. Let

$$d(x) = (x - z)(x - \bar{z}) = x^2 - (z + \bar{z})x + z\bar{z}.$$

By Theorem 8–2.2(f), $z + \bar{z} = 2\Re(z)$ is real, and by Theorem 8–2.4(b), $z\bar{z} = |z|^2$ is real. Therefore, $d(x) \in R[x]$. By the division algorithm, we can write

$$p(x) = q(x) \cdot d(x) + r(x),$$

where $q(x)$ and $r(x)$ are in $R[x]$, and either $r(x) = 0$, or else $\text{Deg}\,[r(x)] < \text{Deg}\,[d(x)] = 2$. Since

$$r(z) = p(z) - q(z) \cdot d(z) = 0 - q(z) \cdot 0 = 0,$$

and

$$r(\bar{z}) = p(\bar{z}) - q(\bar{z}) \cdot d(\bar{z}) = 0 - q(\bar{z}) \cdot 0 = 0,$$

it follows that $r(x)$ must be the zero polynomial. Indeed, otherwise the number of roots of $r(x)$ would exceed $\text{Deg}\,[r(x)]$, which is impossible by Theorem 9–7.6. Thus, $d(x)$ divides $p(x)$ in $R[x]$. Since $p(x)$ is irreducible,

$$p(x) = a \cdot d(x) = ax^2 + bx + c,$$

where a is some nonzero real number, and $b = -a \cdot (z + \bar{z})$, $c = a \cdot z\bar{z}$ are also real. Moreover, by Theorem 8–2.2(f),

$$b^2 - 4ac = a^2(z^2 + 2z\bar{z} + \bar{z}^2) - 4a^2z\bar{z} = a^2(z^2 - 2z\bar{z} + \bar{z}^2)$$
$$= a^2(z - \bar{z})^2 = a^2[2i\mathcal{I}(z)]^2 = -4a^2\mathcal{I}(z)^2 < 0,$$

since $a \neq 0$ and $\mathcal{I}(z) \neq 0$ (because z is not real). This shows that every irreducible polynomial in $R[x]$ is either linear or of the form $ax^2 + bx + c$ with $b^2 - 4ac < 0$. Conversely, all such polynomials are irreducible in $R[x]$ (see Problem 3, Section 9–5). The last statement of Theorem 9–8.4 is a specialization of the unique factorization theorem to the ring of polynomials with real coefficients.

EXAMPLE 1. The knowledge of a single root of a polynomial often simplifies the task of finding the remaining roots. For instance, if we are given that $1 + i$ is a root of $x^4 - 4x^3 + 5x^2 - 2x - 2$, then it follows from Theorem 9–8.3 that $1 - i$ is also a root. Dividing $x^4 - 4x^3 + 5x^2 - 2x - 2$ by

$$[x - (1 + i)][x - (1 - i)] = x^2 - 2x + 2$$

gives the quotient $x^2 - 2x - 1$. By Theorem 8–2.7, the roots of $x^2 - 2x - 1$ are

$$\tfrac{1}{2}(2 + \sqrt{4 + 4}) = 1 + \sqrt{2},$$

and

$$\tfrac{1}{2}(2 - \sqrt{4 + 4}) = 1 - \sqrt{2}.$$

Therefore, all of the roots of $x^4 - 4x^3 + 5x^2 - 2x - 2$ are

$$1 + i, \qquad 1 - i, \qquad 1 + \sqrt{2}, \qquad \text{and} \qquad 1 - \sqrt{2}.$$

EXAMPLE 2. Sometimes it is necessary to determine a polynomial from the knowledge of its roots. If the polynomial belongs to $C[x]$ and the leading coefficient, and all of the complex roots, together with their multiplicities, are given, then Theorem 9–8.2 solves this problem. For example, the monic polynomial which has i as a double root, $1 + i$ as a simple root, and 1 as a simple root is

$$(x - i)^2[x - (1 + i)](x - 1)$$
$$= x^4 - (2 + 3i)x^3 - (2 - 5i)x^2 + (4 - i)x - (1 + i).$$

Very often in such problems, the information about the roots is incomplete, so that it is necessary to use other data. For example, suppose that we wish to find every real, cubic polynomial $a(x)$ with leading coefficient 1 and constant term 1, which has i as one of its roots. Since $a(x)$ is to have real coefficients and i is a root, it follows from Theorem 9–8.3 that $-i$ is also a root. Let z be the remaining root. Then

$$(x - i)[x - (-i)](x - z) = a(x) = x^3 + bx^2 + cx + 1.$$

Multiplying out the left-hand side of this equality gives

$$x^3 - zx^2 + x - z = x^3 + bx^2 + cx + 1.$$

Therefore, $b = -z$, $c = 1$, $1 = -z$. Thus, the only polynomial with the required property is $x^3 + x^2 + x + 1$. Of course it can also be seen that $z = -1$ by observing that the product of the roots of a cubic polynomial is equal to the negative of the constant term divided by the leading coefficient.

PROBLEMS

1. Using Fig. 9–1, estimate roughly the absolute values of the roots of the polynomial $x^3 + x + i$.

2. Find all of the roots of the following polynomials, making use of the given data.
   (a) $x^3 + 6x^2 - 24x + 160$, one root of which is $2 - 2\sqrt{3}\, i$.
   (b) $x^3 + (1 - 2i)x^2 - (1 + 2i)x - 1$, which has a double root.
   (c) $x^5 - 3x^4 + 4x^3 - 4x + 4$, which has $1 + i$ as a double root.

3. Find the monic polynomial $a(x)$ in $C[x]$ from the given data.

(a) $a(x)$ has simple roots 1, 2, i, $1 + 4i$, and $1 - 4i$, and no others.

(b) $a(x)$ has i as a root of multiplicity three and Deg $[a(x)] = 3$.

(c) $a(x)$ is real, of the fourth degree, and has $1 - i$ and i among its roots.

(d) $a(x)$ is a real cubic polynomial of the form $x^3 + bx + c$, and $2 + i$ is a root of $a(x)$.

4. Let r_1, r_2, and r_3 be the roots of the cubic polynomial

$$x^3 + ax^2 + bx + c.$$

Express a, b, and c in terms of r_1, r_2, and r_3. Obtain similar results for monic polynomials of degree four.

5. Using Theorem 9–8.4, prove that every real polynomial of odd degree has at least one real root. [*Remark.* In Section 9–10, we will give a proof of this fact which does not make indirect use of the fundamental theorem of algebra.]

6. Let $f(x)$ be a monic polynomial in $R[x]$ such that $f(x)$ has no roots in R. Prove that $f(a) > 0$ for all real numbers a.

7. Let $f(x) = ax^{2n} + bx^n + c$ be a polynomial in $C[x]$, where $a \neq 0$ and $n \geq 1$.

(a) Show how Theorems 8–2.7 and 8–4.3 can be used to find all of the roots of $f(x)$.

(b) Find the roots of $x^6 - 2ix^3 + (-1 - i)$.

8. Prove that if $f(x) \in R[x]$ has the complex root c with multiplicity m, then $f(x)$ also has $\bar{c}$ as a root of multiplicity m.

*9–9 The solution of third- and fourth-degree equations. The fundamental theorem of algebra is what mathematicians call an *existence theorem*. It asserts that certain numbers always exist, but it gives no method for finding them. The Italian mathematicians of the Renaissance period were mainly concerned with methods by which they could actually determine roots of particular equations. It was a remarkable achievement that they† discovered formulas which explicitly exhibited the solutions of third- and fourth-degree equations.

The expressions which give the roots of the general cubic equation can easily be derived by formal manipulation. Suppose that $x = z$ is a solution of

$$x^3 + bx^2 + cx + d = 0, \tag{9–3}$$

---

† Scipio Ferro discovered a solution of $x^3 + ax = b$, where a and b are positive real numbers. This was rediscovered and generalized somewhat by Tartaglia, who showed his work to Cardan under a pledge of secrecy. Cardan published the result of Ferro and Tartaglia, together with some discoveries of his own, but he neglected to mention that the solution of the cubic equation was not his own work.

where b, c, and d are arbitrary complex numbers. Let $w = z + b/3$. Then

$$
\begin{aligned}
0 &= z^3 + bz^2 + cz + d \\
&= (w - b/3)^3 + b(w - b/3)^2 + c(w - b/3) + d \\
&= [w^3 - bw^2 + (b^2/3)w - (b/3)^3] + b[w^2 - 2(b/3)w + (b/3)^2] \\
&\qquad\qquad\qquad\qquad\qquad\qquad + c(w - b/3) + d \\
&= w^3 + (c - b^2/3)w + [d - bc/3 + 2(b/3)^3].
\end{aligned}
$$

Conversely, if w satisfies

$$w^3 + (c - b^2/3)w + [d - bc/3 + 2(b/3)^3] = 0,$$

then it is easy to see that $x = w - b/3$ is a solution of $x^3 + bx^2 + cx + d = 0$. Therefore, we can restrict our attention to *reduced cubic equations*, that is, equations of the form

$$x^3 + px + q = 0, \tag{9-4}$$

where the coefficients p and q are related to the coefficients of the general cubic equation (9-3) by

$$p = c - b^2/3, \qquad q = d - bc/3 + 2(b/3)^3. \tag{9-5}$$

If $p = 0$ in (9-4), then the reduced cubic equation has the special form

$$x^3 = -q.$$

In this case, the three roots of the equation are the three complex cube roots of $-q$ which can be found by Theorem 8-4.3. Thus, we may assume that $p \neq 0$ in (9-4). Suppose that w is a solution of (9-4). Let u satisfy $u^2 - wu - p/3 = 0$. Then, since $p \neq 0$, it follows that $u \neq 0$. Therefore,

$$w = u - p/3u.$$

Substituting in (9-4), we have

$$(u - p/3u)^3 + p(u - p/3u) + q = 0,$$

that is,

$$u^3 - (p/3u)^3 + q = 0.$$

Consequently

$$(u^3)^2 + q(u^3) - (p/3)^3 = 0.$$

It follows from Theorem 8-2.7 that u satisfies

$$u^3 = -q/2 \pm \sqrt{(q/2)^2 + (p/3)^3}.$$

Therefore, u is a solution of one of the two equations

$$x^3 = -q/2 + \sqrt{(q/2)^2 + (p/3)^3}, \tag{9-6}$$

$$x^3 = -q/2 - \sqrt{(q/2)^2 + (p/3)^3}. \tag{9-7}$$

Suppose that u satisfies the equation (9–6). By Theorem 8–4.3, this equation has three solutions. If u is any one solution, then the other two are ζu and $\zeta^2 u$, where

$$\zeta = \cos 120 + i \sin 120 = -\tfrac{1}{2} + \tfrac{1}{2}\sqrt{3}\, i,$$
$$\zeta^2 = \cos 240 + i \sin 240 = -\tfrac{1}{2} - \tfrac{1}{2}\sqrt{3}\, i = 1/\zeta$$

(see Problem 7, Section 8–4). The next step is to check directly that

$$w_1 = u - p/3u, \qquad w_2 = \zeta u - p/3\zeta u = \zeta u - \zeta^2 p/3u,$$
$$w_3 = \zeta^2 u - p/3\zeta^2 u = \zeta^2 u - \zeta p/3u$$

are actually roots of the reduced cubic equation $x^3 + px + q = 0$. We first note that

$$\left(\frac{p}{3u}\right)^3 = \frac{(p/3)^3}{u^3} = \frac{(p/3)^3}{-q/2 + \sqrt{(q/2)^2 + (p/3)^3}}$$

$$= \frac{(p/3)^3}{-q/2 + \sqrt{(q/2)^2 + (p/3)^3}} \cdot \frac{-q/2 - \sqrt{(q/2)^2 + (p/3)^3}}{-q/2 - \sqrt{(q/2)^2 + (p/3)^3}}$$

$$= \frac{(p/3)^3 \cdot [-q/2 - \sqrt{(q/2)^2 + (p/3)^3}]}{(q/2)^2 - [(q/2)^2 + (p/3)^3]}$$

$$= -[-q/2 - \sqrt{(q/2)^2 + (p/3)^3}].$$

Therefore,

$$(-p/3u)^3 = -q/2 - \sqrt{(q/2)^2 + (p/3)^3}. \tag{9-8}$$

Substituting $w_1 = u - p/3u$ in $x^3 + px + q$, we have

$$(u - p/3u)^3 + p(u - p/3u) + q = u^3 + (-p/3u)^3 + q$$
$$= [-q/2 + \sqrt{(q/2)^2 + (p/3)^3}]$$
$$+ [-q/2 - \sqrt{(q/2)^2 + (p/3)^3}] + q = 0,$$

by (9–8). Similarly, since $\zeta^3 = 1$,

$$(\zeta u - \zeta^2 p/3u)^3 + p(\zeta u - \zeta^2 p/3u) + q$$
$$= (\zeta u)^3 + (-\zeta p/3u)^3 + q = u^3 + (-p/3u)^3 + q = 0.$$

In the same way, $\zeta^2 u - \zeta p/3u$ satisfies (9–4). Therefore, w_1, w_2, and w_3 are roots of the reduced cubic. These roots were obtained by assuming that u satisfies (9–6). However, (9–8) shows that if u is a solution of (9–6), then $v = -p/3u$ is a solution of (9–7). Therefore, the three solutions of (9–7) are v, ζv, and $\zeta^2 v$. These lead to the roots

$$v - \frac{p}{3v} = \frac{-p}{3u} - \frac{p}{3(-p/3u)} = \frac{-p}{3u} + u = w_1,$$

$$\zeta v - \frac{\zeta^2 p}{3v} = w_3, \quad \text{and} \quad \zeta^2 v - \frac{\zeta p}{3v} = w_2$$

of the reduced cubic. Thus, (9–7) does not lead to new solutions of (9–4). We summarize our results in the following theorem.

THEOREM 9–9.1. Let $p \neq 0$ and q be complex numbers. Then the solutions of the reduced cubic equation

$$x^3 + px + q = 0$$

are given by the expressions

$$x = \sqrt[3]{-q/2 + \sqrt{(q/2)^2 + (p/3)^3}} + \sqrt[3]{-q/2 - \sqrt{(q/2)^2 + (p/3)^3}},$$

$$x = \zeta\sqrt[3]{-q/2 + \sqrt{(q/2)^2 + (p/3)^3}} + \zeta^2\sqrt[3]{-q/2 - \sqrt{(q/2)^2 + (p/3)^3}},$$

$$x = \zeta^2\sqrt[3]{-q/2 + \sqrt{(q/2)^2 + (p/3)^3}} + \zeta\sqrt[3]{-q/2 - \sqrt{(q/2)^2 + (p/3)^3}},$$

where

$$\sqrt[3]{-q/2 + \sqrt{(q/2)^2 + (p/3)^3}}$$

is any one of the three solutions u of the equation

$$u^3 = -q/2 + \sqrt{(q/2)^2 + (p/3)^3}$$

and

$$\sqrt[3]{-q/2 - \sqrt{(q/2)^2 + (p/3)^3}}$$

is a solution v of $v^3 = -q/2 - \sqrt{(q/2)^2 + (p/3)^3}$ such that $uv = -p/3$. Of course

$$v = \frac{-p/3}{\sqrt[3]{-q/2 + \sqrt{(q/2)^2 + (p/3)^3}}},$$

and

$$\zeta = -\tfrac{1}{2} + \tfrac{1}{2}\sqrt{3}\,i.$$

The expressions in this theorem for the solutions of the reduced cubic equation are known as *Cardan's formulas*.

EXAMPLE 1.   Let us solve $x^3 + 3x^2 + 2 = 0$. The corresponding reduced equation is obtained by letting $x = y - 1$: $y^3 - 3y + 4 = 0$. Thus, $p = -3$, $q = 4$, and

$$\sqrt[3]{-q/2 + \sqrt{(q/2)^2 + (p/3)^3}} = \sqrt[3]{-2 + \sqrt{3}}.$$

Taking

$$\sqrt[3]{-2 + \sqrt{3}} \qquad \text{and} \qquad \sqrt[3]{-2 - \sqrt{3}}$$

to be the real cube roots of $-2 + \sqrt{3}$ and $-2 - \sqrt{3}$, respectively, we have

$$\sqrt[3]{-2 + \sqrt{3}} \cdot \sqrt[3]{-2 - \sqrt{3}} = \sqrt[3]{4 - 3} = 1 = -(-3)/3 = -p/3.$$

Hence, the solutions of the reduced equation are

$$\sqrt[3]{-2 + \sqrt{3}} + \sqrt[3]{-2 - \sqrt{3}}, \qquad \zeta\sqrt[3]{-2 + \sqrt{3}} + \zeta^2\sqrt[3]{-2 - \sqrt{3}},$$

and

$$\zeta^2\sqrt[3]{-2 + \sqrt{3}} + \zeta\sqrt[3]{-2 - \sqrt{3}},$$

and the solutions of $x^3 + 3x^2 + 2 = 0$ are

$$\sqrt[3]{-2 + \sqrt{3}} + \sqrt[3]{-2 - \sqrt{3}} - 1,$$

$$\zeta\sqrt[3]{-2 + \sqrt{3}} + \zeta^2\sqrt[3]{-2 - \sqrt{3}} - 1$$

$$= \tfrac{1}{2}(\sqrt[3]{2 - \sqrt{3}} + \sqrt[3]{2 + \sqrt{3}} - 2) + \tfrac{3}{2}(\sqrt[3]{2 + \sqrt{3}} - \sqrt[3]{2 - \sqrt{3}})i,$$

$$\zeta^2\sqrt[3]{-2 + \sqrt{3}} + \zeta\sqrt[3]{-2 - \sqrt{3}} - 1$$

$$= \tfrac{1}{2}(\sqrt[3]{2 - \sqrt{3}} + \sqrt[3]{2 + \sqrt{3}} - 2) - \tfrac{3}{2}(\sqrt[3]{2 + \sqrt{3}} - \sqrt[3]{2 - \sqrt{3}})i.$$

The solution of the general quartic equation can be obtained from the solution of a cubic equation by an ingenious trick discovered by Ferrari (1522–1565), a student of Cardan. As in the case of cubic equations, it is convenient to reduce the general quartic equation,

$$x^4 + bx^3 + cx^2 + dx + e = 0, \tag{9–9}$$

to the special form

$$y^4 + ry^2 + sy + t = 0, \tag{9–10}$$

by substituting $x = y - b/4$. If y is a solution of (9–10) and u is any complex number, then

$$(y^2 + u)^2 = y^4 + 2uy^2 + u^2 = (2u - r)y^2 - sy + (u^2 - t),$$

since $y^4 = -ry^2 - sy - t$. Let us try to choose u so that

$$(2u - r)y^2 - sy + (u^2 - t) = (my + n)^2$$

for suitable complex numbers m and n. This equation will certainly hold no matter what y may be, provided $m^2 = (2u - r)$, $n^2 = u^2 - t$, and $2mn = -s$. These requirements impose the condition $(-s)^2 = (2mn)^2 = 4m^2n^2 = 4(2u - r)(u^2 - t)$. In other words, u must satisfy the *resolvent cubic equation*

$$u^3 - \frac{r}{2}u^2 - tu + \left(\frac{rt}{2} - \frac{s^2}{8}\right) = 0. \qquad (9\text{--}11)$$

If this condition is fulfilled, then

$$(y^2 + u)^2 = (my + n)^2,$$

where

$$m = \sqrt{2u - r}, \qquad n = -s/(2\sqrt{2u - r}). \qquad (9\text{--}12)$$

Therefore, $y^2 + u = \pm(my + n)$, and y is a root of one of the equations

$$y^2 - my - (n - u) = 0, \qquad y^2 + my + (n + u) = 0. \qquad (9\text{--}13)$$

The four roots of the two equations (9–13) are the roots of the reduced quartic equation (9–10), as is easily shown by reversing our steps in the derivation of (9–13). Since a solution u of (9–11) can be obtained, using Theorem 9–9.1, it follows that (9–10), and hence (9–9), can be solved explicitly.

EXAMPLE 2. Consider the quartic equation

$$x^4 - 4x^3 + 12x^2 - 12x + 5 = 0.$$

To reduce this equation, let $y = x - 1$. We obtain

$$\begin{aligned} 0 &= (y + 1)^4 - 4(y + 1)^3 + 12(y + 1)^2 - 12(y + 1) + 5 \\ &= y^4 + 6y^2 + 4y + 2. \end{aligned}$$

Thus, $r = 6$, $s = 4$, and $t = 2$, so that the resolvent cubic equation is

$$u^3 - 3u^2 - 2u + 4 = 0.$$

Clearly, $u = 1$ is a solution of this resolvent cubic, and we obtain

$$m = \sqrt{2u - r} = 2i, \qquad n = -\frac{4}{4i} = i.$$

Thus, y is obtained as a solution of

$$y^2 - 2iy + (1 - i) = 0 \qquad \text{or} \qquad y^2 + 2iy + (1 + i) = 0.$$

The quadratic formulas, Theorem 8–2.7, give

$$y = i \pm \sqrt{(-i)^2 - (1 - i)} = i \pm \sqrt{-2 + i}$$

and

$$y = -i \pm \sqrt{i^2 - (1 + i)} = -i \pm \sqrt{-2 - i}.$$

The square roots $\sqrt{-2 + i}$ and $\sqrt{-2 - i}$ can be computed from (8–9):

$$\sqrt{-2 + i} = \frac{\sqrt{5} + (-2 + i)}{\sqrt{2(\sqrt{5} - 2)}} = (\sqrt{2}/2)(\sqrt{\sqrt{5} - 2} + i\sqrt{\sqrt{5} + 2}),$$

$$\sqrt{-2 - i} = (\sqrt{2}/2)(\sqrt{\sqrt{5} - 2} - i\sqrt{\sqrt{5} + 2}).$$

Combining these results, we obtain all of the solutions of the original equation $x^4 - 4x^3 + 12x^2 - 12x + 5 = 0$:

$$x = \left[1 + (\sqrt{2}/2)\sqrt{\sqrt{5} - 2}\right] + i\left[1 + (\sqrt{2}/2)\sqrt{\sqrt{5} + 2}\right],$$

$$x = \left[1 - (\sqrt{2}/2)\sqrt{\sqrt{5} - 2}\right] + i\left[1 - (\sqrt{2}/2)\sqrt{\sqrt{5} + 2}\right],$$

$$x = \left[1 + (\sqrt{2}/2)\sqrt{\sqrt{5} - 2}\right] - i\left[1 + (\sqrt{2}/2)\sqrt{\sqrt{5} + 2}\right],$$

$$x = \left[1 - (\sqrt{2}/2)\sqrt{\sqrt{5} - 2}\right] - i\left[1 - (\sqrt{2}/2)\sqrt{\sqrt{5} + 2}\right].$$

Success in solving the cubic and quartic equations led mathematicians from the time of Bombelli to seek similar results for the general fifth-degree equation $x^5 + bx^4 + cx^3 + dx^2 + ex + f = 0$. However, all efforts failed. The reason for this failure was finally discovered in 1824 by the young Norwegian genius, N. H. Abel (1802–1829), who proved that the general fifth-degree equation *cannot* be solved by means of radicals. That is, there are no expressions (involving only the operations of addition, multiplication, subtraction, division, and the operation of taking square roots, cube roots, fourth roots, etc.) which explicitly exhibit the roots of an arbitrary monic fifth-degree polynomial in terms of the coefficients of the polynomial. Even deeper insight into the solutions of polynomial equations resulted from the investigations of Abel's French contemporary, Evariste Galois* (1811–1832). Galois' theory not only showed why it is

---

* Galois was perhaps the greatest of all mathematical prodigies. Of him it can truly be said that he was neither appreciated nor understood during his lifetime. His mathematical work was not published until 14 years after his death, and was not absorbed into the body of mathematical knowledge for another 25 years. Yet the ideas in this work revolutionized algebra. Galois was killed in a duel at the age of 21.

impossible to solve the general fifth-degree equation by radicals, but also revealed why the third- and fourth-degree equations can be solved. Even today, Galois' work stands, practically unchanged, as one of the most beautiful theories of modern mathematics.

PROBLEMS

1. Solve the following equations.

   (a) $x^3 - 9x - 12 = 0$
   (b) $x^3 - 18x - 30 = 0$
   (c) $x^3 - 6x^2 - 6x - 2 = 0$
   (d) $x^3 - 3ix + (1 - i) = 0$
   (e) $x^4 - 4x^2 + 8x - 4 = 0$
   (f) $x^4 - 4x^3 - 5x^2 + 12x + 6 = 0$
   (g) $x^4 - x^2 - 2ix + 6 = 0$

2. (a) Prove in detail that any solution y of one of the equations (9–13) is a solution of (9–10), provided m and n are given by (9–12) and u is any solution of (9–11). (b) Write on a large piece of paper an expression which gives a solution y of (9–10) in terms of r, s, and t.

3. Let $f(x)$ be a monic cubic polynomial with roots r_1, r_2, and r_3. The *discriminant* D of $f(x)$ is defined to be

$$D = (r_1 - r_2)^2(r_2 - r_3)^2(r_3 - r_1)^2.$$

Use Theorem 9–9.1 to prove that the discriminant of $x^3 + px + q$ is

$$-(4p^3 + 27q^2).$$

[*Hint:* By definition, $\zeta^3 = 1$, and by Problem 8, Section 8–4, $1 + \zeta + \zeta^2 = 0$.]

4. Let $f(x) = x^3 + bx^2 + cx + d$. Find the discriminant of $f(x)$.

5. Prove that a cubic polynomial $f(x)$ in $R[x]$ has three distinct real roots if the discriminant D of $f(x)$ is positive, real roots, one of which is a multiple root, if $D = 0$, and a single real root and two (nonreal) complex conjugate roots if $D < 0$.

6. Use the results of Problems 3 and 5 to determine the number of real roots of the following polynomials.

   (a) $x^3 + 2x - 1$ (b) $x^3 - \sqrt[3]{10}\,x - 1$ (c) $2x^3 - x + 1$

7. Find the roots of $x^3 - 2x + 1$ by observing that 1 is a root. Find the expression, given by Theorem 9–9.1, for each of these roots.

8. Let $a(x) = x^3 + px + q$, where p and q are real and $(p/3)^3 + (q/2)^2 < 0$ (so that $p < 0$). Prove that the three roots of $a(x)$ are

$$2\sqrt{-p/3}\,\cos(\phi/3), \qquad 2\sqrt{-p/3}\,\cos(\phi/3 + 120),$$
$$2\sqrt{-p/3}\,\cos(\phi/3 + 240),$$

where ϕ is an angle such that

$$\cos \phi = (-q/2)/\sqrt{-p^3/27}.$$

[*Hint:* Let $-q/2 + i\sqrt{-[(p/3)^3 + (q/2)^2]} = r(\cos \phi + i \sin \phi)$. Show that $r = \sqrt{-p^3/27}$ and $\cos \phi = (-q/2)/\sqrt{-p^3/27}$. Substitute into Theorem 9-9.1, and use Theorem 8-4.3.]

9. Use the result of Problem 8 to find the roots of the following polynomials.

(a) $x^3 - 2x + 1$ (b) $x^3 - 9x + 9$ (c) $x^3 - 3x^2 - 3x - 4$

9-10 Graphs of real polynomials. An important part of the theory of equations in $R[x]$ is concerned with finding the real roots of polynomials. For a given polynomial $a(x) \in R[x]$, the problem is to determine the number of real roots of $a(x)$ and obtain decimal approximations of each real root. In this section and the following one, we will discuss some of the basic methods for solving these problems.

Let $a(x) = a_n x^n + a_{n-1} x^{n-1} + \cdots + a_1 x + a_0$ be a polynomial with real coefficients. Associated with each real number c is the value $a(c)$ of $a(x)$ at $x = c$. Of course, $a(c)$ is also a real number. The set of all ordered pairs of real numbers

$$\{\langle c, a(c) \rangle | c \in R\}$$

is called the *graph of* $a(x)$. Since each ordered pair of real numbers can be represented by a point in a coordinate plane, the graph of $a(x)$ can be represented by a set of points in the plane. It is customary to also refer to this set of points as the graph of $a(x)$.

Experience shows that the graph of a real polynomial $a(x)$ is a smooth unbroken curve. For example, if $a(x)$ is a constant polynomial, then the graph of $a(x)$ is a horizontal line. If $\text{Deg}\,[a(x)] = 1$, then the graph of $a(x)$ is a straight line which is neither horizontal nor vertical [see Fig. 9-2(a)]. If $\text{Deg}\,[a(x)] = 2$, then the graph of $a(x)$ is a parabola [see Fig. 9-2(b)].

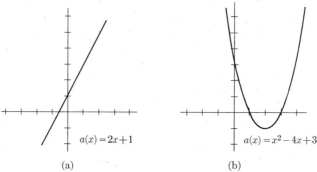

$a(x) = 2x + 1$ $a(x) = x^2 - 4x + 3$

(a)   (b)

FIGURE 9-2

From the graph of a real polynomial $a(x)$, it is possible to obtain a great deal of information about $a(x)$. For example, the real roots of $a(x)$ are the numbers c such that $a(c) = 0$, that is, they are the points at which the graph of $a(x)$ either touches or crosses the X-axis of the coordinate plane. Thus the graph of $a(x)$ tells us (at least roughly) where the real roots of $a(x)$ are located.

EXAMPLE 1. Let us sketch the graph of $a(x) = x^3 - 3x^2 - 2x + 6$. It is convenient to make a table of values of $a(c)$ corresponding to various choices of c:

c	-2	$-\frac{3}{2}$	-1	$-\frac{1}{2}$	0	$\frac{1}{2}$	1	$\frac{3}{2}$	2	$\frac{5}{2}$	3	$\frac{7}{2}$	4
$a(c)$	-10	$-\frac{9}{8}$	4	$\frac{49}{8}$	6	$\frac{35}{8}$	2	$-\frac{3}{8}$	-2	$-\frac{17}{8}$	0	$\frac{41}{8}$	14

We plot the points determined by the pairs $\langle c, a(c) \rangle$ from the above table in a coordinate plane, and sketch an unbroken curve which passes through these points (see Fig. 9–3). It is seen from this graph that $a(x)$ has three real roots at approximately -1.5, 1.5, and 3. Actually 3 is an exact root of $a(x)$ as our table shows, and factoring out $x - 3$ gives

$$a(x) = (x - 3)(x^2 - 2) = (x - 3)(x + \sqrt{2})(x - \sqrt{2}).$$

Hence, for $a(x) = x^3 - 3x^2 - 2x + 6$ it is not necessary to plot the graph in order to find the real zeros. However, for polynomials of higher degree, graphical methods may be the most effective way of approximating the roots.

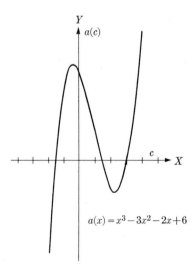

FIGURE 9–3

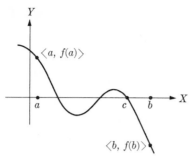

FIGURE 9–4

The fact that the graph of a polynomial is an unbroken curve suggests the following important result.

THEOREM 9–10.1. Let $f(x)$ be a polynomial in $R[x]$. Suppose that a and b are real numbers such that $a < b$, and $f(a)$ and $f(b)$ have opposite signs. Then $f(x)$ has at least one real root c with $a < c < b$.

This result is intuitively obvious. In fact, by assumption, the points $\langle a, f(a) \rangle$ and $\langle b, f(b) \rangle$ are on opposite sides of the X-axis in the coordinate plane. Since the graph of $f(x)$ is an unbroken curve which passes through these two points, this graph must, at one or more points between a and b, cross the X-axis (see Fig. 9–4). That is, there is a real number c with $a < c < b$, such that $f(c) = 0$.

Of course, the above remarks do not constitute a proof of the theorem. The completeness property of the real numbers will be used to locate the largest root c of $a(x)$ in the interval from a to b. The argument is a slight modification of the proof of Theorem 7–6.3. The proof of Theorem 9–10.1 will not make use of the fundamental theorem of algebra. This remark is important, because our proof of the fundamental theorem given in the appendix is based on Theorem 9–10.1.

Before giving the proof, it is convenient to establish a simple property of real polynomials.

(9–10.2). Let $g(x) \in R[x]$. Then there is a positive real number m which depends only on $g(x)$ such that $-m \le g(h) \le m$ for all $h \in R$ satisfying $|h| \le 1$.

Proof. Let $g(x) = b_0 + b_1 x + \cdots + b_n x^n$. Then if $|h| \le 1$, it follows from Theorem 4–6.7 that

$$|g(h)| = |b_0 + b_1 h + \cdots + b_n h^n| \le |b_0| + |b_1| \cdot |h| + \cdots + |b_n| \cdot |h|^n$$
$$\le |b_0| + |b_1| + \cdots + |b_n|.$$

Thus, we can let $m = |b_0| + |b_1| + \cdots + |b_n|$ if $g(x)$ is not the zero polynomial, and $m = 1$ if $g(x) = 0$.

Proof of Theorem 9–10.1.   Since $f(a)$ and $f(b)$ have opposite signs, it follows that either $f(a) > 0 > f(b)$, or $f(a) < 0 < f(b)$. We will prove the theorem for the case $f(a) > 0$ and $f(b) < 0$. The proof in the other case is similar. Let $S = \{t \in R | a \le t \le b \text{ and } f(t) > 0\}$.   That is, S is the set of all real numbers between a and b for which the value of $f(x)$ is positive. The set S is not empty since $a \in S$. Moreover, b is an upper bound for S. Since R is a complete ordered field, the set S has a least upper bound (see Definition 7–5.4).   Let $c = $ l.u.b. S.   Then $a \le c$, because $a \in S$ and c is an upper bound of S, and $c \le b$, since b is an upper bound of S and c is the *least* upper bound of S. The definitions of S and c imply two facts which we will use:

(1) if $c < t \le b$, then $f(t) \le 0$;

(2) if $h > 0$, then there is a real number t such that $c - h < t \le c$ and $f(t) > 0$.

Indeed, if $c < t \le b$, then $t \notin S$, since c is an upper bound for S. However, $a \le c < t \le b$ and $f(t) > 0$ implies that $t \in S$, by the definition of S. Therefore, $f(t) > 0$ is impossible. That is, $f(t) \le 0$.   Moreover, $h > 0$ means that $c - h$ is not an upper bound of S, so that $c - h < t$ for some $t \in S$. Furthermore, $t \in S$ implies $t \le c$ and $f(t) > 0$. The proof will be completed by showing that both of the inequalities $f(c) > 0$ and $f(c) < 0$ lead to contradictions. Indeed, it then follows that $f(c) = 0$, so that $c \ne a$ and $c \ne b$. Thus, $a < c < b$. Consider the polynomial $f(x + c) - f(c)$, where $f(x + c)$ is obtained from $f(x)$ by substituting $x + c$ for x in $f(x)$. Since $f(0 + c) - f(c) = 0$, it follows that 0 is a root of this polynomial. Consequently, by the factor theorem, we have

(3) $f(x + c) - f(c) = x \cdot g(x)$,

where $g(x)$ is some polynomial in $R[x]$. Let m be a positive real number such that

(4) if $h \in R$ and $|h| \le 1$, then $-m \le g(h) \le m$.

Such a number exists, by (9–10.2).

Suppose that $f(c) > 0$. Then $c < b$, since $f(b) < 0$. Define

$$h = (\tfrac{1}{2}) \cdot \min \{2, b - c, f(c)/m\}.$$

This definition is so contrived that h satisfies

(5) $h > 0$,   (6) $h \le 1$,

(7) $h + c < b$,   (8) $h \cdot m < f(c)$.

By (3), (4), (5), (6), and (8), we obtain

$$f(h + c) = f(c) + h \cdot g(h) \ge f(c) - h \cdot m > f(c) - f(c) = 0.$$

However, it follows from (5) and (7) that $c < h + c < b$, so that this inequality is in contradiction with (1). Therefore, $f(c) > 0$ is impossible.

Suppose that $f(c) < 0$. Define

$$h = \min \{1, -f(c)/m\}.$$

This choice of h leads to the inequalities

(9) $h > 0$,

(10) $h \leq 1$,

(11) $h \cdot m \leq -f(c)$.

By (2), there is a real number t such that $c - h < t \leq c$ and $f(t) > 0$. Consequently, $-h < t - c \leq 0 < h$, so that $|t - c| < h \leq 1$. Therefore, by (3), (4), and (11) (substituting $t - c$ for x),

$$0 < f(t) = f(c) + (t - c)g(t - c) \leq f(c) + |t - c| \cdot |g(t - c)|$$
$$\leq f(c) + h \cdot m \leq f(c) - f(c) = 0.$$

This contradiction shows that $f(c) < 0$ is impossible, so that the proof of Theorem 9–10.1 is complete.

———————

EXAMPLE 2. Another proof that each positive real number d has a real nth root (Theorem 7–6.3) can be obtained very easily from Theorem 9–10.1. Consider the polynomial $f(x) = x^n - d$. Since $n \geq 1$, $(d + 1)^n \geq d + 1$. Hence, $f(d + 1) = (d + 1)^n - d \geq d + 1 - d = 1 > 0$, and because $f(0) = -d < 0$, it follows from Theorem 9–10.1 that $f(x)$ has a positive root. That is, d has a positive nth root.

EXAMPLE 3. Theorem 9–10.1 can be used to locate the real roots of the polynomial $f(x) = x^3 - 12x^2 - 13x + 6$. We make a table of values for $f(x)$:

t	$f(t)$	t	$f(t)$
-3	-90	1	-18
-2	-24	2	-60
-1	6	3	-114
0	6	12	$12^3 - 12^3 - 13 \cdot 12 + 6 = -150$
		13	$13^3 - 12 \cdot 13^2 - 13^2 + 6 = 6$

By Theorem 9–10.1, $f(x)$ has three real roots t_1, t_2, and t_3 such that

$$-2 < t_1 < -1, \qquad 0 < t_2 < 1, \qquad \text{and} \qquad 12 < t_3 < 13.$$

Since $f(x)$ can have at most three roots, t_1, t_2, and t_3 are all of the roots of $f(x)$.

To make the most effective use of the method used in Example 3 to locate the real roots of a polynomial $f(x) \in R[x]$, it is desirable to have an upper and a lower bound for the real roots of $f(x)$. Otherwise, we will usually not know how large or small to take t in calculating $f(t)$ for a table of values of $f(x)$.

THEOREM 9–10.3. Let $f(x) = x^n + a_{n-1}x^{n-1} + a_{n-2}x^{n-2} + \cdots + a_0$ be a polynomial in $R[x]$. Define

$$M = \max \{-a_{n-1}, -a_{n-2}, \ldots, -a_0, 0\}$$

and

$$m = \max \{a_{n-1}, -a_{n-2}, \ldots, (-1)^{n-1}a_0, 0\}.$$

Then $f(t) > 0$ for all $t > M + 1$, and $(-1)^n f(t) > 0$ for all $t < -(m + 1)$. In particular, if $f(x)$ has a real root c, then $-(m + 1) \leq c \leq M + 1$.

Proof. By the definition of M, we have $M \geq -a_j$, and hence $-M \leq a_j$, for $j = 0, 1, \ldots, n - 1$. Thus, if $t > M + 1 \geq 1$, then

$$
\begin{aligned}
f(t) &= a_0 + a_1 t + \cdots + a_{n-1}t^{n-1} + t^n \\
&\geq -M(1 + t + \cdots + t^{n-1}) + t^n \\
&= -M[(t^n - 1)/(t - 1)] + t^n \\
&= ([t - (M + 1)]t^n + M)/(t - 1) > 0
\end{aligned}
$$

[see Problem 6(a), Section 2–1]. To prove that $t < -(m + 1)$ implies that $(-1)^n f(t) > 0$, simply apply the result which has just been proved to the polynomial

$$(-1)^n f(-x) = x^n - a_{n-1}x^{n-1} + a_{n-2}x^{n-2} + \cdots + (-1)^n a_0.$$

We leave the details for the reader to work out.

It should be emphasized that the bounds $-(m + 1)$ and $M + 1$ obtained in Theorem 9–10.3 for the real roots of a polynomial are not in general the best possible. For instance, the theorem gives the bounds -1 and 6 for the real roots of $x^2 - 5x + 9$, although this polynomial actually has no real root.

EXAMPLE 4. Let us obtain upper and lower bounds for the real roots of the polynomial

$$f(x) = 2x^4 - 3x^3 + x - 4.$$

Since $f(x)$ is not a monic polynomial, Theorem 9–10.3 does not apply directly to give bounds for the roots of $f(x)$. However, the roots of $f(x)$ are evidently the same as those of the monic polynomial

$$\tfrac{1}{2}f(x) = x^4 - \tfrac{3}{2}x^3 + \tfrac{1}{2}x - 2.$$

We have

$$\max \{-(-\tfrac{3}{2}), -0, -\tfrac{1}{2}, -(-2), 0\} = 2$$

and

$$\max \{-\tfrac{3}{2}, -0, \tfrac{1}{2}, -(-2), 0\} = 2.$$

Therefore, if c is a real root of $f(x)$, then $-3 \le c \le 3$ by Theorem 9–10.3.

An important consequence of Theorems 9–10.1 and 9–10.3 is the following result.

THEOREM 9–10.4. If $f(x)$ is a nonzero polynomial in $R[x]$ such that Deg $[f(x)]$ is odd, then $f(x)$ has at least one real root.

Proof. Let $f(x) = a_0 + a_1 x + \cdots + a_{n-1}x^{n-1} + a_n x^n$, where a_0, $a_1, \ldots, a_{n-1}$, and a_n are real numbers, $a_n \ne 0$, and n is odd. Define $g(x) = a_n^{-1} \cdot f(x)$. Then

$$g(x) = x^n + b_{n-1}x^{n-1} + \cdots + b_1 x + b_0,$$

where $b_{n-1} = a_{n-1}/a_n, \ldots, b_1 = a_1/a_n$, and $b_0 = a_0/a_n$. Since every root of $g(x)$ is also a root of $f(x)$, it is sufficient to show that $g(x)$ has at least one real root. Let u and v be real numbers such that

$$u > \max \{-b_{n-1}, -b_{n-2}, \ldots, -b_1, -b_0, 0\} + 1,$$

and

$$v < -[\max \{b_{n-1}, -b_{n-2}, \ldots, (-1)^{n-2}b_1, (-1)^{n-1}b_0, 0\} + 1].$$

Then by Theorem 9–10.3,

$$f(u) > 0 \quad \text{and} \quad (-1)^n f(v) > 0.$$

Since n is odd, $(-1)^n = -1$, so that $f(v) < 0$. Therefore, by Theorem 9–10.1, $f(x)$ has a real root between v and u.

The above proof does not depend on the fundamental theorem of algebra. A proof of Theorem 9–10.4 *can* be based on the fundamental theorem of algebra (see Problem 5, Section 9–8), but then it would not be logically correct to turn around and use Theorem 9–10.4 in the proof of the fundamental theorem, as we will do in Appendix 3.

PROBLEMS

1. By plotting points at $\frac{1}{2}$ unit intervals from -3 to 3, sketch the graphs of the following polynomials.

(a) $x^2 - 2x + 1$
(b) $-2x^3 + x - 3$
(c) $x^4 + x^3 + x^2 + x + 1$
(d) $x^3 - 2x^2 - 3$

2. By graphing the following polynomials, estimate the location of their real roots.

(a) $x^4 - 2x^2 - 8x - 3$
(b) $x^4 - 28x^2 + 24x + 12$
(c) $x^3 - 4x + 1$

3. Find upper and lower bounds for the real roots of the following polynomials.

(a) $x^7 - x^6 - x^5 + x^4 - x^3 + x - 1$
(b) $x^{12} - 23x^2 + 72x - 1$
(c) $4x^5 - 2x - 1$
(d) $99x^{99} + x^7 + 1$

4. Use the method of Example 3 to find the largest integer $\leq c$ for all of the real roots c of the following polynomials.

(a) $x^3 - 7x + 5$
(b) $x^4 - 4x^2 + x + 1$
(c) $x^5 - 7x^3 + 3x^2 + 5x - 1$

5. Prove that a monic polynomial in $R[x]$ which has even degree must have at least two real roots if the constant term is negative.

6. Prove the last part of Theorem 9–10.3 in detail.

7. Let $a_1, a_2, \ldots, a_n$ be real numbers with $a_1 < a_2 < \cdots < a_n$. Let b_0, $b_1, b_2, \ldots, b_n$ be positive real numbers. Define

$$g(x) = (x - a_1)(x - a_2) \cdots (x - a_n)$$

and

$$f(x) = b_0 g(x) + \frac{b_1 g(x)}{x - a_1} + \frac{b_2 g(x)}{x - a_2} + \cdots + \frac{b_n g(x)}{x - a_n}.$$

Prove that $f(x)$ has n different real roots.

8. Let $f(x)$ be a polynomial of positive degree in $R[x]$. Prove that if $f'(x)$ has no real root, then $f(x)$ has exactly one real root. [*Hint:* Use Theorem 9–10.4 to show that $f(x)$ has at least one real root; use Theorem 9–6.4 to show that $f(x)$ has no multiple real roots; prove that if

$$f(x) = (x - a)(x - b) \cdot g(x),$$

where $f(x)$ has no root between a and b, then $f'(a)$ and $f'(b)$ have opposite signs; from these facts, deduce the assertion of Problem 8.]

9–11 Sturm's theorem. Theorem 9–10.1 guarantees the existence of *at least one* real root between c and d if the values of the polynomial $f(x) \in R[x]$ at c and d have opposite signs. There may be more than one. For example, if

$$f(x) = 64x^3 - 88x^2 + 34x - 3,$$

then $f(0) = -3$ and $f(1) = 7$. The roots of $f(x)$ are $\frac{1}{8}$, $\frac{1}{2}$, and $\frac{3}{4}$. In sketching a graph of $f(x)$ from a table of values, it would be easy to overlook two of these roots:

c	-1	$-\frac{1}{2}$	0	$\frac{1}{2}$	1		2
$f(c)$	-189	-50	-3	0	7	66	225

From this data, we would probably sketch the graph pictured in Fig. 9–5. The actual graph of $f(x)$, with the three zeros indicated, is shown in Fig. 9–6.

Sturm's theorem* makes it possible to determine the number of real roots of a polynomial between any two numbers. Applying this theorem to the polynomial $f(x) = 64x^3 - 88x^2 + 34x - 3$, we would be able to see that $f(x)$ has three real roots between 0 and 1, and thereby avoid the error of sketching the graph of $f(x)$ as in Fig. 9–5.

Let $f(x)$ be a polynomial of positive degree. We will describe a process which assigns to every real number t a nonnegative integer $N(t)$, such that the value of $N(t)$ is diminished by 1 whenever t passes a root of $f(x)$. Then for any real numbers $c < d$ such that $f(c) \neq 0$ and $f(d) \neq 0$, the integer $N(c) - N(d)$ is the number of real roots of $f(x)$ between c and d.

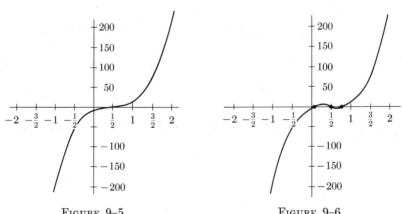

FIGURE 9–5   FIGURE 9–6

* Named for its discoverer, Jacques Charles François Sturm (1803–1855).

The first step in defining $N(t)$ is to alter slightly the Euclidean algorithm (see Section 9–4). By the division algorithm,

$$f(x) = q_1(x)f'(x) + r_1(x).$$

Let $s_1(x) = -r_1(x)$, and divide $f'(x)$ by $s_1(x)$:

$$f'(x) = q_2(x)s_1(x) + r_2(x).$$

Let $s_2(x) = -r_2(x)$, and divide $s_1(x)$ by $s_2(x)$:

$$s_1(x) = q_3(x)s_2(x) + r_3(x).$$

If this process is continued, we obtain the following sequence of equations:

$$f(x) = q_1(x)f'(x) - s_1(x),$$
$$f'(x) = q_2(x)s_1(x) - s_2(x),$$
$$\vdots$$
$$s_{k-2}(x) = q_k(x)s_{k-1}(x) - s_k(x),$$
$$s_{k-1}(x) = q_{k+1}(x)s_k(x),$$

where $s_k(x)$ is the last nonzero remainder. Except possibly for sign, the remainders $s_1(x), s_2(x), \ldots, s_k(x)$ obtained in this way are the same as the remainders obtained in applying the Euclidean algorithm to find a greatest common divisor of $f(x)$ and $f'(x)$. Therefore, the last nonzero remainder $s_k(x)$ is a g.c.d. of $f(x)$ and $f'(x)$.

The sequence of polynomials

$$\begin{aligned}
&f(x),\\
&f'(x),\\
&s_1(x) = q_1(x)f'(x) - f(x),\\
&s_2(x) = q_2(x)s_1(x) - f'(x),\\
&s_3(x) = q_3(x)s_2(x) - s_1(x),\\
&\quad\vdots\\
&s_k(x) = q_k(x)s_{k-1}(x) - s_{k-2}(x)
\end{aligned} \qquad (9\text{–}14)$$

is called the *Sturm sequence* of $f(x)$.

EXAMPLE 1. Let $f(x) = 64x^3 - 88x^2 + 34x - 3$. Then $f'(x) = 192x^2 - 176x + 34$. By dividing, we obtain

$$64x^3 - 88x^2 + 34x - 3 = (\tfrac{1}{3}x - \tfrac{11}{72})(192x^2 - 176x + 34) - (\tfrac{38}{9}x - \tfrac{79}{36}),$$
$$192x^2 - 176x + 34 = (\tfrac{864}{19}x - \tfrac{6516}{361})(\tfrac{38}{9}x - \tfrac{79}{36}) - (\tfrac{2025}{361}).$$

Therefore, the Sturm sequence of $f(x)$ is

$$64x^3 - 88x^2 + 34x - 3,$$
$$192x^2 - 176x + 34,$$
$$\tfrac{38}{9}x - \tfrac{79}{36},$$
$$\tfrac{2025}{361}.$$

For each real number t, the values at $x = t$ of the polynomials given in (9–14) form a finite sequence of real numbers:

$$f(t), f'(t), s_1(t), s_2(t), \ldots, s_k(t). \qquad (9\text{–}15)$$

A *variation in sign* occurs in the sequence (9–15) whenever one of the numbers is positive, and the next nonzero number in the sequence is negative, or vice versa. For instance, in the sequence $3, 0, -1, -2, 0, 0, 1$, variations in sign occur at 3 and -2. Let $N(t)$ be the total number of variations in sign for the sequence (9–15). The number $N(t)$ can be computed by discarding the numbers in the sequence (9–15) which are 0, and counting the number of variations in sign for the new sequence which consists of positive and negative real numbers.

EXAMPLE 2.   Let $f(x)$ be the polynomial $64x^3 - 88x^2 + 34x - 3$, whose Sturm sequence was obtained in Example 1. The values of the polynomials in the Sturm sequence of $f(x)$ corresponding to $x = 0$ and $x = 1$ are, respectively,

$$-3, \qquad 34, \qquad -\tfrac{79}{36}, \qquad \tfrac{2025}{361};$$
$$7, \qquad 50, \qquad \tfrac{73}{36}, \qquad \tfrac{2025}{361}.$$

Consequently, for the polynomial $64x^3 - 88x^2 + 34x - 3$,

$$N(0) = 3, \qquad N(1) = 0.$$

THEOREM 9–11.1.   *Sturm's theorem.*   Let $f(x)$ be a polynomial in $R[x]$ whose Sturm sequence is given by (9–14). Let c and d be real numbers such that $c < d$ and $f(c) \neq 0$ and $f(d) \neq 0$. For each real number t, let $N(t)$ be the number of variations in sign in the sequence (9–15). Then the number of distinct roots of $f(x)$ between c and d is equal to $N(c) - N(d)$.

The proof of Sturm's theorem is elementary, but rather long. For this reason, we will not prove Theorem 9–11.1 in this section. The interested reader can find a proof of Sturm's theorem in Appendix 1.

EXAMPLE 3. Returning to the polynomial $f(x) = 64x^3 - 88x^2 + 34x - 3$, we note that by Sturm's theorem and the result of Example 2, $f(x)$ must have three roots between 0 and 1. This is in agreement with the observation made at the beginning of this section that $\frac{1}{8}$, $\frac{1}{2}$, and $\frac{3}{4}$ are roots of $f(x)$. There can be no others, because the degree of $f(x)$ is three.

It is to be emphasized that Sturm's theorem gives a way of finding the number of *distinct* real roots of a polynomial. This theorem does not give any information about the multiplicity of these roots. However, if the last term $s_k(x)$ in the Sturm sequence of a polynomial $f(x)$ is not a constant, then $f(x)$ *may* have multiple real roots, which can be located by applying Sturm's theorem to $s_k(x)$, since this polynomial is a g.c.d. of $f(x)$ and $f'(x)$.

EXAMPLE 4. Let $f(x) = 4x^3 - 3x + 1$. Then $f'(x) = 12x^2 - 3$, and

$$4x^3 - 3x + 1 = (\tfrac{1}{3}x) \cdot (12x^2 - 3) - (2x - 1),$$
$$12x^2 - 3 = (6x + 3)(2x - 1).$$

Therefore, the Sturm sequence of $f(x)$ is

$$4x^3 - 3x + 1, \qquad 12x^2 - 3, \qquad 2x - 1.$$

For the values $x = -2$, $x = 0$, $x = 2$, the Sturm sequence of $f(x)$ becomes

$$
\begin{array}{llll}
x = -2: & -25, & 45, & -5, \\
x = 0: & 1, & -3, & -1, \\
x = 2: & 27, & 45, & 3.
\end{array}
$$

Therefore, $N(-2) = 2$, $N(0) = 1$, and $N(2) = 0$. It follows from Sturm's theorem that $f(x)$ has one root between -2 and 0, and one root between 0 and 2. It is easy to see (by Theorem 9–10.3, for example) that $f(x)$ has no root smaller than -2, and none larger than 2. Thus, $f(x)$ has only two distinct real roots. Clearly, one of these must be a double root, since the complex roots of a real polynomial occur in pairs, by Theorem 9–8.3. If we note that $2x - 1$ is a greatest common divisor of $f(x)$ and $f'(x)$, then it becomes clear from Theorem 9–5.4 that $\frac{1}{2}$ is a double root of $f(x)$. By inspection, the other real root is -1.

EXAMPLE 5. Let $f(x) = x^4 + 4x^3 + x^2 - 6x + 2 = 0$. Then

$$f'(x) = 4x^3 + 12x^2 + 2x - 6,$$

and

$$f(x) = (\tfrac{1}{4}x + \tfrac{1}{4})f'(x) - (\tfrac{5}{2}x^2 + 5x - \tfrac{7}{2}),$$
$$f'(x) = (\tfrac{8}{5}x + \tfrac{8}{5})(\tfrac{5}{2}x^2 + 5x - \tfrac{7}{2}) - (\tfrac{2}{5}x + \tfrac{2}{5}),$$
$$\tfrac{5}{2}x^2 + 5x - \tfrac{7}{2} = (\tfrac{25}{4}x + \tfrac{25}{4})(\tfrac{2}{5}x + \tfrac{2}{5}) - 6.$$

Therefore, the Sturm sequence of $f(x)$ is

$$x^4 + 4x^3 + x^2 - 6x + 2,$$
$$4x^3 + 12x^2 + 2x - 6,$$
$$\tfrac{5}{2}x^2 + 5x - \tfrac{7}{2},$$
$$\tfrac{2}{5}x + \tfrac{2}{5},$$
$$6.$$

By Theorem 9–10.3, every real root of $f(x)$ is between -7 and 7. Computing the values of the Sturm sequence for each integral value beginning at $x = -7$, we find that $N(-7) = 4$, $N(-6) = 4$, $N(-5) = 4$, $N(-4) = 4$, $N(-3) = 4$, $N(-2) = 2$, $N(-1) = 2$, $N(0) = 2$, and $N(1) = 0$. This shows that all four roots of $f(x)$ are real, and there are two roots between -3 and -2 and two roots between 0 and 1. Since $f(-3) > 0$, $f(-2) > 0$, $f(0) > 0$, and $f(1) > 0$, the existence of these real roots would not be detected by Theorem 9–10.1 if we calculated $f(x)$ only for integer values of x. The calculation of $N(-\tfrac{5}{2}) = 3$ and $N(\tfrac{1}{2}) = 1$ locates the roots of $f(x)$ in the intervals

$$-3 < x < -\tfrac{5}{2}, \qquad -\tfrac{5}{2} < x < -2, \qquad 0 < x < \tfrac{1}{2}, \qquad \text{and} \qquad \tfrac{1}{2} < x < 1.$$

Having isolated each real root of $f(x)$, we can use Theorem 9–10.1* to obtain the n-place decimal approximation of these roots. For example, since $f(0) = 2$, $f(0.1) = 1.9541$, $f(0.2) = 0.8736$, $f(0.3) = 0.4061$, $f(0.4) = 0.0416$, and $f(0.5) = -0.1875$, it follows from Theorem 9–10.1 that the root of $f(x)$ in the interval $0 < x < \tfrac{1}{2}$ is between 0.4 and 0.5. Repeating this process, we obtain $f(0.41) = 0.0120$ and $f(0.42) = -0.0768$ (with four decimal accuracy). Thus, the 2-place decimal approximation of this root is 0.41. Continuing in this way, we can locate the root between successive thousandths, ten thousandths, etc. There are various schemes for systematizing and shortening the calculations involved in finding decimal approximations of the real roots of a polynomial in $R[x]$. The interested reader can find these methods discussed in standard college algebra and theory of equations textbooks.

Problems

1. Give the Sturm sequence of each of the following polynomials.
   (a) $x^3 + x^2 + x + 1$
   (b) $x^4 - 3x^2 - 10x - 6$
   (c) $x^5 - 5x - 2$

---

* If the multiplicity of the isolated root is even, then Theorem 9–10.1 will not help in locating the root. For the polynomial which we are considering, it is obvious that all of the roots are simple, because the sum of the multiplicities of all the roots is four, and there are four distinct roots.

2. Use Sturm's theorem to locate (between consecutive integers) all the real roots of the polynomials in Problem 1.

3. Let $f(x) = ax^2 + bx + c$, where a, b, and c are real numbers, with $a \neq 0$. Find the Sturm sequence of $f(x)$. Use Sturm's theorem to show that $f(x)$ has real roots if and only if $b^2 > 4ac$.

4. Let p and q be real numbers, with $p \neq 0$. Show that the Sturm sequence of the polynomial $x^3 + px + q$ is

$$x^3 + px + q,$$
$$3x^2 + p,$$
$$-(\tfrac{2}{3}px + q),$$
$$-[\tfrac{27}{4}(q^2/p^2) + p],$$

provided $27q^2 + 4p^3 \neq 0$. Use Sturm's theorem to show that $x^3 + px + q$ has one real root if $27q^2 + 4p^3 > 0$ and three real roots if $27q^2 + 4p^3 < 0$. [*Hint: Consider the cases $p > 0$, $p < 0$ separately.*]

5. Show that if $s_k(t) = 0$ in the sequence (9–15), then every term in the sequence is zero.

6. Find the 3-place decimal approximations of all the roots of the polynomial of Example 5.

9–12 Polynomials with rational coefficients. The fundamental theorem of algebra leads to a complete solution of the problem "what are the irreducible polynomials in $C[x]$ and in $R[x]$?" (See Theorems 9–8.2 and 9–8.4.) Determining the irreducible polynomials in $Q[x]$ is much more difficult. There are ways of testing whether or not a polynomial in $Q[x]$ is irreducible. However, all of these methods are rather complicated, and they do not lead to very interesting general results. For this reason, we will only consider a part of the general problem of determining the complete factorization of polynomials in $Q[x]$, namely, the determination of the linear factors.

By the factor theorem, a polynomial $x - r$ with $r \in Q$ is a factor of $a(x)$ in $Q[x]$ if and only if r is a root of $a(x)$. Suppose that

$$a(x) = (u_0/v_0) + (u_1/v_1)x + (u_2/v_2)x^2 + \cdots + (u_n/v_n)x^n,$$

where the numbers u_i and $v_i \neq 0$ are integers. Let v be a common multiple of the denominators $v_0, v_1, v_2, \ldots, v_n$, for example, $v = v_0 v_1 v_2 \ldots v_n$, or $v = [v_0, v_1, v_2, \ldots, v_n]$. Then the polynomial $b(x) = v \cdot a(x)$ has integral coefficients. Moreover, $b(r) = v \cdot a(r) = 0$ if and only if $a(r) = 0$. Thus, the problem of finding the monic linear factors of a polynomial in $Q[x]$ can be reduced to the problem of finding the rational roots of a polynomial in $Z[x]$. The following theorem shows that the rational roots of a polynomial in $Z[x]$ can be found by trial.

THEOREM 9–12.1. Let $a(x) = a_0 + a_1x + \cdots + a_{n-1}x^{n-1} + a_nx^n$ be a polynomial with integral coefficients. Suppose that $a_0 \neq 0$, $a_n \neq 0$, and $n \geq 1$. If b and c are relatively prime integers such that b/c is a root of $a(x)$, then b divides a_0 and c divides a_n.

Proof. If b/c is a root of $a(x)$, then

$$a_0 + a_1(b/c) + \cdots + a_{n-1}(b/c)^{n-1} + a_n(b/c)^n = 0.$$

Multiplying this equation by c^n, we obtain

$$a_0c^n + a_1bc^{n-1} + \cdots + a_{n-1}b^{n-1}c + a_nb^n = 0.$$

Therefore,

$$-(a_0c^{n-1} + a_1bc^{n-2} + \cdots + a_{n-1}b^{n-1}) \cdot c = a_nb^n,$$

and

$$a_0c^n = b \cdot [-(a_1c^{n-1} + \cdots + a_{n-1}b^{n-2}c + a_nb^{n-1})].$$

These equalities imply that c divides a_nb^n and b divides a_0c^n. Since b and c have no common prime factor by hypothesis, it follows that $(c, b^n) = 1$ and $(b, c^n) = 1$. Thus, by Theorem 5–2.6, c divides a_n and b divides a_0.

EXAMPLE 1. We will use Theorem 9–12.1 to show that 0 is the only rational root of the polynomial $a(x) = x^7 - 3x^6 + 2x^3 + x^2$. Clearly, 0 is a root of $a(x)$, and $a(x) = x^2(x^5 - 3x^4 + 2x + 1)$. If $r \neq 0$ is a rational root of $a(x)$, then r is a root of $x^5 - 3x^4 + 2x + 1$. We can write $r = b/c$, where b and c are relatively prime integers. By Theorem 9–12.1, b divides the constant term of $x^5 - 3x^4 + 2x + 1$, and c divides the leading coefficient of this polynomial. That is, b and c both divide 1. Hence, b and c are either 1 or -1, so that $r = \pm 1$ also. However, $a(1) = 1^7 - 3 \cdot 1^6 + 2 \cdot 1^3 + 1^2 = 1$ and $a(-1) = (-1)^7 - 3 \cdot (-1)^6 + 2(-1)^3 + (-1)^2 = -5$. Therefore, 0 is the only rational root of $a(x)$.

EXAMPLE 2. Let

$$a(x) = x^4 + \tfrac{11}{6}x^3 + \tfrac{4}{3}x^2 - x - \tfrac{2}{3}.$$

The roots of $a(x)$ are the same as the roots of

$$6a(x) = 6x^4 + 11x^3 + 8x^2 - 6x - 4.$$

If $r = b/c$ is a rational root of $6a(x)$, where b and c are relatively prime integers, then by Theorem 9–12.1, b divides 4 and c divides 6. Therefore, the possibilities for r are

$$\pm 1, \quad \pm 2, \quad \pm 4, \quad \pm\tfrac{1}{2}, \quad \pm\tfrac{1}{3}, \quad \pm\tfrac{2}{3}, \quad \pm\tfrac{4}{3}, \quad \pm\tfrac{1}{6}.$$

Testing each of these numbers, we find that $a(-\tfrac{1}{2}) = 0$, $a(\tfrac{2}{3}) = 0$, and $-\tfrac{1}{2}$ and

$\frac{2}{3}$ are the only rational roots of $a(x)$. The division algorithm gives the factorization

$$a(x) = (x + \tfrac{1}{2})(x - \tfrac{2}{3})(x^2 + 2x + 2),$$

and it is easy to see that $x^2 + 2x + 2$ is irreducible in $Q[x]$.

EXAMPLE 3. Theorem 9–12.1 can be used in combination with some of the previous results in this chapter to obtain considerable information about the complete set of roots in C of a polynomial in $Q[x]$. Let

$$a(x) = x^6 - \tfrac{4}{3}x^5 - \tfrac{10}{3}x^4 + \tfrac{1}{3}x^3 + \tfrac{8}{3}x^2 + \tfrac{11}{3}x + \tfrac{7}{3}.$$

Since $a(x) \in Q[x]$, it follows that $a(x) \in R[x]$. By Theorem 9–10.3, a real root c of $a(x)$ satisfies

$$-\tfrac{14}{3} \le c \le \tfrac{13}{3}.$$

The complete set of roots in C of $a(x)$ is the same as the set of roots of

$$b(x) = 3a(x) = 3x^6 - 4x^5 - 10x^4 + x^3 + 8x^2 + 11x + 7.$$

By Theorem 9–12.1, the possible rational roots of $b(x)$ are ± 1, ± 7, $\pm \tfrac{1}{3}$, and $\pm \tfrac{7}{3}$. Since $-7 < -\tfrac{14}{3}$ and $7 > \tfrac{13}{3}$, it follows that 7 and -7 cannot be roots of $b(x)$ [for otherwise $a(x)$ would have a root in $Q \subset R$ which is not between the bounds for the real roots of $a(x)$]. Testing the numbers ± 1, $\pm \tfrac{1}{3}$, $\pm \tfrac{7}{3}$ in $b(x)$, we find that $b(-1) = 0$, $b(\tfrac{7}{3}) = 0$, and that -1 and $\tfrac{7}{3}$ are the only rational roots of $b(x)$. The division algorithm yields

$$b(x) = (x + 1)(x - \tfrac{7}{3})(3x^4 - 3x^2 - 3x - 3)$$
$$= 3(x + 1)(x - \tfrac{7}{3})(x^4 - x^2 - x - 1)$$

in $Q[x]$. Further roots of $b(x)$ in C are roots of

$$c(x) = x^4 - x^2 - x - 1.$$

From Theorem 9–12.1, the only possible rational roots of $c(x)$ are 1 and -1. Of course, 1 cannot be a root of $c(x)$, since it is not a root of $b(x)$. By substituting, we find that $c(-1) = 0$. Division gives

$$c(x) = (x + 1)(x^3 - x^2 - 1)$$

so that

$$b(x) = 3(x + 1)^2(x - \tfrac{7}{3})(x^3 - x^2 - 1)$$

in $Q[x]$. Let $d(x) = x^3 - x^2 - 1$. Since $d(-1) \ne 0$, it follows $x^3 - x^2 - 1$ is irreducible in $Q[x]$ (see Problem 3). Thus $a(x) = (x + 1)^2(x - \tfrac{7}{3})(x^3 - x^2 - 1)$ is the complete factorization of $a(x)$ into irreducibles in $Q[x]$. Further roots of $b(x)$ in C are roots of $d(x)$. Regarding $d(x)$ as a polynomial in $R[x]$, we use Theorem 9–10.3 again, and find that every real root c of $d(x)$ satisfies $-2 \le$

$c \leq 2$. The Sturm sequence for $d(x)$ is

$$d(x) = x^3 - x^2 - 1,$$
$$d'(x) = 3x^2 - 2x,$$
$$s_1(x) = \tfrac{2}{9}x + 1,$$
$$s_2(x) = \tfrac{279}{4},$$

and $N(-2) = 2$, $N(2) = 1$. Therefore, by Sturm's theorem, $d(x)$ has exactly one real root. This root is located between 1 and 2 since $d(1) = -1$ and $d(2) = 3$. The other roots of $d(x)$ are a pair of conjugate complex numbers (Theorem 9–8.3). In summary, we have obtained the following information about the roots in C of the polynomial $a(x)$: -1 is a double root; $\tfrac{7}{3}$ is a simple root; there is a simple real root between 1 and 2 which is not rational; there is a pair of conjugate complex roots. Of course, real and complex roots of $x^3 - x^2 - 1$ can be found in terms of square roots and cube roots, using the methods of Section 9–9.

The roots of polynomials in $Q[x]$ have many interesting properties. In the remainder of this section, we will examine some of the simplest ideas which are used in the study of the roots of rational polynomials. Our discussion will scratch the surface of an extensive branch of mathematics known as algebraic number theory.

DEFINITION 9–12.2. A complex number u is called an *algebraic number* if u is a root of some nonzero polynomial with rational coefficients. Complex numbers which are not algebraic are called *transcendental*.

Every rational number r is an algebraic number, because r is a root of $x - r$. Any number of the form $u = \sqrt[m]{r}$, where r is rational, is algebraic, because u is a root of $x^m - r$. The complex unit $i = \sqrt{-1}$ is an algebraic number. More generally, any number of the form $r + i \cdot s$, $r \in Q$, $s \in Q$, is an algebraic number, because $r + i \cdot s$ is a root of $x^2 - 2rx + (r^2 + s^2)$. Later we will show that the sum and product of any two algebraic numbers is an algebraic number, so that numbers such as $\sqrt{3} + \sqrt{5}$, $\sqrt{2} + \sqrt[3]{2}$, $\sqrt[4]{7} + i$, $2 \cdot \sqrt[3]{5}$, etc., are algebraic.

We observed in Section 1–2 that the set of all algebraic numbers is denumerable (see the discussion following Example 5). Since the set C of complex numbers is not denumerable, there must be many complex numbers which are not algebraic. That is, transcendental numbers certainly exist. However, it is not very easy to produce specific examples of transcendental numbers, and it is quite difficult to prove that particular numbers such as π and $2^{\sqrt{2}}$ are transcendental.

According to Definition 9–12.2, a number u is algebraic if it is a root of *any* nonzero polynomial in $Q[x]$. Of course, if u is algebraic, then u is a root of infinitely many polynomials with coefficients in Q. The following theorem tells us exactly what this set of polynomials can be.

THEOREM 9–12.3. Let u be an algebraic number. Then there is a unique monic polynomial $p(x)$ of least degree having u as a root. This polynomial $p(x)$ is irreducible, and it has the following property: if $a(x) \in Q[x]$, and u is a root of $a(x)$, then $p(x)$ divides $a(x)$ in $Q[x]$.

The unique polynomial $p(x)$ described in this theorem is called the *minimal polynomial of* u. The *degree* of u is defined to be the degree of the minimal polynomial of u. Thus, the rational numbers are exactly the algebraic numbers of degree one, and the numbers $r + \sqrt{s}$ where r, $s \in Q$ and s is not a square in Q are of degree two.

To prove Theorem 9–12.3, let $J = \{a(x) \in Q[x] | a(u) = 0\}$. That is, J is the set of all polynomials in $Q[x]$ which have u as a root. The assumption that u is an algebraic number means that J is a subset of $Q[x]$ which contains at least one nonzero polynomial. Therefore,

$$S = \{\mathrm{Deg}\,[a(x)] | a(x) \in J,\, a(x) \neq 0\}$$

is a nonempty subset of the set N of all natural numbers. (Note that no nonzero constant polynomial belongs to J.) Consequently, by the well-ordering principle, S contains a smallest number. That is, there is a non-zero polynomial $f(x) \in J$ such that $\mathrm{Deg}\,[f(x)] \leq \mathrm{Deg}\,[a(x)]$ for all nonzero $a(x) \in J$. Let $f(x) = a_0 + a_1 x + \cdots + a_{n-1}x^{n-1} + a_n x^n$, where $a_n \neq 0$. Define

$$p(x) = a_n^{-1} f(x) = (a_n^{-1} a_0) + (a_n^{-1} a_1)x + \cdots + (a_n^{-1} a_{n-1})x^{n-1} + x^n.$$

Then $p(x)$ is a monic polynomial such that $p(u) = 0$ and $\mathrm{Deg}\,[p(x)] \leq \mathrm{Deg}\,[a(x)]$ for all nonzero $a(x) \in J$. We will show: (i) $p(x)$ is irreducible, and (ii) if $a(x) \in J$, then $p(x)$ divides $a(x)$ in $Q[x]$. It will then follow easily that $p(x)$ is unique. Suppose that $p(x)$ is reducible. Then $p(x) = b(x) \cdot c(x)$, where $b(x)$ and $c(x)$ are nonzero polynomials in $Q[x]$ which have degrees less than $\mathrm{Deg}\,[p(x)]$. Since $b(u) \cdot c(u) = p(u) = 0$, it follows that either $b(u) = 0$, or $c(u) = 0$. Hence, by definition of J, either $b(x) \in J$, or $c(x) \in J$. This is impossible however, because $\mathrm{Deg}\,[p(x)] \leq \mathrm{Deg}\,[a(x)]$ for all nonzero $a(x) \in J$. Therefore, $p(x)$ is irreducible. In order to prove (ii), let $a(x) \in J$. By the division algorithm, it is possible to write

$$a(x) = q(x) \cdot p(x) + r(x),$$

where $q(x) \in Q[x]$, $r(x) \in Q[x]$, and either $r(x) = 0$, or else $\mathrm{Deg}\,[r(x)] < \mathrm{Deg}\,[p(x)]$. Suppose that $r(x) \neq 0$. Then $\mathrm{Deg}\,[r(x)] < \mathrm{Deg}\,[p(x)]$.

Moreover, $r(u) = a(u) - q(u) \cdot p(u) = 0 - q(u) \cdot 0 = 0$,   because $a(x) \in J$ and $p(x) \in J$. Thus, $r(x) \in J$. However, this is impossible, since $r(x) \in J$ implies that $\text{Deg}\,[p(x)] \leq \text{Deg}\,[r(x)]$.   Consequently, $r(x) \neq 0$ is impossible. Therefore, $r(x) = 0$ and $a(x) = q(x) \cdot p(x)$. That is, $p(x)$ divides $a(x)$, which proves (ii). It remains to show that $p(x)$ is unique. By choice, $p(x)$ is one monic polynomial of minimal degree in J. Suppose that $a(x)$ is another one. Then $\text{Deg}\,[a(x)] = \text{Deg}\,[p(x)]$. By what we have just proved, $p(x)|a(x)$. Therefore, $a(x)$ is a nonzero, constant multiple of $p(x)$ (see 9–4.1d). Since $a(x)$ and $p(x)$ are both monic, the constant must be one. That is, $a(x) = p(x)$. This establishes the uniqueness of $p(x)$.

———————————

EXAMPLE 4. Let $u = \sqrt{2}$. Then the minimal polynomial of u is $x^2 - 2$, since u is a root of this polynomial, but not of any polynomial of lower degree in $Q[x]$. Thus $\sqrt{2}$ is an algebraic number of degree two. The polynomials in $Q[x]$ which have $\sqrt{2}$ as a root are exactly those polynomials which are divisible by $x^2 - 2$. In particular, if $\sqrt{2}$ is a root of the rational polynomial $a(x)$, then $-\sqrt{2}$ is also a root of $a(x)$.

———————————

We wish to prove that the set of all algebraic numbers is a subring of the ring C of all complex numbers. A preliminary result is needed, which is important in its own right.

THEOREM 9–12.4. Let u be an algebraic number of degree n. Define

$$Q[u] = \{r_0 + r_1 u + \cdots + r_{n-1} u^{n-1} | r_0, r_1, \ldots, r_{n-1} \in Q\}.$$

Then $Q[u]$ is closed under addition, multiplication, negation, and the inverse of every nonzero element of $Q[u]$ is in $Q[u]$. Thus, $Q[u]$ is a field which is a subring* of C.

Proof. Let $U = \{a(u)|a(x) \in Q[x]\}$. Then it follows from (9–7.2) that U is a subring of C. We will first prove that $Q[u] = U$. It is clear that $Q[u] \subseteq U$. Indeed $Q[u]$ is just the set of all complex numbers $r(u)$, where $r(x) \in Q[x]$ is such that either $r(x) = 0$, or else $\text{Deg}\,[r(x)] < n$. On the other hand, suppose that $w \in U$. Then $w = a(u)$ for some $a(x) \in Q[x]$. Let $p(x)$ be the minimal polynomial of u. Then the degree of $p(x)$ is,

———————————

* In general, if D is a subring of a ring A and $a \in A$, then $D[a]$ denotes the smallest subring of A containing D and a. This notation seems to conflict with the use of $D[x]$ to denote the ring of polynomials with coefficients in D, but there is no contradiction because $D[x]$ is the smallest subring of $D[x]$ which contains D and x. Throughout the rest of this section, the symbols u and v will always stand for algebraic numbers, and x will denote an indeterminate as usual.

by definition, the degree n of u. By the division algorithm, we can write $a(x) = q(x) \cdot p(x) + r(x)$, where $r(x) \in Q[x]$, and either $r(x) = 0$, or else $\text{Deg}\,[r(x)] < \text{Deg}\,[p(x)] = n$. Thus,

$$r(x) = r_0 + r_1 x + \cdots + r_{n-1} x^{n-1},$$

where $r_0, r_1, \ldots,$ and r_{n-1} are rational numbers. Moreover,

$$w = a(u) = q(u) \cdot p(u) + r(u) = q(u) \cdot 0 + r(u) = r(u)$$
$$= r_0 + r_1 u + \cdots + r_{n-1} u^{n-1}.$$

Consequently $w \in Q[u]$. Since w was any element of U, we have proved that $U \subseteq Q[u]$. Thus, $Q[u] = U$. The only thing left to show is that every nonzero element of $Q[u]$ has an inverse in $Q[u]$. Let $w = r_0 + r_1 u + \cdots + r_{n-1} u^{n-1}$ be an element of $Q[u]$ which is not zero. Then in particular, the polynomial $r(x) = r_0 + r_1 x + \cdots + r_{n-1} x^{n-1}$ is not zero. Moreover, $\text{Deg}\,[r(x)] \leq n - 1 < \text{Deg}\,[p(x)]$. Hence, $p(x)$ does not divide $r(x)$. Since $p(x)$ is irreducible by Theorem 9–12.3, it follows that $p(x)$ and $r(x)$ are relatively prime [see (9–5.2)]. Therefore, by Theorem 9–4.4, polynomials $g(x)$ and $h(x)$ exist in $Q[x]$, such that

$$1 = g(x) \cdot r(x) + h(x) \cdot p(x).$$

Substituting $x = u$ in this identity, we obtain

$$1 = g(u) \cdot r(u) + h(u) \cdot p(u) = g(u) \cdot r(u) + h(u) \cdot 0 = g(u) \cdot r(u).$$

Therefore, $w^{-1} = r(u)^{-1} = g(u) \in U = Q[u]$. This completes the proof.

THEOREM 9–12.5. If u and v are algebraic numbers, then $u + v$, $u \cdot v$, and $-u$ are algebraic numbers. If u is a nonzero algebraic number, then u^{-1} is an algebraic number.

In order to prove this theorem, it is necessary to use a result which will be established in Section 10–2 (see Theorem 10–2.9). The special case of Theorem 10–2.9 which we will use here can be stated as follows.

(9–12.6). Let $\{r_{i,j} | 1 \leq i \leq g, 0 \leq j \leq g\}$ be a set of rational numbers. Then there exist rational numbers $s_0, s_1, s_2, \ldots, s_g$ not all of which are zero such that

$$\sum_{j=0}^{g} r_{i,j} s_j = 0,$$

for $i = 1, 2, \ldots, g$.

Proof of Theorem 9–12.5. Suppose that the degree of u is m and the degree of v is n. We will prove that $u + v$ is a root of a nonzero polynomial in $Q[x]$ which has degree at most $m \cdot n$. Therefore $u + v$ is algebraic of degree $\leq m \cdot n$. By Theorem 9–12.4, for any natural numbers i and j, there exist rational numbers $a_{i,0}, \ a_{i,1}, \ a_{i,2}, \ \ldots, \ a_{i,m-1}$ and $b_{j,0}, \ b_{j,1}, \ b_{j,2}, \ \ldots, \ b_{j,n-1}$ such that

$$u^i = \sum_{k=0}^{m-1} a_{i,k} u^k, \qquad v^j = \sum_{l=0}^{n-1} b_{j,l} v^l.$$

Hence, by the binomial theorem, we have for $h = 1, 2, 3, \ldots, m \cdot n$.

$$\begin{aligned}
(u + v)^h &= \sum_{i=0}^{h} \binom{h}{i} u^i v^{h-i} \\
&= \sum_{i=0}^{h} \binom{h}{i} \left(\sum_{k=0}^{m-1} a_{i,k} u^k \right) \left(\sum_{l=0}^{n-1} b_{h-i,l} v^l \right) \\
&= \sum_{k=0}^{m-1} \sum_{l=0}^{n-1} \left(\sum_{i=0}^{h} a_{i,k} b_{h-i,l} \binom{h}{i} \right) u^k v^l \\
&= \sum_{k=0}^{m-1} \sum_{l=0}^{n-1} r_{k,l,h} u^k v^l,
\end{aligned}$$

where

$$r_{k,l,h} = \sum_{i=0}^{h} a_{i,k} b_{h-i,l} \binom{h}{i}.$$

Since all of the binomial coefficients $\binom{h}{i}$ are natural numbers, it follows that each of the numbers $r_{k,l,h}$ is rational. It is also convenient to define $r_{k,l,0} = 1$ if $k = l = 0$ and $r_{k,l,0} = 0$ if $k > 0$ or $l > 0$, so that

$$(u + v)^0 = \sum_{k=0}^{m-1} \sum_{l=0}^{n-1} r_{k,l,0} u^k v^l.$$

By (9–12.6) (taking $g = m \cdot n$ and replacing the indices $i = 1, 2, \ldots, g$ by the $m \cdot n$ pairs $\langle k, l \rangle$, $0 \leq k \leq m - 1$, $0 \leq l \leq n - 1$ in some order), there exist rational numbers $s_0, s_1, \ldots, s_{m \cdot n}$ not all of which are zero, such that

$$\sum_{h=0}^{m \cdot n} r_{k,l,h} s_h = 0$$

for all pairs $\langle k, l \rangle$ with $0 \leq k \leq m - 1$ and $0 \leq l \leq n - 1$.

Consequently,

$$\sum_{h=0}^{m \cdot n} s_h (u+v)^h = \sum_{h=0}^{m \cdot n} \sum_{k=0}^{m-1} \sum_{l=0}^{n-1} s_h r_{k,l,h} u^k v^l$$

$$= \sum_{k=0}^{m-1} \sum_{l=0}^{n-1} \left(\sum_{h=0}^{m \cdot n} r_{k,l,h} s_h \right) u^k v^l$$

$$= \sum_{k=0}^{m-1} \sum_{l=0}^{n-1} 0 \cdot u^k v^l = 0.$$

That is, $u + v$ is a root of the nonzero polynomial

$$\sum_{h=0}^{m \cdot n} s_h x^h \in Q[x].$$

Therefore, $u + v$ is an algebraic number. A similar proof shows that $u \cdot v$ is a root of a nonzero polynomial of degree at most $m \cdot n$. Thus, $u \cdot v$ is algebraic. In particular $-u = (-1) \cdot u$ is algebraic. Finally, suppose that $u \neq 0$, and let the minimal polynomial of u be

$$p(x) = c_0 + c_1 x + c_2 x^2 + \cdots + c_{m-1} x^{m-1} + x^m.$$

Then $c_0 \neq 0$, because $p(x)$ is irreducible, so that

$$1 = c_0^{-1} \cdot c_0$$

$$= u \cdot [(-c_0^{-1} c_1) + (-c_0^{-1} c_2) u + \cdots$$

$$+ (-c_0^{-1} c_{m-1}) u^{m-2} + (-c_0^{-1}) u^{m-1}].$$

Therefore,

$$u^{-1} = (-c_0^{-1} c_1) + (c_0^{-1} c_2) u + \cdots + (-c_0^{-1} c_{m-1}) u^{m-2} + (-c_0^{-1}) u^{m-1}.$$

Since the sums and products of algebraic numbers are algebraic, and since u and each of the rational numbers $-c_0^{-1} c_1$, $-c_0^{-1} c_2$, $\ldots$, $-c_0^{-1} c_{m-1}$, $-c_0^{-1}$ is algebraic, it follows that u^{-1} is algebraic. This completes the proof of Theorem 9–12.5.

EXAMPLE 5. It is instructive to carry out the proof of Theorem 9–12.5 in a special case.

Let $u = 1 + \sqrt{2}$ and $v = \sqrt{3}$. Then the minimal polynomials of u and v are $x^2 - 2x - 1$ and $x^2 - 3$, respectively. We have

$$u^2 = 2u + 1, \quad u^3 = 2u^2 + u = 5u + 2,$$

$$u^4 = uu^3 = 5u^2 + 2u = 12u + 5,$$

$$v^2 = 3, \quad v^3 = 3v, \quad v^4 = 9,$$

so that

$$(u + v)^2 = u^2 + 2uv + v^2 = 2u + 1 + 2uv + 3$$
$$= 4 + 2u + 2uv,$$
$$(u + v)^3 = u^3 + 3u^2v + 3uv^2 + v^3 = (5u + 2) + 3(2u + 1)v + 9u + 3v$$
$$= 2 + 14u + 6v + 6uv,$$
$$(u + v)^4 = u^4 + 4u^3v + 6u^2v^2 + 4uv^3 + v^4$$
$$= (12u + 5) + 4(5u + 2)v + 6(2u + 1)3 + 4u(3v) + 9$$
$$= 32 + 48u + 8v + 32uv.$$

We wish to find rational numbers s_0, s_1, s_2, s_3, and s_4, not all zero, satisfying

$$1 \cdot s_0 + 0 \cdot s_1 + 4 \cdot s_2 + 2 \cdot s_3 + 32 \cdot s_4 = 0,$$
$$0 \cdot s_0 + 1 \cdot s_1 + 2 \cdot s_2 + 14 \cdot s_3 + 48 \cdot s_4 = 0,$$
$$0 \cdot s_0 + 1 \cdot s_1 + 0 \cdot s_2 + 6 \cdot s_3 + 8 \cdot s_4 = 0,$$
$$0 \cdot s_0 + 0 \cdot s_1 + 2 \cdot s_2 + 6 \cdot s_3 + 32 \cdot s_4 = 0.$$

A method for solving such systems of equations will be developed in Section 10–2. However, it is easy to verify that

$$s_0 = -8, \qquad s_1 = 16, \qquad s_2 = -4, \qquad s_3 = -4, \qquad s_4 = 1$$

is a solution. Consequently,

$$(u + v)^4 - 4(u + v)^3 - 4(u + v)^2 + 16(u + v) - 8$$
$$= (1 \cdot (-8) + 0 \cdot 16 + 4 \cdot (-4) + 2 \cdot (-4) + 32 \cdot 1)$$
$$+ (0 \cdot (-8) + 1 \cdot 16 + 2 \cdot (-4) + 14 \cdot (-4) + 48 \cdot 1)u$$
$$+ (0 \cdot (-8) + 1 \cdot 16 + 0 \cdot (-4) + 6 \cdot (-4) + 8 \cdot 1)v$$
$$+ (0 \cdot (-8) + 0 \cdot 16 + 2 \cdot (-4) + 6 \cdot (-4) + 32 \cdot 1)uv$$
$$= 0.$$

Therefore, $u + v = 1 + \sqrt{2} + \sqrt{3}$ is a root of $x^4 - 4x^3 - 4x^2 + 16x - 8$. The proof that uv is an algebraic number is somewhat simpler in this special case. Note that

$$(uv)^2 = u^2v^2 = (2u + 1) \cdot 3 = 3 + 6u,$$
$$(uv)^3 = u^3v^3 = (5u + 2)(3v) = 6v + 15uv,$$
$$(uv)^4 = u^4v^4 = (12u + 5) \cdot 9 = 45 + 108u.$$

Thus,

$$(uv)^4 - 18(uv)^2 + 9 = (45 - 3 \cdot 18 + 9) + (108 - 6 \cdot 18 + 0) \cdot u = 0.$$

Consequently, $uv = \sqrt{3} + \sqrt{2} \cdot \sqrt{3}$ is a root of $x^4 - 18x^2 + 9$.

It can be shown that the polynomials $x^4 - 4x^3 - 4x^2 + 16x - 8$ and $x^4 - 18x^2 + 9$ are irreducible in $Q[x]$, so that if $u = 1 + \sqrt{2}$ and $v = \sqrt{3}$, then the degree of $u + v$ and uv is exactly 4, the product of the degree of u and the degree of v. It may happen however that the degree of $u + v$ or of uv is less than the product of the degrees of u and v. For example, if $u = \sqrt{2}$ and $v = \sqrt[4]{2}$, then the degree of u is 2, the degree of v is 4, and the degrees of $u + v$ and uv are both 4: $u + v$ is a root of $x^4 - 4x^2 - 8x + 2$, uv is a root of $x^4 - 8$.

It is convenient to reformulate our main results on algebraic numbers.

THEOREM 9–12.7. The set A of all algebraic numbers is a field which is a subring of C. If u is any algebraic number, then the field $Q[u]$ is a subring of A.

Proof. By Theorem 9–12.5, the set A of all algebraic numbers is a field with respect to the operations of addition, multiplication, and negation in C. That is, A is a subring of C. If v is any element of $Q[u]$, where u is an algebraic number, then by the definition of $Q[u]$, v is a sum of products of algebraic numbers. Thus, by Theorem 9–12.5, $v \in A$. Therefore, $Q[u] \subseteq A$.

PROBLEMS

1. Find all of the rational roots of the following polynomials.
   (a) $2x^3 - 7x^2 + 10x - 6$
   (b) $x^3 - \frac{2}{3}x^2 + 3x - 2$
   (c) $x^3 - \frac{1}{4}x^2 - \frac{1}{4}x + \frac{1}{16}$
   (d) $x^3 - 48x + 64$
   (e) $x^4 - 5x - 1$
   (f) $2x^6 - x^5 - 2x^4 + x^3 + 2x^2 + 3x - 2$

2. Prove that if r is a rational root of a monic polynomial with integral coefficients, then r is an integer.

3. Prove that a polynomial of degree 2 or 3 in $Q[x]$ is irreducible in $Q[x]$ if it has no rational root. Use this result to show that the following polynomials are irreducible in $Q[x]$.
   (a) $x^2 + x + 1$ (b) $x^2 + \frac{1}{2}x - 1$
   (c) $x^3 + 37x^2 + 211x - 1$ (d) $x^3 - 25x - 5$

4. Give the complete factorization in $Q[x]$ of the following polynomials.
   (a) $x^4 - 1$
   (b) $2x^4 - x^3 + 2x^2 + x - 1$
   (c) $x^4 + x^2 + 1$

5. For the following polynomials in $Q[x]$ determine all rational roots, and the number and approximate location of all real roots.
   (a) $x^4 + \frac{19}{10}x^3 + \frac{28}{10}x^2 + \frac{7}{10}x - \frac{1}{10}$
   (b) $x^5 + 4x^4 + 7x^3 + 7x^2 + 4x + 1$
   (c) $x^7 + \frac{25}{6}x^6 + \frac{9}{2}x^5 - \frac{21}{2}x^4 - \frac{35}{6}x^3 - 3x^2 + 6x - \frac{4}{3}$

6. Find the minimal polynomial of the following algebraic numbers: $\frac{1}{2}$, $1 + \sqrt{3}$, $-\frac{1}{2} - i\sqrt{3}/2$, $3\sqrt[3]{2}$.

7. Suppose that r and s are rational numbers and s is not the square of a rational number. Prove (a) the minimal polynomial of $r + \sqrt{s}$ is $x^2 - 2rx + (r^2 - s)$; (b) if $a(x) \in Q[x]$ is such that $r + \sqrt{s}$ is a root of $a(x)$, then $r - \sqrt{s}$ is also a root of $a(x)$.

8. Carry out the proof that if u and v are algebraic numbers, then $u + v$ is an algebraic number in the following special case.
    (a) $u = \sqrt{2}, v = \sqrt{5}$
    (b) $u = \sqrt{2}, v = \sqrt[3]{2}$.

9. Give the details of the proof that if u and v are algebraic numbers of degree m and n, respectively, then uv is algebraic of degree at most $m \cdot n$.

10. Let $p(x)$ and $q(x)$ be distinct monic irreducible polynomials in $Q[x]$. Prove that there is no complex number which is a root of both $p(x)$ and $q(x)$.

11. Show that if u is an algebraic number of degree n, then $-u$ is of degree n.

12. Let $p(x)$ be irreducible in $Q[x]$. Suppose that u and v are two roots of $p(x)$. Prove that the fields $Q[u]$ and $Q[v]$ are isomorphic.

CHAPTER 10

SYSTEMS OF EQUATIONS AND MATRICES

10–1 Polynomials in several indeterminates. In Section 9–2 we showed that beginning with any integral domain D, a domain $D[x]$ of polynomials with coefficients in D could be constructed. In particular, D itself can be taken to be a domain of polynomials. In fact, this process can be repeated any number of times to obtain polynomials in several indeterminates. In order to avoid confusion, it is of course necessary to use different symbols to designate the various indeterminates. The symbols x, y, and z are usually used in discussing polynomials in one, two, or three indeterminates; in discussions involving larger numbers of indeterminates, x_1, x_2, x_3, $\ldots$ are more convenient.

DEFINITION 10–1.1. Let D be an integral domain. The *domain of polynomials in the distinct indeterminates* x_1, x_2, $\ldots$, x_r *with coefficients in* D is defined by induction on r. For $r = 1$, $D[x_1]$ is the integral domain of polynomials in x_1 with coefficients in D, defined as in Section 9–2. If $r > 1$ and $D[x_1, x_2, \ldots, x_{r-1}]$ has been defined, let

$$D[x_1, x_2, \ldots, x_{r-1}, x_r] = (D[x_1, x_2, \ldots, x_{r-1}])[x_r]$$

be the integral domain of polynomials in x_r with coefficients in

$$D[x_1, x_2, \ldots, x_{r-1}].$$

The elements of $D[x_1, x_2, \ldots, x_r]$ are called *polynomials in* $x_1, x_2, \ldots, x_r$ *with coefficients in* D.

According to Definitions 10–1.1 and 9–2.1, each element of

$$D[x_1, x_2, \ldots, x_r]$$

can be expressed uniquely in the form

$$\sum_{i=0}^{n} f_i x_r^i, \tag{10–1}$$

where $f_i \in D[x_1, x_2, \ldots, x_{r-1}]$. If $r = 2$, then each f_i is a polynomial in x_1, which can be expressed in the form $\sum_{j=0}^{mi} a_{i,j} x_1^j$ with $a_{ij} \in D$. Choose m to be the largest of the integers m_0, m_1, $\ldots$, m_n and define $a_{i,j} = 0$ if

$m_i < j \leq m$. Then the polynomial (10–1) (in the case $r = 2$) is

$$\sum_{i=0}^{n} \sum_{j=0}^{m} a_{i,j} x_1^j x_2^i.$$

Moreover, this expression is unique. That is, if

$$\sum_{i=0}^{n} \sum_{j=0}^{m} a_{i,j} x_1^j x_2^i = \sum_{i=0}^{n} \sum_{j=0}^{m} b_{i,j} x_1^j x_2^i,$$

where all $a_{i,j}$ and $b_{i,j}$ are in D, then $a_{i,j} = b_{i,j}$ for all i and j. In fact, define

$$f_i = \sum_{j=0}^{m} a_{i,j} x_1^j$$

and

$$g_i = \sum_{j=0}^{m} b_{i,j} x_1^j$$

for all i. Then $\sum_{i=0}^{n} f_i x_2^i = \sum_{i=0}^{m} g_i x_2^i$. By uniqueness of the representation (10–1), it follows that

$$\sum_{j=0}^{m} a_{i,j} x_1^j = f_i = g_i = \sum_{j=0}^{m} b_{i,j} x_1^j$$

for all i. Therefore, by Definition 9–2.1, $a_{i,j} = b_{i,j}$ for all i and j. In general, it can be shown by induction on r that each polynomial in $D[x_1, x_2, \ldots, x_r]$ can be expressed uniquely as a multiple sum

$$\sum_{i_1=0}^{n_1} \sum_{i_2=0}^{n_2} \cdots \sum_{i_r=0}^{n_r} a_{i_1, i_2, \ldots, i_r} x_1^{i_1} x_2^{i_2} \cdots x_r^{i_r}, \tag{10–2}$$

where for each string $i_1, i_2, \ldots, i_r$ of integers satisfying $0 \leq i_1 \leq n_1$, $0 \leq i_2 \leq n_2, \ldots, 0 \leq i_r \leq n_r$, $a_{i_1, i_2, \ldots, i_r}$ is an element of D. The existence of a representation of the form (10–2) is the reason why the elements of $D[x_1, x_2, \ldots, x_r]$ are called polynomials in $x_1, x_2, \ldots, x_r$, with coefficients in D.

Because it is cumbersome, the expression (10–2) is frequently shortened to

$$\sum_{i} a_i x_1^{i_1} x_2^{i_2} \cdots x_r^{i_r},$$

where i stands for the ordered string $\langle i_1, i_2, \ldots, i_r \rangle$, and the sum is over a finite number of such strings. It is sometimes convenient to denote polynomials in r indeterminates by expressions such as

$$a(x_1, x_2, \ldots, x_r), \qquad b(x_1, x_2, \ldots, x_r), \qquad f(x_1, x_2, \ldots, x_r).$$

The statement that the representation $\sum_i a_i x_1^{i_1} x_2^{i_2} \cdots x_r^{i_r}$ of a polynomial in $D[x_1, x_2, \ldots, x_r]$ is unique means that

$$\sum_i a_i x_1^{i_1} x_2^{i_2} \cdots x_r^{i_r} = \sum_i b_i x_1^{i_1} x_2^{i_2} \cdots x_r^{i_r}$$

only if $a_i = b_i$ for all $i = \langle i_1, i_2, \ldots, i_r \rangle$. This fact is very important. Many definitions concerning polynomials in several indeterminates are stated in terms of the representation of polynomials in the form

$$\sum_i a_i x_1^{i_1} x_2^{i_2} \cdots x_r^{i_r}.$$

The concepts introduced in this way are well defined because of the uniqueness of the representation (a fact which is often not mentioned).

Those polynomials in $D[x_1, x_2, \ldots, x_r]$ which contain only the indeterminates $x_{j_1}, x_{j_2}, \ldots, x_{j_s}$, where $j_1, j_2, \ldots, j_s$ are distinct elements of the set $\{1, 2, \ldots, r\}$, form a subring of $D[x_1, x_2, \ldots, x_r]$. This subring is isomorphic to the ring of all polynomials in any s indeterminates with coefficients in D. It is natural to denote this subring of $D[x_1, x_2, \ldots, x_r]$ by $D[x_{j_1}, x_{j_2}, \ldots, x_{j_s}]$. For example, a polynomial $\sum_i \sum_j \sum_k a_{i,j,k} x^k y^j z^i$ such that $a_{i,j,k} = 0$ for all $k > 0$ can be expressed as

$$\sum_i \sum_j \sum_k a_{i,j,k} x^k y^j z^i = \sum_i \sum_j (a_{i,j,0} x^0) y^j z^i = \sum_i \sum_j b_{i,j} y^j z^i,$$

where $a_{i,j,0} x^0 = b_{i,j} \in D$. The set of all such polynomials is the subring of $D[x, y, z]$, which we denote by $D[y, z]$. In this way, the rings of polynomials in the various subsets of $\{x_1, x_2, \ldots, x_r\}$ are identified with subrings of $D[x_1, x_2, \ldots, x_r]$.

If $a(x_1, x_2, \ldots, x_r)$ is a polynomial in $D[x_1, x_2, \ldots, x_r]$, then it is clear from the representation (10–2) that for each natural number $j \leq r$, we can think of $a(x_1, x_2, \ldots, x_r)$ as a polynomial in x_j with coefficients in $D[x_1, \ldots, x_{j-1}, x_{j+1}, \ldots, x_r]$. Thus, no distinction is made between $D[x_1, x_2, \ldots, x_r]$ and $D[x_1, \ldots, x_{j-1}, x_{j+1}, \ldots, x_r, x_j]$. In general, if $i_1, i_2, \ldots, i_r$ is any permutation of $1, 2, \ldots, r$, then $D[x_{i_1}, x_{i_2}, \ldots, x_{i_r}]$ is regarded as the same domain of polynomials as $D[x_1, x_2, \ldots, x_r]$.

For example, the polynomial

$$a(x, y, z) = x^4 + 5y - 3z + 2x^2 yz + 3x^3 z^2$$

is expressed as

$$(x^4 + 5y) + (2x^2 y - 3)z + (3x^3)z^2$$

when considered as a polynomial in $D[x, y][z] = D[x, y, z]$. On the other hand, the same polynomial can be written in the form

$$(5y - 3z) + (2yz)x^2 + (3z^2)x^3 + x^4,$$

which is a polynomial in $D[y, z][x] = D[y, z, x]$.

The notion of the degree of a polynomial can be generalized in several ways to polynomials in several indeterminates. When $a(x_1, x_2, \ldots, x_r) \in D[x_1, x_2, \ldots, x_r]$ is regarded as a polynomial in x_j with coefficients in $D[x_1, \ldots, x_{j-1}, x_{j+1}, \ldots, x_r]$, we can use Definition 9–3.1 to define the x_j-degree of $a(x_1, x_2, \ldots, x_r)$. That is, if

$$a(x_1, x_2, \ldots, x_r) = \sum_{i=0}^{n} f_i(x_1, \ldots, x_{j-1}, x_{j+1}, \ldots, x_r)x_j^i,$$

where $f_n(x_1, \ldots, x_{j-1}, x_{j+1}, \ldots, x_r) \neq 0$, then the x_j-degree of $a(x_1, x_2, \ldots, x_r)$ is n. For example, $\frac{1}{2}x^2y + 2xy^3 + 1 = 1 + (2y^3)x + (\frac{1}{2}y)x^2 = 1 + (\frac{1}{2}x^2)y + (2x)y^3$, so that

$$\mathrm{Deg}_x\,[\tfrac{1}{2}x^2y + 2xy^3 + 1] = 2, \qquad \mathrm{Deg}_y\,[\tfrac{1}{2}x^2y + 2xy^3 + 1] = 3.$$

Of course, the properties of the degree of a polynomial listed in Theorem 9–3.2 are satisfied by Deg_{x_j} for each x_j.

It is also possible to define the *total degree* of

$$a(x_1, x_2, \ldots, x_r) = \sum_{i_1=0}^{n_1} \sum_{i_2=0}^{n_2} \cdots \sum_{i_r=0}^{n_r} a_{i_1, i_2, \ldots, i_r} x_1^{i_1} x_2^{i_2} \cdots x_r^{i_r}$$

to be the largest of the sums $i_1 + i_2 + \cdots + i_r$ for which $a_{i_1, i_2, \ldots, i_r}$ is not zero. For example, the total degree of $\frac{1}{2}x^2y + 2xy^3 + 1$ is four. It is easy to prove the analogue of Theorem 9–3.2 for the total degree.

(10–1.2). Let $a(x_1, x_2, \ldots, x_r)$ and $b(x_1, x_2, \ldots, x_r)$ be nonzero polynomials of total degrees m and n respectively. Then

    (a) $a(x_1, x_2, \ldots, x_r) \cdot b(x_1, x_2, \ldots, x_r)$ has total degree $m + n$;

    (b) $a(x_1, x_2, \ldots, x_r) + b(x_1, x_2, \ldots, x_r)$ is either zero, or has total degree $\leq \max \{m, n\}$;

    (c) if $m \neq n$, then the total degree of

$$a(x_1, x_2, \ldots, x_r) + b(x_1, x_2, \ldots, x_r)$$

is equal to $\max \{m, n\}$.

We leave the proof of these facts for the reader to supply.

The arithmetical properties of the rings $F[x]$ with F a field cannot be generalized to polynomial domains $F[x_1, x_2, \ldots, x_r]$ with $r > 1$. The most important results in Sections 9–3 and 9–4 are false in $F[x_1, x_2, \ldots, x_r]$ when $r > 1$. Surprisingly enough, the unique factorization theorem is true in $F[x_1, x_2, \ldots, x_r]$, although it is proved in a different way than Theorem 9–5.4. We will not enter into a discussion of these matters, but will only note the following example.

EXAMPLE 1. The polynomials x and y in $Q[x, y]$ clearly have only nonzero rational numbers as common divisors. Hence, 1 is a greatest common divisor of x and y (in the sense explained in Section 5–2). It is not hard to see, however, that there are no polynomials $f(x, y)$ and $g(x, y)$ in $Q[x, y]$ such that

$$x \cdot f(x, y) + y \cdot g(x, y) = 1.$$

Therefore, the analogue of Theorem 9–4.4 fails in $Q[x, y]$.

The definition of substitution given in 9–7.1 can be extended to polynomials in several indeterminates.

DEFINITION 10–1.3. Let D be an integral domain, and let A be a commutative ring which contains D as a subring. Suppose that

$$a(x_1, x_2, \ldots, x_r) = \sum_{i_1=0}^{n_1} \sum_{i_2=0}^{n_2} \cdots \sum_{i_r=0}^{n_r} a_{i_1, i_2, \ldots, i_r} x_1^{i_1} x_2^{i_2} \cdots x_r^{i_r}$$

is in $D[x_1, x_2, \ldots, x_r]$. Let $\langle u_1, u_2, \ldots, u_r \rangle$ be an ordered string of elements of A. Then the element

$$\sum_{i_1=0}^{n_1} \sum_{i_2=0}^{n_2} \cdots \sum_{i_r=0}^{n_r} a_{i_1, i_2, \ldots, i_r} u_1^{i_1} u_2^{i_2} \cdots u_r^{i_r}$$

in A is called the *value* of $a(x_1, x_2, \ldots, x_r)$ for $x_1 = u_1, x_2 = u_2, \ldots,$ and $x_r = u_r$, and this value is denoted by $a(u_1, u_2, \ldots, u_r)$. The element $a(u_1, u_2, \ldots, u_r)$ is said to be obtained by *substituting* $u_1, u_2, \ldots, u_r$ for $x_1, x_2, \ldots, x_r$ in $a(x_1, x_2, \ldots, x_r)$.

EXAMPLE 2. Let $D = R$, $a(x, y, z) = x^2 + y^2 - z^2$. If $A = C$, the value of $a(x, y, z)$ at $\langle 1, i, -1 \rangle$ is $a(1, i, -1) = 1^2 + (i)^2 - (-1)^2 = -1$. If $A = R$, the value of $a(x, y, z)$ at $\langle \sqrt{2}, \sqrt{2}, 2 \rangle$ is $a(\sqrt{2}, \sqrt{2}, 2) = (\sqrt{2})^2 + (\sqrt{2})^2 - (2)^2 = 0$. Let $A = R[x, y]$. Then the value of $a(x, y, z)$ at

$$\langle x^2 - y^2, 2xy, x^2 + y^2 \rangle$$

is

$$a(x^2 - y^2, 2xy, x^2 + y^2) = (x^2 - y^2)^2 + (2xy)^2 - (x^2 + y^2)^2 = 0.$$

The property of substitution given in (9–7.2) can be generalized.

(10–1.4). Let D be an integral domain which is a subring of the commutative ring A. Let

$$f(x_1, x_2, \ldots, x_r), \qquad a(x_1, x_2, \ldots, x_r), \qquad \text{and} \qquad b(x_1, x_2, \ldots, x_r)$$

be in $D[x_1, x_2, \ldots, x_r]$. Suppose that $u_1, u_2, \ldots, u_r$ are in A.

(a) If $f(x_1, x_2, \ldots, x_r) = a(x_1, x_2, \ldots, x_r) + b(x_1, x_2, \ldots, x_r)$ then

$$f(u_1, u_2, \ldots, u_r) = a(u_1, u_2, \ldots, u_r) + b(u_1, u_2, \ldots, u_r).$$

(b) If $f(x_1, x_2, \ldots, x_r) = a(x_1, x_2, \ldots, x_r) \cdot b(x_1, x_2, \ldots, x_r)$, then

$$f(u_1, u_2, \ldots, u_r) = a(u_1, u_2, \ldots, u_r) \cdot b(u_1, u_2, \ldots, u_r).$$

(c) If $f(x_1, x_2, \ldots, x_r)$ does not contain x_j, then

$$f(u_1, \ldots, u_{j-1}, u_j, u_{j+1}, \ldots, u_r) = f(u_1, \ldots, u_{j-1}, v, u_{j+1}, \ldots, u_r)$$

for all $v \in A$.

(d) Let $g(x_1, x_2, \ldots, x_s) \in D[x_1, x_2, \ldots, x_s]$, $a_i(x_1, x_2, \ldots, x_r) \in D[x_1, x_2, \ldots, x_r]$ for $i = 1, 2, \ldots, s$, and let $u_1, u_2, \ldots, u_r \in A$. If

$$h(x_1, x_2, \ldots, x_r)$$
$$= g(a_1(x_1, x_2, \ldots, x_r), a_2(x_1, x_2, \ldots, x_r), \ldots, a_s(x_1, x_2, \ldots, x_r)),$$

then

$$h(u_1, u_2, \ldots, u_r)$$
$$= g(a_1(u_1, u_2, \ldots, u_r), a_2(u_1, u_2, \ldots, u_r), \ldots, a_s(u_1, u_2, \ldots, u_r)).$$

The statements (a), (b), and (c) are easily proved by means of the generalized commutative, associative, and distributive laws of operation in a ring. (See Section 9–7 for the proof of (b) in the case $r = 1$.) The statement (d) can be obtained from (a), (b), and (c) by induction on s (see Problem 14 below). Part (d) includes (a) and (b) as the special cases in which $g(x_1, x_2) = x_1 + x_2$ and $g(x_1, x_2) = x_1 \cdot x_2$. Another important consequence of (d) is the fact that the result of substituting for the indeterminates in a polynomial does not depend on the way in which the polynomial is expressed. For example,

$$(x_4 - x_1)(x_4 - x_2) + (x_4 - x_3^2)$$
$$= x_4^2 - (x_1 + x_2 - 1)x_4 + x_1 x_2 - x_3^2$$

in $Z[x_1, x_2, x_3, x_4]$. If we let

$$g(x_1, x_2, x_3) = x_1 x_2 + x_3,$$
$$a_1(x_1, x_2, x_3, x_4) = x_4 - x_1,$$
$$a_2(x_1, x_2, x_3, x_4) = x_4 - x_2,$$
$$a_3(x_1, x_2, x_3, x_4) = x_4 - x_3^2,$$

and

$$h(x_1, x_2, x_3, x_4) = x_4^2 - (x_1 + x_2 - 1)x_4 + x_1 x_2 - x_3^2,$$

then

$$h(x_1, x_2, x_3, x_4)$$
$$= g\big(a_1(x_1, x_2, x_3, x_4), a_2(x_1, x_2, x_3, x_4), a_3(x_1, x_2, x_3, x_4)\big).$$

It follows from (10–1.4d) that

$$(u_4 - u_1)(u_4 - u_2) + (u_4 - u_3^2)$$
$$= u_4^2 - (u_1 + u_2 - 1)u_4 + u_1 u_2 - u_3^2$$

for any u_1, u_2, u_3, u_4 in a commutative ring containing Z as a subring. Of course, this fact could be shown directly.

DEFINITION 10–1.5.   Let $a(x_1, x_2, \ldots, x_r) \in D[x_1, x_2, \ldots, x_r]$, where D is an integral domain. Let A be a commutative ring containing D. If $u_1, u_2, \ldots, u_r$ are in A, then the ordered string $\langle u_1, u_2, \ldots, u_r \rangle$ is called a *zero* of $a(x_1, x_2, \ldots, x_r)$ [or a *solution of* $a(x_1, x_2, \ldots, x_r) = 0$] in the ring A if $a(u_1, u_2, \ldots, u_r) = 0$. More generally, if

$$a_1(x_1, x_2, \ldots, x_r), \qquad a_2(x_1, x_2, \ldots, x_r), \qquad \ldots, \qquad a_s(x_1, x_2, \ldots, x_r)$$

are polynomials in $D[x_1, x_2, \ldots, x_r]$, then $\langle u_1, u_2, \ldots, u_r \rangle$ is called a *solution of the system of equations*

$$a_1(x_1, x_2, \ldots, x_r) = 0$$
$$a_2(x_1, x_2, \ldots, x_r) = 0$$
$$\vdots$$
$$a_s(x_1, x_2, \ldots, x_r) = 0$$

if

$$a_1(u_1, u_2, \ldots, u_r) = 0$$
$$a_2(u_1, u_2, \ldots, u_r) = 0$$
$$\vdots$$
$$a_s(u_1, u_2, \ldots, u_r) = 0.$$

EXAMPLE 3. Let $a(x, y) \in R[x, y]$. The zeros $\langle u, v \rangle$ of $a(x, y)$ in R can be considered as the coordinates of points in the cartesian plane. The set of all such points constitutes what is called an *algebraic curve*, (possibly degenerate, that is, the empty set, or a finite number of points). For example, if $a(x, y) = x^2 + y^2 - 1$, the set of all points $\langle u, v \rangle$ which are zeros of $a(x, y)$ is the same as the set of all points which are at a distance one from the origin. Hence, the solutions in R of $a(x, y) = 0$, when plotted as points in the cartesian plane, form a circle of radius one with center at the origin.

EXAMPLE 4. Let $a(x, y, z) \in R[x, y, z]$. The zeros $\langle u, v, w \rangle$ of $a(x, y, z)$ in R can be considered as the coordinates of points in three-dimensional cartesian space (by a process which is similar to the representation of number pairs by points in the plane). The set of all zeros in R of a polynomial $a(x, y, z) \in R[x, y, z]$ constitutes what is called an *algebraic surface* (possibly degenerate, that is, the empty set, or a finite set of points and algebraic curves). For example, let $a(x, y, z) = x^2 + y^2 - z^2$. It is possible to show that the set of all zeros of $a(x, y, z)$ in R lie on two cones with their vertices meeting at the origin and with their axes extending along the z-axis in space (see Fig. 10–1). The zero

$$\langle x^2 - y^2, 2xy, x^2 + y^2 \rangle$$

of $a(x, y, z)$ in $R[x, y]$ is called a *parametrization* of the upper half of this surface. The points on the upper cone are exactly those solutions $\langle w_1, w_2, w_3 \rangle$ in R of $a(x, y, z) = 0$ with $w_3 \geq 0$. If any real numbers u and v are substituted for x and y, respectively, in $\langle x^2 - y^2, 2xy, x^2 + y^2 \rangle$, we obtain a zero $\langle u^2 - v^2, 2uv, u^2 + v^2 \rangle$ in R of $a(x, y, z)$ with $u^2 + v^2 \geq 0$, and therefore a point on the upper cone. The reader can show conversely that any zero $\langle w_1, w_2, w_3 \rangle$ in R of $a(x, y, z)$ with $w_3 \geq 0$ is of the form $w_1 = u^2 - v^2$, $w_2 = 2uv$, $w_3 = u^2 + v^2$ for suitable real numbers u and v.

EXAMPLE 5. Let $a_1(x, y, z) = x^2 + y^2 - z^2$, $a_2(x, y, z) = x^2 + y^2 - 1$ be in $R[x, y, z]$. The zeros in R of the system $a_1(x, y, z) = 0$, $a_2(x, y, z) = 0$ consist of all $\langle u, v, \pm 1 \rangle$ with $u^2 + v^2 = 1$. Thus, in the three-dimensional cartesian coordinates, the set of all these zeros forms two circles of radius one in space (see Fig. 10–2).

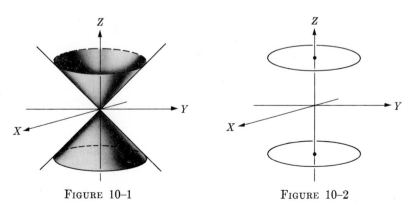

FIGURE 10–1   FIGURE 10–2

The branch of mathematics which is concerned with the zeros of systems of polynomials in several indeterminates is known as *algebraic geometry*. In recent years, the geometric aspects of algebraic geometry have become subordinate to the algebraic features of the theory.

Each of the rings $D[x_1, x_2, \ldots, x_r]$ contains an important class of special polynomials, the symmetric polynomials. Ordinarily, a polynomial is changed into a different polynomial when its indeterminates are permuted. For example, if $a(x, y, z) = x + y^2 + z^3$, then $a(z, x, y) = z + x^2 + y^3$, $a(y, z, x) = y + z^2 + x^3$, etc. However, certain polynomials are left unchanged by all permutations of their indeterminates. For instance, let $a(x, y) = x^2 + xy + y^2$. The only permutations of $\{x, y\}$ are

$$
\begin{array}{cc}
x & y \\
\updownarrow & \updownarrow \\
x & y
\end{array}
\qquad \text{and} \qquad
\begin{array}{cc}
x & y \\
\updownarrow & \updownarrow \\
y & x
\end{array}
$$

Obviously, the first of these permutations does not change $a(x, y)$. The second permutation changes $a(x, y)$ into $a(y, x)$. However,

$$a(y, x) = y^2 + yx + x^2 = x^2 + xy + y^2 = a(x, y)$$

by the commutative and associative laws.

DEFINITION 10–1.6. A polynomial $a(x_1, x_2, \ldots, x_r)$ in $D[x_1, x_2, \ldots, x_r]$ is called *symmetric* if it has the property that for any permutation

$$
\begin{array}{ccccc}
1 & 2 & 3 & \cdots & r \\
\updownarrow & \updownarrow & \updownarrow & \cdots & \updownarrow \\
j_1 & j_2 & j_3 & \cdots & j_r
\end{array}
$$

of the set $\{1, 2, 3, \ldots, r\}$,

$$a(x_{j_1}, x_{j_2}, \ldots, x_{j_r}) = a(x_1, x_2, \ldots, x_r).$$

That is, $a(x_1, x_2, \ldots, x_r)$ is symmetric if every interchange of the indeterminates in $a(x_1, x_2, \ldots, x_r)$ leaves this polynomial unchanged.

It is not necessary to check every permutation of $\{1, 2, \ldots, r\}$ to determine whether a polynomial $a(x_1, x_2, \ldots, x_r)$ is symmetric.

(10–1.7). Let $a(x_1, x_2, \ldots, x_r) \in D[x_1, x_2, \ldots, x_r]$. Then

$$a(x_1, x_2, \ldots, x_r)$$

is symmetric if and only if for every pair i, j of natural numbers with $1 \le i < j \le r$,

$$a(x_1, \ldots, x_{i-1}, x_j, x_{i+1}, \ldots, x_{j-1}, x_i, x_{j+1}, \ldots, x_r) = a(x_1, x_2, \ldots, x_r).$$

That is, interchanging x_i and x_j has no effect on $a(x_1, x_2, \ldots, x_r)$.

Proof. Suppose that $a(x_1, x_2, \ldots, x_r)$ is symmetric. Then since

$$
\begin{array}{ccccccccccc}
1 & \ldots & i-1 & i & i+1 & \ldots & j-1 & j & j+1 & \ldots & r \\
\updownarrow & \ldots & \updownarrow & \updownarrow & \updownarrow & \ldots & \updownarrow & \updownarrow & \updownarrow & \ldots & \updownarrow \\
1 & \ldots & i-1 & j & i+1 & \ldots & j-1 & i & j+1 & \ldots & r
\end{array}
$$

is a permutation of $\{1, 2, \ldots, r\}$, it follows from Definition 10–1.6 that

$$a(x_1, \ldots, x_{i-1}, x_j, x_{i+1}, \ldots, x_{j-1}, x_i, x_{j+1}, \ldots, x_r) = a(x_1, x_2, \ldots, x_r).$$

The proof of the converse will be clearer if we first examine a special case. Let $r = 4$ and suppose that interchanging any two indeterminates has no effect on the polynomial $a(x_1, x_2, x_3, x_4)$. Consider the permutation

$$
\begin{array}{cccc}
1 & 2 & 3 & 4 \\
\updownarrow & \updownarrow & \updownarrow & \updownarrow \\
3 & 4 & 2 & 1
\end{array}
$$

By assumption,

$$a(x_1, x_2, x_3, x_4) = a(x_3, x_2, x_1, x_4),$$

since $a(x_3, x_2, x_1, x_4)$ is obtained from $a(x_1, x_2, x_3, x_4)$ by interchanging x_1 and x_3. For the same reason, we have

$$a(x_1, x_2, x_3, x_4) = a(x_1, x_4, x_3, x_2)$$

and

$$a(x_1, x_2, x_3, x_4) = a(x_1, x_2, x_4, x_3).$$

In the identity

$$a(x_1, x_2, x_3, x_4) = a(x_1, x_4, x_3, x_2)$$

substitute u_1, u_2, u_3, and u_4 for x_1, x_2, x_3, and x_4, where $u_1 = x_3$, $u_2 = x_2$, $u_3 = x_1$, and $u_4 = x_4$. It then follows from (10–1.4d) that

$$a(x_3, x_2, x_1, x_4) = a(x_3, x_4, x_1, x_2).$$

Similarly, in the identity $a(x_1, x_2, x_3, x_4) = a(x_1, x_2, x_4, x_3)$ substitute u_1, u_2, u_3, and u_4 for x_1, x_2, x_3, and x_4, where $u_1 = x_3, u_2 = x_4, u_3 = x_1$, and $u_4 = x_2$. We obtain

$$a(x_3, x_4, x_1, x_2) = a(x_3, x_4, x_2, x_1).$$

Combining the sequence of identities

$$a(x_1, x_2, x_3, x_4) = a(x_3, x_2, x_1, x_4) = a(x_3, x_4, x_1, x_2) = a(x_3, x_4, x_2, x_1)$$

gives the required result that $a(x_1, x_2, x_3, x_4)$ is left unchanged by the permutation

$$
\begin{array}{cccc}
1 & 2 & 3 & 4 \\
\updownarrow & \updownarrow & \updownarrow & \updownarrow \\
3 & 4 & 2 & 1
\end{array}
$$

The proof of the general case follows the same idea, but uses more elaborate notation. First note that if $k_1, k_2, \ldots, k_r$ is any rearrangement of $1, 2, \ldots, r$, then for any pair i, j with $1 \leq i < j \leq r$

$$a(x_{k_1}, \ldots, x_{k_{i-1}}, x_{k_j}, x_{k_{i+1}}, \ldots, x_{k_{j-1}}, x_{k_i}, x_{k_{j+1}}, \ldots, x_{k_r})$$
$$= a(x_{k_1}, \ldots, x_{k_{i-1}}, x_{k_i}, x_{k_{i+1}}, \ldots, x_{k_{j-1}}, x_{k_j}, x_{k_{j+1}}, \ldots, x_{k_r}). \quad (10\text{-}3)$$

In fact, by assumption, $a(x_1, x_2, \ldots, x_r)$ satisfies

$$a(x_1, \ldots, x_{i-1}, x_j, x_{i+1}, \ldots, x_{j-1}, x_i, x_{j+1}, \ldots, x_r)$$
$$= a(x_1, \ldots, x_{i-1}, x_i, x_{i+1}, \ldots, x_{j-1}, x_j, x_{j+1}, \ldots, x_r).$$

Substituting $u_1, u_2, \ldots, u_r$ for $x_1, x_2, \ldots, x_r$, where $u_1 = x_{k_1}$, $u_2 = x_{k_2}$, $\ldots, u_r = x_{k_r}$ gives the required identity (10-3). The identity (10-3) means that in $a(x_{k_1}, x_{k_2}, \ldots, x_{k_r})$, any two of the indeterminates $x_{k_1}, x_{k_2}, \ldots, x_{k_r}$ can be interchanged without changing the polynomial. Moreover, for any permutation

$$
\begin{array}{cccc}
1 & 2 & \ldots & r \\
\updownarrow & \updownarrow & & \updownarrow \\
j_1 & j_2 & \ldots & j_r
\end{array}
$$

it is possible to obtain $a(x_{j_1}, x_{j_2}, \ldots, x_{j_r})$ from $a(x_1, x_2, \ldots, x_r)$ by a finite sequence of such interchanges. Indeed, starting with

$$a(x_1, x_2, \ldots, x_r),$$

we can put x_{j_1} in the first position by substituting x_{j_1} for x_1 and x_1 for x_{j_1}. If $j_1 = 1$, this operation involves no change at all. If $j_1 \neq 1$, then the substitution simply interchanges x_1 and x_{j_1} in $a(x_1, x_2, \ldots, x_r)$. In this case, it follows from (10-3) that

$$a(x_1, x_2, \ldots, x_{j_1-1}, x_{j_1}, x_{j_1+1}, \ldots, x_r)$$
$$= a(x_{j_1}, x_2, \ldots, x_{j_1-1}, x_1, x_{j_1+1}, \ldots, x_r).$$

By a similar substitution, it is possible to get x_{j_2} into the second position. Since $j_2 \neq j_1$ (by the definition of a permutation), the interchange which puts x_{j_2} into the second place will not affect x_{j_1}. Continuing this process, we have

$$a(x_1, x_2, x_3, \ldots, x_r) = a(x_{j_1}, x_2, x_3, \ldots, x_r)$$
$$= a(x_{j_1}, x_{j_2}, x_3, \ldots, x_r)$$
$$= a(x_{j_1}, x_{j_2}, x_{j_3}, \ldots, x_r)$$
$$\vdots$$
$$= a(x_{j_1}, x_{j_2}, x_{j_3}, \ldots, x_{j_r})$$

(making allowance for the inexactness of our notation). Each polynomial in the column on the right side is obtained from the polynomial above it by interchanging two indeterminates or by no change at all. Hence, by the identity (10–3), each polynomial is equal to the one which precedes it. This proves (10–1.7).

THEOREM 10–1.8.   The sum, product, and negative of symmetric polynomials are symmetric. Hence, the set of all symmetric polynomials in $D[x_1, x_2, \ldots, x_r]$ is a subring of $D[x_1, x_2, \ldots, x_r]$.

Proof. Let

$$
\begin{array}{cccc}
1 & 2 & \ldots & r \\
\updownarrow & \updownarrow & & \updownarrow \\
j_1 & j_2 & \ldots & j_r
\end{array}
$$

be a permutation of $\{1, 2, \ldots, r\}$. If $a(x_1, x_2, \ldots, x_r) \in D[x_1, x_2, \ldots, x_r]$, then the polynomial $a(x_{j_1}, x_{j_2}, \ldots, x_{j_r})$ is obtained from $a(x_1, x_2, \ldots, x_r)$ by substituting x_{j_1} for x_1, x_{j_2} for x_2, $\ldots$, and x_{j_r} for x_r. In particular, if $a(x_1, x_2, \ldots, x_r)$ and $b(x_1, x_2, \ldots, x_r)$ are symmetric, and

$$f(x_1, x_2, \ldots, x_r) = a(x_1, x_2, \ldots, x_r) + b(x_1, x_2, \ldots, x_r),$$

then by (10–1.4a),

$$f(x_{j_1}, x_{j_2}, \ldots, x_{j_r}) = a(x_{j_1}, x_{j_2}, \ldots, x_{j_r}) + b(x_{j_1}, x_{j_2}, \ldots, x_{j_r})$$
$$= a(x_1, x_2, \ldots, x_r) + b(x_1, x_2, \ldots, x_r)$$
$$= f(x_1, x_2, \ldots, x_r).$$

It follows that $f(x_1, x_2, \ldots, x_r)$ is symmetric. The fact that the product and negative of symmetric polynomials are symmetric follows in a similar way from (10–1.4).

There is a particularly important class of symmetric polynomials, which can be conveniently defined as follows.

DEFINITION 10–1.9. The *elementary symmetric polynomials* in

$$D[x_1, x_2, \ldots, x_r]$$

are the polynomials $S_1^{(r)}(x_1, x_2, \ldots, x_r)$, $S_2^{(r)}(x_1, x_2, \ldots, x_r)$, ..., $S_r^{(r)}(x_1, x_2, \ldots, x_r)$ defined by the following identity in

$$D[x_1, x_2, \ldots, x_r, x_{r+1}]:$$

$$(x_{r+1} - x_1)(x_{r+1} - x_2) \cdots (x_{r+1} - x_r)$$
$$= x_{r+1}^r - S_1^{(r)}(x_1, x_2, \ldots, x_r)x_{r+1}^{r-1} + S_2^{(r)}(x_1, x_2, \ldots, x_r)x_{r+1}^{r-2}$$
$$- \cdots + (-1)^r S_r^{(r)}(x_1, x_2, \ldots, x_r).$$

For example, if $r = 2$,

$$(x_3 - x_1)(x_3 - x_2) = x_3^2 - (x_1 + x_2)x_3 + x_1 x_2,$$

so that

$$S_1^{(2)}(x_1, x_2) = x_1 + x_2 \quad \text{and} \quad S_2^{(2)}(x_1, x_2) = x_1 x_2.$$

If $r = 3$,

$$(x_4 - x_1)(x_4 - x_2)(x_4 - x_3)$$
$$= x_4^3 - (x_1 + x_2 + x_3)x_4^2 + (x_1 x_2 + x_2 x_3 + x_3 x_1)x_4 - x_1 x_2 x_3,$$

so that

$$S_1^{(3)}(x_1, x_2, x_3) = x_1 + x_2 + x_3,$$
$$S_2^{(3)}(x_1, x_2, x_3) = x_1 x_2 + x_2 x_3 + x_3 x_1,$$
$$S_3^{(3)}(x_1, x_2, x_3) = x_1 x_2 x_3.$$

The fact that the polynomials $S_i^{(r)}(x_1, x_2, \ldots, x_r)$ are symmetric in $D[x_1, x_2, \ldots, x_r]$ is an easy consequence of their definition. If

$$
\begin{array}{cccc}
1 & 2 & \cdots & r \\
\updownarrow & \updownarrow & & \updownarrow \\
j_1 & j_2 & \cdots & j_r
\end{array}
$$

is a permutation of $\{1, 2, \ldots, r\}$, then by (10–1.4d),

$$x_{r+1}^r - S_1^{(r)}(x_{j_1}, x_{j_2}, \ldots, x_{j_r})x_{r+1}^{r-1}$$
$$+ S_2^{(r)}(x_{j_1}, x_{j_2}, \ldots, x_{j_r})x_{r+1}^{r-2} - \cdots + (-1)^r S_r^{(r)}(x_{j_1}, x_{j_2}, \ldots, x_{j_r})$$
$$= (x_{r+1} - x_{j_1})(x_{r+1} - x_{j_2}) \cdots (x_{r+1} - x_{j_r})$$
$$= (x_{r+1} - x_1)(x_{r+1} - x_2) \cdots (x_{r+1} - x_r)$$
$$= x_{r+1}^r - S_1^{(r)}(x_1, x_2, \ldots, x_r)x_{r+1}^{r-1} + S_2^{(r)}(x_1, x_2, \ldots, x_r)x_{r+1}^{r-2}$$
$$- \cdots + (-1)^r S_r^{(r)}(x_1, x_2, \ldots, x_r).$$

Thus, applying Definition 9–2.1 in $(D[x_1, x_2, \ldots, x_r])[x_{r+1}]$, we obtain

$$S_1^{(r)}(x_{j_1}, x_{j_2}, \ldots, x_{j_r}) = S_1^{(r)}(x_1, x_2, \ldots, x_r),$$
$$S_2^{(r)}(x_{j_1}, x_{j_2}, \ldots, x_{j_r}) = S_2^{(r)}(x_1, x_2, \ldots, x_r),$$
$$\vdots$$
$$S_r^{(r)}(x_{j_1}, x_{j_2}, \ldots, x_{j_r}) = S_r^{(r)}(x_1, x_2, \ldots, x_r).$$

This result can easily be generalized.

(10–1.10). Let $f(x_1, x_2, \ldots, x_r) \in D[x_1, x_2, \ldots, x_r]$. Then

$$f(S_1^{(r)}(x_1, x_2, \ldots, x_r), S_2^{(r)}(x_1, x_2, \ldots, x_r), \ldots, S_r^{(r)}(x_1, x_2, \ldots, x_r))$$

is symmetric.

This observation is an immediate consequence of the symmetry of the elementary symmetric polynomials and (10–1.4d). We leave the proof to the reader. The converse of (10–1.10) is a deeper and more important result.

THEOREM 10–1.11. *Fundamental theorem of symmetric polynomials.* Let $a(x_1, x_2, \ldots, x_r)$ be a symmetric polynomial in $D[x_1, x_2, \ldots, x_r]$, where D is any integral domain. Then there is a polynomial $f(x_1, x_2, \ldots, x_r) \in D[x_1, x_2, \ldots, x_r]$ such that

$$a(x_1, x_2, \ldots, x_r)$$
$$= f(S_1^{(r)}(x_1, x_2, \ldots, x_r), S_2^{(r)}(x_1, x_2, \ldots, x_r), \ldots, S_r^{(r)}(x_1, x_2, \ldots, x_r)).$$

We will not prove this theorem here, but the interested reader can find a proof in Appendix 2.

EXAMPLE 6.   Let $a(x_1, x_2, x_3) \in Z[x_1, x_2, x_3]$ be the symmetric polynomial $x_1^3 + x_2^3 + x_3^3$. We have

$$S_1^{(3)} = x_1 + x_2 + x_3, \qquad S_2^{(3)} = x_1 x_2 + x_2 x_3 + x_3 x_1, \qquad S_3^{(3)} = x_1 x_2 x_3,$$

and

$$(x_1 + x_2 + x_3)^3 = x_1^3 + x_2^3 + x_3^3$$
$$+ 3(x_1^2 x_2 + x_1^2 x_3 + x_1 x_2^2 + x_1 x_3^2 + x_2^2 x_3 + x_2 x_3^2)$$
$$+ 6 x_1 x_2 x_3.$$
$$(x_1 + x_2 + x_3)(x_1 x_2 + x_2 x_3 + x_3 x_1) = x_1^2 x_2 + x_1^2 x_3 + x_1 x_2^2 + x_1 x_3^2 + x_2^2 x_3$$
$$+ x_2 x_3^2 + 3 x_1 x_2 x_3.$$

Hence,

$$x_1^3 + x_2^3 + x_3^3 = (S_1^{(3)})^3 - 3S_1^{(3)}S_2^{(3)} + 3S_3^{(3)}.$$

The general procedure followed in Example 6 can be used to express any symmetric polynomial $a(x_1, x_2, \ldots, x_r)$ in $D[x_1, x_2, \ldots, x_r]$ in terms of the elementary symmetric polynomials. Roughly speaking, the process consists of computing all products (including powers) of elementary symmetric polynomials such that the products have total degree no greater than the total degree of $a(x_1, x_2, \ldots, x_r)$. It is then possible (usually by inspection) to express $a(x_1, x_2, \ldots, x_r)$ as a sum with coefficients in D of these products. This procedure can be systematized, but the statement of the exact process is somewhat complicated. In practice, the method of trial and error is usually effective.

PROBLEMS

1. Formulate the definitions of the following concepts for the special case of polynomials in the two indeterminates x and y.

  (a) the total degree of $a(x, y)$
  (b) the value of $a(x, y)$ for $x = u, y = v$
  (c) a zero of $a(x, y)$ in the ring A

2. What are $\text{Deg}_x [a(x, y)]$, $\text{Deg}_y [a(x, y)]$, and the total degree of $a(x, y)$ for the following polynomials?

  (a) $a(x, y) = xy + 1$
  (b) $a(x, y) = x^2y + y^4$
  (c) $a(x, y) = (x + y)^3$

3. Prove by induction on r that every element of $D[x_1, x_2, \ldots, x_r]$ can be expressed uniquely in the form (10–2).

4. Prove (10–1.2).

5. Prove that there are no polynomials $f(x, y)$, $g(x, y)$ in $D[x, y]$ such that $xf(x, y) + yg(x, y) = 1$. [*Hint:* Substitute x for y.]

6. Describe geometrically the zeros in R of the following polynomials in $R[x, y]$.

  (a) $x^2 + y^2$ (b) $x - y$
  (c) xy (d) $(x - 1)^2 + (y + 2)^2 - 4$
  (e) $x^2 + 2x - 3$ (f) $y^2 + 1$

7. Find the solutions in R of the following systems of equations.

  (a) $x + y - 5 = 0,\ x - y + 1 = 0$
  (b) $2x - 3y + 1 = 0,\ 10x - 15y + 2 = 0$
  (c) $2x - 3y + 1 = 0,\ 10x - 15y + 5 = 0$

(d) $x^2 - y^2 - 5 = 0$, $x + y + 1 = 0$
(e) $x^2 - y^2 + 10 = 0$, $x^2 + y^2 - 28 = 0$
(f) $x^3 y = 0$, $x^2 + y^2 - 1 = 0$

8. Determine $S_i^{(4)}(x_1, x_2, x_3, x_4)$ for $1 \leq i \leq 4$ and $S_i^{(5)}(x_1, x_2, x_3, x_4, x_5)$ for $1 \leq i \leq 5$.

9. Which of the following polynomials in $D[x_1, x_2, x_3, x_4]$ are symmetric? Prove your assertions.

(a) $x_1^2 x_2 + x_2^2 x_3 + x_3^2 x_4 + x_4^2 x_1$
(b) $(x_1 + x_2 + x_3)(x_2 + x_3 + x_4)(x_1 + x_3 + x_4)(x_1 + x_2 + x_4)$
(c) $x_1 x_2 + x_2 x_3 + x_3 x_1$.

10. Give the details of the proof of (10–1.10).

11. Express the following symmetric polynomials in $Z[x_1, x_2, x_3]$ in terms of the elementary symmetric polynomials.

(a) $x_1^2 + x_2^2 + x_3^2$
(b) $x_1^2 x_2 + x_2^2 x_3 + x_3^2 x_1 + x_1^2 x_3 + x_2^2 x_1 + x_3^2 x_2$
(c) $x_1^4 + x_2^4 + x_3^4$
(d) $x_1^2 x_2^2 x_3 + x_1 x_2^2 x_3^2 + x_1^2 x_2 x_3^2$

12. Suppose that the roots of the polynomial $x^3 - 2x^2 + x + 1$ are r_1, r_2, and r_3. Find the cubic polynomial whose roots are r_1^2, r_2^2, and r_3^2.

13. (a) Show that in $Q[x, y]$, every symmetric polynomial $a(x, y)$ can be written in the form

$$a(x, y) = \sum_{i=0}^{m} \sum_{j=0}^{n} r_{i,j}(xy)^i (x^j + y^j),$$

where $r_{i,j} \in Q$. [Hint: Let $a(x, y) = \sum s_{k,l} x^k y^l$, and observe that since $a(x, y)$ is symmetric $a(x, y) = \frac{1}{2}[a(x, y) + a(y, x)]$.]

(b) Prove the fundamental theorem on symmetric polynomials for $Q[x, y]$ by showing that for all $j \geq 0$, $x^j + y^j$ can be written in the form $f(x + y, xy)$ for some $f(x, y) \in Q[x, y]$. [Hint: Note that $x^{j+2} + y^{j+2} = (x + y)(x^{j+1} + y^{j+1}) - xy(x^j + y^j)$, and use induction.]

14. (a) Use (10–1.4a, b) to prove by induction on m and n respectively that if

$$f(x_1, x_2, \ldots, x_r) = c_1(x_1, x_2, \ldots, x_r) + c_2(x_1, x_2, \ldots, x_r) + \cdots$$
$$+ c_m(x_1, x_2, \ldots, x_r)$$

and

$$g(x_1, x_2, \ldots, x_r) = d_1(x_1, x_2, \ldots, x_r) \cdot d_2(x_1, x_2, \ldots, x_r) \cdot \cdots$$
$$\cdot d_n(x_1, x_2, \ldots, x_r)$$

in $D[x_1, x_2, \ldots, x_r]$, then for any $u_1, u_2, \ldots, u_r$ in a commutative ring containing D as a subring

$$f(u_1, u_2, \ldots, u_r) = c_1(u_1, u_2, \ldots, u_r) + c_2(u_1, u_2, \ldots, u_r) + \cdots$$
$$+ c_m(u_1, u_2, \ldots, u_r)$$

and

$$g(u_1, u_2, \ldots, u_r) = d_1(u_1, u_2, \ldots, u_r) \cdot d_2(u_1, u_2, \ldots, u_r) \cdot \cdots$$
$$\cdot d_n(u_1, u_2, \ldots, u_r).$$

(b) Use this result to prove (10–1.4d) by induction on s.

10–2 Systems of linear equations. One of the most important special cases of systems of polynomial equations arises when each equation of the system is linear. That is, the system is of the form

$$a_1(x_1, x_2, \ldots, x_r) = 0$$
$$a_2(x_1, x_2, \ldots, x_r) = 0$$
$$\vdots$$
$$a_s(x_1, x_2, \ldots, x_r) = 0,$$

where the total degree of each polynomial

$$a_i(x_1, x_2, \ldots, x_r)$$

is no greater than one. Thus, the equations can be written in the form

$$a_{1,1}x_1 + a_{1,2}x_2 + \cdots + a_{1,r}x_r = b_1$$
$$a_{2,1}x_1 + a_{2,2}x_2 + \cdots + a_{2,r}x_r = b_2 \qquad (10\text{–}4)$$
$$\vdots$$
$$a_{s,1}x_1 + a_{s,2}x_2 + \cdots + a_{s,r}x_r = b_s,$$

where the coefficients $a_{i,j}$ and b_i are elements of an integral domain D. We refer to (10–4) as a *system of s linear equations in r indeterminates* (or *unknowns*) *with coefficients in D.* For example

$$2x_1 - 3x_2 + x_3 + 6x_4 = 0$$
$$x_1 + x_2 - x_3 - x_4 = 7$$

is a system of two equations in four indeterminates with coefficients in Z, and

$$\tfrac{1}{2}x_1 + \tfrac{1}{3}x_2 + \tfrac{1}{4}x_3 + \tfrac{1}{5}x_4 + 0x_5 = 1$$
$$2x_1 + 3x_2 + 4x_3 + 5x_4 + 0x_5 = 1$$
$$0x_1 + 0x_2 + 0x_3 + 0x_4 + 0x_5 = 0$$

is a system of three equations in five unknowns with coefficients in the field Q. Note that the case in which all of the coefficients $a_{i,1}, a_{i,2}, \ldots, a_{i,r}$ and the constant term of one or more equations in a system are zero is not excluded. It is often convenient to omit terms which have zero coefficient, provided that this does not cause confusion. For example, instead of

$$x_1 + 0x_2 + 0x_3 - x_4 = 1$$
$$0x_1 + x_2 + x_3 + x_4 = 0,$$

we would write

$$x_1 - x_4 = 1$$
$$x_2 + x_3 + x_4 = 0.$$

However, it would be confusing to omit the terms $0x_4$ in the system

$$x_1 + x_2 + x_3 + 0x_4 = 1$$
$$2x_1 + x_2 + 3x_3 + 0x_4 = 0,$$

because then it would not be clear that the system is in four indeterminates rather than three, unless this fact were mentioned explicitly. Therefore, whenever such a system is written, all indeterminates will be exhibited.

In dealing with arbitrary systems of linear equations, it is convenient to use the summation notation, and write

$$\sum_{j=1}^{r} a_{i,j}x_j = b_i, \qquad i = 1, 2, \ldots, s, \tag{10–5}$$

instead of (10–4). This notation is not convenient for specific systems in which r and s are small. If $r \le 3$, we will use x, y, and z instead of x_1, x_2, and x_3.

Definition 10–1.5, of a solution of a general system of polynomial equations, applies to systems of linear equations in particular. That is, if

$$\sum_{j=1}^{r} a_{i,j}x_j = b_i, \qquad i = 1, 2, \ldots, s,$$

is a system of s linear equations in r unknowns with coefficients in the integral domain D, and if A is a commutative ring containing D as a subring, then a solution in A of this system consists of an ordered string $\langle c_1, c_2, \ldots, c_r \rangle$ of r elements in A, such that $\sum_{j=1}^{r} a_{i,j}c_j = b_i$, for $i = 1, 2, \ldots, s$.

DEFINITION 10–2.1. A system of linear equations with coefficients in an integral domain D is called *consistent* if it has a solution in some commutative ring containing D as a subring. Otherwise, the system is called *inconsistent*.

When D is a field, there is a way to decide whether or not a system of linear equations with coefficients in D is consistent, and to find all of the solutions of the system if it is consistent. In the remainder of this section we will explain this method of solving systems of linear equations.* The general idea of the process is to construct a new system of equations from the given one. The new system is such that its consistency can be determined by inspection, and when it is consistent, its solutions are easily found. Moreover, the new system is constructed in such a way that it has exactly the same set of solutions as the original system.

DEFINITION 10–2.2. Let

$$\sum_{j=1}^{r} a_{i,j}x_j = b_i, \qquad i = 1, 2, \ldots, s,$$

and

$$\sum_{j=1}^{r} d_{i,j}x_j = e_i, \qquad i = 1, 2, \ldots, t,$$

be systems of linear equations with coefficients in a field F. The systems are *equivalent* if every solution of the first system is a solution of the second, and vice versa.

For example, the system

$$x + y = 0$$
$$2x + 2y = 0$$

is evidently equivalent to the system consisting of the single equation

$$x + y = 0.$$

It is obvious that the relation of equivalence of systems of equations is reflexive, symmetric, and transitive. That is, every system is equivalent to itself; if the system S_1 is equivalent to the system S_2, then S_2 is equivalent to S_1; and if the system S_1 is equivalent to the system S_2 and S_2 is equivalent to a system S_3, then S_1 is equivalent to S_3. Moreover, any two inconsistent systems are equivalent.

---

* The theory of determinants furnishes another method of solving systems of linear equations. In the simplest case of r equations in r unknowns, with the determinant of the coefficients not equal to zero, the familiar Cramer's rule provides explicit formulas for the unknowns as quotients of certain determinants. However, if the number of equations and unknowns exceeds four, then it requires considerable computation to evaluate these determinants, so that Cramer's rule is of more theoretical than practical importance. In this book we will not discuss determinants or their application to the solution of linear equations. A complete discussion of these topics can be found in References 20, 21, 22, 24, and 25 listed at the end of this book.

There are three basic operations called *elementary transformations* which replace a given system of equations with coefficients in a field F by an equivalent system. These operations are described as follows:

(1) interchange two equations;

(2) multiply an equation by an element of F and add the result to a different equation of the system;

(3) multiply an equation by a nonzero element of F.

Thus, if the original system of equations is (10–4), then the forms of systems obtained by applying elementary transformations of the three types are as follows.

Type 1, where $1 \leq m < n \leq s$:

$$a_{1,1}x_1 + a_{1,2}x_2 + \cdots + a_{1,r}x_r = b_1$$
$$\vdots$$
$$a_{n,1}x_1 + a_{n,2}x_2 + \cdots + a_{n,r}x_r = b_n$$
$$\vdots$$
$$a_{m,1}x_1 + a_{m,2}x_2 + \cdots + a_{m,r}x_r = b_m$$
$$\vdots$$
$$a_{s,1}x_1 + a_{s,2}x_r + \cdots + a_{s,r}x_r = b_s.$$

Type 2, where $1 \leq m < n \leq s$, and $c \in F$:

$$a_{1,1}x_1 + a_{1,2}x_2 + \cdots + a_{1,r}x_r = b_1$$
$$\vdots$$
$$a_{m,1}x_1 + a_{m,2}x_2 + \cdots + a_{m,r}x_r = b_m$$
$$\vdots$$
$$(a_{n,1} + ca_{m,1})x_1 + (a_{n,2} + ca_{m,2})x_2 + \cdots + (a_{n,r} + ca_{m,r})x_r = b_n + cb_m$$
$$\vdots$$
$$a_{s,1}x_1 + a_{s,2}x_2 + \cdots + a_{s,r}x_r = b_s.$$

Type 3, where $c \neq 0$ in F:

$$a_{1,1}x_1 + a_{1,2}x_2 + \cdots + a_{1,r}x_r = b_1$$
$$\vdots$$
$$ca_{m,1}x_1 + ca_{m,2}x_2 + \cdots + ca_{m,r}x_r = cb_m$$
$$\vdots$$
$$a_{s,1}x_1 + a_{s,2}x_2 + \cdots + a_{s,r}x_r = b_s.$$

It is clear that each type of elementary transformation takes a system of s linear equations in r unknowns with coefficients in F into a system of linear equations of the same sort, that is, s equations in r unknowns with coefficients in F.

THEOREM 10–2.3. Suppose that S and S' are systems of linear equations with coefficients in a field F such that S' is obtained from S by means of a sequence of elementary transformations. That is, there are systems of linear equations $S_0, S_1, S_2, \ldots, S_n$ such that S_0 is S and S_n is S', and for each natural number $k \leq n$ the system S_k is obtained from the system S_{k-1} by means of an elementary transformation. Then the systems S and S' are equivalent.

Proof. Since the relation of equivalence between two systems of linear equations is transitive, it is sufficient to prove that for each $k \leq n$, S_k is equivalent to S_{k-1}. There are three cases to consider, depending on which type of elementary transformation is used in passing from S_{k-1} to S_k. If S_k is obtained from S_{k-1} by interchanging two equations in the list, then it is obvious that every solution of S_k is a solution of S_{k-1}, and vice versa. Suppose that S_k is obtained from S_{k-1} by adding a multiple of one equation to another. That is,

$$S_{k-1} \quad \text{is} \quad \sum_{j=1}^{r} a_{i,j}x_j = b_i, \quad i = 1, 2, \ldots, s,$$

$$S_k \quad \text{is} \quad \sum_{j=1}^{r} d_{i,j}x_j = e_i, \quad i = 1, 2, \ldots, s,$$

where the equation $\sum_{j=1}^{r} d_{i,j}x_j = e_i$ is the same as $\sum_{j=1}^{r} a_{i,j}x_j = b_i$ for $i \neq n$, and

$$\sum_{j=1}^{r} d_{n,j}x_j = e_n \quad \text{is} \quad \sum_{j=1}^{r} (a_{n,j} + ca_{m,j})x_j = b_n + cb_m,$$

where $m \neq n$. Let $\langle c_1, c_2, \ldots, c_r \rangle$ be a solution of S_{k-1}. Then $\langle c_1, c_2, \ldots, c_r \rangle$ plainly satisfies every equation of S_k, except possibly $\sum_{j=1}^{r} d_{n,j}x_j = e_n$. However,

$$\sum_{j=1}^{r} a_{m,j}c_j = b_m \quad \text{and} \quad \sum_{j=1}^{r} a_{n,j}c_j = b_n.$$

Multiplying the first of these equations by c and adding it to the second, we obtain from the general distributive, associative, and commutative laws

$$\sum_{j=1}^{r} (a_{n,j} + ca_{m,j})c_j = b_n + cb_m.$$

That is, $\sum_{j=1}^{r} d_{n,j}c_j = e_n$. Therefore, $\langle c_1, c_2, \ldots, c_r \rangle$ is a solution of S_k. Conversely if $\langle c_1, c_2, \ldots, c_r \rangle$ is a solution of S_k, then $\sum_{j=1}^{r} a_{i,j}c_j = b_i$ for $i \neq n$ and $\sum_{j=1}^{r} (a_{n,j} + ca_{m,j})c_j = b_n + cb_m$. Subtracting from this equality c times the equation $\sum_{j=1}^{r} a_{m,j}c_j = b_m$ gives $\sum_{j=1}^{r} a_{n,j}c_j = b_n$. Thus, $\langle c_1, c_2, \ldots, c_k \rangle$ is a solution of S_{k-1}. Thus S_k and S_{k-1} are equivalent in this case also. The proof that S_k is equivalent to S_{k-1} if S_k is obtained from S_{k-1} by multiplying some equation by a nonzero element of F is left as an exercise for the reader (see Problem 7 below).

We now illustrate by an example the way in which a system of linear equations can be transformed by a sequence of elementary transformations into an equivalent system which can easily be solved.

EXAMPLE 1. Consider the system

$$-3y + \tfrac{1}{2}z = 4 \qquad 2x + \tfrac{1}{5}y - z = 0 \qquad 3x - 2y + z = 1$$

with coefficients in Q. In Table 10–1, the elementary transformation is described

TABLE 10–1

Interchange the first and second equations	$2x + \tfrac{1}{5}y - z = 0$ $- 3y + \tfrac{1}{2}z = 4$ $3x - 2y + z = 1$
Multiply the first equation by $\tfrac{1}{2}$	$x + \tfrac{1}{10}y - \tfrac{1}{2}z = 0$ $- 3y + \tfrac{1}{2}z = 4$ $3x - 2y + z = 1$
Multiply the first equation by -3 and add to the third equation	$x + \tfrac{1}{10}y - \tfrac{1}{2}z = 0$ $- 3y + \tfrac{1}{2}z = 4$ $- \tfrac{23}{10}y + \tfrac{5}{2}z = 1$
Multiply the second equation by $-\tfrac{1}{3}$	$x + \tfrac{1}{10}y - \tfrac{1}{2}z = 0$ $y - \tfrac{1}{6}z = -\tfrac{4}{3}$ $- \tfrac{23}{10}y + \tfrac{5}{2}z = 1$
Multiply the second equation by $\tfrac{23}{10}$ and add to the third equation	$x + \tfrac{1}{10}y - \tfrac{1}{2}z = 0$ $y - \tfrac{1}{6}z = -\tfrac{4}{3}$ $\tfrac{127}{60}z = -\tfrac{31}{15}$
Multiply the third equation by $\tfrac{60}{127}$	$x + \tfrac{1}{10}y - \tfrac{1}{2}z = 0$ $y - \tfrac{1}{6}z = -\tfrac{4}{3}$ $z = -\tfrac{124}{127}$

on the left and the resulting equivalent system is given on the right. The final system of equations in this table is easily solved. If $\langle c_1, c_2, c_3 \rangle$ is a solution, then $c_3 = -\frac{124}{127}$, $c_2 = \frac{1}{6}c_3 - \frac{4}{3} = -\frac{570}{381}$ (from the second equation), and $c_1 = -\frac{1}{10}c_2 + \frac{1}{2}c_3 = -\frac{129}{381}$ (from the first equation). It is routine to check by direct substitution that $\langle -\frac{129}{381}, -\frac{570}{381}, -\frac{124}{127} \rangle$ is a solution of the system

$$x + \tfrac{1}{10}y - \tfrac{1}{2}z = 0$$
$$y - \tfrac{1}{6}z = -\tfrac{4}{3}$$
$$z = -\tfrac{124}{127}.$$

Therefore, this system has exactly one solution in any commutative ring containing Q as a subring. It follows from Theorem 10–2.3 that the original system

$$- 3y + \tfrac{1}{2}z = 4$$
$$2x + \tfrac{1}{5}y - z = 0$$
$$3x - 2y + z = 1$$

has the unique solution

$$\left\langle -\tfrac{129}{381}, -\tfrac{570}{381}, -\tfrac{124}{127} \right\rangle.$$

It is the special form of the last system of equations in Table 10–1 that makes it possible to obtain these solution so easily. This system is a particular case of a system of equations which is in "echelon form."

DEFINITION 10–2.4. A system of linear equations

$$\sum_{j=1}^{r} a_{i,j}x_j = b_i, \qquad i = 1, 2, \ldots, s,$$

is said to be in *echelon form* if there exists an integer m with $0 \le m \le s$ and a sequence of natural numbers $\langle n_1, n_2, \ldots, n_m \rangle$ such that
   (a) $1 \le n_1 < n_2 < \cdots < n_m \le r$;
   (b) if $1 \le i \le m$, then $a_{i,j} = 0$ for $j < n_i$ and $a_{i,n_i} = 1$;
   (c) if $m < i \le s$, then $a_{i,j} = 0$ for all j.
[If $m = s$, case (c) does not occur].

In Example 1, the last system obtained in Table 10–1 is in echelon form, with $m = 3$, $n_1 = 1$, $n_2 = 2$, and $n_3 = 3$. The system

$$x_1 + 3x_2 + 0x_3 + 0x_4 = 2$$
$$0x_1 + 0x_2 + x_3 + 5x_4 = 1$$
$$0x_1 + 0x_2 + 0x_3 + 0x_4 = 0$$

is in echelon form with

$$m = 2, \qquad n_1 = 1, \qquad \text{and} \qquad n_2 = 3.$$

The system

$$0x + 0y = 1$$
$$0x + 0y = 0$$

is also in echelon form with $m = 0$. Systems of this kind (with the coefficients of all indeterminates equal to zero) seem rather trivial, but it would be inconvenient to exclude them from our discussion. In general, if $m = 0$ in Definition 10–2.4, then the set $\{n_1, n_2, \ldots, n_m\}$ of natural numbers is empty. In this case, the conditions (a) and (b) are satisfied vacuously, and condition (c) implies that $a_{i,j} = 0$ for all i and j.

Note that by condition (a) in Definition 10–2.4, the number m cannot exceed r, because it is impossible to have more than r different natural numbers n_i which satisfy $1 \leq n_i \leq r$.

THEOREM 10–2.5. If S is a system of s linear equations in r unknowns with coefficients in a field F, then it is possible to transform S into a system of linear equations S' in echelon form by means of a finite sequence of elementary transformations.

Proof. The proof of this theorem is by course of values induction on the number t of different indeterminates which have nonzero coefficients in the system. That is, t is the number of indeterminates having at least one nonzero coefficient. Of course, $t \leq r$. If this number is zero, then the system must have the trivial form

$$0x_1 + 0x_2 + \cdots + 0x_r = b_1$$
$$0x_1 + 0x_2 + \cdots + 0x_r = b_2$$
$$\vdots$$
$$0x_1 + 0x_2 + \cdots + 0x_r = b_s,$$

which is already in echelon form (with $m = 0$). Thus, the basis of the induction $t = 0$ offers no difficulty. Assume that $t > 0$ and every system in which fewer than t indeterminates appear with nonzero coefficients can be transformed to a system in echelon form by means of elementary transformations. Suppose that

$$\sum_{j=1}^{r} a_{i,j}x_j = b_i, \qquad i = 1, 2, \ldots, s,$$

is a system in which t indeterminates occur with nonzero coefficients. Let

n_1 be the least natural number such that x_{n_1} has a nonzero coefficient in one of the equations. Since $t > 0$, it follows from the well-ordering principle that such an n_1 exists. If the coefficient of x_{n_1} is zero in the first equation, interchange the first equation with an equation in which the coefficient of x_{n_1} is not zero. Multiply the new first equation by the inverse in F of the coefficient of x_{n_1}. After these elementary transformations, the system has the form

$$0x_1 + \cdots + 0x_{n_1-1} + \quad x_{n_1} + a^*_{1,n_1+1}x_{n_1+1} + \cdots + a^*_{1,r}x_r = b^*_1$$
$$0x_1 + \cdots + 0x_{n\ -1} + a^*_{2,n_1}x_{n_1} + a^*_{2,n_1+1}x_{n_1+1} + \cdots + a^*_{2,r}x_r = b^*_2$$
$$\vdots$$
$$0x_1 + \cdots + 0x_{n_1-1} + a^*_{s,n_1}x_{n_1} + a^*_{s,n_1+1}x_{n_1+1} + \cdots + a^*_{s,r}x_r = b^*_s.$$

In turn, multiply the first equation by $-a^*_{i,n_1}$ and add to the ith equation for $i = 2, 3, \ldots, s$ to obtain

$$0x_1 + \cdots + \quad x_{n_1} + a^*_{1,n_1+1}x_{n_1+1} + \cdots + a^*_{1,r}x_r = b^*_1$$
$$0x_1 + \cdots + 0x_{n_1} + a^{**}_{2,n_1+1}x_{n_1+1} + \cdots + a^{**}_{2,r}x_r = b^{**}_2 \qquad (10\text{–}6)$$
$$\vdots$$
$$0x_1 + \cdots + 0x_{n_1} + a^{**}_{s,n_1+1}x_{n_1+1} + \cdots + a^{**}_{s,r}x_r = b^{**}_s.$$

The construction of (10–6) from the original system is effected by a finite number of elementary transformations. Moreover, it is evident that if an indeterminate x_n occurs with zero coefficient in every equation of the original system

$$\sum_{j=1}^{r} a_{i,j}x_j = b_i, \qquad i = 1, 2, \ldots, s,$$

then every coefficient of x_n in (10–6) is also zero. Consequently, in the system

$$0x_1 + \cdots + 0x_{n_1} + a^{**}_{2,n_1+1}x_{n_1+1} + \cdots + a^{**}_{2,r}x_r = b^{**}_2$$
$$\vdots \qquad\qquad\qquad (10\text{–}7)$$
$$0x_1 + \cdots + 0x_{n_1} + a^{**}_{s,n_1+1}x_{n_1+1} + \cdots + a^{**}_{s,r}x_r = b^{**}_s,$$

at most $t - 1$ indeterminates appear with nonzero coefficients. By the induction hypothesis, the system (10–7) can be transformed into echelon form by a finite sequence of elementary transformations. Clearly, in the resulting echelon system obtained from (10–7), the indeterminates x_j for $j \leq n_1$ will occur with coefficient zero. That is, the echelon system obtained will be of the form

$$0x_1 + \cdots + 0x_{n_1} + \cdots + 0x_{n_2-1} + x_{n_2} + \cdots + d_{2,r}x_r = e_2$$
$$\vdots$$

Consequently, combining this system with the first equation of (10–6), we obtain an echelon system

$$0x_1 + \cdots + \ x_{n_1} + \cdots + a_{1,n_2}^{*}x_{n_2} + \cdots + a_{1,r}^{*}x_r = b_1^{*}$$
$$0x_1 + \cdots + 0x_{n_1} + \cdots + \quad\ x_{n_2} + \cdots + d_{2,r}x_r = e_2$$
$$\vdots$$

Since a sequence of elementary transformations applied to (10–7) can be considered as a sequence of elementary transformations applied to (10–6) which do not involve the first equation, it follows that we can get from our original system to a system in echelon form by applying a finite number of elementary transformations. This completes the induction, and proves Theorem 10–2.5.

By combining the results of Theorems 10–2.3 and 10–2.5, we obtain the most important result of this section.

THEOREM 10–2.6. Any system S of s linear equations in r unknowns with coefficients in a field F is equivalent to a system S' of s linear equations in r unknowns with coefficients in F where S' is in echelon form.

It should be emphasized that a system of linear equations may be equivalent to many different systems in echelon form. The system S' in Theorem 10–2.6 is by no means unique (see Problem 5 below).

The reduction process described in Example 1 and in the proof of Theorem 10–2.5 works for arbitrary fields. When it is used for fields of the form Z_p, where p is a prime number, the results can be interpreted to obtain information concerning the solution of linear congruences with a prime modulus (see the discussion following Theorem 9–7.8).

EXAMPLE 2. Let the system

$$2x_1 + 4x_2 + \ x_3 + \ x_4 = 1$$
$$x_1 + 3x_2 + 2x_3 + \ x_4 = 2$$
$$3x_1 + 4x_2 + \ x_3 + 2x_4 = 3$$
$$4x_1 + \ x_2 + \ x_3 + 3x_4 = 4$$
$$x_1 + \ x_2 + \ x_3 + \ x_4 = 0$$

have coefficients in Z_5, the integers modulo 5. We list the successive equivalent systems, arriving finally at a system in echelon form. The reader should describe the elementary transformations at each step.

$$x_1 + 2x_2 + 3x_3 + 3x_4 = 3$$
$$x_1 + 3x_2 + 2x_3 + x_4 = 2$$
$$3x_1 + 4x_2 + x_3 + 2x_4 = 3$$
$$4x_1 + x_2 + x_3 + 3x_4 = 0$$
$$x_1 + x_2 + x_3 + x_4 = 0;$$

$$x_1 + 2x_2 + 3x_3 + 3x_4 = 3$$
$$x_2 + 4x_3 + 3x_4 = 4$$
$$3x_2 + 2x_3 + 3x_4 = 4$$
$$3x_2 + 4x_3 + x_4 = 3$$
$$4x_2 + 3x_3 + 3x_4 = 2;$$

$$x_1 + 2x_2 + 3x_3 + 3x_4 = 3$$
$$x_2 + 4x_3 + 3x_4 = 4$$
$$4x_4 = 2$$
$$2x_3 + 2x_4 = 1$$
$$2x_3 + x_4 = 1;$$

$$x_1 + 2x_2 + 3x_3 + 3x_4 = 3$$
$$x_2 + 4x_3 + 3x_4 = 4$$
$$2x_3 + 2x_4 = 1$$
$$4x_4 = 2$$
$$2x_3 + x_4 = 1;$$

$$x_1 + 2x_2 + 3x_3 + 3x_4 = 3$$
$$x_2 + 4x_3 + 3x_4 = 4$$
$$x_3 + x_4 = 3$$
$$4x_4 = 2$$
$$2x_3 + x_4 = 1;$$

$$x_1 + 2x_2 + 3x_3 + 3x_4 = 3$$
$$x_2 + 4x_3 + 3x_4 = 4$$
$$x_3 + x_4 = 3$$
$$4x_4 = 2$$
$$4x_4 = 0;$$

$$x_1 + 2x_2 + 3x_3 + 3x_4 = 3$$
$$x_2 + 4x_3 + 3x_4 = 4$$
$$x_3 + x_4 = 3$$
$$x_4 = 3$$
$$4x_4 = 0;$$

$$x_1 + 2x_2 + 3x_3 + 3x_4 = 3$$
$$x_2 + 4x_3 + 3x_4 = 4$$
$$x_3 + x_4 = 3$$
$$x_4 = 3$$
$$0 = 3.$$

This system is not satisfied for any choice of x_1, x_2, x_3, and x_4 because the final equation $0 = 3$ is never satisfied. Therefore the original system has no solution in any commutative ring containing Z_5. The linear system of equations in this example can be regarded as a system of simultaneous linear congruences

$$2x_1 + 4x_2 + x_3 + x_4 \equiv 1 \ (\text{mod } 5)$$
$$x_1 + 3x_2 + 2x_3 + x_4 \equiv 2 \ (\text{mod } 5)$$
$$3x_1 + 4x_2 + x_3 + 2x_4 \equiv 3 \ (\text{mod } 5)$$
$$4x_1 + x_2 + x_3 + 3x_4 \equiv 4 \ (\text{mod } 5)$$
$$x_1 + x_2 + x_3 + x_4 \equiv 0 \ (\text{mod } 5).$$

Our result shows that this system of congruences has no solution $\langle c_1, c_2, c_3, c_4 \rangle$ where $c_i \in Z$.

EXAMPLE 3. The system

$$x_1 + 2x_2 + x_3 - 3x_4 - x_5 = 4$$
$$x_2 + \tfrac{1}{5}x_3 - \tfrac{2}{5}x_4 + x_5 = \tfrac{3}{5}$$
$$x_4 + x_5 = 1$$

with coefficients in Q is in echelon form. Let $x_5 = c$, where c is an element in any commutative ring A containing Q as a subring. Then from the last equation, $x_4 = 1 - c$. Substituting $x_4 = 1 - c$, $x_5 = c$ in the second equation and choosing $x_3 = d \in A$, we have

$$x_2 = -\tfrac{1}{5}d + \tfrac{2}{5}(1 - c) - c + \tfrac{3}{5} = 1 - \tfrac{7}{5}c - \tfrac{1}{5}d.$$

From the first equation

$$x_1 = -2(1 - \tfrac{7}{5}c - \tfrac{1}{5}d) - d + 3(1 - c) + c + 4 = 5 + \tfrac{4}{5}c - \tfrac{3}{5}d.$$

Thus,

$$\langle 5 + \tfrac{4}{5}c - \tfrac{3}{5}d, \ 1 - \tfrac{7}{5}c - \tfrac{1}{5}d, \ d, \ 1 - c, \ c \rangle$$

is a solution of the given system, where c and d are arbitrary elements in A. For example, if $A = Q[x]$ and $c = d = x$, then a solution is

$$\langle 5 + \tfrac{1}{5}x, 1 - \tfrac{8}{5}x, x, 1 - x, x \rangle.$$

It is clear that this system has infinitely many different solutions.

Examples 1, 2, and 3 illustrate the fact that systems of equations in echelon form can be solved (or shown to be inconsistent) without much trouble. In fact, we can prove the following general results.

THEOREM 10–2.7. Let

$$\sum_{j=1}^{r} a_{i,j}x_j = b_i, \qquad i = 1, 2, \ldots, s,$$

be a system of linear equations with coefficients in F, which is in echelon form: $a_{i,j} = 0$ for $j < n_i$, $a_{i,n_i} = 1$ for $1 \le i \le m$ and $a_{i,j} = 0$ for all j if $m < i \le s$, where $1 \le n_1 < n_2 < \cdots < n_m \le r$ and $0 \le m \le s$.

(a) The system is consistent if and only if either $m = s$, or $b_i = 0$ for every i satisfying $m < i \le s$. If the system is consistent, then it has a solution $\langle c_1, c_2, \ldots, c_r \rangle$ with each c_i in F.

(b) If the system is consistent, then its solution is unique if and only if $m = r$. When this condition is not satisfied (that is, the system has more than one solution) then it is always possible to find at least as many solutions $\langle c_1, c_2, \ldots, c_r \rangle$ with $c_i \in F$ as there are elements in F.

Proof. (a) Suppose that $m < s$ and there is an $i > m$ such that $b_i \ne 0$. Then the ith equation of the given system is

$$0x_1 + 0x_2 + \cdots + 0x_r = b_i.$$

This equation plainly has no solution in any ring A containing F as a subring. On the other hand, if either $m = s$, or $b_i = 0$ for all i satisfying $m < i \le s$, then it is easy to see that $\langle c_1, c_2, \ldots, c_r \rangle$ is a solution with $c_i \in F$, where we define recursively

$$c_{n_m} = b_m,$$
$$c_{n_{m-1}} = b_{m-1} - a_{m-1,n_m}c_{n_m},$$
$$c_{n_{m-2}} = b_{m-2} - a_{m-2,n_{m-1}}c_{n_{m-1}} - a_{m-2,n_m}c_{n_m},$$
$$\vdots$$
$$c_{n_1} = b_1 \qquad - a_{1,n_2}c_{n_2} - \cdots - a_{1,n_m}c_{n_m},$$

and $c_j = 0$ for all indices j which are not among the indices $n_1, n_2, \ldots, n_m$.

Note that the c_{n_k} are determined by the $a_{i,j}$ and b_i. For example,

$$c_{n_{m-1}} = b_{m-1} - a_{m-1,n_m}b_m,$$
$$c_{n_{m-2}} = b_{m-2} - a_{m-2,n_{m-1}}(b_{m-1} - a_{m-1,n_m}b_m) - a_{m-2,n_m}b_m.$$

It follows that our system is consistent and has a solution in F.

(b) Suppose that the system is consistent and $m = r$. Since the natural numbers $n_1, n_2, \ldots, n_r$ satisfy $1 \leq n_1 < n_2 < \cdots < n_r \leq r$, it follows that $n_k = k$ for $k = 1, 2, \ldots, r$. That is, the system has the form

$$x_1 + a_{1,2}x_2 + \cdots + a_{1,r}x_r = b_1$$
$$x_2 + \cdots + a_{2,r}x_r = b_2$$
$$\vdots$$
$$x_r = b_r$$
$$0x_r = b_{r+1} = 0$$
$$\vdots$$
$$0x_r = b_s = 0.$$

If $\langle c_1, c_2, \ldots, c_r \rangle$ is a solution of this system, then necessarily

$$c_r = b_r.$$

Suppose inductively that $c_r, c_{r-1}, \ldots, c_{r-k+1}$ are uniquely determined in any solution. Then since

$$c_{r-k} = b_{r-k} - a_{r-k,r-k+1}c_{r-k+1} - \cdots - a_{r-k,r-1}c_{r-1} - a_{r-k,r}c_r,$$

it follows that c_{r-k} is also unique. Hence, by the principle of induction, the system of equations has a unique solution. Conversely, if the system is consistent, but the condition $m = r$ is not satisfied, then there exists an index l such that $l \neq n_k$ for all $1 \leq k \leq m$. Let $c \in F$. Define $e_i = b_i - a_{i,l}c$. Then the system

$$\sum_{j=1}^{r} a_{i,j}x_j = e_i, \qquad i = 1, 2, \ldots, s,$$

is still consistent because if $i > m$, then $a_{i,l} = 0$ and $e_i = b_i = 0$. By the proof of part (a), this new system has a solution $\langle c_1, c_2, \ldots, c_r \rangle$ with $c_i \in F$, such that $c_l = 0$. It is then clear that

$$\langle c_1, c_2, \ldots, c_{l-1}, c, c_{l+1}, \ldots, c_r \rangle$$

is a solution of our original system of equations. Since c can be arbitrary, it follows that the system has at least as many different solutions (in F) as there are elements in F. In particular, since every field contains at least two elements, the system has more than one solution.

As a consequence of Theorems 10–2.6 and 10–2.7, we have the following useful result.

THEOREM 10–2.8. If a system of linear equations in r unknowns with coefficients in a field F is consistent, then the system has a solution $\langle c_1, c_2, \ldots, c_r \rangle$ with $c_i \in F$.

Proof. By Theorem 10–2.6, the given system S is equivalent to a system S' of linear equations with coefficients in F, such that S' is in echelon form. Since S is consistent and S' is equivalent to S, it follows that S' is consistent. By Theorem 10–2.7, S' has a solution $\langle c_1, c_2, \ldots, c_r \rangle$ with $c_i \in F$. Since S' is equivalent to S, it follows that $\langle c_1, c_2, \ldots, c_r \rangle$ is also a solution of S.

When $b_1 = b_2 = \cdots = b_s = 0$ in (10–4), the system is called *homogeneous*. A homogeneous system of linear equations is always consistent since $\langle 0, 0, \ldots, 0 \rangle$ is a solution. An interesting question concerning homogeneous equations is whether or not they have solutions other than the trivial one $\langle 0, 0, \ldots, 0 \rangle$. This problem can always be referred to the case in which the homogeneous system is in echelon form. Indeed, it is clear that every elementary transformation carries a homogeneous system into a homogeneous system. Therefore, by Theorems 10–2.3 and 10–2.5, every homogeneous system is equivalent to a homogeneous system in echelon form. It is clear that if a homogeneous system has a unique solution, then it has no solution other than the trivial one $\langle 0, 0, \ldots, 0 \rangle$. Consequently, Theorem 10–2.7(b) provides a condition for a homogeneous system in echelon form to have a nontrivial solution, namely $m < r$, where m is the number of equations of the system in which some nonzero coefficient appears and r is the number of indeterminates. In particular, if the number s of equations is less than the number r of unknowns, then the system has a nontrivial solution. Consequently, we obtain the following useful result.

THEOREM 10–2.9. Let

$$\sum_{j=1}^{r} a_{i,j} x_j = 0, \qquad i = 1, 2, \ldots, s,$$

be a homogeneous system of s linear equations in r unknowns with coefficients in the field F. Suppose that $s < r$. Then $c_1, c_2, \ldots, c_r$ exist in F, not all zero, such that

$$\sum_{j=1}^{r} a_{i,j} c_j = 0, \qquad i = 1, 2, \ldots, s.$$

Proof. By Theorems 10–2.3 and 10–2.5, the system $\sum_{j=1}^{r} a_{i,j}x_j = 0$, $i = 1, 2, \ldots, s$, is equivalent to a homogeneous system S' of s linear equations in r unknowns with coefficients in F such that S' is in echelon form. Since $m \leq s < r$, it follows from Theorem 10–2.7(b) and the fact that every field contains at least two elements that there is a solution

$$\langle c_1, c_2, \ldots, c_r \rangle$$

of S' which is different from $\langle 0, 0, \ldots, 0 \rangle$. Since S' is equivalent to the given system, it follows that $\sum_{j=1}^{r} a_{i,j}c_j = 0$ for $i = 1, 2, \ldots, s$.

EXAMPLE 4. By elementary transformations, the homogeneous system

$$x_1 + \sqrt{2}\,x_2 - \quad 3x_3 + \sqrt{3}\,x_4 = 0$$
$$2x_1 \qquad + \sqrt{2}\,x_3 + \quad x_4 = 0$$
$$x_1 + \quad x_2 - \quad 5x_3 + \quad 2x_4 = 0$$

can be transformed into the system

$$x_1 + x_2 - \qquad 5x_3 + \qquad\qquad\qquad\qquad 2x_4 = 0$$
$$x_2 + (-5 - \sqrt{2}/2)x_3 + \qquad\qquad\qquad \tfrac{3}{2}x_4 = 0$$
$$x_3 + (-\tfrac{29}{73} - 21\sqrt{2}/146 + 4\sqrt{3}/73 + 9\sqrt{6}/73)x_4 = 0.$$

The value of x_4 can be chosen arbitrarily and the equations solved for x_3, x_2, and x_1.

PROBLEMS

1. Reduce the following systems of linear equations with coefficients in Q to echelon form by means of elementary transformations, describing the elementary transformation being used at each step.

(a) $2x + y = 3$
$\quad x - y = 1$
$\quad x + y = 2$

(b) $\tfrac{1}{2}x_1 + x_2 - \tfrac{1}{2}x_3 + x_4 = 1$
$\quad x_1 - x_2 + \tfrac{1}{6}x_3 - x_4 = 0$

(c) $\quad x - \quad y = 2$
$\qquad x + \quad y = 2$
$\quad 3x - \quad y = 2$
$\qquad x + 7y = 2$

(d) $2x_1 - 3x_2 + \frac{1}{3}x_3 - x_4 + x_5 = 0$

   $x_1 - 2x_2 - x_3 \qquad - x_5 = 1$

   $\frac{1}{3}x_1 - x_2 \qquad + x_4 + \frac{1}{3}x_5 = 2$

   $2x_1 + x_2 + x_3 - x_4 + 2x_5 = 0$

(e) $\sum_{j=1}^{100} (-1)^{ij}x_j = (-1)^i, \ i = 1, 2, \ldots, 100$

2. Discuss the solution of each of the systems in Problem 1. That is, determine whether or not each system is consistent, and if it is describe all possible solutions (as in Example 3).

3. Describe the elementary transformations used at each step in Example 2.

4. Solve the following systems of linear equations with coefficients in Z_7.

   (a) $2x + 2y + 3z = 1$

   $4x + 6y + z = 4$

   $x \qquad + z = 3$

   (b) $x_1 + x_2 + x_3 + x_4 + x_5 + x_6 = 1$

   $x_1 + 2x_2 + 3x_3 + 4x_4 + 5x_5 + 6x_6 = 1$

   $x_1 + 4x_2 + 2x_3 + 2x_4 + 4x_5 + x_6 = 1$

   $x_1 + x_2 + 6x_3 + x_4 + 6x_5 + 6x_6 = 1$

   $x_1 + 2x_2 + 4x_3 + 4x_4 + 2x_5 + x_6 = 1$

   $x_1 + 4x_2 + 5x_3 + 2x_4 + 3x_5 + 6x_6 = 1$

5. Show that by elementary transformations it is possible to reduce the system

$$x + y + z = 1$$
$$x + y - z = 2$$
$$x - y - z = 3$$

to any of the following systems in echelon form

$x + y + z = 1$	$x + y - z = 2$	$x - y - z = 3$
$y + z = -1$	$y = -\frac{1}{2}$	$y + z = -1$
$z = -\frac{1}{2},$	$z = -\frac{1}{2},$	$z = -\frac{1}{2},$
$x + y + z = 1$	$x + y - z = 2$	$x - y - z = 3$
$y = -\frac{1}{2}$	$y + z = -1$	$y = -\frac{1}{2}$
$z = -\frac{1}{2},$	$z = -\frac{1}{2},$	$z = -\frac{1}{2}.$

Does this list of systems include *all* possible echelon forms to which the given system can be reduced?

6. Suppose that the system $\sum_{j=1}^{r} a_{i,j}x_j = b_i, \ i = 1, 2, \ldots, r$, of r linear equations in r unknowns with coefficients in a field F has the unique solution $\langle c_1, c_2, \ldots, c_r \rangle$. Show that it is possible to reduce this system by elementary

transformations to the form

$$x_1 \qquad\qquad = c_1$$
$$x_2 \qquad = c_2$$
$$\vdots$$
$$x_r = c_r.$$

7. Complete the proof of Theorem 10–2.3 by showing that if a system S' is obtained from a system S by an elementary transformation of type 3 (multiplication of an equation in S by a nonzero element of F), then S and S' are equivalent systems.

8. Let a, b, c, d, e, and f be elements of any field with $a \neq 0$. Prove that the system

$$ax + by = e$$
$$cx + dy = f$$

is consistent if and only if either

(i) $ad - bc \neq 0$, or

(ii) $ad - bc = af - ec = 0$.

9. Prove that the homogeneous system

$$a_{1,1}x_1 + a_{1,2}x_2 + a_{1,3}x_3 = 0$$
$$a_{2,1}x_1 + a_{2,2}x_2 + a_{2,3}x_3 = 0$$
$$a_{3,1}x_1 + a_{3,2}x_2 + a_{3,3}x_3 = 0$$

has a solution different from $\langle 0, 0, 0 \rangle$ if and only if

$$a_{1,1}a_{2,2}a_{3,3} + a_{2,1}a_{3,2}a_{1,3} + a_{3,1}a_{1,2}a_{2,3} - a_{1,3}a_{2,2}a_{3,1} - a_{2,3}a_{3,2}a_{1,1}$$
$$- a_{3,3}a_{1,2}a_{2,1} = 0.$$

10. Show that if the system S' is obtained from the system S by an elementary transformation, then there is an elementary transformation which carries the system S' into S.

11. Show that if $\langle c_1, c_2, \ldots, c_r \rangle$ is any solution of the homogeneous system

$$\sum_{j=1}^{r} a_{i,j}x_j = 0, \qquad i = 1, 2, \ldots, s,$$

with all of the c_j belonging to some ring A containing all $a_{i,j}$, and if d is any element of A, then $\langle dc_1, dc_2, \ldots, dc_r \rangle$ is also a solution of the homogeneous system.

12. Show that if $\langle c_1, c_2, \ldots, c_r \rangle$ is any solution of the system S:

$$\sum_{j=1}^{r} a_{i,j}x_j = b_i, \qquad i = 1, 2, \ldots, s,$$

and if $\langle d_1, d_2, \ldots, d_r \rangle$ is a solution of the associated homogeneous system

$$\sum_{j=1}^{r} a_{i,j}x_j = 0, \qquad i = 1, 2, \ldots, s,$$

then $\langle c_1 + d_1, c_2 + d_2, \ldots, c_r + d_r \rangle$ is a solution of S.

10–3 The algebra of matrices. The study of linear equations in the preceding section serves as a natural introduction to the concept of a rectangular matrix. The system of equations S,

$$a_{1,1}x_1 + a_{1,2}x_2 + \cdots + a_{1,r}x_r = b_1$$
$$a_{2,1}x_1 + a_{2,2}x_2 + \cdots + a_{2,r}x_r = b_2$$
$$\vdots$$
$$a_{s,1}x_1 + a_{s,2}x_2 + \cdots + a_{s,r}x_r = b_s,$$

can be completely determined if the coefficients of S are given and the position of each coefficient in the system is known. This information is conveniently presented by the rectangular array

$$\begin{bmatrix} a_{1,1} & a_{1,2} \ldots a_{1,r} & b_1 \\ a_{2,1} & a_{2,2} \ldots a_{2,r} & b_2 \\ \vdots & \vdots \quad\quad \vdots & \vdots \\ a_{s,1} & a_{s,2} \ldots a_{s,r} & b_s \end{bmatrix},$$

which is called a matrix.

DEFINITION 10–3.1. *Let A be a ring. An m by n matrix* (plural: *matrices*) *with elements in A is a rectangular array* *

$$\mathbf{A} = \begin{bmatrix} a_{1,1} & a_{1,2} & \ldots & a_{1,n} \\ a_{2,1} & a_{2,2} & \ldots & a_{2,n} \\ \vdots & \vdots & & \vdots \\ a_{m,1} & a_{m,2} & \ldots & a_{m,n} \end{bmatrix},$$

with m rows and n columns, where the entries $a_{i,j}$ are elements of the ring A.

For example,

$$\begin{bmatrix} 2 & 0 & -1 & 6 \\ 0 & -7 & 2 & 20 \end{bmatrix}$$

---

* In this section and the following one, boldface capital letters will denote matrices.

is a 2 by 4 matrix with elements in the ring Z of integers. In this example,

$$a_{1,1} = 2, \qquad a_{1,2} = 0, \qquad a_{1,3} = -1, \qquad a_{1,4} = 6,$$

and

$$a_{2,1} = 0, \qquad a_{2,2} = -7, \qquad a_{2,3} = 2, \qquad a_{2,4} = 20.$$

The entries $a_{i,j}$ of a matrix are called the *elements of the matrix*, and the position of each element in the matrix is indicated by its subscripts. For instance, $a_{1,1}$ is the element in the first row and first column (the upper left-hand corner) of the matrix, while $a_{3,4}$ is the element in the third row and fourth column. In general, $a_{i,j}$ is the element in the ith row and jth column for $i = 1, 2, \ldots, m$ and $j = 1, 2, \ldots, n$.

The number m of rows and the number n of columns in a matrix can be arbitrary natural numbers. These numbers are called the *dimensions* of the matrix. If $\mathbf{A}$ is an n by n matrix, that is, the number of rows is equal to the number of columns, then $\mathbf{A}$ is called a *square* matrix. A matrix with only one column, that is, an m by 1 matrix, is called a *column matrix*, or a *column vector*. Similarly, a matrix with only one row is called a *row matrix*, or a *row vector*.

The reader should be careful not to confuse matrices with determinants. Corresponding to every square matrix $\mathbf{A}$ with elements in a commutative ring $\mathbf{A}$, there is associated in a certain way an element of A called the *determinant* of $\mathbf{A}$. For example, if $\mathbf{A}$ is the 2 by 2 matrix

$$\mathbf{A} = \begin{bmatrix} a_{1,1} & a_{1,2} \\ a_{2,1} & a_{2,2} \end{bmatrix},$$

then the determinant of $\mathbf{A}$ is

$$a_{1,1}a_{2,2} - a_{1,2}a_{2,1},$$

and if $\mathbf{A}$ is the 3 by 3 matrix

$$\mathbf{A} = \begin{bmatrix} a_{1,1} & a_{1,2} & a_{1,3} \\ a_{2,1} & a_{2,2} & a_{2,3} \\ a_{3,1} & a_{3,2} & a_{3,3} \end{bmatrix},$$

the determinant of $\mathbf{A}$ is

$$a_{1,1}a_{2,2}a_{3,3} + a_{1,2}a_{2,3}a_{3,1} + a_{1,3}a_{2,1}a_{3,2}$$
$$- a_{1,3}a_{2,2}a_{3,1} - a_{1,2}a_{2,1}a_{3,3} - a_{1,1}a_{2,3}a_{3,2}.$$

The matrix $\mathbf{A}$ is *not* an element of the ring A, whereas the determinant of $\mathbf{A}$ is an element of A. For r by s matrices with $r \neq s$, the determinant is not even defined.

Matrices are more than just convenient forms for presenting numerical data. By defining suitable operations of addition, subtraction, and multiplication, it is possible to develop an algebra of matrices which has numerous applications. The purpose of this section is to define these matrix operations and derive their basic properties. Some of the application of the algebra of matrices will be described in examples.

Two matrices will be called *equal* if they are identically the same. That is, if

$$
\mathbf{A} = \begin{bmatrix} a_{1,1} & a_{1,2} & \ldots & a_{1,n} \\ a_{2,1} & a_{2,2} & \ldots & a_{2,n} \\ \vdots & \vdots & & \vdots \\ a_{m,1} & a_{m,2} & \ldots & a_{m,n} \end{bmatrix} \quad \text{and} \quad \mathbf{B} = \begin{bmatrix} b_{1,1} & b_{1,2} & \ldots & b_{1,s} \\ b_{2,1} & b_{2,2} & \ldots & b_{2,s} \\ \vdots & \vdots & & \vdots \\ b_{r,1} & b_{r,2} & \ldots & b_{r,s} \end{bmatrix},
$$

then $\mathbf{A} = \mathbf{B}$ if and only if $m = r$, $n = s$ (thus, $\mathbf{A}$ and $\mathbf{B}$ have the same dimensions), and $a_{i,j} = b_{i,j}$ for $i = 1, 2, \ldots, m$ and $j = 1, 2, \ldots, n$. For example, if

$$
\mathbf{A} = \begin{bmatrix} 1 & 0 \\ 0 & 1 \end{bmatrix} \quad \text{and} \quad \mathbf{B} = \begin{bmatrix} 0 & 1 \\ -1 & 0 \end{bmatrix},
$$

then $\mathbf{A} \neq \mathbf{B}$; if $\mathbf{A} = (1 \ 1 \ 1)$ and $\mathbf{B} = (1 \ 1)$, then $\mathbf{A} \neq \mathbf{B}$; however, if

$$
\mathbf{A} = \begin{bmatrix} 0 & 0 & 0 \\ 0 & 0 & 0 \end{bmatrix} \quad \text{and} \quad \mathbf{B} = \begin{bmatrix} 1 + i^2 & 0 & 0 \\ 0 & 2 - (\sqrt{2})^2 & 0 \end{bmatrix},
$$

then $\mathbf{A} = \mathbf{B}$.

DEFINITION 10–3.2. If $\mathbf{A}$ and $\mathbf{B}$ are m by n matrices with elements $a_{i,j}$ and $b_{i,j}$ in a ring A, then the *sum*, $\mathbf{A} + \mathbf{B}$, of $\mathbf{A}$ and $\mathbf{B}$ is the matrix

$$
\mathbf{C} = \begin{bmatrix} a_{1,1} + b_{1,1} & a_{1,2} + b_{1,2} & \ldots & a_{1,n} + b_{1,n} \\ a_{2,1} + b_{2,1} & a_{2,2} + b_{2,2} & \ldots & a_{2,n} + b_{2,n} \\ \vdots & & \vdots & & \vdots \\ a_{m,1} + b_{m,1} & a_{m,2} + b_{m,2} & \ldots & a_{m,n} + b_{m,n} \end{bmatrix}.
$$

Thus, $\mathbf{C} = \mathbf{A} + \mathbf{B}$ is an m by n matrix with elements in A such that $c_{i,j} = a_{i,j} + b_{i,j}$ for $i = 1, 2, \ldots, m$ and $j = 1, 2, \ldots, n$. It is clear that addition of matrices is a well defined binary operation on the set of all m by n matrices with elements in A. However, the sum $\mathbf{A} + \mathbf{B}$ is not defined unless $\mathbf{A}$ and $\mathbf{B}$ have the same dimensions.

EXAMPLE 1. The matrices

$$\mathbf{A} = \begin{bmatrix} \frac{1}{2} & 6 & 0 \\ -\frac{1}{5} & 1 & 7 \\ 4 & 0 & -\frac{1}{3} \\ 1 & 1 & 1 \end{bmatrix} \quad \text{and} \quad \mathbf{B} = \begin{bmatrix} -\frac{1}{2} & 4 & -8 \\ 2 & 1 & \frac{1}{3} \\ 6 & 9 & 0 \\ -1 & -1 & -1 \end{bmatrix}$$

are 4 by 3 matrices with elements in the field Q of rational numbers.

$$\mathbf{A} + \mathbf{B} = \begin{bmatrix} 0 & 10 & -8 \\ \frac{9}{5} & 2 & \frac{22}{3} \\ 10 & 9 & -\frac{1}{3} \\ 0 & 0 & 0 \end{bmatrix}.$$

Since matrices are added "elementwise", according to Definition 10–3.2, the properties of addition which hold in the ring A are also satisfied by matrix addition.

(10–3.3). Matrix addition is associative.

Proof. Let **A**, **B**, and **C** be m by n matrices with elements $a_{i,j}$, $b_{i,j}$, and $c_{i,j}$ in a ring A. Then by Definition 10–3.2,

$$(\mathbf{A} + \mathbf{B}) + \mathbf{C} = \begin{bmatrix} a_{1,1} + b_{1,1} & a_{1,2} + b_{1,2} & \cdots & a_{1,n} + b_{1,n} \\ a_{2,1} + b_{2,1} & a_{2,2} + b_{2,2} & \cdots & a_{2,n} + b_{2,n} \\ \vdots & \vdots & & \vdots \\ a_{m,1} + b_{m,1} & a_{m,2} + b_{m,2} & \cdots & a_{m,n} + b_{m,n} \end{bmatrix} + \begin{bmatrix} c_{1,1} & c_{1,2} & \cdots & c_{1,n} \\ c_{2,1} & c_{2,2} & \cdots & c_{2,n} \\ \vdots & \vdots & & \vdots \\ c_{m,1} & c_{m,2} & \cdots & c_{m,n} \end{bmatrix}$$

$$= \begin{bmatrix} (a_{1,1} + b_{1,1}) + c_{1,1} & (a_{1,2} + b_{1,2}) + c_{1,2} & \cdots & (a_{1,n} + b_{1,n}) + c_{1,n} \\ (a_{2,1} + b_{2,1}) + c_{2,1} & (a_{2,2} + b_{2,2}) + c_{2,2} & \cdots & (a_{2,n} + b_{2,n}) + c_{2,n} \\ \vdots & \vdots & & \vdots \\ (a_{m,1} + b_{m,1}) + c_{m,1} & (a_{m,2} + b_{m,2}) + c_{m,2} & \cdots & (a_{m,n} + b_{m,n}) + c_{m,n} \end{bmatrix}.$$

Similarly,

$$\mathbf{A} + (\mathbf{B} + \mathbf{C}) = \begin{bmatrix} a_{1,1} + (b_{1,1} + c_{1,1}) & a_{1,2} + (b_{1,2} + c_{1,2}) & \cdots & a_{1,n} + (b_{1,n} + c_{1,n}) \\ a_{2,1} + (b_{2,1} + c_{2,1}) & a_{2,2} + (b_{2,2} + c_{2,2}) & \cdots & a_{2,n} + (b_{2,n} + c_{2,n}) \\ \vdots & \vdots & & \vdots \\ a_{m,1} + (b_{m,1} + c_{m,1}) & a_{m,2} + (b_{m,2} + c_{m,2}) & \cdots & a_{m,n} + (b_{m,n} + c_{m,n}) \end{bmatrix}.$$

Both $(\mathbf{A} + \mathbf{B}) + \mathbf{C}$ and $\mathbf{A} + (\mathbf{B} + \mathbf{C})$ are m by n matrices with elements in A, and since addition is associative in A, it follows that $(a_{i,j} + b_{i,j}) + c_{i,j} = a_{i,j} + (b_{i,j} + c_{i,j})$ for all i, j. Thus, according to the definition of equality of matrices, $(\mathbf{A} + \mathbf{B}) + \mathbf{C} = \mathbf{A} + (\mathbf{B} + \mathbf{C})$.

The commutative law of addition in a ring A leads to the corresponding property of matrix addition.

(10–3.4). Matrix addition is commutative.

It will be left as an exercise for the reader to prove (10–3.4), that is, to show that if $\mathbf{A}$ and $\mathbf{B}$ are m by n matrices with elements in a ring A, then $\mathbf{A} + \mathbf{B} = \mathbf{B} + \mathbf{A}$.

Let $\mathbf{O}$ denote the m by n matrix which has the zero element of A in every position. Then it follows from Definitions 4–2.1(c) and 10–3.2 that

$$\mathbf{A} + \mathbf{O} = \mathbf{A}, \tag{10–8}$$

where $\mathbf{A}$ is any m by n matrix with elements in A. Of course, $\mathbf{O} + \mathbf{A} = \mathbf{A}$ also. Because $\mathbf{O}$ satisfies (10–8), it is called the *zero matrix*.
Let

$$\mathbf{A} = \begin{bmatrix} a_{1,1} & a_{1,2} & \cdots & a_{1,n} \\ a_{2,1} & a_{2,2} & \cdots & a_{2,n} \\ \vdots & \vdots & & \vdots \\ a_{m,1} & a_{m,2} & \cdots & a_{m,n} \end{bmatrix}$$

be an m by n matrix with elements $a_{i,j}$ in a ring A. Define the *negative* of A to be the m by n matrix

$$-\mathbf{A} = \begin{bmatrix} -a_{1,1} & -a_{1,2} & \cdots & -a_{1,n} \\ -a_{2,1} & -a_{2,2} & \cdots & -a_{2,n} \\ \vdots & \vdots & & \vdots \\ -a_{m,1} & -a_{m,2} & \cdots & -a_{m,n} \end{bmatrix}. \tag{10–9}$$

In (10–9), the element $-a_{i,j}$ of A is the negative of $a_{i,j}$ in the ring A. Thus, we have

$$\mathbf{A} + (-\mathbf{A}) = \begin{bmatrix} a_{1,1} + (-a_{1,1}) & a_{1,2} + (-a_{1,2}) & \cdots & a_{1,n} + (-a_{1,n}) \\ a_{2,1} + (-a_{2,1}) & a_{2,2} + (-a_{2,2}) & \cdots & a_{2,n} + (-a_{2,n}) \\ \vdots & \vdots & & \vdots \\ a_{m,1} + (-a_{m,1}) & a_{m,2} + (-a_{m,2}) & \cdots & a_{m,n} + (-a_{m,n}) \end{bmatrix} = \begin{bmatrix} 0 & 0 & \cdots & 0 \\ 0 & 0 & \cdots & 0 \\ \vdots & \vdots & & \vdots \\ 0 & 0 & \cdots & 0 \end{bmatrix} = \mathbf{O}.$$

$$\tag{10–10}$$

Let $_mM_n(A)$ denote the set of all m by n matrices with elements in a ring A. Then with addition and negation defined by Definition 10–3.2 and (10–9), the properties (10–3.3), (10–3.4) and equations (10–8), (10–10) correspond exactly to the conditions of Definition 4–2.1(a) (b), (c), and (d) in the definition of a ring. The reader might expect that the next step would be to introduce an "elementwise" multiplication in the set $_mM_n(A)$, which together with addition and negation would make $_mM_n(A)$ into a ring. Indeed, this can be done (see Problem 6 below). However, it turns out that in the various applications of matrices, a different definition of matrix multiplication is more useful.

DEFINITION 10–3.5. Let **A** be an m by n matrix with elements $a_{i,j}$ in a ring A and let **B** be an n by q matrix with elements $b_{i,j} \in A$. Then the *product* **AB** is the m by q matrix which has the element $\sum_{k=1}^{n} a_{i,k}b_{k,j}$ in the ith row and jth column for $i = 1, 2, \ldots, m$ and $j = 1, 2, \ldots, q$.

According to this definition, it is possible to multiply two matrices with elements in a ring only when the first matrix has the same number of columns as the second matrix has rows. Therefore, if $m \neq n$, Definition 10–3.5 does *not* define the product of two matrices in the set $_mM_n(A)$. However if $m = n$, then it does define a binary operation on the set $_nM_n(A)$.

EXAMPLE 2. Let

$$\mathbf{A} = \begin{bmatrix} \tfrac{1}{2} & -1 & 2 \\ 0 & \tfrac{3}{2} & 1 \end{bmatrix}, \qquad \mathbf{B} = \begin{bmatrix} 1 & 0 & 1 \\ -1 & 1 & 3 \\ 2 & 0 & -2 \end{bmatrix}$$

be matrices with elements in the field Q of rational numbers. Since **A** has three columns and **B** has three rows, the product **AB** is defined. In fact, according to Definition 10–3.5,

$$\mathbf{AB} = \begin{bmatrix} \tfrac{1}{2} \cdot 1 + (-1) \cdot (-1) + 2 \cdot 2 & \tfrac{1}{2} \cdot 0 + (-1) \cdot 1 + 2 \cdot 0 & \tfrac{1}{2} \cdot 1 + (-1) \cdot 3 + 2 \cdot (-2) \\ 0 \cdot 1 + \tfrac{3}{2} \cdot (-1) + 1 \cdot 2 & 0 \cdot 0 + \tfrac{3}{2} \cdot 1 + 1 \cdot 0 & 0 \cdot 1 + \tfrac{3}{2} \cdot 3 + 1 \cdot (-2) \end{bmatrix}$$

$$= \begin{bmatrix} \tfrac{11}{2} & -1 & -\tfrac{13}{2} \\ \tfrac{1}{2} & \tfrac{3}{2} & \tfrac{5}{2} \end{bmatrix}.$$

The product **BA** is not defined, since **B** has three columns, while **A** has only two rows.

EXAMPLE 3. Using the definition of multiplication given in Definition 10–3.5, it is possible to write a system of s linear equations in r unknowns as a single matrix equation. Let

$$\sum_{j=1}^{r} a_{i,j}x_j = b_i, \qquad i = 1, 2, \ldots, s,$$

be a system of linear equations with coefficients in an integral domain D. The s by r matrix

$$\mathbf{A} = \begin{bmatrix} a_{1,1} & a_{1,2} \ldots a_{1,r} \\ a_{2,1} & a_{2,2} \ldots a_{2,r} \\ \vdots & \vdots \qquad \vdots \\ a_{s,1} & a_{s,2} \ldots a_{s,r} \end{bmatrix}$$

is called the *matrix of coefficients* of the system. Define column matrices $\mathbf{X}$ and $\mathbf{B}$ by

$$\mathbf{X} = \begin{bmatrix} x_1 \\ x_2 \\ \vdots \\ x_r \end{bmatrix}, \qquad \mathbf{B} = \begin{bmatrix} b_1 \\ b_2 \\ \vdots \\ b_s \end{bmatrix}.$$

The elements of $\mathbf{A}$, $\mathbf{X}$, and $\mathbf{B}$ can be thought of as being in the ring

$$D[x_1, x_2, \ldots, x_r].$$

Since $\mathbf{A}$ has r columns and $\mathbf{X}$ has r rows, it is possible to form the product $\mathbf{AX}$. By definition, this product is a column matrix with s rows, namely,

$$\mathbf{AX} = \begin{bmatrix} a_{1,1}x_1 + a_{1,2}x_2 + \cdots + a_{1,r}x_r \\ a_{2,1}x_1 + a_{2,2}x_2 + \cdots + a_{2,r}x_r \\ \vdots \\ a_{s,1}x_1 + a_{s,2}x_2 + \cdots + a_{s,r}x_r \end{bmatrix}.$$

Consequently, the matrix equation $\mathbf{AX} = \mathbf{B}$ is identical with the system of equations

$$\sum_{j=1}^{r} a_{i,j}x_j = b_i, \qquad i = 1, 2, \ldots, s.$$

Using this notation, a solution of the system of equations is a column matrix with r rows

$$\mathbf{C} = \begin{bmatrix} c_1 \\ c_2 \\ \vdots \\ c_r \end{bmatrix},$$

with elements in a commutative ring A containing D as a subring, such that

$$AC = B.$$

EXAMPLE 4. Let

$$\sum_{j=1}^{r} a_{i,j}x_j = b_i, \qquad i = 1, 2, \ldots, s,$$

be a system of linear equations with coefficients in the integral domain D. Suppose that $y_1, y_2, \ldots, y_t$ are new unknowns which are related to $x_1, x_2, \ldots, x_r$ by the equations

$$x_1 = d_{1,1}y_1 + d_{1,2}y_2 + \cdots + d_{1,t}y_t$$
$$x_2 = d_{2,1}y_1 + d_{2,2}y_2 + \cdots + d_{2,t}y_t$$
$$\vdots$$
$$x_r = d_{r,1}y_1 + d_{r,2}y_2 + \cdots + d_{r,t}y_t,$$

with $d_{j,k} \in D$ for all j and k. In compact notation,

$$x_j = \sum_{k=1}^{t} d_{j,k}y_k, \qquad j = 1, 2, \ldots, r.$$

Thus, the given system becomes

$$\sum_{j=1}^{r} a_{i,j}\left(\sum_{k=1}^{t} d_{j,k}y_k\right) = b_i, \qquad i = 1, 2, \ldots, s,$$

which, by the generalized distributive, commutative, and associative laws is equivalent to

$$\sum_{k=1}^{t} \left(\sum_{j=1}^{r} a_{i,j}d_{j,k}\right) y_k = b_i, \qquad i = 1, 2, \ldots, s.$$

The matrix of coefficients of this new system of equations is

$$\begin{bmatrix} \sum_{j=1}^{r} a_{1,j}d_{j,1} & \sum_{j=1}^{r} a_{1,j}d_{j,2} & \cdots & \sum_{j=1}^{r} a_{1,j}d_{j,t} \\ \sum_{j=1}^{r} a_{2,j}d_{j,1} & \sum_{j=1}^{r} a_{2,j}d_{j,2} & \cdots & \sum_{j=1}^{r} a_{2,j}d_{j,t} \\ \vdots & \vdots & & \vdots \\ \sum_{j=1}^{r} a_{s,j}d_{j,1} & \sum_{j=1}^{r} a_{s,j}d_{j,2} & \cdots & \sum_{j=1}^{r} a_{s,j}d_{j,t} \end{bmatrix}.$$

That is, if $\mathbf{A}$ is the matrix of coefficients of the original system, and if

$$\mathbf{D} = \begin{bmatrix} d_{1,1} & d_{1,2} & \cdots & d_{1,t} \\ d_{2,1} & d_{2,2} & \cdots & d_{2,t} \\ \vdots & \vdots & & \vdots \\ d_{r,1} & d_{r,2} & \cdots & d_{r,t} \end{bmatrix}$$

is the matrix of the coefficients in the system of equations which relate $x_1, x_2, \ldots,$ x_r to $y_1, y_2, \ldots, y_t$, then the matrix of coefficients of the new system is $\mathbf{AD}$, according to Definition 10–3.5. These calculations can be carried out within the algebra of matrices. Let

$$\mathbf{X} = \begin{bmatrix} x_1 \\ x_2 \\ \vdots \\ x_r \end{bmatrix}, \qquad \mathbf{Y} = \begin{bmatrix} y_1 \\ y_2 \\ \vdots \\ y_t \end{bmatrix}, \qquad \text{and} \qquad \mathbf{B} = \begin{bmatrix} b_1 \\ b_2 \\ \vdots \\ b_s \end{bmatrix}.$$

Then the relation between the x's and y's can be expressed by the matrix equation

$$\mathbf{X} = \mathbf{DY}$$

(see Example 3). Also, the original system of equations can be written in the form

$$\mathbf{AX} = \mathbf{B}.$$

Substituting $\mathbf{DY}$ for $\mathbf{X}$ in this equation gives

$$\mathbf{A(DY)} = \mathbf{B}.$$

It must be noted of course that the number of columns of $\mathbf{A}$ is equal to the number of rows of $\mathbf{DY}$, so that $\mathbf{A(DY)}$ makes sense. In a moment we will show that matrix multiplication is associative. Assuming this fact, it follows that

$$\mathbf{A(DY)} = \mathbf{(AD)Y}.$$

Consequently, the new system of equations in matrix form is

$$\mathbf{(AD)Y} = \mathbf{B}.$$

The matrix of coefficients of this system is clearly $\mathbf{AD}$, which is what we proved above by writing the systems in full. This example illustrates the notational savings which matrices provide.

We will now establish the associativity of matrix multiplication which was mentioned in Example 4.

(10–3.6). Matrix multiplication is associative.

Proof. Let **A** be an m by n matrix with elements $a_{i,j}$ in a ring A, **B** an n by q matrix with elements $b_{i,j}$ in A, and **C** a q by r matrix with elements $c_{i,j}$ in A. Then the products **AB**, **BC**, **(AB)C**, and **A(BC)** are all defined. We wish to prove that these last two products are equal. By Definition 10–3.5,

(AB)C =

$$
\begin{bmatrix}
\sum_{k=1}^{n} a_{1,k}b_{k,1} & \sum_{k=1}^{n} a_{1,k}b_{k,2} & \cdots & \sum_{k=1}^{n} a_{1,k}b_{k,q} \\
\sum_{k=1}^{n} a_{2,k}b_{k,1} & \sum_{k=1}^{n} a_{2,k}b_{k,2} & \cdots & \sum_{k=1}^{n} a_{2,k}b_{k,q} \\
\vdots & \vdots & & \vdots \\
\sum_{k=1}^{n} a_{m,k}b_{k,1} & \sum_{k=1}^{n} a_{m,k}b_{k,2} & \cdots & \sum_{k=1}^{n} a_{m,k}b_{k,q}
\end{bmatrix}
\begin{bmatrix}
c_{1,1} & c_{1,2} \cdots c_{1,r} \\
c_{2,1} & c_{2,2} \cdots c_{2,r} \\
\vdots & \vdots & \vdots \\
c_{q,1} & c_{q,2} \cdots c_{q,r}
\end{bmatrix}
$$

is the m by r matrix which has the element

$$
\sum_{l=1}^{q} \left(\sum_{k=1}^{n} a_{i,k}b_{k,l} \right) c_{l,j}
$$

in the ith row and jth column for $i = 1, 2, \ldots, m$ and $j = 1, 2, \ldots, r$. Again using Definition 10–3.5,

A(BC) =

$$
\begin{bmatrix}
a_{1,1} & a_{1,2} \cdots a_{1,n} \\
a_{2,1} & a_{2,2} \cdots a_{2,n} \\
\vdots & \vdots & \vdots \\
a_{m,1} & a_{m,2} \cdots a_{m,n}
\end{bmatrix}
\begin{bmatrix}
\sum_{l=1}^{q} b_{1,l}c_{l,1} & \sum_{l=1}^{q} b_{1,l}c_{l,2} & \cdots & \sum_{l=1}^{q} b_{1,l}c_{l,r} \\
\sum_{l=1}^{q} b_{2,l}c_{l,1} & \sum_{l=1}^{q} b_{2,l}c_{l,2} & \cdots & \sum_{l=1}^{q} b_{2,l}c_{l,r} \\
\vdots & \vdots & & \vdots \\
\sum_{l=1}^{q} b_{n,l}c_{l,1} & \sum_{l=1}^{q} b_{n,l}c_{l,2} & \cdots & \sum_{l=1}^{q} b_{n,l}c_{l,r}
\end{bmatrix}
$$

is an m by r matrix which has the element

$$
\sum_{k=1}^{n} a_{i,k} \left(\sum_{l=1}^{q} b_{k,l}c_{l,j} \right)
$$

in the ith row and jth column for $i = 1, 2, \ldots, m$ and $j = 1, 2, \ldots, r$. By the distributive laws, Definition 4–2.1(f) and (g), and the commutative law for addition, Definition 4–2.1(a), which are satisfied in the ring A,

$$\sum_{l=1}^{q}\left(\sum_{k=1}^{n} a_{i,k}b_{k,l}\right)c_{l,j} = \sum_{k=1}^{n}\sum_{l=1}^{q} (a_{i,k}b_{k,l})c_{l,j},$$

$$\sum_{k=1}^{n} a_{i,k}\left(\sum_{l=1}^{q} b_{k,l}c_{l,j}\right) = \sum_{k=1}^{n}\sum_{l=1}^{q} a_{i,k}(b_{k,l}c_{l,j}).$$

Since $(a_{i,k}b_{k,l})c_{l,j} = a_{i,k}(b_{k,l}c_{l,j})$ by the associative law for multiplication, in A, it follows that the element in ith row and jth column of $(\mathbf{AB})\mathbf{C}$ is the same as the element in the ith row and jth column of $\mathbf{A}(\mathbf{BC})$ for $i = 1, 2, \ldots, m$ and $j = 1, 2, \ldots, r$. Therefore,

$$(\mathbf{AB})\mathbf{C} = \mathbf{A}(\mathbf{BC})$$

by the definition of equality of matrices.

If $\mathbf{A}$ and $\mathbf{B}$ are m by n and n by q matrices, respectively, with elements in a ring, then $\mathbf{AB}$ is defined, but $\mathbf{BA}$ has no meaning unless $m = q$. However, even in the case where both products $\mathbf{AB}$ and $\mathbf{BA}$ are defined, they are not necessarily equal. Indeed, if $\mathbf{A}$ is an m by n matrix and $\mathbf{B}$ is an n by m matrix, then $\mathbf{AB}$ is m by m and $\mathbf{BA}$ is n by n. Thus, if $m \neq n$, the two products do not have the same dimensions, and are not equal. The following example shows that even when $\mathbf{A}$ and $\mathbf{B}$ are both n by n square matrices (so that $\mathbf{AB}$ and $\mathbf{BA}$ are also n by n matrices), the products $\mathbf{AB}$ and $\mathbf{BA}$ may not be equal.

EXAMPLE 5. Let

$$\mathbf{A} = \begin{bmatrix} 0 & 1 \\ 0 & 1 \end{bmatrix} \quad \text{and} \quad \mathbf{B} = \begin{bmatrix} 1 & 1 \\ 0 & 0 \end{bmatrix}$$

be 2 by 2 matrices with elements in Z. Then

$$\mathbf{AB} = \begin{bmatrix} 0 & 0 \\ 0 & 0 \end{bmatrix} \quad \text{and} \quad \mathbf{BA} = \begin{bmatrix} 0 & 2 \\ 0 & 0 \end{bmatrix}.$$

Let

$$\mathbf{C} = \begin{bmatrix} \frac{1}{2} & 1 & 0 \\ \frac{2}{3} & 0 & -3 \\ 1 & 1 & 1 \end{bmatrix} \quad \text{and} \quad \mathbf{D} = \begin{bmatrix} 2 & -4 & \frac{1}{2} \\ 6 & -7 & \frac{1}{5} \\ 0 & 1 & 2 \end{bmatrix}$$

be 3 by 3 matrices with elements in Q. Then

$$\mathbf{CD} = \begin{bmatrix} 7 & -9 & \frac{9}{20} \\ \frac{4}{3} & -\frac{17}{3} & -\frac{17}{3} \\ 8 & -10 & \frac{27}{10} \end{bmatrix}, \qquad \mathbf{DC} = \begin{bmatrix} -\frac{7}{6} & \frac{5}{2} & \frac{25}{2} \\ -\frac{22}{15} & \frac{31}{5} & \frac{106}{5} \\ \frac{8}{3} & 2 & -1 \end{bmatrix}.$$

We will now adopt the simpler notation $M_n(A)$ for the set $_nM_n(A)$ of all n by n matrices with elements in a ring A. The matrices of $M_n(A)$ are called *n-rowed square matrices with elements in A*. We have already proved most of the results needed for the following theorem.

THEOREM 10–3.7. The set $M_n(A)$ of all n-rowed square matrices with elements in a ring A, with addition, multiplication, and negation, defined by Definitions 10–3.2 and 10–3.5 and (10–9), is a ring. If A contains an identity element 1, then the n by n matrix

$$\mathbf{I} = \begin{bmatrix} 1 & 0 & \cdots & 0 \\ 0 & 1 & \cdots & 0 \\ \vdots & \vdots & & \vdots \\ 0 & 0 & \cdots & 1 \end{bmatrix}$$

(whose elements $e_{i,j}$ are 1 if $i = j$ and 0 if $i \neq j$) is the identity in $M_n(A)$. Moreover, if $n \geq 2$ and $1 \neq 0$ in A, then $M_n(A)$ is not commutative.

Proof. The only identities left to verify in order to prove that $M_n(A)$ is a ring are the distributive laws, Definition 4–2.1(f) and (g), that is,

$$\mathbf{A(B + C)} = \mathbf{AB} + \mathbf{AC}, \qquad \mathbf{(A + B)C} = \mathbf{AC} + \mathbf{BC}.$$

These follow easily from the properties of addition and multiplication in A, and we leave their proof as an exercise for the reader. To prove that $\mathbf{I}$ is an identity in $M_n(A)$, let

$$\mathbf{A} = \begin{bmatrix} a_{1,1} & a_{1,2} & \cdots & a_{1,n} \\ a_{2,1} & a_{2,2} & \cdots & a_{2,n} \\ \vdots & \vdots & & \vdots \\ a_{n,1} & a_{n,2} & \cdots & a_{n,n} \end{bmatrix}$$

be an arbitrary matrix in $M_n(A)$. Then the element of the ith row and

jth column of **AI** is

$$a_{i,1}e_{1,j} + a_{i,2}e_{2,j} + \cdots + a_{i,n}e_{n,j},$$

where $e_{k,j} = 0$ if $k \neq j$ and $e_{j,j} = 1$. Thus, $a_{i,1}e_{1,j} + a_{i,2}e_{2,j} + \cdots + a_{i,n}e_{n,j} = a_{i,j} \cdot 1 = a_{i,j}$. Since i and j are arbitrary, it follows that **AI** = **A**. Similarly, **IA** = **A**. To complete the proof, it will be sufficient to exhibit two matrice **A** and **B** in $M_n(A)$ such that **AB** $\neq$ **BA** (assuming of course that $n \geq 2$ and $1 \neq 0$ in A). Let

$$A = \begin{bmatrix} 1 & 0 & 0 & \cdots & 0 \\ 0 & 0 & 0 & \cdots & 0 \\ \vdots & \vdots & \vdots & & \vdots \\ 0 & 0 & 0 & \cdots & 0 \end{bmatrix}, \qquad B = \begin{bmatrix} 0 & 1 & 0 & \cdots & 0 \\ 0 & 0 & 0 & \cdots & 0 \\ \vdots & \vdots & \vdots & & \vdots \\ 0 & 0 & 0 & \cdots & 0 \end{bmatrix}.$$

Then it follows easily from Definition 10–3.5 that

$$AB = \begin{bmatrix} 0 & 1 & 0 & \cdots & 0 \\ 0 & 0 & 0 & \cdots & 0 \\ \vdots & \vdots & \vdots & & \vdots \\ 0 & 0 & 0 & \cdots & 0 \end{bmatrix}, \quad \text{and} \quad BA = \begin{bmatrix} 0 & 0 & 0 & \cdots & 0 \\ 0 & 0 & 0 & \cdots & 0 \\ \vdots & \vdots & \vdots & & \vdots \\ 0 & 0 & 0 & \cdots & 0 \end{bmatrix}.$$

Therefore **AB** $\neq$ **BA**, so that the proof is complete.

PROBLEMS

1. (a) Write the 5 by 3 matrix with elements in Z which has $a_{i,j} = i \cdot j$ for $i = 1, 2, 3, 4, 5$ and $j = 1, 2, 3$.
   (b) Construct the 2 by 4 matrix with elements in Q which has $a_{i,j} = i/j$ for $i = 1, 2,$ and $j = 1, 2, 3, 4$.

2. List every 2 by 2 matrix which has elements in Z_2, the ring of integers modulo 2.

3. If **A** and **B** are m by n matrices with elements in a ring A, then the *difference* of **A** and **B** is defined by **A** $-$ **B** = **A** $+$ ($-$**B**). Prove that **A** $-$ **B** is the unique solution of the matrix equation **B** $+$ **X** = **A**.

4. Perform the indicated operations.

(a) $\begin{bmatrix} -2 & \frac{1}{7} & 6 & 0 \\ \frac{3}{4} & 2 & 0 & 1 \\ 5 & 1 & -1 & 2 \end{bmatrix} + \begin{bmatrix} 0 & \frac{6}{7} & 4 & -3 \\ \frac{1}{2} & 6 & -1 & 2 \\ 0 & 1 & 0 & 1 \end{bmatrix}$

(b) $\begin{bmatrix} \frac{1}{2} + 2i \\ -5 \\ 1 - i \\ 4 - 7i \end{bmatrix} - \begin{bmatrix} 2i \\ 6 \\ 4 - i \\ \frac{1}{3} - 7i \end{bmatrix}$

(c) $\left(\begin{bmatrix} 2 & 6 \\ 1 & 3 \\ 0 & 2 \end{bmatrix} + \begin{bmatrix} 1 & -4 \\ 2 & 3 \\ 0 & 5 \end{bmatrix} \right) - \begin{bmatrix} 2 & 6 \\ 3 & 0 \\ -7 & -1 \end{bmatrix}$

5. Prove (10–3.4).

6. Define multiplication in $_mM_n(A)$ by the rule

$$\begin{bmatrix} a_{1,1} & a_{1,2} & \cdots & a_{1,n} \\ a_{2,1} & a_{2,2} & \cdots & a_{2,n} \\ \vdots & \vdots & & \vdots \\ a_{m,1} & a_{m,2} & \cdots & a_{m,n} \end{bmatrix} \cdot \begin{bmatrix} b_{1,1} & b_{1,2} & \cdots & b_{1,n} \\ b_{2,1} & b_{2,2} & \cdots & b_{2,n} \\ \vdots & \vdots & & \vdots \\ b_{m,1} & b_{m,2} & \cdots & b_{m,n} \end{bmatrix}$$

$$= \begin{bmatrix} a_{1,1}b_{1,1} & a_{1,2}b_{1,2} & \cdots & a_{1,n}b_{1,n} \\ a_{2,1}b_{2,1} & a_{2,2}b_{2,2} & \cdots & a_{2,n}b_{2,n} \\ \vdots & \vdots & & \vdots \\ a_{m,1}b_{m,1} & a_{m,2}b_{m,2} & \cdots & a_{m,n}b_{m,n} \end{bmatrix}.$$

Prove that with this multiplication and with addition and negation, defined by Definition 10–3.2 and (10–9), $_mM_n(A)$ is a ring. Prove that if A is commutative, then $_mM_n(A)$ is commutative. Is it true that $_mM_n(A)$ is an integral domain if A is an integral domain?

7. Compute the following matrix products.

(a) $\begin{bmatrix} 0 & 1 & 3 \\ -1 & 2 & 0 \end{bmatrix} \begin{bmatrix} 4 & 0 \\ -5 & 1 \\ 0 & 6 \end{bmatrix}$, $\begin{bmatrix} 4 & 0 \\ -5 & 1 \\ 0 & 6 \end{bmatrix} \begin{bmatrix} 0 & 1 & 3 \\ -1 & 2 & 0 \end{bmatrix}$,

(b) $[-5 \quad 6 \quad 1 \quad 3] \begin{bmatrix} -1 & 0 & 3 \\ 7 & -2 & 1 \\ 0 & 0 & 0 \\ 1 & 6 & 2 \end{bmatrix}$

(c)
$$\begin{bmatrix} a_1 \\ a_2 \\ \vdots \\ a_n \end{bmatrix} [b_1 \quad b_2 \dots b_n], \qquad [b_1 \quad b_2 \dots b_n] \begin{bmatrix} a_1 \\ a_2 \\ \vdots \\ a_n \end{bmatrix}$$

(d)
$$\begin{bmatrix} 1 & i \\ 0 & 1+i \end{bmatrix} \begin{bmatrix} -1 & 2-i & 0 \\ 6 & 1 & i \end{bmatrix} \begin{bmatrix} 1 & 1+3i & 4 \\ 0 & 1 & -i \\ 0 & 0 & 1 \end{bmatrix}$$

8. Write the systems of homogeneous linear equations in the unknowns x_1, x_2, x_3, and x_4 whose matrices of coefficients are as follows.

(a) $\begin{bmatrix} 1 & 0 & 0 & 1 \\ 1 & 2 & 1 & 0 \end{bmatrix}$ \qquad (b) $\begin{bmatrix} \frac{1}{2} & \frac{1}{3} & \frac{1}{4} & \frac{1}{5} \\ 1 & \frac{2}{3} & \frac{1}{2} & \frac{2}{5} \\ \frac{3}{2} & 1 & \frac{3}{4} & \frac{3}{5} \end{bmatrix}$

(c) **I**, where **I** is the identity matrix of $M_4(Q)$.

9. Find the matrix of coefficients of the systems obtained from the homogeneous systems in Problem 8 by making the following change of unknowns:

$$\begin{aligned} x_1 &= y_1 + y_2 + y_3 \\ x_2 &= 2y_1 - y_2 - y_3 \\ x_3 &= \qquad\quad y_2 + y_3 \\ x_4 &= y_1 + 2y_2 + y_3. \end{aligned}$$

10. Complete the proof of Theorem 10–3.7 by proving the distributive laws in $M_n(A)$. Prove, more generally, that if

$$\mathbf{A} \in {}_mM_n(A), \qquad \mathbf{B} \in {}_nM_q(A),$$

and

$$\mathbf{C} \in {}_nM_q(A),$$

then

$$\mathbf{A}(\mathbf{B} + \mathbf{C}) = \mathbf{AB} + \mathbf{AC}.$$

State a general form of the other distributive law.

11. Prove that if $n \geq 2$ and the ring A contains an element $a \neq 0$, then $M_n(A)$ contains proper divisors of zero.

12. Let A be a ring with identity. Suppose that $n \geq 2$. Find matrices **A** and **B** in $M_n(A)$ such that

$$(\mathbf{AB})^2 \neq \mathbf{A}^2\mathbf{B}^2.$$

13. Prove that for any ring A, the ring $M_1(A)$ of all 1 by 1 matrices with elements in A is isomorphic to A.

10–4 The inverse of a square matrix. If F is a field, then by Theorem 10–3.7 the ring $M_n(F)$ of all n-rowed square matrices with elements in F has the identity

$$I = \begin{bmatrix} 1 & 0 & \cdots & 0 \\ 0 & 1 & \cdots & 0 \\ \vdots & \vdots & & \vdots \\ 0 & 0 & \cdots & 1 \end{bmatrix},$$

which is the n by n matrix with 1 in every position on the diagonal line from the upper left-hand corner to the lower right-hand corner (the so-called "main diagonal") and 0 in every other position. The existence of an identity element in $M_n(F)$ makes it possible to define inverses.

DEFINITION 10–4.1. Let $\mathbf{A}$ and $\mathbf{B}$ be in $M_n(F)$, where F is a field. If $\mathbf{AB} = \mathbf{BA} = \mathbf{I}$, then the matrix $\mathbf{B}$ is called an *inverse* of the matrix $\mathbf{A}$ in $M_n(F)$.

If $\mathbf{B}$ is an inverse of $\mathbf{A}$, then of course $\mathbf{A}$ is an inverse of $\mathbf{B}$, since Definition 10–4.1 is symmetrical in $\mathbf{A}$ and $\mathbf{B}$. A matrix $\mathbf{A}$ may not have an inverse, but if an inverse does exist, then it is unique. In fact, suppose that $\mathbf{AB} = \mathbf{BA} = \mathbf{I}$ and $\mathbf{AC} = \mathbf{CA} = \mathbf{I}$, where $\mathbf{A}$, $\mathbf{B}$, and $\mathbf{C}$ belong to $M_n(F)$. Then by the associative law,

$$\mathbf{B} = \mathbf{IB} = (\mathbf{CA})\mathbf{B} = \mathbf{C}(\mathbf{AB}) = \mathbf{CI} = \mathbf{C}.$$

We will denote the unique inverse of $\mathbf{A}$, when it exists, by $\mathbf{A}^{-1}$. Matrices which have no inverse are called *singular*; if $\mathbf{A}$ has an inverse, then $\mathbf{A}$ is called *nonsingular*.

EXAMPLE 1. The matrix

$$\mathbf{A} = \begin{bmatrix} \frac{1}{4} & \frac{3}{2} \\ \frac{1}{2} & 3 \end{bmatrix}$$

in $M_2(Q)$ does not have an inverse. Assume that

$$\mathbf{B} = \begin{bmatrix} b_{1,1} & b_{1,2} \\ b_{2,1} & b_{2,2} \end{bmatrix} \in M_2(Q)$$

is such that $\mathbf{AB} = \mathbf{I}$. Then

$$\mathbf{AB} = \begin{bmatrix} \frac{1}{4} & \frac{3}{2} \\ \frac{1}{2} & 3 \end{bmatrix}\begin{bmatrix} b_{1,1} & b_{1,2} \\ b_{2,1} & b_{2,2} \end{bmatrix} = \begin{bmatrix} \frac{1}{4}b_{1,1} + \frac{3}{2}b_{2,1} & \frac{1}{4}b_{1,2} + \frac{3}{2}b_{2,2} \\ \frac{1}{2}b_{1,1} + 3b_{2,1} & \frac{1}{2}b_{1,2} + 3b_{2,2} \end{bmatrix} = \begin{bmatrix} 1 & 0 \\ 0 & 1 \end{bmatrix}.$$

Therefore, the numbers $b_{1,1}$, $b_{1,2}$, $b_{2,1}$, and $b_{2,2}$ must satisfy the following equations:

$$\begin{aligned}
\tfrac{1}{4}b_{1,1} + \tfrac{3}{2}b_{2,1} &= 1 \\
\tfrac{1}{4}b_{1,2} + \tfrac{3}{2}b_{2,2} &= 0 \\
\tfrac{1}{2}b_{1,1} + 3b_{2,1} &= 0 \\
\tfrac{1}{2}b_{1,2} + 3b_{2,2} &= 1.
\end{aligned}$$

Multiplying the first equation by -2 and adding it to the third equation, we get an equivalent system of equations:

$$\begin{aligned}
\tfrac{1}{4}b_{1,1} + \tfrac{3}{2}b_{2,1} &= 1 \\
\tfrac{1}{4}b_{1,2} + \tfrac{3}{2}b_{2,2} &= 0 \\
0 &= -2 \\
\tfrac{1}{2}b_{1,2} + 3b_{2,2} &= 1,
\end{aligned}$$

which is inconsistent. This proves that $\mathbf{A}$ has no inverse in $M_2(Q)$.

EXAMPLE 2. The matrix

$$\mathbf{A} = \begin{bmatrix} i & -i & 1 \\ 3i & 4 & 0 \\ 1 & 0 & 1+i \end{bmatrix}$$

in $M_3(C)$ has an inverse

$$\mathbf{A}^{-1} = \begin{bmatrix} (-20 - 24i)/61 & (6 - 5i)/61 & (22 + 2i)/61 \\ (-18 + 15i)/61 & (23 - 9i)/122 & (3 - 33i)/122 \\ (22 + 2i)/61 & (-1 + 11i)/122 & (37 - 41i)/122 \end{bmatrix}$$

in $M_3(C)$, as the reader can verify by checking that $\mathbf{A}^{-1}\mathbf{A} = \mathbf{A}\mathbf{A}^{-1} = \mathbf{I}$.

An important elementary property of the set of all nonsingular matrices is the fact that this set is closed under multiplication. In fact, the inverse of the product of nonsingular matrices can be given explicitly in terms of the inverses of the given matrices.

THEOREM 10–4.2. Let $\mathbf{A}_1, \mathbf{A}_2, \ldots, \mathbf{A}_k$ be nonsingular matrices in $M_n(F)$, where F is a field. Then $\mathbf{A}_k^{-1} \ldots \mathbf{A}_2^{-1}\mathbf{A}_1^{-1}$ is the inverse of the product $\mathbf{A}_1\mathbf{A}_2 \ldots \mathbf{A}_k$, so that this product is nonsingular.

Proof. If $k = 1$, the assertion to be proved is that $\mathbf{A}_1^{-1}$ is the inverse of $\mathbf{A}_1$. This is true by the definition of $\mathbf{A}_1^{-1}$. Suppose that $k = 2$. Then

$$(\mathbf{A}_2^{-1}\mathbf{A}_1^{-1})(\mathbf{A}_1\mathbf{A}_2) = \mathbf{A}_2^{-1}(\mathbf{A}_1^{-1}\mathbf{A}_1)\mathbf{A}_2 = \mathbf{A}_2^{-1}\mathbf{I}\mathbf{A}_2 = \mathbf{A}_2^{-1}\mathbf{A}_2 = \mathbf{I}$$

and

$$(\mathbf{A}_1\mathbf{A}_2)(\mathbf{A}_2^{-1}\mathbf{A}_1^{-1}) = \mathbf{A}_1(\mathbf{A}_2\mathbf{A}_2^{-1})\mathbf{A}_1^{-1} = \mathbf{A}_1\mathbf{I}\mathbf{A}_1^{-1} = \mathbf{A}_1\mathbf{A}_1^{-1} = \mathbf{I}.$$

Thus, by Definition 10–4.1, $\mathbf{A}_2^{-1}\mathbf{A}_1^{-1}$ is an inverse of $\mathbf{A}_1\mathbf{A}_2$. Since inverses are unique, $(\mathbf{A}_1\mathbf{A}_2)^{-1} = \mathbf{A}_2^{-1}\mathbf{A}_1^{-1}$. The proof of the general case is obtained by induction on k, using the case $k = 2$ to establish the induction step. We omit the details.

If

$$\sum_{j=1}^{n} a_{i,j}x_j = b_i, \qquad i = 1, 2, \ldots, n,$$

is a system of n linear equations in n unknowns with coefficients in a field F, then the matrix of coefficients of this system

$$\mathbf{A} = \begin{bmatrix} a_{1,1} & a_{1,2} & \cdots & a_{1,n} \\ a_{2,1} & a_{2,2} & \cdots & a_{2,n} \\ \vdots & \vdots & & \vdots \\ a_{n,1} & a_{n,2} & \cdots & a_{n,n} \end{bmatrix}$$

belongs to $M_n(F)$. If the matrix $\mathbf{A}$ has an inverse in $M_n(F)$, and if this inverse is known, then the system of equations can easily be solved. In fact, suppose that $\langle c_1, c_2, \ldots, c_r \rangle$ is any solution of the system. As we observed in Example 3, Section 10–3,

$$\mathbf{AC} = \mathbf{B},$$

where

$$\mathbf{C} = \begin{bmatrix} c_1 \\ c_2 \\ \vdots \\ c_n \end{bmatrix} \qquad \text{and} \qquad \mathbf{B} = \begin{bmatrix} b_1 \\ b_2 \\ \vdots \\ b_n \end{bmatrix}.$$

Multiplying each side of this equation by $\mathbf{A}^{-1}$ gives

$$\mathbf{A}^{-1}(\mathbf{AC}) = \mathbf{A}^{-1}\mathbf{B}.$$

Therefore, by the associative law, $\mathbf{C} = \mathbf{IC} = (\mathbf{A}^{-1}\mathbf{A})\mathbf{C} = \mathbf{A}^{-1}(\mathbf{AC}) = \mathbf{A}^{-1}\mathbf{B}$. That is, the solution $\langle c_1, c_2, \ldots, c_n \rangle$ can be obtained in the form of a column matrix by computing $\mathbf{A}^{-1}\mathbf{B}$, *provided that* $\mathbf{A}^{-1}$ is known. Conversely, by direct substitution of $\mathbf{C} = \mathbf{A}^{-1}\mathbf{B}$ for $\mathbf{X}$ in the matrix equation $\mathbf{AX} = \mathbf{B}$, it follows that $\mathbf{C}$ is a solution. Therefore, the elements of $\mathbf{C}$ furnish a solution of the original system of linear equations. Note that the solution of the system is unique since $\mathbf{C} = \mathbf{A}^{-1}\mathbf{B}$ and $\mathbf{A}^{-1}$ is unique.

EXAMPLE 3. Consider the following system of linear equations with coefficients in C:

$$ix_1 - ix_2 + x_3 = 0$$
$$3ix_1 + 4x_2 \quad\quad = i$$
$$x_1 + (1 + i)x_3 = -1.$$

The matrix of the coefficients of this system is the matrix $\mathbf{A}$ whose inverse was given in Example 2. By our discussion, the unique solution of this system is obtained from the column matrix

$$\mathbf{A}^{-1}\mathbf{B} = \begin{bmatrix} (-20 - 24i)/61 & (6 - 5i)/61 & (22 + 2i)/61 \\ (-18 + 15i)/61 & (23 - 9i)/122 & (3 - 33i)/122 \\ (22 + 2i)/61 & (-1 + 11i)/122 & (37 - 41i)/122 \end{bmatrix} \begin{bmatrix} 0 \\ i \\ -1 \end{bmatrix}$$

$$= \begin{bmatrix} (-17 + 4i)/61 \\ (3 + 28i)/61 \\ (-24 + 20i)/61 \end{bmatrix}$$

thus, $\langle (-17 + 4i)/61,\ (3 + 28i)/61,\ (-24 + 20i)/61 \rangle$ is the solution of the given system.

The above discussion gives some indication of why it is important to be able to decide whether or not a matrix has an inverse, and if it has, to find the inverse. In the remainder of this section, we will describe a practical method* of finding the inverse of any nonsingular square matrix with elements in a field. The process is similar to the method of solving systems of linear equations which was explained in Section 10–2.

Suppose that $\sum_{j=1}^{n} a_{i,j}x_j = b_i,\ i = 1, 2, \ldots, m$, is a system of m linear equations in n unknowns with coefficients in the field F. Let $\mathbf{A}$ be the matrix of coefficients of this system. If we apply an elementary transformation to this system, then a system of linear equations is obtained whose matrix of coefficients $\mathbf{B}$ can be described in terms of the matrix $\mathbf{A}$. For example, if the elementary transformation interchanges the equations k and l, then $\mathbf{B}$ is obtained from $\mathbf{A}$ by interchanging the rows k and l. This observation motivates the definition of an *elementary row transformation* of a matrix $\mathbf{A}$ in ${}_mM_n(F)$. There are three types of such elementary transformations, which can be described as follows.

---

* It can be shown that a square matrix $\mathbf{A}$ with elements in a field is nonsingular if and only if the determinant of $\mathbf{A}$ is not zero. An explicit expression can even be given for the inverse of $\mathbf{A}$ in terms of certain determinants. However, the method which we will explain below is a more practical way to find $\mathbf{A}^{-1}$ than by evaluating these determinants.

(1) Interchange two rows of $\mathbf{A}$:

$$\begin{bmatrix} a_{1,1} & a_{1,2} & \cdots & a_{1,n} \\ \vdots & \vdots & & \vdots \\ a_{i,1} & a_{i,2} & \cdots & a_{i,n} \\ \vdots & \vdots & & \vdots \\ a_{j,1} & a_{j,2} & \cdots & a_{j,n} \\ \vdots & \vdots & & \vdots \\ a_{m,1} & a_{m,2} & \cdots & a_{m,n} \end{bmatrix} \rightarrow \begin{bmatrix} a_{1,1} & a_{1,2} & \cdots & a_{1,n} \\ \vdots & \vdots & & \vdots \\ a_{j,1} & a_{j,2} & \cdots & a_{j,n} \\ \vdots & \vdots & & \vdots \\ a_{i,1} & a_{i,2} & \cdots & a_{i,n} \\ \vdots & \vdots & & \vdots \\ a_{m,1} & a_{m,2} & \cdots & a_{m,n} \end{bmatrix}.$$

(2) Multiply a row of $\mathbf{A}$ by some element of F and add to a different row of $\mathbf{A}$:

$$\begin{bmatrix} a_{1,1} & a_{1,2} & \cdots & a_{1,n} \\ \vdots & \vdots & & \vdots \\ a_{i,1} & a_{i,2} & \cdots & a_{i,n} \\ \vdots & \vdots & & \vdots \\ a_{j,1} & a_{j,2} & \cdots & a_{j,n} \\ \vdots & \vdots & & \vdots \\ a_{m,1} & a_{m,2} & \cdots & a_{m,n} \end{bmatrix} \rightarrow \begin{bmatrix} a_{1,1} & a_{1,2} & \cdots & a_{1,n} \\ \vdots & \vdots & & \vdots \\ a_{i,1} & a_{i,2} & \cdots & a_{i,n} \\ \vdots & \vdots & & \vdots \\ ca_{i,1}+a_{j,1} & ca_{i,2}+a_{j,2} & \cdots & ca_{i,n}+a_{j,n} \\ \vdots & \vdots & & \vdots \\ a_{m,1} & a_{m,2} & \cdots & a_{m,n} \end{bmatrix},$$

where $c \in F$, and $i \neq j$.

(3) Multiply a row of $\mathbf{A}$ by some nonzero element of F:

$$\begin{bmatrix} a_{1,1} & a_{1,2} & \cdots & a_{1,n} \\ \vdots & \vdots & & \vdots \\ a_{i,1} & a_{i,2} & \cdots & a_{i,n} \\ \vdots & \vdots & & \vdots \\ a_{m,1} & a_{m,2} & \cdots & a_{m,n} \end{bmatrix} \rightarrow \begin{bmatrix} a_{1,1} & a_{1,2} & \cdots & a_{1,n} \\ \vdots & \vdots & & \vdots \\ ca_{i,1} & ca_{i,2} & \cdots & ca_{i,n} \\ \vdots & \vdots & & \vdots \\ a_{m,1} & a_{m,2} & \cdots & a_{m,n} \end{bmatrix},$$

where $c \in F$, and $c \neq 0$.

It is clear that the method used to prove Theorem 10–2.6 can be employed to show that any matrix can be carried into echelon form:

$$\mathbf{C} = \begin{bmatrix} 0 & \cdots & 0 & 1 & d_{1,n_1+1} & \cdots & d_{1,n_2} & d_{1,n_2+1} & \cdots & d_{1,n_r} & d_{1,n_r+1} & \cdots & d_{1,n} \\ 0 & \cdots & 0 & 0 & 0 & \cdots & 1 & d_{2,n_2+1} & \cdots & d_{2,n_r} & d_{2,n_r+1} & \cdots & d_{2,n} \\ \vdots & & \vdots & \vdots & \vdots & & \vdots & \vdots & & \vdots & \vdots & & \vdots \\ 0 & \cdots & 0 & 0 & 0 & \cdots & 0 & 0 & \cdots & 1 & d_{r,n_r+1} & \cdots & d_{r,n} \\ 0 & \cdots & 0 & 0 & 0 & \cdots & 0 & 0 & \cdots & 0 & 0 & \cdots & 0 \\ \vdots & & \vdots & \vdots & \vdots & & \vdots & \vdots & & \vdots & \vdots & & \vdots \\ 0 & \cdots & 0 & 0 & 0 & \cdots & 0 & 0 & \cdots & 0 & 0 & \cdots & 0 \end{bmatrix} \quad (10\text{–}11)$$

by a sequence of elementary transformations.

EXAMPLE 4. Let

$$\mathbf{A} = \begin{bmatrix} 2 & -3 & 1 \\ 1 & -\frac{1}{2} & 6 \\ 4 & -1 & -1 \end{bmatrix}.$$

By elementary row transformations, $\mathbf{A}$ is taken into echelon form as follows:

$$\begin{bmatrix} 2 & -3 & 1 \\ 1 & -\frac{1}{2} & 6 \\ 4 & -1 & -1 \end{bmatrix} \rightarrow \begin{bmatrix} 1 & -\frac{1}{2} & 6 \\ 2 & -3 & 1 \\ 4 & -1 & -1 \end{bmatrix} \rightarrow \begin{bmatrix} 1 & -\frac{1}{2} & 6 \\ 0 & -2 & -11 \\ 4 & -1 & -1 \end{bmatrix} \rightarrow \begin{bmatrix} 1 & -\frac{1}{2} & 6 \\ 0 & -2 & -11 \\ 0 & 1 & -25 \end{bmatrix}$$

$$\rightarrow \begin{bmatrix} 1 & -\frac{1}{2} & 6 \\ 0 & 1 & -25 \\ 0 & -2 & -11 \end{bmatrix} \rightarrow \begin{bmatrix} 1 & -\frac{1}{2} & 6 \\ 0 & 1 & -25 \\ 0 & 0 & -61 \end{bmatrix} \rightarrow \begin{bmatrix} 1 & -\frac{1}{2} & 6 \\ 0 & 1 & -25 \\ 0 & 0 & 1 \end{bmatrix}.$$

It should be clear which elementary row transformation is applied at each step.

A sequence of elementary row transformations on a matrix $\mathbf{A} \in {}_m M_n(F)$ can be accomplished by multiplying $\mathbf{A}$ by a matrix $\mathbf{P} \in M_m(F)$. This fact can be used to give a necessary and sufficient condition for a square matrix to have an inverse, and to calculate the inverse when it exists. In order to carry out this program, we need several preliminary results.

(10–4.3). Let $\mathbf{I}^{(i,j)}$ be the matrix obtained from the identity matrix $\mathbf{I} \in M_m(F)$ by interchanging the ith and jth rows of $\mathbf{I}$. Let $\mathbf{A} \in {}_m M_n(F)$. Then the matrix $\mathbf{I}^{(i,j)}\mathbf{A}$ is the matrix obtained from $\mathbf{A}$ by interchanging the ith and jth rows of $\mathbf{A}$.

Proof. We have

The matrix $\mathbf{I}^{(i,j)}$ has 1's on the diagonal except in the ith and jth rows where the diagonal element is zero, 1 in the (i, j)-position, 1 in the (j, i)-position, and zeros elsewhere. If $\mathbf{A} \in {}_mM_n(F)$ is a matrix with elements $a_{i,j}$, then it follows from the definition of matrix multiplication that

$$
\mathbf{I}^{(i,j)}\mathbf{A} = \begin{array}{c} \\ \\ i \\ \\ j \\ \\ \\ \end{array}
\begin{bmatrix}
a_{1,1} & a_{1,2} & \cdots & a_{1,n} \\
\vdots & \vdots & & \vdots \\
a_{j,1} & a_{j,2} & \cdots & a_{j,n} \\
\vdots & \vdots & & \vdots \\
a_{i,1} & a_{i,2} & \cdots & a_{i,n} \\
\vdots & \vdots & & \vdots \\
a_{m,1} & a_{m,2} & \cdots & a_{m,n}
\end{bmatrix}.
$$

For example, $\mathbf{I}^{(2,4)}$ is the matrix obtained from the identity matrix in $M_4(F)$ by interchanging the second and fourth rows, and

$$
\mathbf{I}^{(2,4)}\mathbf{A} =
$$

$$
\begin{bmatrix}
1 & 0 & 0 & 0 \\
0 & 0 & 0 & 1 \\
0 & 0 & 1 & 0 \\
0 & 1 & 0 & 0
\end{bmatrix}
\begin{bmatrix}
a_{1,1} & a_{1,2} & a_{1,3} & a_{1,4} \\
a_{2,1} & a_{2,2} & a_{2,3} & a_{2,4} \\
a_{3,1} & a_{3,2} & a_{3,3} & a_{3,4} \\
a_{4,1} & a_{4,2} & a_{4,3} & a_{4,4}
\end{bmatrix}
=
\begin{bmatrix}
a_{1,1} & a_{1,2} & a_{1,3} & a_{1,4} \\
a_{4,1} & a_{4,2} & a_{4,3} & a_{4,4} \\
a_{3,1} & a_{3,2} & a_{3,3} & a_{3,4} \\
a_{2,1} & a_{2,2} & a_{2,3} & a_{2,4}
\end{bmatrix}.
$$

(10–4.4). Let $\mathbf{I}_c^{(i,j)}$ be the matrix obtained from the identity matrix $\mathbf{I} \in M_m(F)$ by multiplying each element of the ith row of $\mathbf{I}$ by $c \in F$ and adding it to the corresponding element of the jth row $(i \neq j)$. Let $\mathbf{A} \in {}_mM_n(F)$. Then the matrix $\mathbf{I}_c^{(i,j)}\mathbf{A}$ is the matrix obtained from $\mathbf{A}$ by multiplying each element of the ith row of $\mathbf{A}$ by c and adding it to the corresponding element of the jth row.

Proof. Observe that

$$
\mathbf{I}_c^{(i,j)} = \begin{array}{c} \\ \\ i \\ \\ j \\ \\ \\ \end{array}
\begin{bmatrix}
1 & & & & & & \\
& \ddots & & \vdots & & & \\
& & & \vdots & & & \\
\cdots & & 1 & & & & \\
& & \vdots & \ddots & & & \\
\cdots & & c & \cdots & 1 & & \\
& & & & & \ddots & \\
& & & & & & 1
\end{bmatrix}
$$

is a matrix with 1's on the diagonal, the element $c \in F$ in the (j, i)-position and zeros elsewhere. Let $\mathbf{A}$ have elements $a_{i,j}$. Then

$$
\mathbf{I}_c^{(i,j)}\mathbf{A} = \begin{matrix} \\ \\ i \\ \\ j \\ \\ \\ \end{matrix}
\begin{bmatrix}
a_{1,1} & a_{1,2} & \cdots & a_{1,n} \\
\vdots & \vdots & & \vdots \\
a_{i,1} & a_{i,2} & \cdots & a_{i,n} \\
\vdots & \vdots & & \vdots \\
ca_{i,1} + a_{j,1} & ca_{i,2} + a_{j,2} & \cdots & ca_{i,n} + a_{j,n} \\
\vdots & \vdots & & \vdots \\
a_{m,1} & a_{m,2} & \cdots & a_{m,n}
\end{bmatrix}.
$$

For instance, $I_c^{(1,3)}$ is the matrix obtained from the identity matrix in $M_4(F)$ by multiplying each element of the first row of $\mathbf{I}$ by c and adding to the corresponding element of the third row. Moreover,

$$
\mathbf{I}_c^{(1,3)}\mathbf{A} =
\begin{bmatrix}
1 & 0 & 0 & 0 \\
0 & 1 & 0 & 0 \\
c & 0 & 1 & 0 \\
0 & 0 & 0 & 1
\end{bmatrix}
\begin{bmatrix}
a_{1,1} & a_{1,2} & a_{1,3} & a_{1,4} \\
a_{2,1} & a_{2,2} & a_{2,3} & a_{2,4} \\
a_{3,1} & a_{3,2} & a_{3,3} & a_{3,4} \\
a_{4,1} & a_{4,2} & a_{4,3} & a_{4,4}
\end{bmatrix}
$$

$$
=
\begin{bmatrix}
a_{1,1} & a_{1,2} & a_{1,3} & a_{1,4} \\
a_{2,1} & a_{2,2} & a_{2,3} & a_{2,4} \\
ca_{1,1} + a_{3,1} & ca_{1,2} + a_{3,2} & ca_{1,3} + a_{3,3} & ca_{1,4} + a_{3,4} \\
a_{4,1} & a_{4,2} & a_{4,3} & a_{4,4}
\end{bmatrix}.
$$

(10–4.5).   Let $\mathbf{I}_c^{(i)}$ be the matrix obtained from the identity matrix $\mathbf{I} \in M_m(F)$ by multiplying each element of the ith row of $\mathbf{I}$ by $c \neq 0$ in F. Let $\mathbf{A} \in {}_mM_n(F)$. Then $\mathbf{I}_c^{(i)}\mathbf{A}$ is the matrix obtained from $\mathbf{A}$ by multiplying each element of the ith row of $\mathbf{A}$ by c.

Proof. The result follows at once when we note that

$$
\mathbf{I}_c^{(i)} =
\begin{matrix} \\ \\ i \\ \\ \\ \end{matrix}
\begin{bmatrix}
1 & & & & & & \\
 & \ddots & & \vdots & & & \\
 & & 1 & \vdots & & & \\
i & \cdots & & c & & & \\
 & & & & 1 & & \\
 & & & & & \ddots & \\
 & & & & & & 1
\end{bmatrix}
$$

is a matrix with 1's on the diagonal except in the ith row where c is on the diagonal, and zeros elsewhere.

We will refer to the matrices $\mathbf{I}^{(i,j)}$, $\mathbf{I}_c^{(i,j)}$, and $\mathbf{I}_c^{(i)}$ as elementary transformation matrices of type 1, 2, and 3, respectively. The results (10–4.4), (10–4.5), and (10–4.6) show that each elementary row transformation on a matrix can be accomplished by multiplying the given matrix on the left by a matrix obtained from $\mathbf{I}$ by this same elementary transformation.

EXAMPLE 5. We will find a matrix $\mathbf{P} \in M_3(Q)$ such that $\mathbf{PA}$ is in echelon form, where

$$\mathbf{A} = \begin{bmatrix} 0 & 1 & -2 \\ \frac{1}{2} & 6 & 1 \\ 2 & \frac{1}{7} & 0 \end{bmatrix}.$$

In Table 10–2, we list a sequence of elementary row transformations which will carry $\mathbf{A}$ into echelon form, the corresponding elementary transformation matrices, and the result of performing these elementary transformations.

TABLE 10–2

Interchange the first and second rows	$\begin{bmatrix} 0 & 1 & 0 \\ 1 & 0 & 0 \\ 0 & 0 & 1 \end{bmatrix}$	$\begin{bmatrix} \frac{1}{2} & 6 & 1 \\ 0 & 1 & -2 \\ 2 & \frac{1}{7} & 0 \end{bmatrix}$
Multiply the first row by 2	$\begin{bmatrix} 2 & 0 & 0 \\ 0 & 1 & 0 \\ 0 & 0 & 1 \end{bmatrix}$	$\begin{bmatrix} 1 & 12 & 2 \\ 0 & 1 & -2 \\ 2 & \frac{1}{7} & 0 \end{bmatrix}$
Multiply the first row by -2 and add to the third row	$\begin{bmatrix} 1 & 0 & 0 \\ 0 & 1 & 0 \\ -2 & 0 & 1 \end{bmatrix}$	$\begin{bmatrix} 1 & 12 & 2 \\ 0 & 1 & -2 \\ 0 & -\frac{167}{7} & -4 \end{bmatrix}$
Multiply the second row by $\frac{167}{7}$ and add to the third row	$\begin{bmatrix} 1 & 0 & 0 \\ 0 & 1 & 0 \\ 0 & \frac{167}{7} & 1 \end{bmatrix}$	$\begin{bmatrix} 1 & 12 & 2 \\ 0 & 1 & -2 \\ 0 & 0 & -\frac{362}{7} \end{bmatrix}$
Multiply the third row by $-\frac{7}{362}$	$\begin{bmatrix} 1 & 0 & 0 \\ 0 & 1 & 0 \\ 0 & 0 & -\frac{7}{362} \end{bmatrix}$	$\begin{bmatrix} 1 & 12 & 2 \\ 0 & 1 & -2 \\ 0 & 0 & 1 \end{bmatrix}$

From the table, we see that

$$\left(\begin{bmatrix} 1 & 0 & 0 \\ 0 & 1 & 0 \\ 0 & 0 & -\frac{7}{362} \end{bmatrix} \begin{bmatrix} 1 & 0 & 0 \\ 0 & 1 & 0 \\ 0 & \frac{167}{7} & 1 \end{bmatrix} \begin{bmatrix} 1 & 0 & 0 \\ 0 & 1 & 0 \\ -2 & 0 & 1 \end{bmatrix} \begin{bmatrix} 2 & 0 & 0 \\ 0 & 1 & 0 \\ 0 & 0 & 1 \end{bmatrix} \begin{bmatrix} 0 & 1 & 0 \\ 1 & 0 & 0 \\ 0 & 0 & 1 \end{bmatrix}\right) \begin{bmatrix} 0 & 1 & -2 \\ \frac{1}{2} & 6 & 1 \\ 2 & \frac{1}{7} & 0 \end{bmatrix}$$

$$= \begin{bmatrix} 1 & 12 & 2 \\ 0 & 1 & -2 \\ 0 & 0 & 1 \end{bmatrix},$$

and the required matrix $\mathbf{P}$ is the product of the five elementary transformation matrices. Since

$$\mathbf{P} = \mathbf{PI} = \begin{bmatrix} 1 & 0 & 0 \\ 0 & 1 & 0 \\ 0 & 0 & -\frac{7}{362} \end{bmatrix} \begin{bmatrix} 1 & 0 & 0 \\ 0 & 1 & 0 \\ 0 & \frac{167}{7} & 1 \end{bmatrix} \begin{bmatrix} 1 & 0 & 0 \\ 0 & 1 & 0 \\ -2 & 0 & 1 \end{bmatrix} \begin{bmatrix} 2 & 0 & 0 \\ 0 & 1 & 0 \\ 0 & 0 & 1 \end{bmatrix} \begin{bmatrix} 0 & 1 & 0 \\ 1 & 0 & 0 \\ 0 & 0 & 1 \end{bmatrix} \mathbf{I},$$

it is evident that $\mathbf{P}$ is obtained from the identity matrix $\mathbf{I}$ by performing the given sequence of elementary transformations on $\mathbf{I}$. Thus, $\mathbf{P}$ can be computed without resorting to matrix multiplication. The following steps carry $\mathbf{I}$ into $\mathbf{P}$ by the elementary transformations listed in Table 10–2:

$$\mathbf{I} = \begin{bmatrix} 1 & 0 & 0 \\ 0 & 1 & 0 \\ 0 & 0 & 1 \end{bmatrix} \to \begin{bmatrix} 0 & 1 & 0 \\ 1 & 0 & 0 \\ 0 & 0 & 1 \end{bmatrix} \to \begin{bmatrix} 0 & 2 & 0 \\ 1 & 0 & 0 \\ 0 & 0 & 1 \end{bmatrix} \to \begin{bmatrix} 0 & 2 & 0 \\ 1 & 0 & 0 \\ 0 & -4 & 1 \end{bmatrix} \to \begin{bmatrix} 0 & 2 & 0 \\ 1 & 0 & 0 \\ \frac{167}{7} & -4 & 1 \end{bmatrix} \to \begin{bmatrix} 0 & 2 & 0 \\ 1 & 0 & 0 \\ -\frac{167}{362} & \frac{14}{181} & -\frac{7}{362} \end{bmatrix} = \mathbf{P}.$$

The reader can check that

$$\mathbf{PA} = \begin{bmatrix} 1 & 12 & 2 \\ 0 & 1 & -2 \\ 0 & 0 & 1 \end{bmatrix}.$$

(10–4.6). Each elementary transformation matrix in $M_m(F)$ has an inverse in $M_m(F)$ which is an elementary transformation matrix of the same type.

Proof. By (10–4.3) when a matrix is multiplied on the left by $\mathbf{I}^{(i,j)}$, the ith and jth rows of the matrix are interchanged. Since $\mathbf{I}^{(i,j)}$ is obtained from $\mathbf{I}$ by interchanging the ith and jth rows of $\mathbf{I}$, it follows that

$$\mathbf{I}^{(i,j)}\mathbf{I}^{(i,j)} = \mathbf{I}.$$

Therefore, the inverse of $\mathbf{I}^{(i,j)}$ is $\mathbf{I}^{(i,j)}$. By (10–4.4), multiplying a matrix on the left by $\mathbf{I}_{-c}^{(i,j)}$, adds $-c$ times each element of the ith row of the matrix to the corresponding element of the jth row. Since $\mathbf{I}_c^{(i,j)}$ is obtained from $\mathbf{I}$ by multiplying each element of ith row of $\mathbf{I}$ by c and adding to the corresponding element of the jth row, it follows that $\mathbf{I}_{-c}^{(i,j)}\mathbf{I}_c^{(i,j)} = \mathbf{I}$. A similar argument shows that $\mathbf{I}_c^{(i,j)}\mathbf{I}_{-c}^{(i,j)} = \mathbf{I}$. Therefore $\mathbf{I}_{-c}^{(i,j)}$ is the inverse of $\mathbf{I}_c^{(i,j)}$. Finally, it is easy to check that $\mathbf{I}_{1/c}^{(i)}$ is the inverse of $\mathbf{I}_c^{(i)}$, and this completes the proof.

Since any product of nonsingular matrices has an inverse, by Theorem 10–4.2, the following result is obtained from (10–4.6).

(10–4.7). A matrix $\mathbf{P} \in M_m(F)$ which is a product of elementary transformation matrices has an inverse in $M_m(F)$.

We now return to the consideration of n-rowed square matrices. One more preliminary result is needed before the main theorem.

(10–4.8). Let the matrix $\mathbf{A}$ in $M_n(F)$ be in the echelon form. If $\mathbf{A}$ has 1 in every main diagonal position, then

$$\mathbf{A} = \begin{bmatrix} 1 & d_{1,2} & d_{1,3} & \cdots & d_{1,n-1} & d_{1,n} \\ 0 & 1 & d_{2,3} & \cdots & d_{2,n-1} & d_{2,n} \\ \vdots & \vdots & \vdots & & \vdots & \vdots \\ 0 & 0 & 0 & \cdots & 1 & d_{n-1,n} \\ 0 & 0 & 0 & \cdots & 0 & 1 \end{bmatrix},$$

and it is possible to transform $\mathbf{A}$ into the identity matrix $\mathbf{I}$ in $M_n(F)$ by a sequence of elementary row transformations.

Proof. If the last row of $\mathbf{A}$ is multiplied by $-d_{1,n}$ and added to the first row, then multiplied by $-d_{2,n}$ and added to the second row, etc., we obtain the matrix which is identical with $\mathbf{A}$ except that $d_{1,n}, d_{2,n}, \ldots, d_{n-1,n}$ are replaced by 0:

$$\begin{bmatrix} 1 & d_{1,2} & d_{1,3} & \cdots & d_{1,n-1} & 0 \\ 0 & 1 & d_{2,3} & \cdots & d_{2,n-1} & 0 \\ \vdots & \vdots & \vdots & & \vdots & \vdots \\ 0 & 0 & 0 & \cdots & 1 & 0 \\ 0 & 0 & 0 & \cdots & 0 & 1 \end{bmatrix}.$$

Next, the $(n - 1)$st row of this new matrix is multiplied by $-d_{1,n-1}$ and added to the first row, then multiplied by $-d_{2,n-1}$ and added to the second row, and so forth. This sequence of elementary row transformations leads to the matrix

$$\begin{bmatrix} 1 & d_{1,2} & d_{1,3} & \cdots & 0 & 0 \\ 0 & 1 & d_{2,3} & \cdots & 0 & 0 \\ \vdots & \vdots & \vdots & & \vdots & \vdots \\ 0 & 0 & 0 & \cdots & 1 & 0 \\ 0 & 0 & 0 & \cdots & 0 & 1 \end{bmatrix}.$$

It is obvious how this process is continued to finally obtain the identity matrix $\mathbf{I}$.

EXAMPLE 6. By using type 2 elementary transformations, the matrix

$$\begin{bmatrix} 1 & 2 & -1 & 1 \\ 0 & 1 & 0 & 1 \\ 0 & 0 & 1 & \frac{1}{2} \\ 0 & 0 & 0 & 1 \end{bmatrix}$$

is reduced to the identity matrix in $M_4(Q)$ in the following five steps:

$$\begin{bmatrix} 1 & 2 & -1 & 1 \\ 0 & 1 & 0 & 1 \\ 0 & 0 & 1 & \frac{1}{2} \\ 0 & 0 & 0 & 1 \end{bmatrix} \rightarrow \begin{bmatrix} 1 & 2 & -1 & 0 \\ 0 & 1 & 0 & 1 \\ 0 & 0 & 1 & \frac{1}{2} \\ 0 & 0 & 0 & 1 \end{bmatrix} \rightarrow \begin{bmatrix} 1 & 2 & -1 & 0 \\ 0 & 1 & 0 & 0 \\ 0 & 0 & 1 & \frac{1}{2} \\ 0 & 0 & 0 & 1 \end{bmatrix} \rightarrow \begin{bmatrix} 1 & 2 & -1 & 0 \\ 0 & 1 & 0 & 0 \\ 0 & 0 & 1 & 0 \\ 0 & 0 & 0 & 1 \end{bmatrix}$$

$$\rightarrow \begin{bmatrix} 1 & 2 & 0 & 0 \\ 0 & 1 & 0 & 0 \\ 0 & 0 & 1 & 0 \\ 0 & 0 & 0 & 1 \end{bmatrix} \rightarrow \begin{bmatrix} 1 & 0 & 0 & 0 \\ 0 & 1 & 0 & 0 \\ 0 & 0 & 1 & 0 \\ 0 & 0 & 0 & 1 \end{bmatrix}.$$

THEOREM 10-4.9. Let F be a field and suppose that $\mathbf{A} \in M_n(F)$. Then $\mathbf{A}$ has an inverse in $M_n(F)$ if and only if $\mathbf{A}$ can be transformed into the identity matrix $\mathbf{I}$ of $M_n(F)$ by a sequence of elementary row transformations. The inverse of $\mathbf{A}$ can be obtained by applying to $\mathbf{I}$ the same sequence of elementary row transformations that is used to get from $\mathbf{A}$ to $\mathbf{I}$.

Proof. Suppose that $\mathbf{A}$ can be transformed into $\mathbf{I}$ by a sequence of elementary transformations. Then by (10–4.3), (10–4.4), and (10–4.5) there is a sequence $\mathbf{E}_1, \mathbf{E}_2, \ldots, \mathbf{E}_{k-1}, \mathbf{E}_k$ of elementary transformation matrices such that

$$\mathbf{E}_k \mathbf{E}_{k-1} \ldots \mathbf{E}_2 \mathbf{E}_1 \mathbf{A} = \mathbf{I}.$$

Let $\mathbf{B} = \mathbf{E}_k \mathbf{E}_{k-1} \ldots \mathbf{E}_2 \mathbf{E}_1$. Then $\mathbf{BA} = \mathbf{I}$. We wish to show that $\mathbf{B}$ is the inverse of $\mathbf{A}$. By Definition 10–4.1, it is sufficient to prove that $\mathbf{AB} = \mathbf{I}$. Note that by (10–4.7), $\mathbf{B}$ has an inverse $\mathbf{B}^{-1}$. From this fact and the identity $\mathbf{BA} = \mathbf{I}$ we obtain the desired result: $\mathbf{AB} = \mathbf{IAB} = \mathbf{B}^{-1}\mathbf{BAB} = \mathbf{B}^{-1}\mathbf{IB} = \mathbf{B}^{-1}\mathbf{B} = \mathbf{I}$. By definition, $\mathbf{B} = \mathbf{E}_k \mathbf{E}_{k-1} \ldots \mathbf{E}_2 \mathbf{E}_1 \mathbf{I}$, so that $\mathbf{B}$ is obtained from $\mathbf{I}$ by applying in order the elementary transformations corresponding to $\mathbf{E}_1, \mathbf{E}_2, \ldots, \mathbf{E}_{k-1}$, and finally $\mathbf{E}_k$. This proves the last statement of the theorem. The only thing left to show is that if $\mathbf{A}$ has an inverse, then $\mathbf{A}$ can be transformed into $\mathbf{I}$ by a sequence of elementary transformations. Suppose that $\mathbf{A}^{-1}$ exists. As we remarked before, any matrix $\mathbf{A}$ can be transformed into the echelon form (10–11) by means of a sequence of elementary row transformations. Consequently, by (10–4.3), (10–4.4), and (10–4.5), there is a matrix $\mathbf{P} \in M_n(F)$, such that $\mathbf{P}$ is a product of elementary transformation matrices and $\mathbf{C} = \mathbf{PA}$ is in echelon form (10–11). To complete the proof, it is sufficient by (10–4.8) to show that $\mathbf{C}$ has the form

$$\begin{bmatrix} 1 & d_{1,2} & d_{1,3} & \ldots & d_{1,n} \\ 0 & 1 & d_{2,3} & \ldots & d_{2,n} \\ \vdots & \vdots & \vdots & & \vdots \\ 0 & 0 & 0 & \ldots & 1 \end{bmatrix}, \qquad (10\text{–}12)$$

with 1 in every diagonal position. Suppose that $\mathbf{C}$ does not have this form. Then because $\mathbf{C}$ is a square matrix in echelon form, it follows that every element of the last row of $\mathbf{C}$ is zero. Therefore, by the definition of matrix multiplication, if $\mathbf{D}$ is any matrix in $M_n(F)$, then every element in the last row of $\mathbf{CD}$ is zero. In particular, $\mathbf{C}$ cannot have an inverse. However, $\mathbf{C} = \mathbf{PA}$. By assumption $\mathbf{A}$ has an inverse, and since $\mathbf{P}$ is a product of elementary transformation matrices, it follows from (10–4.7) that $\mathbf{P}$ has an inverse. Therefore, by Theorem 10–4.2, $\mathbf{C}$ has an inverse. This contradiction shows that $\mathbf{C}$ must have the form (10–12), which completes the proof.

The last part of the above proof shows that no matter how a nonsingular matrix **A** is reduced to echelon form by elementary row transformations, the result will be of the form (10–12). Otherwise **A** could not have an inverse. Therefore, if a matrix $\mathbf{A} \in M_n(F)$ reduces by elementary row transformations to an echelon form different from (10–12) (which means that the last row must contain all zeros), then **A** does not have an inverse in $M_n(F)$.

EXAMPLE 7. We will show that the matrix

$$\mathbf{A} = \begin{bmatrix} 1 & -2 & 3 & 0 \\ 3 & -1 & \frac{7}{2} & 1 \\ 4 & 2 & 1 & 0 \\ 2 & 0 & \frac{8}{5} & 1 \end{bmatrix}$$

in $M_4(Q)$ has no inverse. In fact, by the usual process of carrying **A** into echelon form, we obtain

$$\begin{bmatrix} 1 & -2 & 3 & 0 \\ 3 & -1 & \frac{7}{2} & 1 \\ 4 & 2 & 1 & 0 \\ 2 & 0 & \frac{8}{5} & 1 \end{bmatrix} \rightarrow \begin{bmatrix} 1 & -2 & 3 & 0 \\ 0 & 5 & -\frac{11}{2} & 1 \\ 4 & 2 & 1 & 0 \\ 2 & 0 & \frac{8}{5} & 1 \end{bmatrix} \rightarrow \begin{bmatrix} 1 & -2 & 3 & 0 \\ 0 & 5 & -\frac{11}{2} & 1 \\ 0 & 10 & -11 & 0 \\ 2 & 0 & \frac{8}{5} & 1 \end{bmatrix}$$

$$\rightarrow \begin{bmatrix} 1 & -2 & 3 & 0 \\ 0 & 5 & -\frac{11}{2} & 1 \\ 0 & 10 & -11 & 0 \\ 0 & 4 & -\frac{22}{5} & 1 \end{bmatrix} \rightarrow \begin{bmatrix} 1 & -2 & 3 & 0 \\ 0 & 1 & -\frac{11}{10} & \frac{1}{5} \\ 0 & 10 & -11 & 0 \\ 0 & 4 & -\frac{22}{5} & 1 \end{bmatrix}$$

$$\rightarrow \begin{bmatrix} 1 & -2 & 3 & 0 \\ 0 & 1 & -\frac{11}{10} & \frac{1}{5} \\ 0 & 0 & 0 & -2 \\ 0 & 4 & -\frac{22}{5} & 1 \end{bmatrix} \rightarrow \begin{bmatrix} 1 & -2 & 3 & 0 \\ 0 & 1 & -\frac{11}{10} & \frac{1}{5} \\ 0 & 0 & 0 & -2 \\ 0 & 0 & 0 & \frac{1}{5} \end{bmatrix}.$$

At this point, it is possible to stop, even though complete reduction to echelon form has not been achieved. It is clear however that elementary row transformations applied to the last two rows of this matrix cannot produce a 1 on the main diagonal in the third row and third column. Therefore, **A** can be transformed by elementary transformations into an echelon matrix which is not of the form (10–12). Consequently, **A** has no inverse in $M_4(Q)$. Note that this same conclusion could not be obtained from the next to last matrix in the above sequence, because of the presence of 4 in the fourth row, second column.

EXAMPLE 8. Let us apply the process described in Theorem 10–4.9 to obtain the inverse which was given (without any motivation) for the matrix

$$\mathbf{A} = \begin{bmatrix} i & -i & 1 \\ 3i & 4 & 0 \\ 1 & 0 & 1+i \end{bmatrix}$$

in Example 2. From the second line on, the first column of Table 10–3 describes an elementary row transformation. The second and third columns give the matrices which are obtained by applying these elementary transformations to the corresponding matrices of the preceding lines. The second and third columns of the first line contain the matrices $\mathbf{A}$ and $\mathbf{I}$ in $M_3(C)$, respectively. The second and third columns of the last line of Table 10–3 (see pp. 458 and 459) contain $\mathbf{I}$ and $\mathbf{A}^{-1}$.

PROBLEMS

1. Check that $\mathbf{A}\mathbf{A}^{-1} = \mathbf{A}^{-1}\mathbf{A} = \mathbf{I}$ in Example 2.

2. Complete the induction in the proof of Theorem 10–4.2.

3. Show by an example that the sum of two nonsingular matrices is not necessarily nonsingular. Can the sum of two singular matrices be nonsingular?

4. Carry the following matrices into echelon form (10–11) by elementary row transformations.

(a) $\begin{bmatrix} \frac{1}{2} & -2 & 0 \\ 1 & 3 & 2 \\ 6 & 12 & -1 \end{bmatrix}$ (b) $\begin{bmatrix} -5 & 6 \\ 10 & 1 \end{bmatrix}$ (c) $\begin{bmatrix} i & -i & 1 \\ 0 & -2i & 2 \\ 4 & 3i & -3 \end{bmatrix}$

(d) $\begin{bmatrix} 0 & 0 & 0 & 0 & 1 \\ 0 & 0 & 0 & 1 & 0 \\ 0 & 0 & 1 & 0 & 0 \\ 0 & 1 & 0 & 0 & 0 \\ 1 & 0 & 0 & 0 & 0 \end{bmatrix}$ (e) $\begin{bmatrix} 2 & 2 & 2 & 2 \\ 2 & 2 & 2 & 2 \\ 2 & 2 & 2 & 2 \\ 2 & 2 & 2 & 2 \end{bmatrix}$

5. Write the following elementary transformation matrices in $M_5(Q)$: $\mathbf{I}^{(1,5)}$, $\mathbf{I}^{(2,3)}$, $\mathbf{I}_{1/2}^{(1,2)}$, $\mathbf{I}_{-3}^{(2,4)}$, $\mathbf{I}_2^{(5)}$, $\mathbf{I}_{1/7}^{(3)}$. Describe in words the elementary row transformations to which each of these matrices corresponds.

TABLE 10-3

Operation	Matrix	Matrix
	$\begin{bmatrix} i & -i & 1 \\ 3i & 4 & 0 \\ 1 & 0 & 1+i \end{bmatrix}$	$\begin{bmatrix} 1 & 0 & 0 \\ 0 & 1 & 0 \\ 0 & 0 & 1 \end{bmatrix}$
Multiply the first row by $-i$	$\begin{bmatrix} 1 & -1 & -i \\ 3i & 4 & 0 \\ 1 & 0 & 1+i \end{bmatrix}$	$\begin{bmatrix} -i & 0 & 0 \\ 0 & 1 & 0 \\ 0 & 0 & 1 \end{bmatrix}$
Multiply the first row by $-3i$ and add to the second row	$\begin{bmatrix} 1 & -1 & -i \\ 0 & 4+3i & -3 \\ 1 & 0 & 1+i \end{bmatrix}$	$\begin{bmatrix} -i & 0 & 0 \\ -3 & 1 & 0 \\ 0 & 0 & 1 \end{bmatrix}$
Multiply the first row by -1 and add to the third row	$\begin{bmatrix} 1 & -1 & -i \\ 0 & 4+3i & -3 \\ 0 & 1 & 1+2i \end{bmatrix}$	$\begin{bmatrix} -i & 0 & 0 \\ -3 & 1 & 0 \\ i & 0 & 1 \end{bmatrix}$
Interchange the second and third rows	$\begin{bmatrix} 1 & -1 & -i \\ 0 & 1 & 1+2i \\ 0 & 4+3i & -3 \end{bmatrix}$	$\begin{bmatrix} -i & 0 & 0 \\ i & 0 & 1 \\ -3 & 1 & 0 \end{bmatrix}$
Multiply the second row by $-(4+3i)$ and add to the third row	$\begin{bmatrix} 1 & -1 & -i \\ 0 & 1 & 1+2i \\ 0 & 0 & -(1+11i) \end{bmatrix}$	$\begin{bmatrix} -i & 0 & 0 \\ i & 0 & 1 \\ -4i & 1 & -(4+3i) \end{bmatrix}$

Multiply the third row by $[-(1+11i)]^{-1} = \dfrac{-(1-11i)}{122}$	$\begin{bmatrix} 1 & -1 & -i \\ 0 & 1 & 1+2i \\ 0 & 0 & 1 \end{bmatrix}$	$\begin{bmatrix} -i & 0 & 0 \\ i & 0 & 1 \\ \dfrac{22+2i}{61} & \dfrac{-1+11i}{122} & \dfrac{37-41i}{122} \end{bmatrix}$
Multiply the third row by i and add to the first row	$\begin{bmatrix} 1 & -1 & 0 \\ 0 & 1 & 1+2i \\ 0 & 0 & 1 \end{bmatrix}$	$\begin{bmatrix} \dfrac{-2-39i}{61} & \dfrac{-11-i}{122} & \dfrac{41+37i}{122} \\ i & 0 & 1 \\ \dfrac{22+2i}{61} & \dfrac{-1+11i}{122} & \dfrac{37-41i}{122} \end{bmatrix}$
Multiply the third row by $-(1+2i)$ and add to the second row	$\begin{bmatrix} 1 & -1 & 0 \\ 0 & 1 & 0 \\ 0 & 0 & 1 \end{bmatrix}$	$\begin{bmatrix} \dfrac{-2-39i}{61} & \dfrac{-11-i}{122} & \dfrac{41+37i}{122} \\ \dfrac{-18+15i}{61} & \dfrac{23-9i}{122} & \dfrac{3-33i}{122} \\ \dfrac{22+2i}{61} & \dfrac{-1+11i}{122} & \dfrac{37-41i}{122} \end{bmatrix}$
Add the second row to the first row	$\begin{bmatrix} 1 & 0 & 0 \\ 0 & 1 & 0 \\ 0 & 0 & 1 \end{bmatrix}$	$\begin{bmatrix} \dfrac{-20-24i}{61} & \dfrac{6-5i}{61} & \dfrac{22+2i}{61} \\ \dfrac{-18+15i}{61} & \dfrac{23-9i}{122} & \dfrac{3-33i}{122} \\ \dfrac{22+2i}{61} & \dfrac{-1+11i}{122} & \dfrac{37-41i}{122} \end{bmatrix}$

6. Find a matrix $\mathbf{P}$ such that $\mathbf{PA}$ is in echelon form (10–11) for each matrix $\mathbf{A}$ listed in Problem 4.

7. Find the inverses of the elementary transformation matrices of Problem 5.

8. Which of the matrices of Problem 4 have inverses? Find the inverses when they exist.

9. Prove that $\mathbf{A} \in M_n(F)$ has an inverse if and only if $\mathbf{A}$ is a product of elementary transformation matrices.

10. Let $\mathbf{A}$ be the matrix of coefficients of the homogeneous system of n equations in n unknowns with coefficients in a field F:

$$\sum_{j=1}^{n} a_{i,j} x_j = 0, \qquad i = 1, 2, \ldots, n.$$

Write this system in matrix form,

$$\mathbf{AX} = \mathbf{O}, \qquad \mathbf{X} = \begin{bmatrix} x_1 \\ x_2 \\ \vdots \\ x_n \end{bmatrix}, \qquad \mathbf{O} = \begin{bmatrix} 0 \\ 0 \\ \vdots \\ 0 \end{bmatrix}.$$

(a) Show that if $\mathbf{B}$ is a nonsingular matrix, then the solutions of $\mathbf{AX} = \mathbf{O}$ are the same as the solutions of $(\mathbf{BA})\mathbf{X} = \mathbf{O}$.

(b) Use the result of (a) to prove that $\mathbf{A}$ is nonsingular if and only if $\mathbf{AX} = \mathbf{O}$ has only the trivial solution $\mathbf{X} = \mathbf{O}$. [*Hint:* To prove that this condition is sufficient, let $\mathbf{B}$ be a product of elementary transformation matrices such that $\mathbf{BA}$ is in echelon form. Use the result of Theorem 10–2.7(b), together with (10–4.8) and Theorem 10–4.9.]

(c) Use part (b) to prove that if $\mathbf{A} \in M_n(F)$ is such that $\mathbf{BA} = \mathbf{I}$ for some $\mathbf{B} \in M_n(F)$, then $\mathbf{A}$ is nonsingular, and $\mathbf{B} = \mathbf{A}^{-1}$.

11. Prove that the matrix

$$\begin{bmatrix} a_{1,1} & a_{1,2} & a_{1,3} \\ a_{2,1} & a_{2,2} & a_{2,3} \\ a_{3,1} & a_{3,2} & a_{3,3} \end{bmatrix}$$

is nonsingular if and only if its determinant

$$a_{1,1}a_{2,2}a_{3,3} + a_{1,3}a_{3,2}a_{2,1} + a_{1,2}a_{2,3}a_{3,1} - a_{1,3}a_{2,2}a_{3,1} - a_{1,1}a_{3,2}a_{2,3}$$
$$- a_{1,2}a_{2,1}a_{3,3}$$

is not zero.

APPENDIX 1

THE PROOF OF STURM'S THEOREM

THEOREM A1–1. *Sturm's theorem.* Let $f(x)$ be a polynomial in $R[x]$ with Sturm sequence

$$
\begin{aligned}
&f(x), \\
&f'(x), \\
&s_1(x) = q_1(x)f'(x) - f(x), \\
&s_2(x) = q_2(x)s_1(x) - f'(x), \\
&s_3(x) = q_3(x)s_2(x) - s_1(x), \\
&\quad\vdots \\
&s_k(x) = q_k(x)s_{k-1}(x) - s_{k-2}(x).
\end{aligned}
\tag{1}
$$

Let c and d be real numbers such that $c < d$ and $f(c) \neq 0$ and $f(d) \neq 0$. For each real number t, let $N(t)$ be the number of variations in sign in the sequence (1). Then the number of distinct real roots of $f(x)$ between c and d is equal to $N(c) - N(d)$.

Proof. The first step in the proof is to replace the Sturm sequence (1) by a modified sequence for which the value of $N(c) - N(d)$ is the same as for (1). The last Sturm polynomial $s_k(x)$ is a g.c.d. of $f(x)$ and $f'(x)$ (see Section 9–11), and is a divisor of every polynomial in the Sturm sequence (1). The modified sequence is

$$
\begin{aligned}
&g(x) = f(x)/s_k(x), \\
&g_0(x) = f'(x)/s_k(x), \\
&g_1(x) = s_1(x)/s_k(x) = q_1(x)g_0(x) - g(x), \\
&g_2(x) = s_2(x)/s_k(x) = q_2(x)g_1(x) - g_0(x), \\
&\quad\vdots \\
&g_k(x) = s_k(x)/s_k(x) = 1.
\end{aligned}
\tag{2}
$$

Since $s_k(x)$ divides $f(x)$ and $f(c) \neq 0$, it follows that $s_k(c) \neq 0$. Therefore, dividing each polynomial of sequence (1) by $s_k(x)$ leaves the signs the same at $x = c$ if $s_k(c) > 0$, and reverses each sign at $x = c$ if $s_k(c) < 0$. In either case, the number of variations in sign in the sequence

$$
g(c), \quad g_0(c), \quad g_1(c), \quad \ldots, \quad g_k(c)
$$

461

is the same as the number of variations in

$$f(c), \quad f'(c), \quad s_1(c), \quad \ldots, \quad s_k(c).$$

That is, $N(c)$ is the same for sequence (2) as for sequence (1). Similarly, $s_k(d) \neq 0$ since $f(d) \neq 0$, and $N(d)$ calculated from (2) is the same as $N(d)$ computed from (1). Thus, the modified Sturm sequence (2) yields the same value of $N(c) - N(d)$ as the original sequence (1).

We next observe that the real roots of $g(x)$ are the same as the real roots of $f(x)$, although possibly with different multiplicities. In fact, suppose that the distinct real roots of $f(x)$ are $u_1, u_2, \ldots, u_r$. Then

$$f(x) = a(x - u_1)^{m_1}(x - u_2)^{m_2} \ldots (x - u_r)^{m_r}q_1(x)^{n_1}q_2(x)^{n_2} \ldots q_s(x)^{n_s},$$

where a is a nonzero real number, $m_1, m_2, \ldots, m_r, n_1, n_2, \ldots, n_s$ are natural numbers, and $q_1(x), q_2(x), \ldots, q_s(x)$ are distinct monic polynomials of degree greater than one which are irreducible in $R[x]$ and consequently have no real roots. By Theorem 9–6.4,

$$s_k(x) = b(x - u_1)^{m_1-1}(x - u_2)^{m_2-1} \ldots$$
$$\ldots (x - u_r)^{m_r-1}q_1(x)^{n_1-1}q_2(x)^{n_2-1} \ldots q_s(x)^{n_s-1},$$

where b is some nonzero real number. Hence,

$$g(x) = \frac{f(x)}{s_k(x)} = ab^{-1}(x - u_1)(x - u_2) \ldots (x - u_r)q_1(x)q_2(x) \ldots q_s(x).$$

Thus, the different real roots of $g(x)$ are also $u_1, u_2, \ldots,$ and u_r. Moreover, we note for future reference that each u_i is a simple root of $g(x)$. Thus, to prove the theorem, it is sufficient to show that $N(c) - N(d)$ calculated from sequence (2) is the number of roots of $g(x)$ in the interval from c to d.

Divide the interval between c and d at each point which corresponds to a root of any one of the polynomials in the sequence (2). We then have a finite set of real numbers

$$c = x_0 < x_1 < x_2 < \cdots < x_{r-1} < x_r = d,$$

such that each x_i for $1 \le i < r$ is a root of some polynomial in (2), and every root of every polynomial in (2) in the interval from c to d is in the set $\{x_0, x_1, x_2, \ldots, x_{r-1}, x_r\}$. Thus if t satisfies $x_{i-1} < t < x_i$ for $i = 1, 2, \ldots, r$, then none of the polynomials in (2) is equal to 0 at $x = t$. The proof is carried out by showing that

(i) the value of $N(t)$ remains unchanged in each interval $x_{i-1} < t < x_i$,

(ii) the value of $N(t)$ is the same in two adjacent intervals $x_{i-1} < t < x_i$ and $x_i < t < x_{i+1}$ if x_i is not a root of $g(x)$, and

(iii) the value of $N(t)$ for $x_i < t < x_{i+1}$ is one less than the value of $N(t)$ for $x_{i-1} < t < x_i$ if x_i is a root of $g(x)$.

Proof of (i). Suppose that one of the polynomials in sequence (2) changes sign in an interval $x_{i-1} < t < x_i$. Denote this polynomial by $h(x)$. Then $h(t_1)$ and $h(t_2)$ have opposite signs where $x_{i-1} < t_1 < t_2 < x_i$. By Theorem 9–10.1, $h(x)$ has a root between t_1 and t_2. However, this contradicts the fact that every root of $h(x)$ between c and d is in the set $\{x_0, x_1, x_2, \ldots, x_{r-1}, x_r\}$. Therefore, every polynomial in sequence (2) has the same sign for all t such that $x_{i-1} < t < x_i$. This implies that $N(t)$, which is the number of variations in sign in the sequence

$$g(t), \quad g_0(t), \quad g_2(t), \quad \ldots, \quad g_k(t) = 1$$

is the same for all t such that $x_{i-1} < t < x_i$.

Proof of (ii). Suppose that x_i is not a root of $g(x)$. We will compare the sequences

$$g(t), \quad g_0(t), \quad g_1(t), \quad \ldots, \quad g_k(t) = 1, \tag{3}$$

where $x_{i-1} < t < x_i$, and

$$g(x_i), \quad g_0(x_i), \quad g_1(x_i), \quad \ldots, \quad g_k(x_i) = 1. \tag{4}$$

By the proof of (i), the signs of the numbers in (4) are the same as those for the corresponding numbers in (3), except that some of the numbers in sequence (4) may be zero. Observe that the first and last terms in (4) are not zero, since x_i is not a root of $g(x)$ and $g_k(x_i) = 1$. Moreover, no two consecutive terms in (4) are zero. For otherwise, examination of the equations (2) shows that all following terms would be zero. In particular, $g_k(x_i) = 0$, which is impossible. It also follows from (2) that those numbers in sequence (4) which are adjacent to a zero have opposite signs. For example, if $g_2(x_i) = 0$, then since $g_3(x) = q_3 g_2(x) - g_1(x)$, we have $0 \neq g_3(x_i) = -g_1(x_i)$. Therefore, at a place where a zero occurs in (4), there are the following possibilities for the signs in the sequences (3) and (4):

$$
\begin{array}{ll}
\cdots + - - \cdots & \cdots + 0 - \cdots \\
\cdots + + - \cdots & \cdots + 0 - \cdots \\
\cdots - - + \cdots \quad (3) & \cdots - 0 + \cdots \quad (4) \\
\cdots - + + \cdots & \cdots - 0 + \cdots
\end{array}
$$

Thus, the variation in sign that occurs in (3) is preserved in (4). Hence, $N(t)$, the total number of variations in sign in (3), is the same as $N(x_i)$, the total number of variations in sign in (4). If t satisfies $x_i < t < x_{i+1}$ in (3), then the above argument shows that $N(x_i) = N(t)$. Therefore, $N(t)$ is the same for all t such that $x_{i-1} < t < x_{i+1}$, which completes the proof of (ii). The reader should observe that since $g(c) \neq 0$, $g(d) \neq 0$, we have incidentally proved that $N(t)$ is the same for all t such that $c = x_0 \le t < x_1$ as well as for all t such that $x_{r-1} < t \le x_r = d$.

Proof of (iii). Note first that if x_i is a root of $g(x)$, then $i \ne 0$ and $i \ne r$, since $g(x_0) = g(c) \ne 0$ and $g(x_r) = g(d) \ne 0$. Suppose that x_i is a root of $f(x)$ of multiplicity m. Then

$$f(x) = (x - x_i)^m a(x), \tag{5}$$

where x_i is not a root of $a(x)$. Moreover, $s_k(x) = (x - x_i)^{m-1} s(x)$, where x_i is not a root of $s(x)$. Thus, $s(x)$ and $x - x_i$ are relatively prime, so that $s(x)$ divides $a(x)$. Since $s_k(x)$ divides

$$f'(x) = m(x - x_i)^{m-1} a(x) + (x - x_i)^m a'(x),$$

it follows that $s(x)$ also divides $a'(x)$. Let $b(x) = a(x)/s(x)$ and $c(x) = a'(x)/s(x)$. Then we have

$$g(x) = \frac{f(x)}{s_k(x)} = (x - x_i) b(x), \tag{6}$$

$$g_0(x) = \frac{f'(x)}{s_k(x)} = m b(x) + (x - x_i) c(x), \tag{7}$$

where x_i is not a root of $b(x)$. It follows that $b(t) \ne 0$ for all t such that $x_{i-1} < t < x_{i+1}$. Indeed, $b(x_i) \ne 0$, since x_i is not a root of $b(x)$. If $b(t) = 0$ for $t \ne x_i$, then by (6) $g(t) = 0$. This is impossible because x_i is the only root of $g(x)$ between x_{i-1} and x_{i+1}. It therefore follows from Theorem 9–10.1 that $b(t)$ has the same sign throughout the interval $x_{i-1} < t < x_{i+1}$. Suppose that $b(t) > 0$ for all t in this interval. Then

$$g(t) = (t - x_i) b(t) < 0$$

if $x_{i-1} < t < x_i$, and

$$g(t) = (t - x_i) b(t) > 0$$

if $x_i < t < x_{i+1}$.
  By (7),

$$g_0(x_i) = m b(x_i) + (x_i - x_i) c(x_i) = m b(x_i) > 0.$$

Therefore, $g_0(t) > 0$ for all t such that $x_{i-1} < t < x_{i+1}$. Hence, for $x_{i-1} < t < x_i$, the signs of the sequence

$$g(t), \quad g_0(t), \quad g_1(t), \quad \dots, \quad g_k(t) = 1$$

are

$$- + \cdots + ,$$

and for $x_i < t < x_{i+1}$, the signs are

$$+ + \cdots + .$$

This same result is obtained if we suppose that $b(x_i) < 0$. If x_i is not a root of any polynomial in (2) except $g(x)$, then each term of the abbreviated sequence

$$g_0(t), \quad g_1(t), \quad \ldots, \quad g_k(t)$$

has the same sign throughout the interval $x_{i-1} < t < x_{i+1}$. In this case, the complete sequence

$$g(t), \quad g_0(t), \quad g_1(t), \quad \ldots, \quad g_k(t)$$

has exactly one less variation in sign when $x_i < t < x_{i+1}$ than when $x_{i-1} < t < x_i$. If x_i is a root of some polynomial in (2) other than $g(x)$, then x_i must be a root of one of the polynomials $g_1(x), g_2(x), \ldots, g_{k-1}(x)$, since $g_0(x_i) \neq 0$ and $g_k(x_i) = 1 \neq 0$. It is now possible to use the result of (ii) applied to the sequence

$$g_0(x), \quad g_1(x), \quad g_2(x), \quad \ldots, \quad g_{k-1}(x), \quad g_k(x).$$

That is, since $g_0(x_i) \neq 0$ and $g_k(x_i) \neq 0$, the number of variations in sign in

$$g_0(t), \quad g_1(t), \quad g_2(t), \quad \ldots, \quad g_{k-1}(t), \quad g_k(t)$$

is the same for $x_{i-1} < t < x_i$ as for $x_i < t < x_{i+1}$. Therefore, in every case, the value of $N(t)$ is exactly one less in the interval $x_i < t < x_{i+1}$ than in the interval $x_{i-1} < t < x_i$. This completes the proof of (iii).

Combining the results (i), (ii), and (iii), we have proved that the only change which occurs in the value of $N(t)$ for $c \leq t \leq d$ is that $N(t)$ is diminished by 1 at each root of $g(x)$ in the given interval. Therefore, the number of roots of $g(x)$ [which is the number of distinct real roots of the polynomial $f(x)$] between c and d is $N(c) - N(d)$.

APPENDIX 2

THE PROOF OF THE FUNDAMENTAL THEOREM OF SYMMETRIC POLYNOMIALS

In this appendix we will prove the fundamental theorem on symmetric polynomials. Actually, a slightly stronger result than Theorem 10–1.11 will be obtained. This strengthening is motivated by the following observation:

(1) If $a(x_1, x_2, \ldots, x_r)$ is symmetric in $D[x_1, x_2, \ldots, x_r]$, then for $1 \leq i < j \leq r$

$$\text{Deg}_{x_i}[a(x_1, x_2, \ldots, x_r)] = \text{Deg}_{x_j}[a(x_1, x_2, \ldots, x_r)].$$

In fact, it is easily seen that

$$\text{Deg}_{x_i}[a(x_1, \ldots, x_i, \ldots, x_j, \ldots, x_r)]$$
$$= \text{Deg}_{x_j}[a(x_1, \ldots, x_j, \ldots, x_i, \ldots x_r)],$$

for any $a(x_1, x_2, \ldots, x_r) \in D[x_1, x_2, \ldots, x_r]$. Since

$$a(x_1, \ldots, x_j, \ldots, x_i, \ldots x_r) = a(x_1, \ldots, x_i, \ldots, x_j, \ldots, x_r)$$
$$= a(x_1, x_2, \ldots, x_r)$$

if $a(x_1, x_2, \ldots, x_r)$ is symmetric, the assertion (1) is proved.

The result which we will prove is the following.

THEOREM A2–1. Let $a(x_1, x_2, \ldots, x_r)$ be a nonzero symmetric polynomial in $D[x_1, x_2, \ldots, x_r]$ such that $\text{Deg}_{x_1}[a(x_1, x_2, \ldots, x_r)] = \cdots = \text{Deg}_{x_r}[a(x_1, x_2, \ldots, x_r)] = n$. Then there is a polynomial

$$f(x_1, x_2, \ldots, x_r)$$

of total degree n such that

$$a(x_1, x_2, \ldots, x_r)$$
$$= f(S_1^{(r)}(x_1, x_2, \ldots, x_r), S_2^{(r)}(x_1, x_2, \ldots, x_r), \ldots, S_r^{(r)}(x_1, x_2, \ldots, x_r)).$$

Proof. The proof is in the form of a double induction. The first induction is on the number r of indeterminates. The second induction is on n, and it occurs in proving the induction step: if the theorem is true for symmetric polynomials in fewer than r indeterminates, then it is true for polynomials

466

in r indeterminates. Before carrying out this induction, it is convenient to establish some preliminary facts.

(2) If $a(x_1, x_2, \ldots, x_{r-1}, x_r)$ is symmetric in $D[x_1, x_2, \ldots, x_r]$, and

$$a(x_1, x_2, \ldots, x_{r-1}, x_r)$$
$$= b_0(x_1, x_2, \ldots, x_{r-1}) + b_1(x_1, x_2, \ldots, x_{r-1}) \cdot x_r + \cdots$$
$$+ b_n(x_1, x_2, \ldots, x_{r-1}) \cdot x_r^n,$$

then each of the polynomials $b_i(x_1, x_2, \ldots, x_{r-1})$ is symmetric in

$$D[x_1, x_2, \ldots, x_{r-1}].$$

In fact, if

$$\begin{matrix} 1 & 2 & \cdots & r-1 \\ \updownarrow & \updownarrow & \cdots & \updownarrow \\ j_1 & j_2 & \cdots & j_{r-1} \end{matrix}$$

is any permutation of $\{1, 2, \ldots, r-1\}$, then

$$\begin{matrix} 1 & 2 & \cdots & r-1 & r \\ \updownarrow & \updownarrow & \cdots & \updownarrow & \updownarrow \\ j_1 & j_2 & \cdots & j_{r-1} & r \end{matrix}$$

is a permutation of $\{1, 2, \ldots, r-1, r\}$. Since $a(x_1, x_2, \ldots, x_{r-1}, x_r)$ is symmetric in $D[x_1, x_2, \ldots, x_{r-1}, x_r]$, it follows that

$$a(x_{j_1}, x_{j_2}, \ldots, x_{j_{r-1}}, x_r) = a(x_1, x_2, \ldots, x_{r-1}, x_r).$$

That is,

$$\sum_{i=0}^{n} b_i(x_{j_1}, x_{j_2}, \ldots, x_{j_{r-1}})x_r^i = \sum_{i=0}^{n} b_i(x_1, x_2, \ldots, x_{r-1})x_r^i.$$

Thus by Definition 9–2.1, for $i = 0, 1, \ldots, n$,

$$b_i(x_{j_i}, x_{j_2}, \ldots, x_{j_{r-1}}) = b_i(x_1, x_2, \ldots, x_{r-1}).$$

Since $j_1, j_2, \ldots, j_{r-1}$ was an arbitrary permutation of $1, 2, \ldots, r-1$, it follows that each $b_i(x_1, x_2, \ldots, x_{r-1})$ is symmetric in $D[x_1, x_2, \ldots, x_{r-1}]$.

The elementary symmetric polynomials in $D[x_1, x_2, \ldots, x_r]$ were defined in Definition 10–1.9 by the identity

$$(x_{r+1} - x_1)(x_{r+1} - x_2) \ldots (x_{r+1} - x_r)$$
$$= x_{r+1}^r - S_1^{(r)} \cdot x_{r+1}^{r-1} + S_2^{(r)} \cdot x_{r+1}^{r-2} - \cdots + (-1)^r S_r^{(r)},$$

(where we have written $S_i^{(r)}$ instead of $S_i^{(r)}(x_1, x_2, \ldots, x_r)$ for simplicity). It is convenient to also define

$$S_0^{(r)} = S_0^{(r)}(x_1, x_2, \ldots, x_r) = 1,$$
$$S_{r+1}^{(r)} = S_{r+1}^{(r)}(x_1, x_2, \ldots, x_r) = 0.$$

Using this convention, we obtain the next result.

(3) If $r > 1$, then

$$S_i^{(r)}(x_1, x_2, \ldots, x_r) = S_i^{(r-1)}(x_1, x_2, \ldots, x_{r-1})$$
$$+ S_{i-1}^{(r-1)}(x_1, x_2, \ldots, x_{r-1}) \cdot x_r$$

for $1 \le i \le r$.

By definition,

$$(x_{r+1} - x_1) \ldots (x_{r+1} - x_{r-1})(x_{r+1} - x_r)$$
$$= x_{r+1}^r - S_1^{(r)} \cdot x_{r+1}^{r-1} + S_2^{(r)} \cdot x_{r+1}^{r-2} - \cdots + (-1)^r S_r^{(r)}.$$

Also, since $r > 1$,

$$(x_{r+1} - x_1) \ldots (x_{r+1} - x_{r-1})(x_{r+1} - x_r)$$
$$= [(x_{r+1} - x_1) \ldots (x_{r+1} - x_{r-1})](x_{r+1} - x_r)$$
$$= [x_{r+1}^{r-1} - S_1^{(r-1)} \cdot x_{r+1}^{r-2} + S_2^{(r-1)} \cdot x_{r+1}^{r-3} - \cdots$$
$$+ (-1)^{r-1} S_{r-1}^{(r-1)}](x_{r+1} - x_r)$$
$$= (x_{r+1}^r - S_1^{(r-1)} \cdot x_{r+1}^{r-1} + S_2^{(r-1)} \cdot x_{r+1}^{r-2} - \cdots + (-1)^{r-1} S_{r-1}^{(r-1)} \cdot x_{r+1})$$
$$+ (-x_r x_{r+1}^{r-1} + S_1^{(r-1)} \cdot x_r x_{r+1}^{r-2} - \cdots + (-1)^{r-1} S_{r-2}^{(r-1)} \cdot x_r x_{r+1}$$
$$+ (-1)^r S_{r-1}^{(r-1)} x_r)$$
$$= x_{r+1}^r - (S_1^{(r-1)} + S_0^{(r-1)} x_r) x_{r+1}^{r-1} + (S_2^{(r-1)} + S_1^{(r-1)} x_r) x_{r+1}^{r-2} + \cdots$$
$$+ (-1)^{r-1}(S_{r-1}^{(r-1)} + S_{r-2}^{(r-1)} x_r) x_{r+1} + (-1)^r (S_r^{(r-1)} + S_{r-1}^{(r-1)} x_r).$$

Therefore,

$$S_1^{(r)} = S_1^{(r-1)} + S_0^{(r-1)} x_r, \qquad S_2^{(r)} = S_2^{(r-1)} + S_1^{(r-1)} x_r, \qquad \ldots,$$
$$S_r^{(r)} = S_r^{(r-1)} + S_{r-1}^{(r-1)} x_r.$$

(4) For $r \ge 1$ and $1 \le i \le r$, $S_i^{(r)}(x_1, x_2, \ldots, x_r) \ne 0$ and

$$\text{Deg}_{x_r}[S_i^{(r)}(x_1, x_2, \ldots, x_r)] = 1.$$

If $r = i = 1$, then $S_i^{(r)}(x_1) = x_1$, for which the statement (4) is true. We can therefore make the induction hypothesis that (4) is true for $r - 1$. Note that also $S_0^{(r-1)} = 1 \neq 0$. Hence, if $1 \leq i \leq r$, it follows from (3) that $S_i^{(r)}(x_1, x_2, \ldots, x_r) \neq 0$ and its degree in x_r is exactly one.

(5) Suppose that $g(x_1, x_2, \ldots, x_r) \in D[x_1, x_2, \ldots, x_r]$ has total degree m. Then $g(S_1^{(r)}, S_2^{(r)}, \ldots, S_r^{(r)})$ is symmetric in $D[x_1, x_2, \ldots, x_r]$. Moreover, if* $g(S_1^{(r)}, S_2^{(r)}, \ldots, S_r^{(r)}) \neq 0$, then $\mathrm{Deg}_{x_r}[g(S_1^{(r)}, S_2^{(r)}, \ldots, S_r^{(r)})] \leq m$.

The fact that $g(S_1^{(r)}, S_2^{(r)}, \ldots, S_r^{(r)})$ is symmetric was observed in (10–1.10). To prove the second statement, note that by (4),

$$\mathrm{Deg}_{x_r}[(S_1^{(r)})^{i_1} \cdot (S_2^{(r)})^{i_2} \cdot \cdots \cdot (S_r^{(r)})^{i_r}]$$
$$= i_1 \, \mathrm{Deg}_{x_r}[S_1^{(r)}] + i_2 \, \mathrm{Deg}_{x_r}[S_2^{(r)}] + \cdots + i_r \, \mathrm{Deg}_{x_r}[S_r^{(r)}]$$
$$= i_1 + i_2 + \cdots + i_r.$$

Let
$$g(x_1, x_2, \ldots, x_r) = \sum c_i x_i^{i_1} x_2^{i_2} \ldots x_r^{i_r}.$$

If $g(S_1^{(r)}, S_2^{(r)}, \ldots, S_r^{(r)}) \neq 0$, then

$$\mathrm{Deg}_{x_r}[g(S_1^{(r)}, S_2^{(r)}, \ldots, S_r^{(r)})]$$
$$\leq \max \{\mathrm{Deg}_{x_r}[(S_1^{(r)})^{i_1} \cdot (S_2^{(r)})^{i_2} \cdot \cdots \cdot (S_r^{(r)})^{i_r}] | c_i \neq 0\}$$
$$= \max \{i_1 + i_2 + \cdots + i_r | c_i \neq 0\},$$

which by definition is the total degree m.

(6) Let $a(x_1, x_2, \ldots, x_{r-1}, x_r)$ be symmetric in $D[x_1, x_2, \ldots, x_r]$. If $a(x_1, x_2, \ldots, x_{r-1}, 0) \neq 0$, then

$$\mathrm{Deg}_{x_{r-1}}[a(x_1, x_2, \ldots, x_{r-1}, 0)] \leq \mathrm{Deg}_{x_r}[a(x_1, x_2, \ldots, x_r)].$$

This statement is a direct consequence of (1), because obviously

$$\mathrm{Deg}_{x_{r-1}}[a(x_1, x_2, \ldots, x_{r-1}, 0)] \leq \mathrm{Deg}_{x_{r-1}}[a(x_1, x_2, \ldots, x_{r-1}, x_r)]$$
$$= \mathrm{Deg}_{x_r}[a(x_1, x_2, \ldots, x_{r-1}, x_r)].$$

(7) Let $a(x_1, x_2, \ldots, x_{r-1}, x_r)$ be symmetric in $D[x_1, x_2, \ldots, x_r]$. If $a(x_1, x_2, \ldots, x_{r-1}, 0) = 0$, then there is a polynomial $b(x_1, x_2, \ldots, x_r)$ which is symmetric in $D[x_1, x_2, \ldots, x_r]$, and such that

$$a(x_1, x_2, \ldots, x_r) = S_r^{(r)}(x_1, x_2, \ldots, x_r) \cdot b(x_1, x_2, \ldots, x_r).$$

---

* It can be proved that if $g(x_1, x_2, \ldots, x_r) \neq 0$, then $g(S_1^{(r)}, S_2^{(r)}, \ldots, S_r^{(r)}) \neq 0$. However, this fact will not be needed.

Let

$$a(x_1, x_2, \ldots, x_{r-1}, x_r) = b_0(x_1, x_2, \ldots, x_{r-1}) + b_1(x_1, x_2, \ldots, x_{r-1})x_r$$
$$+ \cdots + b_m(x_1, x_2, \ldots, x_{r-1})x_r^m.$$

Our assumption is that $0 = a(x_1, x_2, \ldots, x_{r-1}, 0) = b_0(x_1, x_2, \ldots, x_{r-1})$. If $r = 1$, then

$$a(x_1) = x_1(b_1 + b_2 x_1 + \cdots + b_m x_1^{m-1}) = S_1^{(1)}(x_1) \cdot b(x_1),$$

which proves (1) in the case $r = 1$, because every polynomial in $D[x_1]$ is symmetric. Assume that (7) holds for $r - 1$. We have

$$a(x_1, x_2, \ldots, x_{r-1}, x_r) = \sum_{k=1}^m b_k(x_1, x_2, \ldots, x_{r-1})x_r^k.$$

By (2), each $b_k(x_1, x_2, \ldots, x_{r-1})$ is symmetric in $D[x_1, x_2, \ldots, x_{r-1}]$. Moreover, since $a(x_1, x_2, \ldots, x_{r-1}, x_r)$ is symmetric in $D[x_1, x_2, \ldots, x_r]$,

$$a(x_1, x_2, \ldots, x_{r-1}, x_r) = a(x_1, x_2, \ldots, x_r, x_{r-1})$$
$$= \sum_{k=1}^m b_k(x_1, x_2, \ldots, x_{r-2}, x_r)x_{r-1}^k.$$

From the assumption that $a(x_1, x_2, \ldots, x_{r-1}, 0) = 0$, it follows that

$$\sum_{k=1}^m b_k(x_1, x_2, \ldots, x_{r-2}, 0)x_{r-1}^k = 0.$$

Hence, for $k = 1, 2, \ldots, m$, we obtain $b_k(x_1, x_2, \ldots, x_{r-2}, 0) = 0$. Therefore, by the induction hypothesis,

$$b_k(x_1, x_2, \ldots, x_{r-2}, x_{r-1})$$
$$= S_{r-1}^{(r-1)}(x_1, x_2, \ldots, x_{r-1}) \cdot c_k(x_1, x_2, \ldots, x_{r-1}).$$

By (3),

$$S_r^{(r)}(x_1, x_2, \ldots, x_r)$$
$$= S_r^{(r-1)}(x_1, x_2, \ldots, x_{r-1})$$
$$+ S_{r-1}^{(r-1)}(x_1, x_2, \ldots, x_{r-1}) \cdot x_r$$
$$= 0 + S_{r-1}^{(r-1)}(x_1, x_2, \ldots, x_{r-1}) \cdot x_r,$$

so that

$$a(x_1, x_2, \ldots, x_{r-1}, x_r)$$
$$= S_{r-1}^{(r-1)}(x_1, x_2, \ldots, x_{r-1}) \cdot x_r \cdot \left(\sum_{k=1}^m c_k(x_1, x_2, \ldots, x_{r-1})x_r^{k-1} \right)$$
$$= S_r^{(r)}(x_1, x_2, \ldots, x_r) \cdot b(x_1, x_2, \ldots, x_r).$$

If

$$
\begin{array}{cccc}
1 & 2 & \ldots & r \\
\updownarrow & \updownarrow & \ldots & \updownarrow \\
j_1 & j_2 & \ldots & j_r
\end{array}
$$

is any permutation of $\{1, 2, \ldots, r\}$, then

$$S_r^{(r)}(x_1, x_2, \ldots, x_r) \cdot b(x_1, x_2, \ldots, x_r)$$

$$
\begin{aligned}
&= a(x_1, x_2, \ldots, x_r) = a(x_{j_1}, x_{j_2}, \ldots, x_{j_r}) \\
&= S_r^{(r)}(x_{j_1}, x_{j_2}, \ldots, x_{j_r}) \cdot b(x_{j_1}, x_{j_2}, \ldots, x_{j_r}) \\
&= S_r^{(r)}(x_1, x_2, \ldots, x_r) \cdot b(x_{j_1}, x_{j_2}, \ldots, x_{j_r}).
\end{aligned}
$$

Consequently, since $D[x_1, x_2, \ldots, x_r]$ is an integral domain and

$$S_r^{(r)}(x_1, x_2, \ldots, x_r) \neq 0,$$

$$b(x_1, x_2, \ldots, x_r) = b(x_{j_1}, x_{j_2}, \ldots, x_{j_r}).$$

Therefore, $b(x_1, x_2, \ldots, x_r)$ is symmetric in $D[x_1, x_2, \ldots, x_r]$. This completes the induction which proves (7).

(8) We can now give the inductive proof of the fundamental theorem on symmetric polynomials. For $r = 1$, there is essentially nothing to prove: every polynomial in $D[x_1]$ is symmetric, and $S_1^{(1)}(x_1) = x_1$. Assume therefore that $r > 1$, and that Theorem A2–1 is true for polynomials which are symmetric in $D[x_1, x_2, \ldots, x_{r-1}]$. Let

$$a(x_1, x_2, \ldots, x_r) = \sum_{k=0}^{n} b_k(x_1, x_2, \ldots, x_{r-1}) x_r^k,$$

where $b_n(x_1, x_2, \ldots, x_{r-1}) \neq 0$ in $D[x_1, x_2, \ldots, x_{r-1}]$. If $n = 0$, then $\mathrm{Deg}_{x_r}[a(x_1, x_2, \ldots, x_r)] = 0$. Hence, by (1), $\mathrm{Deg}_{x_i}[a(x_1, x_2, \ldots, x_r)] = 0$ for all i with $1 \leq i \leq r$. That is $a(x_1, x_2, \ldots, x_r) = a \in D$. In this case, take $f(x_1, x_2, \ldots, x_r) = a(x_1, x_2, \ldots, x_r) = a$, and $a(x_1, x_2, \ldots, x_r) = f(S_1^{(r)}, S_2^{(r)}, \ldots, S_r^{(r)})$, where $f(x_1, x_2, \ldots, x_r)$ has total degree zero. Therefore, let us make our second induction hypothesis: Theorem A2–1 is true for polynomials which are symmetric in $D[x_1, x_2, \ldots, x_r]$ and have degree in x_r less than n. By (2), $b_0(x_1, x_2, \ldots, x_{r-1}) = a(x_1, x_2, \ldots, x_{r-1}, 0)$ is symmetric in $D[x_1, x_2, \ldots, x_{r-1}]$. The two cases $a(x_1, x_2, \ldots, x_{r-1}, 0) = 0$ and $a(x_1, x_2, \ldots, x_{r-1}, 0) \neq 0$ are treated separately. Suppose first that $a(x_1, x_2, \ldots, x_{r-1}, 0) = 0$. By (7),

$$a(x_1, x_2, \ldots, x_r) = S_r^{(r)}(x_1, x_2, \ldots, x_r) \cdot d(x_1, x_2, \ldots, x_r),$$

where $d(x_1, x_2, \ldots, x_r)$ is symmetric in $D[x_1, x_2, \ldots, x_r]$. Since

$$\text{Deg}_{x_r} [S_r^{(r)}(x_1, x_2, \ldots, x_r)] = 1,$$

it follows that

$$\text{Deg}_{x_r} [d(x_1, x_2, \ldots, x_r)] = \text{Deg}_{x_r} [a(x_1, x_2, \ldots, x_r)] - 1 = n - 1.$$

By the second induction hypothesis, there is a polynomial $h(x_1, x_2, \ldots, x_r)$ of total degree $n - 1$, such that

$$d(x_1, x_2, \ldots, x_r) = h(S_1^{(r)}, S_2^{(r)}, \ldots, S_r^{(r)}).$$

Let $f(x_1, x_2, \ldots, x_r) = x_r \cdot h(x_1, x_2, \ldots, x_r)$. Then $f(x_1, x_2, \ldots, x_r)$ has total degree n, and

$$a(x_1, x_2, \ldots, x_r) = S_r^{(r)} \cdot h(S_1^{(r)}, S_2^{(r)}, \ldots, S_r^{(r)})$$

$$= f(S_1^{(r)}, S_2^{(r)}, \ldots, S_r^{(r)}).$$

Now suppose that

$$a(x_1, x_2, \ldots, x_{r-1}, 0) = b_0(x_1, x_2, \ldots, x_{r-1}) \neq 0.$$

By (6),

$$\text{Deg}_{x_{r-1}} [b_0(x_1, x_2, \ldots, x_{r-1})] \leq \text{Deg}_{x_r} [a(x_1, x_2, \ldots, x_r)] = n.$$

By the first induction hypothesis, there is a polynomial $g(x_1, x_2, \ldots, x_{r-1})$ in $D[x_1, x_2, \ldots, x_{r-1}]$, having total degree at most n, such that

$$b_0(x_1, x_2, \ldots, x_{r-1}) = g(S_1^{(r-1)}, S_2^{(r-1)}, \ldots, S_{r-1}^{(r-1)}).$$

Let

$$c(x_1, x_2, \ldots, x_r) = a(x_1, x_2, \ldots, x_r) - g(S_1^{(r)}, S_2^{(r)}, \ldots, S_{r-1}^{(r)}).$$

If $c(x_1, x_2, \ldots, x_r) = 0$, then

$$a(x_1, x_2, \ldots, x_r) = g(S_1^{(r)}, S_2^{(r)}, \ldots, S_{r-1}^{(r)}).$$

In this case, let $f(x_1, x_2, \ldots, x_{r-1}, x_r) = g(x_1, x_2, \ldots, x_{r-1})$. Then

$$a(x_1, x_2, \ldots, x_r) = f(S_1^{(r)}, S_2^{(r)}, \ldots, S_r^{(r)}),$$

where the total degree of $f(x_1, x_2, \ldots, x_r)$ is at most n. If the total degree of $f(x_1, x_2, \ldots, x_r)$ were less than n, then by (5), we would have

$$\text{Deg}_{x_r} [f(S_1^{(r)}, S_2^{(r)}, \ldots, S_r^{(r)})] < n.$$

This is impossible since $\text{Deg}_{x_r} [a(x_1, x_2, \ldots, x_r)] = n$. Therefore, the total degree of $f(x_1, x_2, \ldots, x_r)$ is exactly n. Finally, if $c(x_1, x_2, \ldots, x_r) \neq 0$, then by (5),

$$\mathrm{Deg}_{x_r}\, [c(x_1, x_2, \ldots, x_r)] \leq \max\ \{\mathrm{Deg}_{x_r}\, [a(x_1, x_2, \ldots, x_r)],$$
$$\mathrm{Deg}_{x_r}\, [g(S_1^{(r)}, S_2^{(r)}, \ldots, S_{r-1}^{(r)})]\} = n.$$

Moreover, by (3), $S_i^{(r)}(x_1, x_2, \ldots, x_{r-1}, 0) = S_i^{(r-1)}(x_1, x_2, \ldots, x_{r-1})$ for $1 \leq i \leq r - 1$, so that

$$c(x_1, x_2, \ldots, x_{r-1}, 0)$$
$$= a(x_1, x_2, \ldots, x_{r-1}, 0)$$
$$\quad - g(S_1^{(r)}(x_1, x_2, \ldots, x_{r-1}, 0), \ldots, S_{r-1}^{(r)}(x_1, x_2, \ldots, x_{r-1}, 0))$$
$$= b_0(x_1, x_2, \ldots, x_{r-1}) - g(S_1^{(r-1)}, S_2^{(r-1)}, \ldots, S_{r-1}^{(r-1)}) = 0.$$

At this point we have reached essentially the same situation as when we assumed that $a(x_1, x_2, \ldots, x_{r-1}, 0) = 0$: $c(x_1, x_2, \ldots, x_r)$ is symmetric in $D[x_1, x_2, \ldots, x_r]$, has degree in x_r at most n, and

$$c(x_1, x_2, \ldots, x_{r-1}, 0) = 0.$$

Therefore, by the proof for that case, there is a polynomial $e(x_1, x_2, \ldots, x_r)$ of total degree at most n such that

$$c(x_1, x_2, \ldots, x_r) = e(S_1^{(r)}, S_2^{(r)}, \ldots, S_r^{(r)}).$$

Let $f(x_1, x_2, \ldots, x_r) = e(x_1, x_2, \ldots, x_r) + g(x_1, x_2, \ldots, x_{r-1})$. Then

$$a(x_1, x_2, \ldots, x_r) = f(S_1^{(r)}, S_2^{(r)}, \ldots, S_r^{(r)}),$$

where the total degree of $f(x_1, x_2, \ldots, x_r)$ is at most n. As before, it follows from (5), that the total degree of $f(x_1, x_2, \ldots, x_r)$ is exactly n. The induction is therefore complete and Theorem A2–1 is proved.

APPENDIX 3

THE PROOF OF THE FUNDAMENTAL THEOREM OF ALGEBRA

The purpose of this appendix is to give a proof of Theorem 9–8.1, the fundamental theorem of algebra. Several of the preliminary results needed for the proof are interesting and important, and we will prove them in a more general form than is needed for our immediate purposes.

The first step in our program is to obtain a weak first approximation to Theorem 9–8.1.

THEOREM A3–1. Let F be any field, and let $p(x)$ be a polynomial which is irreducible in $F[x]$. Then there is a field K which contains F as a subring, such that $p(x)$ has a root in K.

Proof. The construction of K uses the method indicated in Problem 3, Section 6–5. We will leave most of the details for the reader to fill in. Define a relation $\sim$ on $F[x]$ by the condition

$$a(x) \sim b(x) \text{ if } p(x) \text{ divides } a(x) - b(x) \text{ in } F[x].$$

The following facts can easily be verified, using the properties of divisibility in $F[x]$.

(1) $\sim$ is an equivalence relation.
(2) If $a(x) \sim b(x)$ and $c(x) \sim d(x)$, then $a(x) + c(x) \sim b(x) + d(x)$, $a(x) \cdot b(x) \sim c(x) \cdot d(x)$, and $-a(x) \sim -b(x)$.
(3) If a and b are in F, then $a \sim b$ if and only if $a = b$.
(4) $p(x) \sim 0$.

Define K to be the set of all equivalence classes $[a(x)]$ of elements of $F[x]$ under the equivalence relation $\sim$ (see Definition 6–4.3). Define operations $\oplus$, $\odot$, and $\ominus$ in K by the conditions:

$$
\begin{aligned}
[a(x)] \oplus [b(x)] &= [a(x) + b(x)], \\
[a(x)] \odot [b(x)] &= [a(x) \cdot b(x)] \\
\ominus [a(x)] &= [-a(x)].
\end{aligned}
$$

(5)

Using (2), it is easy to show that $\oplus$, $\odot$, and $\ominus$ are well-defined operations on K (see the discussion at the beginning of Section 6–5). Moreover, with these operations, K is easily seen to be a commutative ring with an identity [1]. By (3),

$$a \leftrightarrow [a]$$

is a one-to-one correspondence between F and a subring $\{[a] | a \in F\}$ of K.

474

It follows easily from (5) that this correspondence is an isomorphism: for example
$$a + b = c \text{ implies } [a] \oplus [b] = [c].$$

Conversely, if $[a] \oplus [b] = [c]$, then $a + b \sim c$, so that by (3), $a + b = c$. As usual, we identify F with the subring $\{[a] | a \in F\}$ of K, and for simplicity write a instead of $[a]$. Let us also write u for $[x]$. It then follows by induction from (5) that

(6) $[a_0 + a_1 x + \cdots + a_n x^n] = a_0 \oplus a_1 u \oplus \cdots \oplus a_n u^n,$

(where $a_1 u = [a_1] \odot u$, $a_2 u^2 = [a_2] \odot u \odot u$, and so forth) for any $a_0, a_1, \ldots, a_n$ in F. In particular, considering $p(x)$ to be an element of $K[x]$, we can substitute u for x in $p(x)$ to obtain from (4),

(7) $p(u) = [p(x)] = [0] = 0.$

Therefore, u is a root of $p(x)$ in K.

The only thing left to show is that K is a field. Here, for the first time, we use the assumption that $p(x)$ is irreducible in $F[x]$. We must show that any nonzero element of K has an an inverse (see Problem 12, Section 6–2). If v is any element of K, then v is of the form $[a(x)]$ for some $a(x) \in F[x]$. The assumption $v = [a(x)] \neq 0$ means that $a(x)$ is not equivalent to 0, that is, $p(x)$ does not divide $a(x) - 0$. Since $p(x)$ is irreducible, the monic greatest common divisor of $a(x)$ and $p(x)$ must therefore be 1. Thus, by Theorem 9–4.4, there exist polynomials $g(x)$ and $h(x)$ in $F[x]$ such that $g(x)a(x) + h(x)p(x) = 1$. Therefore, $g(x)a(x) \sim 1$, so that
$$[g(x)] \odot [a(x)] = [g(x)a(x)] = [1].$$

This proves that every nonzero element of K has an inverse.

Having constructed K in this proof, we will now revert to our usual notation $+$, $\cdot$, and $-$ for the operations in K as well as in F.

Although the proof of Theorem A3–1 makes essential use of the fact that $p(x)$ is irreducible, this restriction is not really necessary, as the following strengthened version of Theorem A3–1 shows.

THEOREM A3–2. Let F be any field, and let $a(x)$ be a polynomial of degree $m > 0$ in $F[x]$. Then there is a field K containing F as a subring, such that in $K[x]$
$$a(x) = a_0(x - u_1)(x - u_2) \ldots (x - u_m),$$

where a_0 is a nonzero element of F and $u_1, u_2, \ldots, u_m$ are elements of K.

Proof. The theorem is clearly true for polynomials of degree one, in which case we can let $K = F$. Therefore, assume that $m > 1$ and that the theorem holds for all polynomials of degree less than m, with coefficients in *any* field. If $a(x)$ is not irreducible in $F[x]$, then it is possible to write $a(x) = b(x) \cdot c(x)$, where $0 < \text{Deg}\,[b(x)] < m$ and $0 < \text{Deg}\,[c(x)] < m$. Consequently, the induction hypothesis applies to $b(x)$ and $c(x)$. Hence there is a field L containing F as a subring, such that

$$b(x) = b_0(x - u_1) \ldots (x - u_r),$$

where $r = \text{Deg}\,[b(x)]$, $b_0 \neq 0$, and $u_1, u_2, \ldots, u_r$ belong to L. Now think of $c(x)$ as a polynomial in $L[x]$, and apply the induction hypothesis again to obtain $c(x) = c_0(x - v_1) \ldots (x - v_s)$, where $s = \text{Deg}\,[c(x)]$, $c_0 \neq 0$ and $v_1, \ldots, v_s$ are in a field K which contains L as a subring. Thus, $F \subseteq L \subseteq K$, and F is a subring of K. In K, we have

$$a(x) = b(x)c(x) = (b_0 c_0)(x - u_1) \ldots (x - u_r)(x - v_1) \ldots (x - v_s).$$

Let $a_0 = b_0 c_0 \neq 0$. Obviously a_0 is the leading coefficient of $a(x)$, so that $a_0 \in F$. Since $u_1, \ldots, u_r, v_1, \ldots, v_s$ belong to K, and $r + s = \text{Deg}\,[b(x)] + \text{Deg}\,[c(x)] = \text{Deg}\,[a(x)] = m$, the proof of Theorem A3–2 is complete in the case that $a(x)$ is not irreducible.

Suppose therefore that $a(x)$ is irreducible. By Theorem A3–1, there exists a field L containing F as a subfield such that $a(x)$ is *not* irreducible in $L[x]$. Indeed, by the factor theorem, Theorem 9–7.5,

$$a(x) = (x - u)\,d(x),$$

where $u \in L$ and $d(x) \in L[x]$. Hence, by what we have just shown, there is a field K containing L as a subring (therefore also containing F as a subring) such that

$$a(x) = a_0(x - u_1)(x - u_2) \ldots (x - u_m),$$

where $u_1, u_2, \ldots, u_m$ are in K, and $a_0 \neq 0$. Again, since a_0 is the leading coefficient of $a(x)$, it must belong to F. This completes the induction and proves Theorem A3–2.

The proof of the fundamental theorem makes use of some special polynomials, which are defined as follows. Let h be a natural number, and let $x, x_1, x_2, \ldots, x_m$ be distinct indeterminates, with $m \geq 2$. Let

$$g_h(x) = \prod_{1 \leq i < j \leq m} (x - x_i - x_j - h x_i x_j).$$

It is useful to consider $g_h(x)$ in two ways: as an element of

$$(Z[x])[x_1, x_2, \ldots, x_m],$$

and as an element of $(Z[x_1, x_2, \ldots, x_m])[x]$. The notation $g_h(x)$ conforms with this second viewpoint.

(A3–3). $\mathrm{Deg}_x[g_h(x)] = \frac{1}{2}m(m-1)$.

This is clear, because the number of distinct pairs $\langle i, j \rangle$ satisfying $1 \le i < j \le m$ is exactly $\binom{m}{2} = \frac{1}{2}m(m-1)$ (see Section 1–3).

(A3–4). Considered as an element of $(Z[x])[x_1, x_2, \ldots, x_m]$, the polynomial $g_h(x)$ is symmetric. Consequently, we can write

$$g_h(x) = k_h(x, S_1^{(m)}(x_1, \ldots, x_m), S_2^{(m)}(x_1, \ldots, x_m), \ldots, S_m^{(m)}(x_1, \ldots, x_m)),$$

where $k_h(x, x_1, x_2, \ldots, x_m) \in Z[x, x_1, x_2, \ldots, x_m]$.

Proof. To prove this, it is sufficient, by Theorem 10–1.7, to show that $g_h(x)$ is left unchanged when x_k and x_l are interchanged, for each pair $\langle k, l \rangle$ with $1 \le k < l \le m$. Note that $g_h(x)$ can be written in the form

$$P_1 \cdot P_2 \cdot P_3 \cdot P_4 \cdot P_5 \cdot P_6 \cdot P_7 \cdot P_8,$$

where

$P_1 = \prod_{1 \le i < j \le m,\, i \ne k,\, i \ne l,\, j \ne k,\, j \ne l} (x - x_i - x_j - hx_ix_j),$
$P_2 = \prod_{i<k} (x - x_i - x_k - hx_ix_k),$
$P_3 = \prod_{j>l} (x - x_l - x_j - hx_lx_j),$
$P_4 = \prod_{i<k} (x - x_i - x_l - hx_ix_l),$
$P_5 = \prod_{k<i<l} (x - x_i - x_l - hx_ix_l),$
$P_6 = \prod_{k<j<l} (x - x_k - x_j - hx_kx_j),$
$P_7 = \prod_{j>l} (x - x_k - x_j - hx_kx_j),$
$P_8 = x - x_k - x_l - hx_kx_l.$

The effect of interchanging x_k with x_l in these various products is clearly that

P_1 is left unchanged,
P_2 goes into P_4 and P_4 goes into P_2,
P_3 goes into P_7 and P_7 goes into P_3,
P_5 goes into P_6 and P_6 goes into P_5, and
P_8 is left unchanged.

Consequently, $g_h(x) = P_1 \cdot P_2 \cdot P_3 \cdot P_4 \cdot P_5 \cdot P_6 \cdot P_7 \cdot P_8$ goes into $P_1 \cdot P_4 \cdot P_7 \cdot P_2 \cdot P_6 \cdot P_5 \cdot P_3 \cdot P_8 = g_h(x)$. Hence, $g_h(x)$ is symmetrical in $x_1, x_2, \ldots, x_m$. The last statement of (A3–4) is a consequence of the fundamental theorem on symmetric polynomials, Theorem 10–1.11.

We are now in a position to show that every real polynomial has at least one root in the field C of complex numbers.

THEOREM A3–5. Let $a(x) \in R[x]$ have degree $m > 0$. Then there is at least one complex number u such that $a(u) = 0$.

Proof. The proof of this theorem is carried out by induction on the highest power of 2 which divides m, that is, on the nonnegative integer n for which $m = 2^n k$, where k is odd. If $n = 0$, then m is odd, and $a(x)$ has a real root, by Theorem 9–10.4. Therefore, we can assume that $n > 0$ and make the induction hypothesis that every polynomial $f(x) \in R[x]$ for which the highest power of 2 dividing $\text{Deg}\,[f(x)]$ is 2^{n-1} has a complex root. Our objective is to prove that the polynomial $a(x)$ which is of degree $2^n k$ (with k odd) has a complex root.

Consider $a(x)$ as an element of $C[x]$. By Theorem A3–2, there is a field K containing C such that

$$a(x) = a_0(x - u_1)(x - u_2) \ldots (x - u_m),$$

where $a_0 \neq 0$, and $u_1, u_2, \ldots, u_m$ belong to K. We wish to prove that at least one of the u_i is in C. Since a_0 is the leading coefficient of $a(x)$, it must be a real number. Thus, we have

$$
\begin{aligned}
a(x) = a_0 x^m &- a_0 S_1^{(m)}(u_1, u_2, \ldots, u_m) x^{m-1} \\
&+ a_0 S_2^{(m)}(u_1, u_2, \ldots, u_m) x^{m-2} - \cdots \\
&+ (-1)^m a_0 S_m^{(m)}(u_1, u_2, \ldots, u_m).
\end{aligned}
$$

Since $a(x) \in R[x]$ and $a_0 \neq 0$, it follows that

$$S_1^{(m)}(u_1, u_2, \ldots, u_m), \quad S_2^{(m)}(u_1, u_2, \ldots, u_m), \quad \ldots, \quad S_m^{(m)}(u_1, u_2, \ldots, u_m)$$

are real numbers. For each natural number h, let

$$f_h(x) = \prod_{1 \le i < j \le m} (x - u_i - u_j - h u_i u_j).$$

That is, $f_h(x)$ is obtained from $g_h(x)$ by substituting u_1 for x_1, u_2 for x_2, $\ldots$, and u_m for x_m. By (A3–4), $f_h(x)$ can be considered as a polynomial in x, $S_1^{(m)}(u_1, u_2, \ldots, u_m)$, $S_2^{(m)}(u_1, u_2, \ldots, u_m)$, $\ldots$, and $S_m^{(m)}(u_1, u_2, \ldots, u_m)$, with integral coefficients. Thus, considered as a polynomial in x, $f_h(x)$ belongs to $R[x]$. Moreover, by (A3–3)

$$\text{Deg}\,[f_h(x)] = \tfrac{1}{2} m(m - 1) = 2^{n-1} k(2^n k - 1).$$

Therefore, since $n > 0$, the highest power of 2 which divides $\text{Deg}\,[f_h(x)]$

is 2^{n-1}. Consequently, the induction hypothesis applies to $f_h(x)$, that is, $f_h(x)$ has at least one complex root. However, we know from the definition of $f_h(x)$ that its roots are

$$u_i + u_j + hu_iu_j, \qquad 1 \le i < j \le m.$$

Thus, for some pair $\langle k, l \rangle$ with $1 \le k < l \le m$, the element $u_k + u_l + hu_ku_l$ belongs to C. Note that k and l may depend on the integer h. However, such a k and l exist for every natural number h. In particular, among the integers $1, 2, \ldots, \frac{1}{2}m(m-1) + 1$, there must be two *different* values of h, say $h = r$ and $h = s$, such that $u_k + u_l + ru_ku_l$ is in C and $u_k + u_l + su_ku_l$ is in C for the *same* pair $\langle k, l \rangle$. Otherwise, we could obtain a one-to-one mapping of the set $\{1, 2, \ldots, \frac{1}{2}m(m-1) + 1\}$ into the set $\{\langle i, j \rangle | 1 \le i < j \le m\}$, which contains only $\frac{1}{2}m(m-1)$ elements. If $u_k + u_l + ru_ku_l \in C$ and $u_k + u_l + su_ku_l \in C$, then $(r - s)u_ku_l \in C$, so that $u_ku_l \in C$, and hence also $u_k + u_l \in C$. By Theorem 8–2.7, the polynomial

$$(x - u_k)(x - u_l) = x^2 - (u_k + u_l)x + u_ku_l$$

has two roots in C, and of course these must be u_k and u_l. Thus, u_k and u_l are both in C. This completes the induction.

It is worth the reader's effort to examine the proof of Theorem A3–5 very carefully. This proof is the deepest argument which he will find in this book. Both the basis of the induction and the induction step use fundamental results from algebra and the theory of the real number system. The induction itself is somewhat unusual in that the induction variable is the exponent n of 2 in the factorization of $\mathrm{Deg}\,[a(x)]$ into powers of primes.

Our objective can now be easily attained.

THEOREM A3–6. *Fundamental theorem of algebra.* Every polynomial of positive degree in $C[x]$ has at least one root in C.

Proof. Let $f(x) = c_0 + c_1x + \cdots + c_nx^n$, $c_n \ne 0$, $n \ge 1$, and $c_0, c_1, \ldots, c_n$ in C. Define $\bar{f}(x) = \bar{c}_0 + \bar{c}_1x + \cdots + \bar{c}_nx^n$, where $\bar{c}_i$ is the complex conjugate of c_i. Let

$$a(x) = f(x) \cdot \bar{f}(x) = \sum_{k=0}^{2n} a_kx^k,$$

where $a_k = \sum_{i+j=k} c_i\bar{c}_j$. Note that

$$a_k = c_0\bar{c}_k + c_1\bar{c}_{k-1} + \cdots + c_{k-1}\bar{c}_1 + c_k\bar{c}_0,$$

and

$$\bar{a}_k = \bar{c}_0c_k + \bar{c}_1c_{k-1} + \cdots + \bar{c}_{k-1}c_1 + \bar{c}_kc_0,$$

for $0 \leq k \leq n$, and

$$a_k = c_{k-n}\bar{c}_n + c_{k-n+1}\bar{c}_{n-1} + \cdots + c_{n-1}\bar{c}_{k-n+1} + c_n\bar{c}_{k-n},$$

and

$$\bar{a}_k = \bar{c}_{k-n}c_n + \bar{c}_{k-n+1}c_{n-1} + \cdots + \bar{c}_{n-1}c_{k-n+1} + \bar{c}_n c_{k-n},$$

for $n < k \leq 2n$. In both cases, $\bar{a}_k$ is the same sum as a_k, except in reverse order. Hence, $a_k = \bar{a}_k$ for all k. This means that the numbers $a_0, a_1, \ldots, a_{2n}$ are all real, and therefore $a(x) \in R[x]$. The degree of $a(x)$ is $2n$, because $a_{2n} = c_n\bar{c}_n = |c_n|^2 \neq 0$. Thus, $a(x)$ has positive degree, so that by Theorem A3–5 there is a complex number u such that $a(u) = 0$. That is, $f(u) \cdot \bar{f}(u) = 0$. Therefore, either $f(u) = 0$, in which case $f(x)$ has the complex root u, or else $\bar{f}(u) = 0$. However,

$$\bar{f}(u) = \sum_{k=0}^n \bar{c}_k u^k = \overline{\sum_{k=0}^n c_k \bar{u}^k} = \overline{f(\bar{u})},$$

so that $\bar{f}(u) = 0$ implies $f(\bar{u}) = 0$. Thus, $f(x)$ has a complex root in this case also.

REFERENCES

There are many fine books on mathematics. Our purpose here is to call the reader's attention to some of these. We have selected a few of the good English language textbooks which deal mainly with the topics considered in this book. Most of them will carry the reader beyond his present state of knowledge, even assuming that he has mastered every word up to this point.

General references. There are several excellent books which deal with many of the topics we have considered. The three which are listed here are not textbooks in the usual sense, although they have been used as such. They are perhaps read with the most enjoyment and profit by someone who knows (or thinks he knows) something about everything in them.

1. RICHARD COURANT and HERBERT ROBBINS, *What is Mathematics?*, Oxford Press, New York, 1941. This book comes closer than any other we know to answering the question posed in its title.

2. R. L. WILDER, *The Foundations of Mathematics*, Wiley, New York, 1952. This book should be read first and studied afterward. It does an excellent job of presenting an honest picture of the foundations of mathematics.

3. FELIX KLEIN, *Elementary Mathematics from an Advanced Standpoint*, Macmillan, New York, 1932 (reprinted by Dover, New York, 1945). This book was taken from lectures delivered around 1908 by Professor Klein to German secondary school teachers. Modern college teachers can learn a great deal from Klein's lectures.

References on mathematical logic and reasoning. (Introduction.)

4. ALFRED TARSKI, *Introduction to Logic*, Oxford University Press, New York, 1941.

5. PATRICK SUPPES, *Introduction to Logic*, Van Nostrand, Princeton, 1957.

The books of Suppes and Tarski both present elementary mathematical logic with admirable clarity.

6. GEORGE POLYA, *How to Solve It*, Princeton University Press, Princeton, 1957.

7. JACQUES HADAMARD, *The Psychology of Invention in the Mathematical Field*, Princeton University Press, Princeton, 1949.

The aim of Polya's book is to teach the reader to think like a mathematician. Hadamard's study demonstrates by examples that only a born mathematician can think like a mathematician. Both books are interesting.

8. ERNEST NAGEL and JAMES NEWMAN, *Godel's Proof*, New York University Press, New York, 1958. A popular exposition of the work of Godel which brought a revolution in the philosophy of mathematics. This is an interesting book for light reading, but it leaves a craving for the complete story.

9. S. C. KLEENE, *Introduction to Metamathematics*, Van Nostrand, Princeton, 1952. Kleene's book shows what happens when mathematics is used to study logic. The book is heavy and difficult, but the first two parts of it are within the reach of good college undergraduates.

References on set theory. (Chapter 1.)

10. F. HAUSDORFF, *Set Theory*, translated and reprinted by Chelsea, New York, 1957. Although it is essentially a monograph, Hausdorff's book has been a standard source of information on informal set theory for many years.

11. P. R. HALMOS, *Naive Set Theory*, Van Nostrand, Princeton, 1960.

12. PATRICK SUPPES, *Axiomatic Set Theory*, Van Nostrand, Princeton, 1960.

These two recent books by Suppes and Halmos approach set theory in a more formal way. Nevertheless, both books are clearly written and not too difficult. A more elementary discussion of set theory than is found in either Hausdorff, Halmos, or Suppes is given in the following recently published textbook.

13. NORMAN HAMILTON and JOSEPH LANDIN, *Set Theory: The Structure of Arithmetic*, Allyn and Bacon, Boston, 1961.

References on mathematical induction. (Chapter 2.)

14. I. S. SOMINSKII, *The Method of Mathematical Induction*, Blaisdell, New York, 1961. This work is a pamphlet recently translated from Russian which contains numerous interesting examples of the use of mathematical induction.

References on the development of the number systems. (Chapters 3, 4, 6, 7, and 8.)

15. E. G. H. LANDAU, *The Foundations of Analysis*, Chelsea, New York, 1951. Landau's classical monograph begins with Peano's axioms and relentlessly proceeds to construct each number system from N to C. Nothing essential is omitted, and nothing inessential is included. More leisurely developments of the number systems can be found in Suppes' book (12), and in the work (13) of Hamilton and Landin.

References on the theory of numbers. (Chapter 5.)

There are many first rate textbooks on the elementary theory of numbers. The following four are particularly noteworthy. They are listed in the order of increasing comprehensiveness.

16. W. J. LE VEQUE, *Elementary Theory of Numbers*, Addison-Wesley, Reading, Mass., 1962.

17. IVAN NIVEN and H. S. ZUCKERMAN, *An Introduction to the Theory of Numbers*, Wiley, New York, 1960.

18. G. H. HARDY and E. M. WRIGHT, *An Introduction to the Theory of Numbers*, 4th ed., Oxford University Press, London, 1960.

19. W. J. LE VEQUE, *Topics in Number Theory*, Volumes I and II, Addison-Wesley, Reading, Mass., 1956.

References on the theory of equations and linear algebra. (Chapters 9 and 10.)

20. LOUIS WEISNER, *Introduction to the Theory of Equations*, Macmillan, New York, 1938. Weisner's work is one of the best books on the theory of equations which is written from a modern point of view.

21. ROSS A. BEAUMONT and RICHARD W. BALL, *Introduction to Modern Algebra and Matrix Theory*, Holt, Rinehart, Winston, New York, 1954. Beaumont and Ball covers most of the subjects which we have discussed, plus several others: groups, vector spaces, linear transformations, and canonical forms for

matrices. The reader will find that the style of Beaumont and Ball is remarkably similar to what he has encountered in this book.

22. B. L. VAN DER WAERDEN, *Modern Algebra*, Translated and reprinted from the second revised edition, Ungar, New York, 1949. This classical textbook has served many generations of mathematics graduate students, and it will probably serve many more. Volume II and the last few chapters of Volume I are fairly advanced. If possible, the German fourth edition should be used. It is the best-known example of "easy" mathematical German.

23. HARRY POLLARD, *The Theory of Algebraic Numbers*, Carus Monograph number nine, New York, 1950. This monograph is an excellent elementary introduction to algebraic number theory.

24. D. C. MURDOCH, *Linear Algebra for Undergraduates*, Wiley, New York, 1957.

25. L. J. PAIGE and J. D. SWIFT, *Elements of Linear Algebra*, Ginn, Boston, 1961.

26. P. R. HALMOS, *Finite Dimensional Vector Spaces*, 2nd edition, Van Nostrand, Princeton, 1958.

The books of Murdoch, Paige and Swift, and Halmos are all textbooks on matrices and linear algebra. They are listed in increasing order of sophistication. Halmos' work has an especially interesting collection of problems.

References on the history of mathematics. The literature on the history of mathematics is not as large as it might be. For example, practically nothing has been written about the mathematics of the 20th century—a period during which more mathematics has been done than in all of the years up to 1900. Choosing "good books" on the history of mathematics is largely a matter of taste. The following two books are very different, but both of them are enjoyable.

27. D. J. STRUIK, *A Concise History of Mathematics*, Dover, New York, 1948.

28. E. T. BELL, *Men of Mathematics*, Simon and Schuster, New York, 1937.
Bell presents a collection of short biographies of leading mathematicians up to the 20th century. Although it is not a scholarly history, Bell's book is certainly a classic of its kind.

INDEX

484

ABCDE698765432